A Charlton Standard Catalogue

BORDER FINE ARTS
FIGURINES

rd Edition

By
Marilyn Sweet

W.K. Cross
Publisher

The Charlton Press

TORONTO, ONTARIO · PALM HARBOR, FLORIDA

EDITORIAL

Editor	Jean Dale
Assistant Editor	Davina Rowan
Graphic Technician	Davina Rowan

ACKNOWLEDGEMENTS

The Charlton Press and the author wish to thank those who have helped with the third edition of *The Charlton Standard Catalogue of Border Fine Arts Figurines*

CONTRIBUTORS

Lynne Thomson and May George (Border Fine Arts Society); Ray Ayres; Jane South, Enesco; Staff at Enesco; Bruce Wheeler (Wheelers of Loughborough); Staff at the Posthorn; Mary (Grays China); fellow collectors Tina Banger, Derek and Marion Branthwaite, Richard Crompton, Harry Grainger, Bryan and Mavis Kelly, Bryan and Val Leech; Lynne Thomsin, Border Fine Arts, Roy Wylde, Drew Weatherstone, former BFA Master Painter and current BFA repairer at Glenfirra, and several other enthusiasts who have offered their encouragement and spurred me on! I must also thank my husband Peter for taking many of the photographs in a variety of locations and our daughters Natalie and Joanna for helping me check, double and triple check (and more!) all the information.

DISCLAIMERS

While every care has been taken to ensure accuracy in the compilation of the data in this catalogue, the author and the publisher cannot accept responsibility for errors and omissions.

A SPECIAL NOTE TO COLLECTORS

We welcome and appreciate any comments or suggestions you may have in regard to *The Charlton Standard Catalogue of Border Fine Arts Figurines*. If any errors or omissions come to your attention, please write to us, or if you would like to participate in pricing or supplying previously unavailable data or information, please contact Jean Dale at (416) 488-1418, or e-mail us at chpress@charltonpress.com.

Canadian Cataloguing In Publication Data

Border Fine Arts figurines : a Charlton standard catalogue
Biennial.
2nd ed.-
Continues: Charlton standard catalogue of Border Fine Arts figurines.
ISSN 1711-0009
ISBN 0-88968-310-7 (3rd edition)
ISBN 978-0-88968-310-5
    1. Border Fine Arts--Collectors and collecting--Catalogs.
2. Figurines--Scotland--Collectors and collecting--Catalogs.

NK8473.S35C3   738.8'2'075   C2004-900319-4

The Charlton Press

Editorial Office
P. O. Box 820, Station Willowdale B
North York, Ontario M2K 2R1 Canada
Telephone: (416) 488-1418 Fax: (416) 488-4656
Telephone: (800) 442-6042 Fax: (800) 442-1542
www.charltonpress.com, e-mail: chpress@charltonpress.com

PRICING AND THE INTERNET

Over the past thirty years we have gathered pricing information from auctions, dealer submissions, direct mail catalogues and newsletters, all contributed prices on one of two levels, wholesale or retail. We, at the Charlton Press, consider auctions basically a dealer affair, while price lists, naturally retail. To equate both prices, we needed to adjust the auction results upward, by a margin of 30% to 40%, allowing for dealer markups, before comparing and then looking for a consensus on retail prices.

The marketplace has changed, the internet and on-line auctions are growing at such a rate that all other pricing sources we used are being completely overwhelmed by the sheer weight of the items being offered.

The impact the Internet will have on collectables has yet to be appreciated by collectors and dealers alike. All the old avenues such as fairs, shows, dealer stores, retail outlets, direct mail houses and auction rooms are being forced to change due to the extreme pressure of this marketing venue. Margins have come under pressure, wholesale and retail prices are starting to blend, and competition for the Collectors' budget will intensify. We feel this is for the best, as the collectors will receive more value for their money because of competition and also, the large number of participants in the on-line auction process will add greater interest to all collectables.

HOW TO USE THIS CATALOGUE

On the pages that follow, Border Fine Arts figurines are listed, illustrated, described and cross-referenced in alphabetical order by their **Names**. When two or more figures have the same name - but different physical modelling characteristics - they are listed as Style One, Style Two and so on after their names, starting with the first one issued. Such figures will also have different model numbers. When known, the figurine's modeller or **Designer** is listed next. What then follows is the figure's **Height**, given in inches and centimetres. The actual **Colourway** of the figure is listed next. The **Dates** of issue and discontinuation are next.

The Model numbers of all **Varieties** are then listed. Varieties are minor mould changes, decorative alterations, and slight size differences due to firing. Different physical modelling characteristics constitute different styles, dictating different model numbers, and so are not varieties. If the figure is part of a **Series,** then a series name is given next.

The final listing gives the **Price**, the current market value of the figure described. The price appears in U.K. Sterling Pounds, then U.S. funds and then Canadian dollars.

INSURING YOUR FIGURINES

As with any other of your valuables, making certain figurines are protected is a very important concern. It is paramount that you display or store any items in a secure place - preferably one safely away from traffic in the home.

Your figurines are most often covered under your basic homeowner's policy and there are generally three kinds of such policies - standard, broad and comprehensive. Each has its own specific deductible and terms.

Under a general policy, your figurines are considered 'contents' and are covered for all of the perils covered under the contractual terms of your policy (fire, theft, water damage and so on).

However, since figurines are extremely delicate, breakage is treated differently by most insurance companies. There is usually an extra premium attached to insure figures against accidental breakage by, or carelessness of the owner. This is sometimes referred to as 'fine arts' rider. You are advised to contact your insurance professional to get all the answers.

In order to help you protect yourself, it is critical that you take inventory of your figurines and have Colour photographs taken of all your pieces. This is the surest method of clearly establishing, for the police and your insurance company, the items lost or destroyed. It is also the easiest way to establish their replacement value in the event of a tragedy.

WHERE TO BUY

Border Fine Arts can be purchased from retail shops throughout the UK. The BFA web site now lists the addresses and telephone numbers of current UK stockists. Many retailers carry quite a range and can, of course, order anything in current production. Retailers are allocated pieces produced in limited editions, and as the editions tend to be quite small, there are usually not enough to go round. This has become a considerable problem with regard to certain pieces where there are evidently not enough to satisfy the demand. Such pieces seem to be any tractors or pieces featuring machinery. Rarely are these seen on display in retail outlets as they have been reserved as soon as the news is out that they are to be produced!

The market for secondary pieces is developing at a considerable rate at present and internet auctions now regularly feature many desirable early pieces as well as more recently retired figurines. Pieces may be found at both specialists and general auctions and at general Collectors Fairs held throughout the UK. The BFA Society magazine issues a "Seek 'n' Sell" catalogue, and obviously other transactions occur on a private basis. There are a handful of specialist outlets offering secondary market pieces. In the UK collectors "Table Top" sales are being held and are well attended.

TABLE OF CONTENTS

INTRODUCTION
By Marilyn Sweet

I first became aware of Border Fine Arts on a trip to Scotland during the early 1980s. I saw and admired the fantastic detail of the pieces in shops – mainly the ponies and mice on fruit – and on enquiry found they were made in Langholm. Our route home was subsequently amended so that we could visit the Borders and the home of Border Fine Arts! On arrival a local retailer directed us to the factory. It was late in the day and the factory had just shut. A man came out to talk to us. He invited us into his office, enthused about "Thorionware"™ and its properties, showed us some pieces and gave me some leaflets. That man was John Hammond! Little did I realise then that 20 or so years later we would meet again to discuss the book which became the first edition of Border Fine Arts Collectables! In the intervening years I became a Border Fine Arts collector, not just of pieces but also of brochures, leaflets and price lists (in the case of the latter items my long-suffering family would say a "hoarder" – but how useful my carefully "hoarded" items have now become for they formed the basis of this book)! In every new town we visited the local stockist was sought! I was well and truly "hooked". I became a founder member of the BFA Society and attended many BFA events. I have visited Langholm and Border Fine Arts many times now but it is that original occasion that still sticks in my mind, rather like John Hammond's own initial visit to Langholm. The third edition of this book is the result of continuing accumulation of all these "Border Fine Arts" experiences and I hope that collectors old and new enjoy it alike!

THE HISTORY OF BORDER FINE ARTS

The Early Days

The tourist guide "Discover Eskdale and Liddesdale" begins with an excerpt from a poem which reads:

"Amidst the rolling Cheviots,
The town of Langholm lies.
A little off the beaten track,
That's why it's Paradise."

It was to this place of peace and tranquility that the founder of the Company, John Hammond was attracted during a chance visit to the Borders. Langholm lies about 22 miles north of Carlisle and nestles in the hills beside the famous sea trout River Esk. John had come north investigating the possibilities of setting up a business making figurines. He had toured Northern England and arrived in the Lake District. Being so close to the Scottish Border he decided to cross it just to say he had been to Scotland! On his return south the mists descended and with visibility so poor he decided to find accommodation for the night. Staying overnight in Langholm he was taken by the kindness, warmth and general friendliness of the Border people and he spent the next day exploring the area before returning south to Winchester.

A few short weeks later John returned to see Middleholms, an 18th century farmhouse on the outskirts of Langholm which had outbuildings offering workshop potential. Middleholms was acquired – for once the swirling Scottish mists had a positive outcome – who knows what might have happened had John been able to safely journey south that night! John and sculptor Victor Hayton set up "Border Craft and Design," with just three employees and began to make cold-cast bronze and silver figurines in late 1972.

John travelled miles at the beginning promoting the company and gaining a foothold in the market. One day Jedburgh antique dealer Ron Turner informed him that "people likes 'em small and likes 'em painted." The advice was to be acted upon and back at

Middleholms he and the workforce discussed this. Experiments began to research materials and paint, the latter involving paint-makers in Portsmouth who specialised in anti-fouling paints. Finally, a special cold casting process was developed which allowed the sculptures to be subsequently painted. The material developed was named "Thorionware"™ and in October 1974 the name "Border Fine Arts" was registered. "Thorionware"™ offered the opportunity to make figurines with an incredible amount of detail.

In the early years Border Fine Arts was a very small craft operation with three employees, including Ray Ayres, based around the kitchen table at Middleholms Farm. John advertised locally for people with the ability to paint and found a wealth of talent in and around Langholm. The Border area has a long tradition of cloth dyeing and weaving, with its tweed being world famous. The Borderers' natural understanding of colour, with a little training, was quickly transferred to ceramic painting. The Company developed new designs which were carefully researched, well-detailed, and painted in natural colours. They were extremely well-received by a growing band of appreciative collectors. The workforce was expanded and Middleholms was full to capacity. The 1977 price list (the earliest I have a copy of) comprised of 24 Natural History Sculptures by Victor Hayton, with singular contributions from Anne Wall and Mairi Laing. It was produced on a typewriter with the few product codes in existence written on – far removed from the professional full-colour brochures of the future! Victor's limited editions included L02 *Red Squirrels* (edition of 100) and *Weasel and Wren* (edition of 125), which make these amongst the smallest edition numbers issued by Border. Few of the early pieces had a product code, but the distinction of being L01 (edition of 250) went to *Peregrine Falcon, Style One*, as Border's first hand-painted piece. Depicting a falcon pinning down his prey, this impressive sculpture is highly sought after today, as indeed are all these early pieces.

New premises were soon required and, in 1978, Border Fine Arts moved to its present location, Townfoot, in Langholm itself. The initial buildings there also had to be added to as demand for Border Fine Arts products continued to increase. In 1986, Border Fine Arts won the Scottish Business Achievement Award in recognition of growth of the Company and commitment to making a quality product.

In 2004 Border Fine Arts celebrated their thirtieth year under their founder, John Hammond, M.B.E. During the following year he decided to retire.

Subsidiary Companies/Merchanting Division

Around 1987, Border Fine Arts developed their "Merchanting Division," a subsidiary company based in Northampton. Here, The Chiltern Collection including *Thelwell's Riding Academy* and the *Flower Fairies* were manufactured. Over the years the Merchanting Division has also marketed a wide variety of products including Flower Fairies fine bone china giftware, collectors plates from "American Artists," various art prints, Waterford Porcelain Dolls, *The Lowell Davis Farm Collection*, *The Legend of King Arthur*, and *Pups and Dogs Galore*. The collections of *Finesse Bone China Birds* and *The Imagined World of Fleur Cowles* were manufactured in Worcester. The Carrickfergus factory in Northern Ireland manufactured *The Irish Heritage Collection*, which consists of cottages, pubs, and historical monuments of Ireland, as well as *The Wee Folk*, and a small number of figurines.

Enesco

In November 1995 Border Fine Arts became a division of Enesco European Giftware Group Ltd., and the manufacturing of some products was transferred to the Far East. These included the *Beatrix Potter* range, and *Dogs*, and *Cats and Kittens Galore*. Enesco is one of the world's leading producers of giftware, collectables and decorative accessories. Their ranges include the well known *Cherished Teddies, Snowbabies, David Winter Cottages* and *Lilliput Lane*. Enesco had become associated with Border Fine Arts in 1989 with BFA distributing Enesco's products in the UK. Border Fine Arts own ranges were extended to include novelty type and decorative accessories, housewares and other ceramic items. In order to clarify the situation, John Hammond issued a letter in January 1999, to all BFA Society members. In this he explained that in recent years Border Fine Arts had diversified into new ranges of products marketed under the brand name **Border Fine Arts Studio**. In order that these could be marketed at realistic prices, the products had to be sourced from high-quality manufacturers in the Orient. The traditional, James Herriot, wildlife and agricultural product on which Border Fine Arts' reputation is based would carry the name **Border Fine Arts Classic**. This guaranteed such products were manufactured in the UK. Hence distinguishing the place of manufacture, which had until then been rather hazy with regard to some products. Efforts have been made to establish the place of manufacture of the items contained in this book. Generally, any piece noted as "Border Fine Arts Studio" (i.e. *The Cubist Cats* or *Hay Days*), are manufactured in Far Eastern Countries. All the Border Fine Arts "Character" series are manufactured abroad as are the James Herriot introductions (from 2001).

Special Interest and Portrait Items

Border Fine Arts issued some pieces as "Special Interest." As such, these models were generally only available to a customer's specific order. However, some were available to purchase directly from retailers who had decided to stock them. They usually appeared on separate leaflets and had their own price lists. These pieces tended to be subjects of interest to specific collectors rather than the general public. Many of the subjects were field sports themes such as shooting, racehorses (painted entirely to customer's instructions, including the jockey silks), and rarer breeds of dogs and British wild animals. Some pieces which were on general sale to start with were transferred to the special interest category. As special interest pieces were not generally on show in retail shops nor in the brochures, they were not as widely available as general release pieces and therefore rarer to find today. The Special Interest category ceased at the end of 1995.

Until early 2000, most Border pieces could be ordered as a portrait, or painted to individual instructions for an additional percentage fee. This practice ceased at the beginning of 2000 in respect of Limited Edition pieces, with open editions still available painted to order. In 2004 Border Fine Arts re-introduced an "Exclusive Painting Service" whereby the artists at the Langholm Studios can be commissioned, for a percentage fee, to create specially painted versions of Classic figurines, making them unique pieces.

Limited Editions

Border Fine Arts limited edition pieces are probably the most sought after and tend to be the more prestigious pieces which are most readily associated with the BFA name.

In terms of numbers, the smallest editions are of only 100. These are the early piece *Red Squirrels* (L02), and the much later piece *Carriage Horse* (L94). Initially, Border's limited edition pieces were never more than an edition of 500, which makes finding them in perfect condition today a very difficult task!

Limited editions which number less than 500 are: *Weasel and Wren* (edition size 125); *Cleveland Bay Stallion* (L63) and *The Queen's Haflinger at Balmoral* (edition sizes 200); *Peregrine*

Falcon, Style One (L01), *Common Teal, Cheviot Ewe with Lambs* and *Red Stag* (B0437) (250 editions); several of *The Imagined World of Fleur Cowles* series (300 editions) and *Jewel of the East* (L152), *Afghan Hound, Style One* (L12), *Felling the Furrow* (L57), *Harvesting* (L62), *Welsh Cob, Style One* (L11), *Otter On A Stone Base, Ospreys* (L38), and *Red Grouse with Young* (all 350 editions). Later, limited edition pieces tend to be near or over 1,000, with some such as *Ebb and Flow* (B0187), issued in an edition size of 2,500 and two USA Black Stallion pieces produced in an edition size of 3,500 each.

Where limited editions were available in painted resin and cold cast bronze and/or different colourways, the total number of the edition is made up of pieces produced in all media/colours, unless stated otherwise. There is no information as to the proportion of different media/colourways produced for a piece. Whilst the majority of limited edition pieces were sold out rather than retired, there are some editions thought not to have been completed such as *Arab Stallion with Saluki*, and *The Military Collection*.

Limited edition pieces are issued with an accompanying numbered certificate. If the piece is being purchased on the secondary market it is particularly important to check that the certificate numbers matches that on the piece itself.

The Numbering System and Collection Names

Initially, limited edition pieces were given numbers preceded by the letter "L" which easily identified them. However, confusingly, *Chaser* (L50), *Hurdler* (L51), and *The Finish* (L52) were not actually limited editions. Also, all the James Herriot collection pieces were preceded by JH whether they were open or limited editions. Other series were identified with the modeller's initials, such as JB – Judy Boyt Woodland Collection; MT – Dogs by Margaret Turner; or the initials of the series' name, such as DG – Dogs Galore; MTR – Masters of the River; NP – Native Ponies; FE – First Encounters; and ED – Early Days. This simplified things somewhat and made a series easily identifiable. Others simply had a three digit number. However, in the mid-1990s Border began to change the system. The majority of Border pieces have a comparatively short production life of a few years and belong to a particular series. However, one piece which has been produced for many years has confusingly been part of several collections. In 1982, *Black-Faced Ewe and Collie* (104) was part of the "Farm Series – Open Editions." In 1983 it was part of "Agricultural Series – Open Editions" and, in 1984, "Agricultural and Sporting Series – Open Editions." In 1996, it's number was changed to *B104* and it became a James Herriot Collection piece! It also formed part of the sequentially numbered combination piece *S1*, and in 1999 was chosen as one of Border's most popular models to be done as *B0505* in cold-cast bronze as part of Border Fine Art's 25th Anniversary Collection.

June 1996 saw the change to B0 numbers, and the introduction of 6-digit numbers which are not very meaningful to collectors – somehow a collector in conversation saying "I'm looking for 739448" doesn't quite have the same ring to it as "I'm looking for ED9 to complete my collection" has. The former statement is likely to receive a totally blank reception whereas the latter is likely to result in some sort of knowing response.

Commissions

Over the years Border Fine Arts have made a number of pieces commissioned by a variety of customers – mainly retail shops, but also societies and individuals. Pieces commissioned by retail shops are those sold exclusively from the commissioning individual retailer (e.g. The Heavy Horse Collection Gold Edition; *Home From School* (B0403); *Cashmere Goat* (CG1); *Leicester Fox* (L58), or a group of 25 major retailers from throughout the UK known as "The Guild of Specialist China and Glass Retailers." The "Guild" pieces include such diverse subjects as *At the Water's Edge* (EG05), and

Off to the Fair (EG06). There are other pieces for which a group of shops have priority of sale, usually in late Autumn as a sort of "pre-release" and then become general release items the following January, e.g. *All In A Day's Work* (B0593), which are not commissioned pieces as such.

In the early 1980s Border Fine Arts produced exclusive designs for the Northumbria Sporting Company Ltd. based at Alnwick, Northumberland. These included *Felling The Furrow* (L57) and the very detailed *Harvesting* (L62), which were sold with the option of a specially made glass case with metal edges.

Pieces commissioned by Breed Societies included *The Suffolk Punch Stallion* (L70). Several such pieces subsequently went on release either as "Special Interest" items or generally.

Border themselves took out a licence to produce *Paschal Lamb* (L114) for the Preston Guild, and it is understood that an individual commissioned *Police Handler and German Shepherd Dog* (L122). It is not always easy to find out about these commissioned pieces. The best way is to contact the major retailers and ask to be put on their mailing lists.

The American Market

Schmid of Massachusetts, an American Company, distributed Border Fine Arts products throughout the U.S.A. from the late 1970s until they ceased trading in 1995. CS Kellogg and Co. Inc. of Colorado did likewise but on a much smaller scale. The Border Fine Arts ranges available in the USA included many which were American exclusives being, for example, of native North American animals, but there were also others which were issued on both sides of the Atlantic. American artists such as Daniel Parker, Boyd Perry, Chris Leiter and Stan Sparre all produced wildlife studies for Border Fine Arts/Schmid, whilst Ben Black designed his Clown collections and Fleur Cowles her jungle cats with flowers. The American company American Artists also commissioned Border Fine Arts to produce four equine studies by Fred Stone, one of which (*The Black Stallion*, on a sandy base) was a USA exclusive. Border Fine Arts produced a vast diverse range of figurines for the American market, the majority of which belonged to the various *Lowell Davis Collections*.

MAKING A BORDER FINE ARTS FIGURINE

The inherent qualities of the Thorionware™ process allows the artist great scope for exciting and complex compositions previously impossible in ceramic sculptures. The sculptor uses a special modelling wax to make the original. The actual creation of the design can take many hours as every detail has to be carved by hand using intricate dentistry tools. The original wax sculpture then has to be approved.

The process begins with the "blocking" of the sculpture's original design. A special mould-making silicone compound is carefully applied over the wax original to produce the master mould. This is a crucial part of the process, as a mistake could result in the loss of the original and all the hours and hours of work it represents.

Having removed the wax original from the master mould, a metal composition casting is then poured which becomes the production master pattern. This master pattern is carefully worked with engraving tools to ensure that every detail is clear and accurate. This master forms the basis for the production process. Production moulds and cases are made with great precision from this master, for they must not distort in any way during the casting cycle.

BFA's unique resin Thorionware™ is injected as a liquid "slip" into the moulds. A chemical reaction takes place under pressure, which results in a white porcelain-like casting – a faithful rendering of the sculptor's original.

The whiteware castings in their moulds are then moved to the demoulding room. Here they are very carefully and skilfully removed (demoulded) and set aside to finish curing. They are also inspected and any piece not up to BFA's exacting standards will be destroyed. The moulds are reassembled and sent back to the casting room for further use.

The figurines are then carefully fettled using dentistry drills to remove excess material from the figurine. Any pieces composed of several parts may be assembled at this point. Precise quality controls are implemented at this time and all imperfect figurines are immediately discarded.

The surface of the sculpture is treated to accept the enamel paints. If the piece is a new addition, the whiteware goes back to the design studio where the master painter decorates the new piece under the guidance of the sculptor. Many "proofs" will be developed before one is decided upon as the production standard.

All Border Fine Arts sculptures are hand-painted from start to finish by a highly trained artist. The artist uses a wide palette of special enamel colours to build up to the finished piece with several applications. Being individually hand-painted meant that no two pieces would ever be exactly identical. The studio manager continually inspects for quality and style. Finally the finished pieces are initialled by the painter. Many sculptures are accompanied by a small certificate signed by the painter and certificates of prestigious pieces even have a small photograph of the artist.

In the finishing department any complicated sculptures which require painting in several parts are carefully assembled. A further quality check follows and then a clear enamel is applied before the sculptures are baked in an oven which fuses the colours to the body of the piece. This produces a durable and natural finish.

Where appropriate the pieces are mounted on fine mahogany bases. Limited editions are numbered and registered. The final quality check then takes place and the base is baized or felted to protect the purchaser's furniture. The sculptures are carefully packed to begin their journeys all over the world.

It is the attention to detail at every stage of the manufacturing process that has become the hallmark of Border Fine Arts. Throughout the world, Border Fine Arts is widely acknowledged for its "craftsmanship in sculpture" – truly the Collector's Choice.

COLLECTING BORDER FINE ARTS FIGURINES

There is such a vast range of BFA figurines and many collectors seem to specialise in one or two aspects. Others perhaps start with "anything – as long as it's Border" before becoming more focused and refining their collection. The James Herriot series is very large and covers a wide variety of agricultural subjects with pieces of varying sizes (and prices!). Within the James Herriot range are several "sub-series" such as James Herriot's Favourite Characters, which would make pleasing smaller displays. Most species of wildlife, both British and foreign, are covered and, for example, just collecting foxes would make a sizeable collection. Dogs or horses/ponies would also provide a considerable challenge to collect. Especially since the latter include some elusive very limited editions and short production run pieces. Birds are another vast subject and perhaps could be limited to garden, wildfowl, owls (even just Barn Owls!) or subjects by a particular modeller. Available space for display will also play a part – some pieces such as *Call of the Falcon* (L162) would require a large area in order to do the piece justice, and preferably in a central position so that the detail on all sides of the piece could be appreciated.

The majority of pieces illustrated in the first edition of this book were manufactured in the UK. However, times change and today the BFA "Studio" pieces which are sourced from the Far East outnumber the Classic sculptures. From 2004 Border Fine Arts reverted to separate brochures for *The Classic Collection*, *The Studio Collections*, *World of Beatrix Potter*, and *Studio Character Collections*.

EXAMPLES OF COLLECTING BY SUBECT

The James Herriot Collection

One of Border Fine Arts major collections is based on the characters created by the UK's favourite vet, "James Herriot".

James Herriot (real name Alf Wight) " was a veterinarian in the Yorkshire Dales. In 1970 he published his first book *If Only They Could Talk* . His words painted such a rich picture of Yorkshire rural life in the thirties and forties, a place full of characters whose lives revolved around the farm and its animals, the market and the seasons in those "good ol' days." He went on to write several more books based on his experiences and these extremely humorous recollections were turned into films for the cinema and a TV series. It was whilst watching these that John Hammond had the brainwave of turning the people, animals and situations into figurines by Border Fine Arts. John Hammond met with Alf Wight and in 1985 the "All Creatures Great and Small" collection consisting of ten pieces (JH1-JH10) was issued. These initial pieces ranged from individual figurines to scenes, and this practice has continued giving the collector plenty to choose from to suit pocket and shelf space!

Subjects in the James Herriot ranges reflect the plethora of rural life: the fact that farmers were wall builders *(A Warm Day Walling* JH31), fence makers (*Hedge Laying* JH65), as well as stockmen (*Steady Lad, Steady* JH90). Initially they relied on horse power (*Stout Hearts* JH34 and *No Foot No 'Oss* JH94) until machinery came to the Dales (*New Technology Arrives Today* JH46). People on which the farming community depended have also been depicted – *The Country Doctor* (JH63) and *Daily Delivery* (JH103). Figurines such as *Winter Feeding* (JH10) and *Winter Rescue* (JH41) depict the harshness of a Yorkshire winter whilst new life in spring is also a popular subject with such pieces as *Spring Lambing* (JH6) and *Spring Pastures* (JH32). Collectors can delight in the detail shown in complete scenes such as *Viewing the Practice* (JH8), *New Shoes for Dolly* (JH29) and *Milking at Peter Trenholms* (JH7). Smaller pieces of the vet's favourite animal characters include Mrs. Pumphrey's pampered Pekinese *Tricky Woo* (JH16) and the piglet *Nugent* (JH12).

Since the initial models were issued, the collections of the James Herriot range have been an enormous on-going success, and new models continue to be added at least annually. Initially, the interpretations of the subjects and incidents described in the stories were directly influenced by Herriot's characters. More recent figurines are more indirectly influenced with the design team pondering what happened next? Or what happened before? When new figurines are to be planned, the design team meet and have a brainstorming session considering any areas not fully catered for. Designs are then allocated to sculptors. Each sculptor then produces a rough maquette (preliminary model) which is then scrutinized by the sales and marketing team.

Within the James Herriot range there are sub-collections, including *All Creatures Great and Small, Every Living Thing, All Things Wise and Wonderful, James Herriot's Favourite Characters, James Herriot's Yorkshire* and *James Herriot's Cat Stories.* A spin-off from the James Herriot series is one about a Border Collie Pup and his feline friend, *The Adventures of Ruff and Reddy.*

In the Border Fine Arts catalogues, each James Herriot piece usually has an extract from the relevant book which can enhance the collector's pleasure in the piece. An article written in *Issue 3* of *The Borderer* ends with the following: *James Herriot has shared his warmth for the countryside and its people with us through his books.*

Border Fine Arts brings it alive through its figurines, every one meticulously researched from his stories. Each piece is lovingly created by skilled craftspeople to illustrate the nostalgia and feeling of rural life in the first half of the century – "the good ol' days." It is the art of the raconteur to tell the stories and the vision of the sculptor to bring the character to life for the reader. James Herriot will always live on through the figurines of Border Fine Arts.

Tractors

The single most popular subject produced by Border Fine Arts is apparently ... Tractors! Amazingly, each year the announcement of THE Tractor piece is guaranteed to send many a collector into a collecting frenzy! The tractor pieces have also caused the most controversy. In the decade since the first issue, every limited edition tractor has been eagerly sought by collectors and there have simply not been enough to go round.

The first tractor piece *New Technology Arrives Today* (JH46) was issued in January 1991. This James Herriot model featured a Fordson Tractor and was a limited edition of 1,250. Like all the tractor pieces, it was modelled by Ray Ayres. Tractor "fever" really got a grip when *The Fergie* (JH64) was issued the following year, also in an edition size of 1,250. Subsequently, the edition size of tractor pieces increased to 1,500, then 1,750, then 2,000, then, *Cut and Crated* B0649 was issued in an edition of 2001.

In 2003 Border introduced annual "Classic Member-only Tractor Figurines" and also tractors in the Studio range of unlimited editions. Classic Collection tractors continue to be issued in limited editions (now of 1,500 or more). So there are now a variety of tractors available, limited and unlimited editions to suit every collectors pocket!

Lowell Davis

Collecting figurines designed by Lowell Davis would result in a wide variety of subjects varying in size from the very small "Club" pieces to the large significant limited editions. Many of the pieces include Lowell himself and his wife "Miss Charlotte". A personal favourite of mine is *What Rat Race?* which portrays them seated in the horse drawn sleigh enjoying a ride in the snow. There are also several models featuring Lowell's beloved dogs *Hooker* and *Ozark Belle* – the "coon" (racoon) hound. Through the models you will be introduced to many of the animals on the farm – most of which have names including the rooster *Big Jack*. As all Lowell Davis pieces are now retired they would have to be obtained on the secondary market and if you are not in the USA it would involve a significant amount of "International" trade. One of the appealing features of the Lowell Davis collections is the "story" behind the figurine. Each of Lowell's figurines came with a "story card" explaining the figurine. Here is an example of one! *HIS EYES ARE BIGGER THAN HIS STOMACH* "*Winter is setting in and after a dry year with the wild food sources having been a might scarce...Mr. Fox has to make some changes in his diet. The more hunger sets in the braver he becomes...so he moves in closer and closer to the chicken house. There he waits, slobbering at the mouth, waiting for dusk to set in...and old Mr. Fox, he's thinking, "Now, if I wait until dark, Mr. Lowell is going to come down and shut the trap door...so maybe I'd better take the chance...look at those plump beauties! Ahhh!!! Dominicker and Dumplings, Leg of Leghorn, Wyandotte Stew...Roasted Rhode Island Red...slurp! I just got to go for it...!*"

In 1987 Schmid set up the "Lowell Davis Farm Club" issuing a *Farm Gazette* three times each year (with the last volume being number 8, in 1995) and these have now become collectable items themselves. Members were given pieces for renewing their membership, a club cap and had the opportunity to purchase pieces made exclusively for Club members.

The Border Fine Arts Pottery Company Collection

This division of BFA was launched in 2004 with a variety of farm animals and wild birds being produced in high gloss ceramic. All figurines are designed and sculpted by a BFA artist in the Langholm Studios before being passed for production by a BFA international manufacturing partner. Being well modelled and competitively priced the collection has proved a success and as a result has expanded.

Beatrix Potter

It is now over a hundred years since Beatrix Potter wrote a picture letter to the sick son of a former governess, four-year-old Noel Moore. In it she told the tale of four little rabbits by the names of Flopsy, Mopsy, Cottontail and Peter. Eight years later she privately published *The Tale of Peter Rabbit.*

It was an immediate success and as a result Frederick Warne agreed to publish her book commercially provided that Beatrix redid the illustrations in colour. By the end of 1903, 50,000 copies of *Peter Rabbit* had been sold and it has never been out of print since! Beatrix went on using her talents as author and illustrator of many books about her animal characters.

In 1987 John Hammond was considering the possibility of adding to the Border Fine Arts range by introducing models of animal writers. He happened to have illustrations of Beatrix Potter's characters on his desk when Richard Wawrzesta, the Managing Director of Chiltern, BFA's Northampton subsidiary company was attending a meeting. Richard suggested that he would like to attempt to model some of the Beatrix Potter subjects. Although he had never seriously sculpted before his models met with the approval of BFA and Frederick Warne. Richard went on to model all the Beatrix Potter characters and indeed the Brambly Hedge ones too. The vast majority of the BFA pieces in this book are his work.

Richard was born in Northampton in 1952. He went to Art College and then tried several ventures of an artistic nature before becoming managing director of Chiltern.

The early Beatrix Potter collection figurines were issued in beautiful painted gift tins which have become collectable in their own right. The initial models BP1 to BP12 were extended over the next few years until a total of 28 formed the main series entitled "The World of Beatrix Potter." The first retired models were *Cecily Parsley Ran Away* (BP10), and *Amiable Guinea Pig* (BP12), which were both withdrawn in December 1989. A year later *Henny Penny Meets Jemima Puddle-duck* (BP18) was retired after only being available for two years. The last three in the series *Little Black Pig* [Pig-Wig] (BP26), *Benjam Bunny Eating Lettuce* (BP27), and *Old Mr. Benjamin Bunny* (BP28) also had very short production runs making these very difficult to find today. "The World of Beatrix Potter Miniatures" forms quite an extensive collection of 37 models. Thirty-five of these (prefixed by BPM) were manufactured by BFA in this country. The BFA Beatrix Potter Miniatures include a number of characters unique to them. These include *Kep the Collie Dog* (BPM1), *Lucinda the Doll* (BPM5), *Jane and Clock (BPM6),* and *Cat with Watering Can* (BPM10).

Following ENESCO's acquisition of Border Fine Arts manufacture transferred to the Far East and the figures were quite considerably reduced in price. They lost their BPM prefix and were allocated a six-figure number. These figures have "Made in China" printed on the underside of the base. Since 1998, however, special commissions have returned to the UK for production. These figures are larger and more expensive, and include intricate tableau pieces designed by Richard Wawrzesta.

In 2003 there were new developments for the Beatrix Potter range. Enesco set up The "Friends of Peter Rabbit Club" (contact details are at the end of this section) in response to numerous requests from avid collectors of Border Fine Arts' *The World of Beatrix Potter* figurines. The club issues a club exclusive magazine twice a year, and members receive a "Symbol of Membership" figurine annually. Border Fine Arts also introduced a range of ceramic figures, including limited editions based on the well-known illustrations of the Beatrix Potter books. Also launched in June 2003 were a series of porcelain figurines for the "Peter Rabbit and Friends" retail outlets. This collection of contemporary porcelain figures, in a mixture of matt and gloss finish, was based on the new Peter Seedlings artwork inspired by Beatrix Potter's much-loved and timeless Original Peter Rabbit books. They were modelled by Janet Miller and featured favourite characters in dynamic new poses. Two more models were issued in January 2004 but by December 2004 the whole range was retired.

Brambly Hedge

Jill Barklem's series of books about the mouse community living in the English hedgerow of Brambly Hedge were published in 1980. The first four, *Spring, Summer, Autumn,* and *Winter* were such an immediate success that manufacturers were soon requesting licences to reproduce the characters in a variety of media. Brambly Hedge characters modelled by Richard Wawrzesta were received with enthusiasm by Jill Barklem, who was impressed with the fine detail the "Thorionware" resin allowed. BFA's licence issued in January 1987, expired in December 1997. Richard Wawrzesta modelled the entire collection which was first issued in 1988, with the first eight figures of the Store Stump Kitchen Collection. These were initially packed in attractive metal tins. The pieces are impressed at the back "B.H. c J.B. date year B.F.A." A paper label is stuck to the underside of the base.

Furniture from the Brambly Hedge illustrations also joined the collection and again much detail was able to be included. Cardboard display stands of Brambly Hedge scenes could be purchased which gave the figurines a lovely background setting. These were withdrawn by 1992 and are sought after but not easily found today. Other items were added to the range, such as picture frames, clocks, cameos and waterballs. From 1989 these novelty type items were often manufactured in collaboration with the American Enesco Corporation. Enesco themselves had their own licence to manufacture Brambly Hedge items. Their resin figurines, also modelled by Richard Wawrzesta, were the same as the BFA designs. They were manufactured in China and were available between 1990 and 1994, mainly in the USA. Whereas Enesco's figurines tend to have a waxy finish, the models produced by Border Fine Arts do not.

The UK retailers, Wheelers of Loughborough, commissioned Brambly Hedge figurines. These were two collections of tableaux and trinket boxes: *The Four Seasons* and *The Special Occasions* which have proved to be extremely popular with Brambly Hedge enthusiasts.

Fairies

The world of make-believe enjoyed a high-profile in the 19th century. The existence of "little people" as featured in the works of Hans Christian Anderson, Lewis Carroll and J. M. Barrie brought them to the fore. Cicely Mary Barker (1895-1973) became the "flower fairy painter" in 1923 when her book of illustrations entitled *Flower Fairies of the Spring* was printed by Blackie. Cicely was the daughter of a partner in a seed company. She sent botanical specimens for identification to Kew Gardens and received others to paint. She had a convenient source of child models for her fairies as her sister ran a kindergarten in the family home. Cicely regularly added new books to the Flower Fairy Series until the last one, *Flower Fairies of the Wayside* was published in 1948.

There are three BFA fairies series. The initial four were modelled by David Geenty (more well-known for his animal sculptures) as open editions and were listed as "Fairies by Linda Pagett". These had a short production run being issued in 1981 and retired in December 1982 which makes them very difficult to find today. The thirteen initial *Flower Fairies* were also modelled by David Geenty and they also had production runs lasting for two years only. Again they were open editions. There was a gap of three years before Flower Fairies were produced again, and in 1993 Glenis Devereux's models were issued. These were all limited editions of 1950. In January 2000 a series of six open edition Flower Fairy mini figurines were issued. During the next few years the "Fairies Collection" continued to expand with new figurines and assorted other items being regularly introduced. In 2005 Border did not renew the licence and so at the end of 2005 the whole Fairies Collection was retired.

The Fairies are all quite delicate designs, with thin stems and petals adorning the majority. Any being offered on the secondary market would require careful scrutiny to ascertain condition.

The Legend of King Arthur

This collection of eight figurines appeared in the Border Fine Arts Merchanting catalogues.

Oliver Otter and Friends

Kate Veale began her career as a commercial artist in a design studio in Leicester in the 1980s after studying History at Durham University. Here she was noticed and subsequently tutored by Roland Hilder, popular artist and director of Royle Publications. In 1988 she joined Gordon Fraser to work on the well known greetings card range "Country Companions". Drawing her inspiration from her love of animals and vivid childhood memories of growing up in the English countryside she wrote and illustrated a series of four children's books about Oliver Otter and his friends which were published by Sapling in 1996. The four books are *Drew the Shrew and the Star*, *Did You Swim Today Oliver Otter?*, *Follow the Trail Digsby the Mole* and *Will Squirrel's Big Fizz*. Each of the four characters portrayed by Border Fine Arts features in their own book. The model of Drew the Shrew also includes his friend Trevelyan the Newt.

The Border Fine Arts range was issued in 1997 and included bookends, a clock, nurseryware and picture frames. The models included in this book were manufactured in China.

Peter Pan

In 1995 Glenis Devereux modelled six characters from J. M. Barrie's play *Peter Pan*. In 1929 Barrie had donated all the rights of his play to Great Ormond Street Children's Hospital and the royalties from the sale of BFA's Peter Pan range were similarly to benefit this famous London hospital.

Ruff and Ready

The antics of Ruff the Border Collie pup and his friend Reddy the ginger and white kitten were interpreted by long-time Border Fine Arts modeller Anne Wall and introduced in 1995. The set of ten models depict them getting involved in the typical mischief of young animals such as in *Washday Blues* (RR04) pouncing on newly washed overalls to get them just like the farmer likes them – covered in mud and farmyard stains.

Thelwell

Norman Thelwell drew cartoons for *Punch* magazine and many of these were included in his books. *Thelwell's Riding Academy* and *Angels on Horseback* were just two of several books featuring rather plump little girls and their equally endowed shaggy and rather appealing ponies getting up to a wide variety of mischief. BFA's Chiltern Division accurately reproduced the humour in the two series *Thelwell's Riding Academy* and *Thelwell Goes West*. The former featuring the English style of riding whilst the latter half dozen have cowboys! The Thelwells were initially modelled by Fred Moore and latterly by Richard Wawrzesta. Each piece is incised with Thelwell's signature and a copyright date. The underside of the base has a paper sticker giving the model name and number and states "Made in England". Each year from 1984 until 1995 a special Christmas theme piece was issued. Several models had a production run of only a year and three lasted for just six months.

Wind in the Willows

These four characters were based on Kenneth Graham's 4 main riverbank characters of *Ratty, Mole, Toad* and *Badger* from his book *Wind in the Willows*. Very little is known about the actual models. The series was entitled "Miniatures on Bronze". A limited number were possibly issued between July and December 1983 and as such must be considered very elusive today. Please note that *Ratty* (M30) and *Mole* (M31) share their allocated numbers with Running Fox (M30) and *Otter* (M31) from the "Miniature on Bronze Animals" series. In 2002 Wheelers of Loughborough commissioned a limited edition tableau *The Riverbank Picnic* featuring a riverbank base and Mr. Toad, Mole, Ratty and Mr. Badger as separate figures to place on it.

Winnie the Pooh

Alan Alexander (always known as A.A.) Milne's well-known stories of Winnie the Pooh were first published by Mathuen in 1926. The stories were written for, and about, his son Christopher Robin, involving adventures with his teddy bear "Winnie the Pooh" and his companions in the nursery. Ernest Shepherd drew the original illustrations but he did not produce the coloured-in versions until 1973. Christopher Robin and his toy animal friends from the Hundred Acre Wood are still popular with today's children. Children, and indeed adults too, are vivid fans of Winnie the Pooh merchandise. Like other characters covered by this book, many diverse products have been manufactured over the years by a wide variety of companies on the Winnie the Pooh theme. In 2000 Border Fine Arts issued their "Classic Pooh" collection and they have continued to add to it every year since. This consists of two quite distinct yet related product ranges: "Lifestyle", which are a selection of home décor accessories such as pencil boxes, candlesticks and mirrors with a Winnie the Pooh figurines as part of the piece, and "Figurines" featuring Pooh, Tigger, Piglet and Eeyore. Although the collection is called "Classic Pooh" all the pieces are in actual fact "Studio" pieces and as such are manufactured abroad.

MODELLERS AND DESIGNERS

There are now more than 3000 models detailed in this book and they have been sculpted/designed by a wide variety of people some of which are, or have been resident sculptors and others employed on a freelance basis.

Ray Ayres

Although not quite first on an alphabetical basis, Ray fully deserves to head this listing for he has been involved with Border Fine Arts from the very beginning. He first met John Hammond in the Student Union Bar at Winchester College of Art in 1973. Ray was studying fine art and at the time John was a sub contractor working for a building construction firm but actively looking into starting a company manufacturing figurines in bronze. Ray went to work for John's fledgling company initially working on the manufacturing/production side involving regular travelling between Langholm and Winchester for 2 years until he moved to Middleholms in 1976. The company needed more figurines and Ray began to sculpt to ensure a regular supply of the product. Little did he realise then that he was embarking on a lifetime's career as Border Fine Arts' Master Sculptor! To date Ray has been Border's most prolific sculptor with more than 400 models to his credit. Ray's repertoire is wide, proving his ability to sculpt anything be it living or mechanical! His models of mice on fruit were among the first I personally admired for their attention to detail making them so realistic that the fruit seemed edible (prior to the mice getting there first)! Ray has sculpted all the tractor pieces, many dogs, farm animals, British mammals, birds, several James Herriot "scenes" and the Society models. Ray leaves no stone unturned in his efforts to accurately represent the subject with much of his research being first-hand observing, taking photographs and discussing with acknowledged experts. Back at the factory numerous books, photographs and videos are available to consult.

Despite being a giant of a man at 6' 6" tall he is able to sculpt the most exquisite detail into relatively small models. Just look at all the minute detail put into the Millennium piece *The Threshing Mill* (B0361) and the tiny kittens in the scene *Milking at Peter Trenholm's* (JH7). Rest assured that any flora, plant, bush or wall appearing in a piece will have received its fair share of attention to detail too!

Ray is currently Vice-President of Design and as such you might expect him to rarely emerge from his studio – not so! He is very accessible to collectors of Border Fine Arts, attending many Collectors Events throughout the country every year demonstrating his sculpting skills and giving illustrated talks about Border. He is always extremely affable and approachable, willing to discuss Border on a one-to-one basis with both new and established collectors and is very open to suggestions for future pieces. This is an aspect much appreciated by Border collectors. Indeed my own ideas for models of Arabian horses resulted in Border models *Arab Stallion, Trotting, Style Two* (L135) and *Arab Mare and Foal, Style Two* (L136) (actually modelled by Anne Wall).

In 2006 Ray celebrated Thirty Years with Border Fine Arts. To commemorate this, all January 2006 new introductions that were sculpted by him have a peregrine falcon etched into the model, together with his initials in raised relief.

Kirsty Armstrong (also known as Kirsty Riley)

Kirsty Armstrong joined the team at Border Fine Arts in 1995. Having successfully completed courses at Cumbria College of Art and Design and Lancashire Polytechnic she set up her own studio and shop which she named "Art Ducko"! Here she produced, among other models her locally well known "chair persons". When she decided to give up working for herself she approached Border Fine Arts and sent them a model of a tiger. Ray considered that Kirsty had some promise of ability and gave her some work to try out. Those initial pieces were not the hoped for success but Kirsty was determined and working under Ray's watchful eye her talent and "biddability" paid off and she became involved in sculpting pigs! Several years on Kirsty is still considered the pig expert but is now equally adept at sculpting other farm animals such as cattle, sheep and goats and she also modelled the James Herriot Cat Stories Series. Her *Under the Hammer* (B066) depicting cattle in an auction ring proved a very popular piece last year. Kirsty Armstrong is also known as Kirsty Riley.

Paul Back

Paul Back has modelled some quite diverse subjects such as "The Crosser", "Admiral Lord Nelson" and the motorbike piece "Wheel to Wheel".

Kerry Bell

Kerry began her career with Border Fine Arts in 2003 with her model of piglets entitled *Odd One Out* (A3398) for the James Herriot Studio Collection and she has gone on to produce further models including a series of Butterflies.

Ben Black

In the brochure illustrating the Ben Black Collection the artist states: *To me, design is a bit of poetry. It captures certain qualities about life and says it in a very special way. I chose clowns with flowers as a subject because I wanted to create something beautiful and light, something people would enjoy living with.* David Geenty actually modelled the pieces from Ben Black's designs. "The Garden of Clowns" with their delicately coloured flowers are poised on a glossy black base whilst those of "The Intermission Series" are on the usual Border Fine Arts wooden bases. The two wall masks have removable material hats and net ruffs around their necks. They were available in the UK but the majority went to the USA where Schmid distributed them.

Judy Boyt

Judy Boyt was an early modeller for Border. Her series included "A Cat Around the House", "Early Days", "Native Ponies of Great Britain" and the Judy Boyt Woodland Collection.

Don Briddell

Don Briddell is one of America's foremost wood carvers, acclaimed for his lifelike decoy ducks. In 2001 he modelled three ducks for the Border Fine Arts Studio collection entitled "Waterfowl of the World". He also modelled the superb limited edition pair of mallards *Leonardo* (L145) and *Mona* (L144).

John Brown

John Brown has modelled birds and from 2001 he has extended his skills to cover cats and kittens and British wildlife.

David Burnham Smith

David's models are few in number but are of a wide-ranging variety. He modelled the CL Cats, The Military Collection, Gordon-Crosby's Classic Cars and the eagerly sought (but rarely found) *Hobby and Dragonfly* (RB33).

Anne Butler

Anne worked at Border for many years in various capacities. During the early 1990's she modelled some James Herriot pieces such as *Egg Money* (JH71); dogs, pigs and cats (including all the Ivory Cats Collection). She also modelled the very elusive commissioned piece *Police Handler and German Shepherd Dog* (L122). She left Border in order to set up her own successful studio concentrating on equine studies initially in the Lake District before emigrating to the USA to continue her sculpting there.

Fleur Cowles

As a painter Fleur Cowles is well known on both sides of the Atlantic. Her paintings, including those of outsize flowers and oddly serene jungle cats, show how she prefers the world she'd like to see rather than painting the harsh realities of the world around us. Border Fine Arts took inspiration from Fleur's work on canvas and translated it into three-dimensional figurines, creating majestic jungle cats with decorative flowers in fine bone china at the Finesse studio in Worcester. Schmid exclusively distributed "The Imagined World of Fleur Cowles" and "Fleur's Flowers" in the USA. These models were limited editions and are not easy to come across today.

Jack Crewdson

Jack Crewdson is a relatively recent Border modeller with his first pieces *Roe Buck* (B0330) and *Fallow Buck, Style Two*, (B0329) being issued in 1998. Jack has over 35 years experience as a taxidermist which provides him a wealth of knowledge he can apply to his Border Fine Arts sculptures. For Border Fine Arts Jack modelled deer, sheep and cattle all of which tended to be quite large-scale requiring considerable shelf space!

James Harvey/Geoff Dashwood

James Harvey produced three sporting birds for Border *Woodcock* (085), *Partridge, Style Three* (086) and *Red Grouse, Style One*, (087). He also produced models under the name Geoff Dashwood.

Lowell Davis

"Mr. Lowell" as he is frequently referred to is, by all accounts, a rather eccentric American artist who devoted his life to transforming his farm and neighbourhood back to the 1930s. He lived in the foothills of the Ozark Mountain area of Missouri where he painstakingly created a living museum by transporting decaying buildings from his native village back to his farm for restoration. In the 1986 Schmid catalogue he wrote *Some things never change and I'm one of 'em. I just love being with my family and spinnin' yarns about my animals and tendin' my farm. And I have the extra good fortune to be able to share all that by doin' something else I love: paintin' and sculptin'. Yep. I've been blessed with the things that make me happy, So I work at keepin' a good thing going. I'm just tickled that there are so many folks that want to share the things that I treasure most in life.*

Border Fine Arts became involved with Lowell Davis in the late 1970s when he was searching for a company which could reproduce his finely detailed sculptures in ceramic. Border Fine Arts began to issue pieces designed by Lowell Davis and issued in the USA by Schmid in 1979 and continued until Schmid ceased trading in early 1995. For most of that period the models were manufactured in Scotland but towards the end they were being manufactured overseas (Taiwan), Lowell Davis' series include the RFD Series (Rural Federal Delivery) of Lowell Davis' FoxFire Farm depicting animals, scenes and incidents which occurred on Mr. Lowell's farm; the Route 66 series depicting a variety of scenes (including buildings) seen along the famous American Highway Route 66; and the "Little Critters" series of animals getting up to human exploits. Many Lowell Davis pieces are of the humorous variety, with their modelling sometimes comical and each piece was issued with an illustrated "story" card detailing the incident portrayed. A book of all the Story Cards was produced in the USA and this makes a lovely read and brings the sculptures even more to life. These figurines with their "story" cards could be considered as the fore-runner to the James Herriot collections. Lowell Davis pieces form an appealing and very distinctive collection and there are plenty to lookout for with prices covering a wide range. The pieces include those made only for Members of the Lowell Davis Farm Club (run by Schmid) or special event pieces; numerous small individual pieces; and complicated limited editions. The range of Lowell Davis pieces which BFA made for the USA is vast. A limited number of Lowell Davis pieces were released in the UK.

Robert Dockwray

Robert Dockwray contributed a single piece for Border which was *Lord of the Glen* (L161).

Frank DiVita (also known as Frank Falco)

Frank DiVita, a native of Italy, but living in Montana, contributed pieces which tended to be for the American market. These were distributed initially by Kellogg and Co. and illustrated in a brochure entitled "Wildlife by Frank DiVita" and later by Schmid. However those of British subjects were available in the UK including *Pheasant Rising* (L46).

Rob Donaldson

Rob Donaldson specialises in equine subjects and modelled the "Three Day Event" series for Border Fine Arts. Like David Geenty he also produces horses for other manufacturers.

Debbie Edelman

Debbie Edelman modelled an early Border piece *Otter on a Stone Base* which was issued in 1978. She went on to become a sculptress for another Scottish company, "Teviotdale" and with associates she has now acquired the company.

Andrew Edwards

Andrew has revived a former old Border Fine Arts series by modelling some new "Cats Around the House" series for the Studio Collection.

David Fryer

David Fryer's contributions were the series of eight birds forming the series "Miniatures on Bronze" M10-M17 which were all modelled in 1983.

David Geenty

David Geenty modelled a variety of animals for Border for almost a decade commencing in 1979. He also sculpted the "Ben Black Clowns". His last Border piece was *Riding Out* (L18). He is also well known for modelling mainly horses for other manufacturers.

Toni Goffe

Mid 2003 saw the launch of Toni's two very humorous initial series for the Border Fine Arts Studio Character Collection. Toni's art begins as "work in progress sketches", which are developed into watercolours, on which various materials may be worked to achieve the desired colour and effect, including pastel, gouache and acrylic. Toni's award winning art is collected worldwide and has now inspired the "Cool Cats" and "Hot Dogs" collections. Since then he has gone on to design another series this time featuring pigs - "Porkie Pies". Most of Toni's ideas are inspired by watching his own treasured family pets.

Raewyn Greggain

Raewyn's first models for the Border Fine Arts Studio appeared in January 2001 – the Merrie Mice Series and Comic and Curious Cats.

Craig Harding

Craig was born in 1971 in a small village just north of Stoke-on-Trent and he studied at Loughborough College of Art graduating with a BA (Hons) Degree in Fine Art Painting. On his return to the Potteries he gained employment working as a sculptor for one of the many figurine manufacturers in the area. He then went freelance, eventually setting up his own Arts and Crafts business in Alnwick, Northumberland. From there he began working as a freelance sculptor for Border Fine Arts in 1996. This reignited an interest in realistic representation of the human form and he decided to concentrate on sculpting. He accepted a permanent full-time position with Border Fine Arts in November 2000. His contributions include *Thirsty Work* and his portrayal of the Queen on horseback *Morning Exercise at Balmoral*.

Jacqueline Frances Harris-Brown

Jacqueline was born in 1961 in rural Northamptsonshire and studied at Nottingham, Camberwell and Bristol School of Art, obtaining an Honours Degree in Illustration and Graphic Design. After more than 10 years working as an illustrator and portrait artist, a meeting with a well-known sculptor led to a new career, focusing on sculpture. She has produced a large number of equestrian sculptures, but also enjoys working on other animals. Jacqueline's initial models for Border Fine Arts are the limited editions *Off and Pacing* (B0656), depicting an unusual type of racehorse (at least in the UK) – a saddlebred horse trained to "pace" (lateral trotting) pulling a sulky, and "The Trotter".

Victor Hayton

Victor Hayton was Border's original sculptor and co-founder of the company. His models were almost all of a variety of British wildlife but he also modelled a couple of equine studies – *Arab Stallion* and *Arab Mare and Foal*. These original Border studies were available in cold-cast bronze and painted versions and most were only produced in small numbers. Victor's sculptures are generally quite distinct tending to be quite "chunky" and more crudely modelled as they were originally designed to be manufactured in bronze and precious metals rather than in painted resin. These figurines continue to be desirable in their painted version to today's collectors. Victor Hayton produced work other than for Border and these do appear from time to time at auction and are sometimes described as Border Fine Arts which they are not, so care needs to be taken.

Adrian Hughes

Adrian Hughes is the modeller of *10 O'Clock Break* (L158), a pair of bookends, and two of the "Young Farmers" series.

Mairi Laing Hunt

Mairi Laing Hunt (also known as Mairi Laing) was an early Border modeller who contributed a variety of British animal subjects. Her *Fell Hound with Lakeland Terrier* (L92) is an elusive piece sought by many.

Leslie Anne Ivory

Lesley Anne Ivory's name is synonymous with cat designs. Her feline portraits appear on mats and trays for Cloverleaf, plates by Danbury Mint, greeting cards by Hunkydorey, pop-up books by Pavilion and her work is regularly seen in the top London stores. During the early 1990s admirers of Lesley Anne's work could add Border Fine Arts models to their collections. Her famous cats *Octopussy, Phuan, Chesterton* and *Agneatha* were turned into three-dimensional models by Anne Butler in two versions - free "sitting" or on a revolving musical base decorated with characteristic ivory motifs.

Hans Kendrick

Hans is now firmly established as an increasingly prolific sculptor who can turn his hand to a wide variety of subjects. His first models for Border Fine Arts were *Prickly Moments* and *Well Warmed* for the James Herriot Collection, and *Racing Pigeon*. Since then his work has included Border's first (and to date only) boat *The Bonny Fisher Lad* which depicts a Coble boat – a traditional boat used from the Humber Estuary to the Firth of Forth. Hans' personal favourite of his sculptures is *Finishing Off,* which is a wonderfully detailed scene of a horse being shod. Hans is very accessible to collectors as he often attends BFA Events, where he will happily talk about his work and ideas he has for furture models.

Davis Maass

David Maass modelled just one piece, *Resuming the Journey* (147).

Elizabeth MacAllister

The late Elizabeth MacAllister was a much-admired modeller of horses and dogs. Her contributions included the much sought after limited edition pieces *Carriage Horse* (L94), *Charlie's Retreat* (L69), and *Market Day* (JH27).

Lesley McKenzie

Lesley McKenzie was new to Border in 2001 modelling the Border Fine Arts Studios "Fireside Dogs" collection. Leslie's additions to the Border range now include cattle and sheep breeds.

Steve McKeown

Steve McKeown modelled the initial "Dogs Galore" in 1991.

Janet Miller

Janet has turned 2D pictures into models with many of the "Comic and Curious Cats", "Merry Mice" and "Porkie Pies" to her credit.

David Mayer

David is a modeller new to Border Fine Arts and has contributed three "Mouse and..." pieces for the Studio "Natural Mice" collection,

and several bird models in the "Garden Guests" collection. He also modelled Welsh black cattle, "The Grand Parade" and the recent very limited "Hackney and Welsh Cob".

Janet Nightingale

Janet Nightingale modelled three early pieces including Salmon [Atlantic] (080).

Daniel Parker

Daniel Parker specialised in modelling the wildlife of North America. He produced four pieces for Border Fine Arts/Schmid in the 1980s.

Boyd Perry

Boyd Perry completed three series for Border Fine Arts/Schmid in the 1980s. These were *Little Heavyweights* – a curious series of 24 stylized children, wearing oversized clothes pretending to be adults; *Little Rascals* – comical/cartoon-like young creatures with names such as "Sleepy" the owl; and "Wind River" – small scale tableau scenes of a variety of North American wildlife.

Don Polland

In the 1984 Schmid brochure Don Polland wrote *To me, there's nothing quite as powerful and majestic as the buffalo and the horse. These were the fine animals that supported the lives of the Plains Indians in the 18th and 19th centuries. I spent my youth studying this incredible era in American history and working as a cowhand, a stable boy and a jockey. My sculpture is a tribute to the thunder of hooves that was once heard on the open plains.* For Border Fine Arts/Schmid Don Polland produced a series of sculptures depicting aspects of the Plains Indians life-style – including the huge piece *The Great Hunt* made up of several individual sculptures surrounding a central herd of buffalo from his "Western Frontier" collection.

Richard Roberts

Richard Roberts has contributed a number of exotic birds and animals including *Bengal Tiger* (L117) and several "top of the range" pieces such as *Jewel of the East* (L152). He also modelled the Cubist Collection for the Border Fine Arts Studio. These latter pieces are advertised in the brochure as "Abstract interpretations of our favourite animals in a range of colours to complement every home décor." Recently, he modelled the four clowns which form the Classic "Masquerade Clowns" series.

Linda Jane Smith

Linda Jane Smith's humorous feline prints have been delighting fans around the world for two decades, and her highly detailed scenes, populated by cartoon cats have become much sought-after international best sellers. It was no surprise, when in 2001 the Border Fine Arts Studio launched the "Comic and Curious Cats" collection, it proved to be a great success. The initial six felines were modelled by **Raewyn Greggain** with **Janet Miller** sculpting the next series. The "Comic and Curious Cats" collection has continued to expand, with some of the figurines being numbered Limited Editions featuring several cats. There are also smaller models featuring a solo cat. All very detailed. There is something to appeal to every feline fancier – whatever their budget! Many sculptures feature a named cat and have a short verse which appears is on the hang-tag. The *Going Cuckoo* details are – *My name's Alfie, ace bird catcher. I usually have to go out, but suddenly saw an easy opportunity on the inside.*

Barry Snelson

Barry initially modelled a selection of felines for the "Cats and Kittens Galore" collection. He has gone on to produce studies of mischievous puppies for the Studio "Puppy Trouble" series.

Stan Sparre

Stan Sparre modelled some young birds including the *White Heron Fledgling* for Border Fine Arts/Schmid in the 1980s which were issued in North America.

Zoe Stokes

Zoe Stokes' art work depicting comical cats appeared on a series of plates retailed by Border Fine Arts Merchanting division. "American Artists" commissioned by Border Fine Arts to turn four of these cats into three-dimensional models. *Sniffer, Sunshine, Tarzan* and *Waiting* were modelled by Mairi Laing Hunt.

Fred Stone

Fred Stone is extremely well known in the USA for his artwork connected with famous racehorses. He modelled four equines commissioned by "American Artists" and manufactured by Border, which included the two "Black Stallion" pieces from the Walter Farley stories and films of the same name. Border's Merchanting Division also marketed many of Fred Stone's equine collectors plates.

Margaret Turner

Margaret Turner is now acknowledged as Border Fine Arts' canine expert. Margaret, a former graphic designer and teacher of art, has been an animal lover all her life.

Whilst attending dog shows with her black and tan, smooth-haired dachshund Tania, Margaret found fellow showers and spectators had an appetite for anything depicting the short-legged canine! Margaret modelled a seven inch plasticine dachshund and approached companies with it. Border Fine Arts made her the best offer and her dachshund was cast in cold resin and went on to sell well to breed enthusiasts. Other varieties of dachshund followed and when Margaret retired from teaching Ray asked her to sculpt on a regular basis. Margaret's dogs form part of the Dogs and Pups Galore collections and also form her own Border Fine Arts Classic section – "Dogs by Margaret Turner". Nowadays Margaret attends shows as a championship show judge for the six varieties of dachshund and is always ready with her camera to take photographs from all angles of and breed of dog which form the basis for a future model.

Anne Wall

Anne Wall is one of Border Fine Arts longest serving employees. On leaving school Anne was working on a local stud farm when she received a phone call from John Hammond. He was looking for potential painters and had enquired at the local school for details of any former pupils with artistic talents. Anne went for an interview and started painting figurines. She used to ride one of her horses, Dawn or Soldier, for the three or so miles from her home over the hill to Middleholms with a school bag of food for her mount on her back! (Sounds like a potential Border model for the future!). Anne's horses spent the day in the stable at Middleholms and used to be ridden by fellow sculptor Mairi Laing during dinner breaks! Anne rather "fell into" sculpting when her obviously natural talent was noted by John Hammond when she was just "having a go" during breaks from painting at Middleholms and she modelled her first commercial piece in 1978. Anne's number one joy is her horses which she keeps on her small-holding straddling the Scottish-English border. These real horses provide "instant" models for her Border Fine Arts equivalents. However, over the years Anne has modelled a wide variety of animals such as her 1978 piece *Long-tailed Fieldmice and Family* (L13), several North American animals for the American market only, and the major hunting piece *Halloa Away* (L104).

David Walton

David Walton was a prolific contributor to the Border range from 1990 to 1997. He modelled a variety of subjects including British mammals, exotic animals, birds and a fish. For the James Herriot collection he modelled the two "vehicle" pieces – *A Day in the Country* (JH93) and *To the Tup Sale* (JH72).

John Warren

John Warren modelled four sporting subjects (BB01-BB04) in bronze which were designed as trophies.

Elizabeth Waugh

Elizabeth Waugh modelled for Border in the late 1980s and specialised in otters and dogs. Her pieces included *Ladies of the Stream* (L97) and *Jake* (JH35) an eagerly sought James Herriot piece which was only available for 2 years

Richard Wawrzesta

Richard Wawrzesta is well known for his immense contribution to the Border Fine Arts licensed products of Beatrix Potter, Winnie-the-Pooh and Brambly Hedge collections. However, he also demonstrated further talents by modelling a number of wildlife subjects for the "World Wildlife" collection.

Russell Willis

When Border Fine Arts was looking to expand its range to fill an increasing market, they commissioned the talents of Russell Willis.

Initially, Chiltern Border Fine Arts Northampton subsidiary manufactured these but they are now generally produced in the Far East. Prior to this Russell had produced work for Royal Doulton, Crown Derby and Boeham. For the latter he made full size creatures from porcelain so it was quite a contrast to scale down and change the medium!

At Border Fine Arts he has produced numerous studies of our feathered friends, mainly British garden birds and owls, ranging from quite small pieces through to large bird "scenes". Indeed concentrating on Russell Willis birds alone would form a major collection! Many Russell Willis birds have a short production run and if you are an avid collector you need to "keep on your toes" not to miss them!

Richard Young

Richard Young modelled the buildings for the "James Herriot's Yorkshire" series.

CARE AND REPAIR OF YOUR FIGURINES

To care for your figurine Border Fine Arts recommend washing the sculpture carefully in warm soapy water or wiping with a damp soft cloth or paintbrush. The piece is then best left to dry. Please note that abrasives must not be used.

Border Fine Arts used to repair figurines but in August 2000 the repair department was closed. However there are independent repairers available. Glenfirra of Langholm have had a close association with Border Fine Arts since its inception in 1997 and has undertaken with full approval of Border Fine Arts the repair of damaged figurines produced by the company. Glenfirra is run by a group of former Border Fine Arts employees including the former "master painter" Drew Weatherstone, and further details are available from them at:

Glenfirra of Langholm
70 High Street
Langholm, Dumfriesshire DG13 0JH
Website: www.glenfirra.fsnet.co.uk
email: glenfirra@aol.com
Telephone 01387 381713 (Mon. to Fri. 9 am to 3 pm)

THE BORDER FINE ARTS SOCIETY

As a response to the interest shown by a group of avid collectors and in order to encourage new collectors The Border Fine Arts Society was launched by the company on Thursday 1st June 1989. Members receive a copy of the Society magazine *The Borderer* twice a year. This is in full colour and contains a variety of articles on the modellers, the process, new models and promotions, local places of interest and traditions, the stories behind the models, and competitions. Members can contact the Society if they are "seeking" or wishing to sell a figurine and the Society then produces a "Seek 'n' Sell" Catalogue. The Society keeps members informed of Society Events and Painting Demonstrations which are held throughout the year at locations all over the UK (usually in connection with a BFA stockist). Ray Ayres, or another modeller along with a paintress attend these and are always very approachable and willing to converse at length with anyone attending. Enthusiasts can see the sculptors at work, and have purchases signed, or even painted individually. Members receive a miniature figurine each year as part of the membership package and are entitled to purchase an Annual Society Figurine. Lynne Thomson is the current Society Manager.

CONTACTING BORDER FINE ARTS

Border Fine Arts
Brunthill Road
Kingstown Industrial Estate, Carlisle
Cumbria, England, CA3 0EN
Tel.: 01228 404370   Fax: 01228 404390
Email: enquiries@borderfinearts.com
Website: www.borderfinearts.com

Friends of Peter Rabbit Club
Brunthill Road
Kingstown Industrial Estate, Carlisle
Cumbria, England, CA3 0EN
Tel.: 01228 404363   Fax: 01228 404390
Email: enquiries@friendsofpeterrabbitclub.co.uk
Website: www.friendsofpeterrabbitclub.co.uk

ENESCO European Giftware Group Ltd.
Customer Services and Distribution Centre
Brunthill Road
Kingstown Industrial Estate, Carlisle
Cumbria, England, CA3 0EN
UK Customer Services
Tel.: 01228 404040   Fax: 01228 404080
Overseas Customer Services:
Tel.: 44 1228 404040
Fax: 44 1228 404080
Email: uksales@enesco.co.uk

FURTHER READING

The Borderer, Border Fine Arts Society Magazine
Brambly Hedge Collectors Book, Louise Irving

CHAPTER ONE

BORDER FINE ARTS FIGURINES

A BIG FIRST STEP
(Girl and pony)

Model:	A6239
Modeller:	Anne Wall
Height:	5", 12.7 cm
Colour:	Brown, black, white, green and pink
Issued:	01/06 - 12/06
Series:	Hay Days

U.K.:	£30.00
U.S.:	$60.00
Can.:	$60.00

A BRAVE NEW WORLD
(Fox Cubs)

Model:	B0368
Modeller:	Ray Ayres
Height:	4 ¾", 12.1 cm
Colour:	Reddish-brown, brown, white and green
Issued:	07/99 - 06/00
Series:	Event Special

U.K.:	£ 60.00
U.S.:	$120.00
Can.:	$120.00

A CASE OF LOVE
(Golden Retriever puppies)

Model:	A5906
Modeller:	Kerry Bell
Height:	2 ½", 6.4 cm
Colour:	Brown and creamy golden brown
Issued:	06/05 to the present
Series:	On The Farm

U.K.:	£16.00
U.S.:	$35.00
Can.:	$35.00

A DAY IN THE COUNTRY
(Morris 100 Traveller)

Model:	JH93
Modeller:	David Walton
Height:	5", 12.7 cm
Colour:	Taupe, black, blue, grey
Issued:	01/94 in a limited edition of 850
Series:	1. All Things Wise and Wonderful
	2. The James Herriot Collection

U.K.:	£250.00
U.S.:	$500.00
Can.:	$500.00

A DAY WITH THE HOUNDS
(Huntsman and hounds)

Model:	B0789, 0789A
Modeller:	Anne Wall
Height:	8", 20.3 cm
Colour:	B0789 Bay horse
	B0789A Grey horse
Issued:	01/03 in a limited edition of 1,500
Series:	Classic Collection

U.K.:	£200.00
U.S.:	$400.00
Can.:	$400.00

A DAY'S WORK DITCHING

Model:	B0832
Modeller:	Ray Ayres
Height:	7 ¾", 19.7 cm
Colou	Blue, yellow, red, green, brown and black
Issued:	01/03 in a limited edition of 2,003
Series:	Classic Collection

U.K.:	£425.00
U.S.:	$850.00
Can.:	$850.00

A EWE AND A PAIR
(Black-faced)

Model:	B0238
Modeller:	Ray Ayres
Height:	9", 22.9 cm
Colour:	Tan, cream and green
Issued:	01/98 in a limited edition of 1,750
Series:	Agricultural and Sporting

U.K.:	£175.00
U.S.:	$350.00
Can.:	$350.00

A FINE MESS
(Puppy, kitten and wool)

Model:	A6247
Modeller:	Anne Wall
Height:	1 ¾", 4.4 cm
Colour:	Ginger, white, black, green, crimson, lemon
Issued:	01/06 - 12/06
Series:	On The Farm

U.K.:	£12.00
U.S.:	$25.00
Can.:	$25.00

A GOOD DAY OUT
(Labrador)

Model:	115A, B
Modeller:	David Walton
Height:	5 ¼", 13.3 cm
Colour:	A. Black
	B. Yellow
Issued:	01/89 - 12/92
Series:	Agricultural and Sporting

	Black	Yellow
U.K.:	£150.	£125.
U.S.:	$300.	$250.
Can.:	$300.	$250.

A HARD DAY
(Girl holding winner's cup, standing beside pony)

Model:	A0600
Modeller:	Anne Wall
Height:	6 ¼", 15.9 cm
Colour:	Dark brown, black and cream
Issued:	01/01 - 12/04
Series:	Hay Days

U.K.:	£30.00
U.S.:	$60.00
Can.:	$60.00

A HELPING HAND
(Border collie and sheep)

Model:	A5893
Modeller:	Hans Kendrick
Height:	5 ½", 14.0 cm
Colour:	Red, black, white, blue and green
Issued:	06/05 to the present
Series:	On The Farm

U.K.:	£ 97.00
U.S.:	$200.00
Can.:	$200.00

A LONG DAY AHEAD
(Two border collies)

Model:	B0037/SOC9
Modeller:	Ray Ayres
Height:	8", 20.3 cm
Colour:	Black, white and browns
Issued:	06/96 -05/97
Series:	Annual Society Figurine (1996/97)

U.K.:	£175.00
U.S.:	$350.00
Can.:	$350.00

A LUCKY ESCAPE
(Golden Eagle attacking a hare)

Model:	L88/L89
Modeller:	David B. Smith
Height:	17 ¾", 45.1 cm
Colour:	L88 Brown, yellow, white
	L89 Bronze
Issued:	L88 01/89 limited edition of 950
Series:	L89 Studio Bronzes

	Brown	Bronze
U.K.:	£400.	£350.
U.S.:	$800.	$700.
Can.:	$800.	$700.

A LUCKY FIND
(Fox)

Model:	B0703
Modeller:	Ray Ayres
Height:	8 ¾, 22.2 cm
Colour	Reddish-brown, white green, black and brown
Issued:	01/02 in a limited edition of 1,750
Series:	Classic Collection

U.K.:	£150.00
U.S.:	$300.00
Can.:	$300.00

A MAJOR DECISION
(Fordson Major E1ADDN Tractor)

Model:	JH92
Modeller:	Ray Ayres
Height:	6 ¼", 15.9 cm
Colour:	Blue, orange, brown, grey and white
Issued:	01/94 in a limited edition of 1,500
Series:	All Creatures Great and Small

U.K.:	£1,000.00
U.S.:	$2,000.00
Can.:	$2,000.00

A MOMENT TO REFLECT
(Lamp)
(Shepherd and Border Collies)

Model:	B0516
Modeller:	Ray Ayres
Height:	20", 50.8 cm
Colour:	Brown, black , white
Issued:	01/00 - 12/06
Varieties:	Flash and Lightning (B0668)
Series:	The James Herriot Classic Collection

U.K.:	£250.00
U.S.:	$500.00
Can.:	$500.00

Note: Only available in the UK.

A NEW HOME
(Border Collie Pup)

Model:	CEV03
Modeller:	Ray Ayres
Height:	3", 7.6 cm
Colour:	Black, white, blue and red
Issued:	01/95 - 12/98
Series:	Event Special
U.K.:	£20.00
U.S.:	$40.00
Can.:	$40.00

Note: One of a set of four.

A NIGHT AT THE DOGS
(Greyhounds)

Model:	B0905
Modeller:	Margaret Turner
Height:	7", 19.1 cm
Colour:	Reddish-brown, black, white, light brown, red, blue, yellow, and beige
Issued:	01/04 in a limited edition of 500
Series:	Classic Collection
U.K.:	£300.00
U.S.:	$600.00
Can.:	$600.00

A PAIR FOR THE ROYAL
(Shepherd, Sheep and Two Lambs)

Model:	B0580
Modeller:	Kirsty Armstrong
Height:	6 ¾", 17.2 cm
Colour:	Grey, brown, cream and yellow
Issued:	06/00 - 12/01
Series:	The James Herriot Collection
U.K.:	£100.00
U.S.:	$200.00
Can.:	$200.00

A RIGHT AND LEFT
(Labrador and Master)

Model:	B0253A, B
Modeller:	Ray Ayres
Height:	7", 17.8 cm
Colour:	A. Yellow dog B. Black dog
Issued:	01/99 - 06/01
Series:	1. Agricultural and Sporting 2. County Show
U.K.:	£ 90.00
U.S.:	$175.00
Can.:	$175.00

A WARM DAY WALLING
(Dry Stone Dyking)

Model:	JH31
Modeller:	Ray Ayres
Height:	7 ½", 19.1 cm
Colour:	White, grey and green
Issued:	01/90 in a limited edition of 1,250
Series:	All Creatures Great and Small
U.K.:	£ 500.00
U.S.:	$1,000.00
Can.:	$1,000.00

A WATCHFUL EYE
(Female Tawny Owl and Owlets)

Model:	SOC8
Modeller:	Ray Ayres
Height:	7 ¾", 19.7 cm
Colour:	Browns and cream
Issued:	06/95 - 05/96
Series:	Annual Society Figurine (1995/96)
U.K.:	£125.00
U.S.:	$250.00
Can.:	$250.00

A WILD GOOSE CHASE
(Border Collie and Three Geese)

Model:	B0088
Modeller:	Ray Ayres
Height:	4 ½", 11.9 cm
Colour:	Black and white collie, white and brown geese
Issued:	01/97 - 12/99
Series:	1. Every Living Thing 2. The James Herriot Collection
U.K.:	£ 75.00
U.S.:	$150.00
Can.:	$150.00

ABERDEEN ANGUS BULL
Style One

Model:	L59
Modeller:	Ray Ayres
Height:	6 ¼", 15.9 cm
Colour:	Black
Issued:	01/84 in a limited edition of 500
Series:	Special Interest
U.K.:	£1,100.00
U.S.:	$2,200.00
Can.:	$2,200.00

ABERDEEN ANGUS BULL
Style Two

Model:	A0740
Modeller:	Lesley McKenzie
Height:	5 ½", 14.0 cm
Colour:	Black
Issued:	06/01 - 12/05
Series:	Cattle Breeds
U.K.:	£40.00
U.S.:	$80.00
Can.:	$80.00

ABERDEEN ANGUS BULL
Style Three

Model:	B0773
Modeller:	Jack Crewdson
Height:	9", 22.9 cm
Size:	Large
Colour:	Black
Issued:	06/02 in a limited edition of 750
Series:	Classic Collection
U.K.:	£175.00
U.S.:	$350.00
Can.:	$350.00

ABERDEEN ANGUS

	BULL Style Four	CALF	COW
Model:	A5234	A5237	A5277
Modeller:	R. Ayres	K. Armstrong	K. Armstrong
Height:	4 ¼" 10.8 cm	2 ¾" 7.0 cm	4 ¼" 10.8 cm
Colour:	Black		
Issued:	01/05 to the present		
Series:	BFA Pottery Company		
U.K.:	£25.00	£14.95	£25.00
U.S.:	$50.00	$30.00	$50.00
Can.:	$50.00	$30.00	$50.00

ABERDEEN ANGUS COW AND CALF
Style One

Model:	B0204
Modeller:	Kirsty Armstrong
Height:	4 ½", 11.9 cm
Colour:	Black
Issued:	06/97 in a limited edition of 1,250
Series:	Agricultural and Sporting
U.K.:	£175.00
U.S.:	$350.00
Can.:	$350.00

ABERDEEN ANGUS COW AND CALF
Style Two

Model:	A1251
Modeller:	Lesley McKenzie
Height:	5", 12.7 cm
Colour:	Black
Issued:	06/02 - 12/04
Series:	Cattle Breeds
U.K.:	£ 50.00
U.S.:	$100.00
Can.:	$100.00

ABERDEEN ANGUS COW AND CALF
Style Three

Model:	B0807
Modeller:	Jack Crewdson
Height:	9 ½", 24.0 cm
Colour:	Black and green
Issued:	01/04 in a limited edition of 750
Series:	Cattle Breeds
U.K.:	£250.00
U.S.:	$500.00
Can.:	$500.00

ADMIRAL LORD NELSON

Model:	B0969
Modeller:	Paul Back
Height:	8", 20.3 cm
Colour:	Blue, white, red, grey and gold
Issued:	06/05 in a limited edition of 500
Series:	Classic Collection
U.K.:	£125.00
U.S.:	$250.00
Can.:	$250.00

Note: Issued to celebrate the bicentenary of the Battle of Trafalger.

AFGHAN HOUND, Lying

Model:	B0119
Modeller:	Margaret Turner
Height:	3 ½", 8.9 cm
Colour:	Golden brown
Issued:	01/97 - 06/00
Series:	Dogs Galore
U.K.:	£25.00
U.S.:	$50.00
Can.:	$50.00

AFGHAN HOUND, Walking Style One

Model:	L12
Modeller:	Mairi Laing Hunt
Height:	6", 15.0 cm
Colour:	A. Golden and dark brown
	B. Bronze
Issued:	07/78 in a limited edition of 350

	Brown	Bronze
U.K.:	£225.	£100.
U.S.:	$450.	$200.
Can.:	$450.	$200.

AFGHAN HOUND, Walking Style Two

Model:	DL5
Modeller:	Ray Ayres
Height:	5", 12.7 cm
Colour:	Cream and grey
Issued:	01/83 - 12/87
Series:	The World of Dogs
U.K.:	£100.00
U.S.:	$200.00
Can.:	$200.00

AFGHAN HOUND, Walking Style Three

Model:	B0588
Modeller:	Margaret Turner
Height:	6 ¼", 15.9 cm
Colour:	Cream
Issued:	06/00 - 06/01
Series:	Dogs by Margaret Turner
U.K.:	£ 70.00
U.S.:	$140.00
Can.:	$140.00

AFRICAN COW ELEPHANT AND CALF

Model:	RW16
Modeller:	Richard Wawrzesta
Height:	5", 12.7 cm
Colour:	Grey
Issued:	01/90 - 12/95
Series:	Endangered Species (WWF)
U.K.:	£ 50.00
U.S.:	$100.00
Can.:	$100.00

AFRICAN LION

Model:	L105
Modeller	Richard Roberts
Height:	12", 30.5 cm
Colour:	Golden, brown and beige
Issued:	01/91 in a limited edition of 750
Series:	WWFN
U.K.:	£225.00
U.S.:	$450.00
Can.:	$450.00

AFRICAN LIONESS AND CUBS

Model:	L106
Modeller:	Richard Roberts
Height	8", 20.3 cm
Colour:	Golden, brown and beige
Issued:	01/91 in a limited edition of 750
Series:	WWFN
U.K.:	£250.00
U.S.:	$500.00
Can.:	$500.00

AFTER THE RAIN
(Robin, Chaffinch, Blue Tit)

Model:	SOC5
Modeller:	Ray Ayres
Height:	7 ¼", 18.4 cm
Colour:	Red, brown, yellow and blue
Issued:	06/93 - 05/94
Series:	Annual Society Figurine (1993/94)
U.K.:	£150.00
U.S.:	$300.00
Can.:	$300.00

AFTERNOON DELIVERIES
(Lorry, geese and pig)

Model:	B1022
Modeller:	Ray Ayres
Height:	5 ¼" x 12 ¼"
	13.3 x 31.1 cm
Colour:	Browns, green, red,
	white and black
Issued:	01/07 in a limited
	edition of 500
U.K.:	£275.00
U.S.:	$550.00
Can.:	$550.00

AGNEATHA
(Long-haired tabby)

Model:	LA10
Designer:	Lesley Anne Ivory
Modeller:	Anne Butler
Height:	4 ¼", 10.8 cm
Colour:	Brown and white
Issued:	01/92 - 12/93
Varieties:	LAM1 (Musical)
Series:	Ivory Cats
U.K.:	£35.00
U.S.:	$70.00
Can.:	$70.00

AGNEATHA (Musical)
(Long-haired tabby)

Model:	LAM1
Designer:	Lesley Anne Ivory
Modeller:	Anne Butler
Height:	6 ¼", 15.9 cm
Colour:	Brown and white
Issued:	01/92 - 12/93
Varieties:	Agneatha, LA10
Series:	Ivory Cats (Musical)
U.K.:	£45.00
U.S.:	$90.00
Can.:	$90.00

AIREDALE TERRIER

Model:	DL8
Modeller:	Ray Ayres
Height:	4 ¼", 10.8 cm
Colour:	Brown and black
Issued:	01/90 - 12/92
Series:	The World of Dogs
U.K.:	£ 65.00
U.S.:	$125.00
Can.:	$125.00

ALFRED THE SWEET-SHOP CAT

Model:	B0177
Modeller:	Kirsty Armstrong
Height:	3 ¼", 8.3 cm
Colour:	Grey tabby
Issued:	06/97 - 05/99
Series:	James Herriot's Cat
	Stories
U.K.:	£20.00
U.S.:	$40.00
Can.:	$40.00

ALL IN A DAY'S WORK
(Farmer on ATV Herding
Sheep)

Model:	B0593
Modeller:	Kirsty Armstrong
Height:	4 ½" x 12 ½",
	11.9 x 31.7 cm
Colour:	Browns, greens, cream,
	red and black
Issued:	09/00 in a limited
	edition of 1,500
U.K.:	£225.00
U.S.:	$450.00
Can.:	$450.00

ALONG THE SHORELINE
(Dog Otter)

Model:	B0858
Modeller:	Ray Ayres
Height:	4 ½", 11.9 cm
Colour:	Brown, black, white,
	beige, grey, green,
	blue and yellow
Issued:	01/04 in a limited
	edition of 950
Series:	Classic Collection
U.K.:	£125.00
U.S.:	$250.00
Can.:	$250.00

AMERICAN COCKER SPANIEL

Model:	B0608/B0609
Modeller:	Margaret Turner
Height:	3 ¾", 9.5 cm
Colour:	B0608 - Tan
	B0609 - Black/white
Issued:	06/00 - 06/01
Series:	Dogs Galore
U.K.:	£25.00
U.S.:	$50.00
Can.:	$50.00

AN EARLY START
(Massey Ferguson Tractor)

Model: JH91/JH91B
Modeller: Ray Ayres
Height: 5 ¾", 14.6 cm
Colour: Green, black, brown
Issued: 08/93 - 12/98
Series: 1. All Things Wise and
                Wonderful
            2. The James Herriot
                Collection

U.K.:   £325.00
U.S.: $650.00
Can.: $650.00

Note: The version produced for the
        Hodgson's Massey Ferguson
        Society has a grey oil can.

ANEMONE AND CHEETAH

Model: FC17
Designer: Fleur Cowles
Modeller: Richard Young
Height: Unknown
Colour: Mid-blue, white, black
                and yellow
Issued: 1987 - 12/88
Series: Fleur's Flowers

U.K.:   £ 75.00
U.S.: $150.00
Can.: $150.00

ANXIOUS MOMENT
(Penning Sheep)

Model: B0584
Modeller: Ray Ayres
Height: 5 ¼", 13.3 cm
Colour: Brown, green, tan,
                cream, black, white
Issued: 06/00 in a limited
                edition of 1,750
Series: The James Herriot
                Classic Collection

U.K.:   £250.00
U.S.: $500.00
Can.: $500.00

APPALOOSA MARE AND FOAL

Model: A0184
Modeller: Anne Wall
Height: 4 ¾", 12.1 cm
Colour: White, brown, green
                and grey
Issued: 06/00 - 12/02
Series: Horse Breeds

U.K.:   £ 50.00
U.S.: $100.00
Can.: $100.00

APPALOOSA STALLION

Model: A1463
Modeller: Anne Wall
Height: 6 ¼", 15.9 cm
Colour: Brown/beige/white
Issued: 01/03 - 12/04
Series: Horse Breeds

U.K.:   £40.00
U.S.: $80.00
Can.: $80.00

APPLAUSE, THE
(Clown)

Model: B1045
Modeller: Richard Roberts
Height: 8 ¾" x 6"
                22.2 cm x 15.2 cm
Colour: White, red, blue
                and yellow
Issued: 06/06 in a limted
                edition of 500
Series: Masquerade Clowns

U.K.:   £100.00
U.S.: $200.00
Can.: $200.00

ARAB MARE AND FOAL
Style One

Model: L06A, B
Modeller: Victor Hayton
Height: 6 ½", 16.5 cm
Colour: A. Multicoloured
                B. Bronze
Issued: 01/77 in a limited
                edition of 500

	Multi.	Bronze
U.K.:	£ 650.	£200.
U.S.:	$1,300.	$400.
Can.:	$1,300.	$400.

ARAB MARE AND FOAL
Style Two

Model: L136
Modeller: Anne Wall
Height: 6 ¼", 15.9 cm
Colour: A. Grey mare, bay foal
                B. Chestnut mare,
                    bay foal
                C. Bay mare,
                    chestnut foal
Issued: 09/93 in a limited
                edition of 850

U.K.:   £225.00
U.S.: $450.00
Can.: $450.00

ARAB MARE AND FOAL
Style Three

Model: A0186
Modeller: Anne Wall
Height: 5 ¾", 14.6 cm
Colour: Light grey, brown and sandy brown
Issued: 06/00 - 06/06
Series: Horse Breeds

U.K.: £ 60.00
U.S.: $120.00
Can.: $120.00

ARAB MARE AND FOAL, Bust

Model: K213
Modeller: Fred Stone
Height: 7 ¾", 19.7 cm
Colour: Light grey mare, bay foal
Issued: 01/90 in a limited edition of 2,500

U.K.: £100.00
U.S.: $200.00
Can.: $200.00

ARAB STALLION, Standing
(With authentic saddle)

Model: A2016
Modeller: Anne Wall
Height: 11", 27.9 cm
Colour: White and grey
Issued: 06/02 in a limited edition of 950
Series: Studio Limited Editions

U.K.: £200.00
U.S.: $400.00
Can.: $400.00

ARAB STALLION, Trotting
Style One

Model: L05A, B
Modeller: Victor Hayton
Height: 7 ½", 19.1 cm
Colour: A. Multicoloured
        B. Bronze
Issued: 01/77 in a limited edition of 500

	Multi.	Bronze
U.K.:	£ 600.	£175.
U.S.:	$1,200.	$350.
Can.:	$1,200.	$350.

ARAB STALLION, Trotting
Style Two

Model: L135A, B, C
Modeller: Anne Wall
Height: 7", 17.8 cm
Colour: A. Grey
        B. Chestnut
        C. Bay
Issued: 09/93 in a limited edition of 850

U.K.: £200.00
U.S.: $400.00
Can.: $400.00

ARAB STALLION, Trotting
Style Three

Model: A0731
Modeller: Anne Wall
Height: 6 ½", 16.5 cm
Colour: Grey and black
Issued: 06/01 - 12/04
Series: Horse Breeds

U.K.: £40.00
U.S.: $80.00
Can.: $80.00

ARAB STALLION WITH SALUKI

Model: Unknown
Modeller: David Geenty
Height: 9 ½", 24.0 cm
Colour: Various
Issued: 1984 in a limited edition of 750
Series: Special Interest

U.K.: £475.00
U.S.: $950.00
Can.: $950.00

Note: This model was intended for the U.S. market, but some were sold in the U.K.. The edition of 750 was not completed.

ARCTIC ADVENTURE
(Polar Bear and Cubs)

Model: L146
Modeller: Richard Roberts
Height: 8 ¼", 21.0 cm
Colour: White and grey
Issued: 01/94 in a limited edition of 850
Series: WWFN

U.K.: £275.00
U.S.: $550.00
Can.: $550.00

AROUND THE WORLD
(Horse and Rider)

Model:	A0541
Modeller:	Anne Wall
Height	5 ½", 14.0 cm
Colour:	White, cream and blue
Issued:	01/01 - 06/05
Series:	Hay Days
U.K.:	£25.00
U.S.:	$50.00
Can.:	$50.00

ARRIVING AT APPLEBY FAIR
(Bow Top Wagon and Family)

Model:	B0402
Modeller:	Ray Ayres
Height	8 ¼" x 21 ½" x 7 ½", 21.0 x 53.7 x 19.1 cm
Colour:	Turquoise, black, brown and white
Issued:	06/99 in a limited edition of 600
Series:	Appleby Fair
U.K.:	£ 850.00
U.S.:	$1,700.00
Can.:	$1,700.00

ASKRIGG FIELD BARN

Model:	JH52
Modeller:	Richard Young
Height:	3", 7.6 cm
Colour:	Grey, brown, and white
Issued:	01/89 - 09/90
Series:	James Herriot's Yorkshire
U.K.:	£40.00
U.S.:	$80.00
Can.:	$80.00

AT THE FOREST EDGE
(Roebuck and doe)

Model:	B1092
Modeller:	Ray Ayres
Height:	11 ¼" x 11" 28.5 x 27.9 cm
Colour:	Reddish-brown, brown and green
Issued:	06/07 in a limited edition of 350
U.K.:	£275.00
U.S.:	$550.00
Can.:	$550.00

AT THE SLIP
(Foxhounds)

Model:	B0926
Modeller:	Paul Back
Height:	5 ½" x 9" 14.0 x 22.9 cm
Colour:	Black, browns, white, blue and green
Issued:	01/05 in a limited edition of 500
U.K.:	£195.00
U.S.:	$400.00
Can.:	$400.00

AT THE VINTAGE
(Fordson E27N Tractor)

Model:	B0517
Modeller:	Ray Ayres
Height:	8 ½", 21.6 cm
Colour:	Blue, red, green and brown
Issued:	01/00 in a limited edition of 2,000
Series:	The James Herriot Collection
U.K.:	£ 500.00
U.S.:	$1,000.00
Can.:	$1,000.00

AT THE WATER'S EDGE
(Otters)

Model:	EG05
Modeller:	Ray Ayres
Height:	7", 17.8 cm
Colour:	Browns, white and blue
Issued:	11/92 in a limited edition of 1,500
U.K.:	£175.00
U.S.:	$350.00
Can.:	$350.00

AUGUSTE (WALL MASK)

Model:	K66
Designer:	Ben Black
Modeller:	David Geenty
Height:	15", 38.1 cm
Colour:	Blue, red, gold and white
Issued:	01/88 in a limited edition of 2,500
Series:	Ben Black's Intermission Series
U.K.:	£125.00
U.S.:	$250.00
Can.:	$250.00

Note: The hat and muff are fabric material.

AULD HEMP
(Border collie and lamb)

Model:	B0360
Modeller:	Margaret Turner
Height:	6 ¼", 15.9 cm
Colour:	Black, white and brown
Issued:	01/99 - 12/99
Series:	1. Annual Figurine (1999)
	2. 25th Anniversary
U.K.:	£125.00
U.S.:	$250.00
Can.:	$250.00

AUTUMN BLUES
(Blue Tit)

Model:	SRE4
Modeller:	Ray Ayres
Height:	2 ½", 6.4 cm
Colour:	Yellow, blue and black
Issued:	06/93 - 05/94
Series:	Membership Gift
U.K.:	£30.00
U.S.:	$60.00
Can.:	$60.00

Note: This model was given with renewal of membership.

AUTUMN FEAST
(Woodmouse)

Model:	BCM05
Modeller:	Anne Wall
Height:	2 ¼", 5.7 cm
Colour:	Brown, red and orange
Issued:	01/92 - 12/93
Series:	The Country Mouse
U.K.:	£ 60.00
U.S.:	$120.00
Can.:	$120.00

AUTUMN GLORY
(Pheasant)

Model:	B0488
Modeller:	Russell Willis
Size:	12" x 20", 30.5 x 50.8 cm
Colour:	Copper, brown, red, purple-green and white
Issued:	01/99 in a limited edition of 950
Series:	Millennium
U.K.:	£425.00
U.S.:	$850.00
Can.:	$850.00

AUTUMN HARVEST
(Squirrel)

Model:	SRE7/B0036
Modeller:	Ray Ayres
Height:	2 ½", 6.4 cm
Colour:	Red and white
Issued:	06/96 - 05/97
Series:	Membership Gift
U.K.:	£15.00
U.S.:	$30.00
Can.:	$30.00

Note: This model was given with renewal of membership.

AUTUMN HAY
(Cheviot Ewes by Hayrack)

Model:	B0419
Modeller:	Ray Ayres
Height:	4", 10.1 cm
Colour:	Cream, white, grey and yellow
Issued:	06/99 in a limited edition of 1,500
Series:	The James Herriot Collection
U.K.:	£ 80.00
U.S.:	$160.00
Can.:	$160.00

AUTUMN HEDGEROW
(Dormice)

Model:	B0193
Modeller:	Anne Wall
Height:	6 ¼", 15.9 cm
Colour:	Reddish-brown, green and pink
Issued:	06/97 - 12/98
Series:	The Country Mouse
U.K.:	£ 75.00
U.S.:	$150.00
Can.:	$150.00

AUTUMN REDS
(Squirrels)

Model:	B0779
Modeller:	Ray Ayres
Height:	9 ½", 24.0 cm
Colour:	Brownish-red, white, green, red, yellow and brown
Issued:	06/02 – 06/03
Series:	Society Classic Member-only Figurine
U.K.:	£100.00
U.S.:	$200.00
Can.:	$200.00

AVOCETS FEEDING
Model: 094
Modeller: Ray Ayres
Height: 2 ¾", 7.0 cm
Colour: Black, white and blue
Issued: 06/89 - 12/91
Series: British Birds

U.K.: £125.00
U.S.: $250.00
Can.: $250.00

AWKWARD COW, THE
Model: B0891
Modeller: Ray Ayres
Height: 6 ¼" x 14"
 15.9 x 35.5 cm
Colour: Black and white cow
Issued: 06/04 in a limited
 edition of 750

U.K.: £295.00
U.S.: $600.00
Can.: $600.00

AYRSHIRE COW
(Horned)
Model: L75
Modeller: Elizabeth MacAllister
Height: 7", 17.8 cm
Colour: Brown and white
Issued: 01/87 in a limited
 edition of 250

U.K.: £400.00
U.S.: $800.00
Can.: $800.00

AYRSHIRE COW
(Polled)
Model: L74
Modeller: Elizabeth MacAllister
Height: 6 ½", 16.5 cm
Colour: Brown and white
Issued: 01/87 in a limited
 edition of 250

U.K.: £400.00
U.S.: $800.00
Can.: $800.00

AYRSHIRE COW AND NEW CALF
Model: A1467
Modeller: Lesley McKenzie
Height: 5 ¼", 13.3 cm
Colour: Brown, white and green
Issued: 01/03 - 06/06
Series: Cattle Breeds

U.K.: £40.00
U.S.: $80.00
Can.: $80.00

BABY BADGER
Model: A7682
Modeller: Unknown
Height: 2 ½", 6.4 cm
Colour: Grey, white, black
 and brown
Issued: 01/07 to the present
Series: Wildlife

U.K.: £13.00
U.S.: $25.00
Can.: $25.00

BABY BARN OWLET
Model: WB64
Modeller: Russell Willis
Height: 2 ¾", 7.0 cm
Colour: White and yellow
Issued: 01/93 - 12/97
Series: 1. Miniature Baby Birds
 2. Russell Willis Birds

U.K.: £15.00
U.S.: $30.00
Can.: $30.00

BABY BLUE TIT
Model: WB61
Modeller: Russell Willis
Height: 2 ½", 6.4 cm
Colour: Yellow, blue, white,
 green and pink
Issued: 01/93 - 12/97
Series: 1. Miniature Baby Birds
 2. Russell Willis Birds

U.K.: £15.00
U.S.: $30.00
Can.: $30.00

BABY BLUE TITS (Three)

Model: WB23
Modeller: Russell Willis
Height: 3 ¾", 9.5 cm
Colour: Yellow, blue, green, and white
Issued: 01/93 - 12/94
Series: 1. Baby Birds
2. Russell Willis Birds

U.K.: £35.00
U.S.: $70.00
Can.: $70.00

BABY BLUE TITS (Two)

Model: WB22
Modeller: Russell Willis
Height: 4", 10.1 cm
Colour: Yellow, blue, green, white and pink
Issued: 07/92 - 12/93
Series: 1. Baby Birds
2. Russell Willis Birds

U.K.: £35.00
U.S.: $70.00
Can.: $70.00

BABY BROCKS

Model: A0724
Modeller: John Brown
Height: 4", 10.1 cm
Colour: Dark grey, black, white, brown and green
Issued: 06/01 - 12/02
Series: 1. Country Characters
2. Young Ones by John Brown

U.K.: £30.00
U.S.: $60.00
Can.: $60.00

BABY BUNNIES

Model: A0726
Modeller: John Brown
Height: 3 ½", 8.9 cm
Colour: Brown, white, green and pink
Issued: 06/01 - 12/02
Series: 1. Country Characters
2. Young Ones by John Brown

U.K.: £25.00
U.S.: $50.00
Can.: $50.00

BABY CHICKEN

Model: WB66
Modeller: Russell Willis
Height: 2 ½", 6.4 cm
Colour: Yellow and orange
Issued: 01/94 - 12/96
Series: 1. Miniature Baby Birds
2. Russell Willis Birds

U.K.: £15.00
U.S.: $30.00
Can.: $30.00

BABY DUCKLING

Model: WB67
Modeller: Russell Willis
Height: 2 ¼", 5.7 cm
Colour: Yellow and orange
Issued: 01/94 - 12/96
Series: 1. Miniature Baby Birds
2. Russell Willis Birds

U.K.: £15.00
U.S.: $30.00
Can.: $30.00

BABY ELEPHANT

Model: RW26
Modeller: Richard Wawrzesta
Height: 5", 12.7 cm
Colour: Grey
Issued: 01/93 - 12/93
Series: Endangered Species (WWF)

U.K.: £40.00
U.S.: $80.00
Can.: $80.00

BABY ELEPHANTS

Model: RW60
Modeller: Richard Roberts
Height: 4 ½", 11.9 cm
Colour: Grey
Issued: 01/95 - 12/96
Series: Nursery (WWF)

U.K.: £ 65.00
U.S.: $125.00
Can.: $125.00

BABY HEDGEHOG

Model: B0936
Modeller: Ray Ayres
Height: 4", 10.1 cm
Colour: Brown and fawn
Issued: 01/05 - 12/06
Series: Classic Babies

U.K.: £40.00
U.S.: $80.00
Can.: $80.00

BABY KINGFISHER

Model: WB65
Modeller: Russell Willis
Height: 2 ½", 6.4 cm
Colour: Blue, orange and
brown
Issued: 01/93 - 12/97
Series: 1. Miniature Baby Birds
2. Russell Willis Birds

U.K.: £20.00
U.S.: $40.00
Can.: $40.00

BABY LAPWING

Model: WB68
Modeller: Russell Willis
Height: 2 ½", 6.4 cm
Colour: White, brown and
black
Issued: 01/94 - 12/95
Series: 1. Miniature Baby Birds
2. Russell Willis Birds

U.K.: £15.00
U.S.: $30.00
Can.: $30.00

BABY OWLS (Two)

Model: WB20
Modeller: Russell Willis
Height: 4", 10.1 cm
Colour: White and golden
Issued: 07/92 - 12/94
Series: 1. Baby Birds
2. Russell Willis Birds

U.K.: £25.00
U.S.: $50.00
Can.: $50.00

BABY PENGUIN

Model: WB69
Modeller: Russell Willis
Height: 2 ½", 6.4 cm
Colour: Blue-black and cream
Issued: 01/94 - 12/95
Series: 1. Miniature Baby Birds
2. Russell Willis Birds

U.K.: £15.00
U.S.: $30.00
Can.: $30.00

BABY POOL, THE
(Three Otters)

Model: A0727
Modeller: John Brown
Height: 3 ½", 8.9 cm
Colour: Dark brown, cream,
green, tan and blue
Issued: 06/01 - 12/02
Series: 1. Country Characters
2. Young Ones by John
Brown

U.K.: £30.00
U.S.: $60.00
Can.: $60.00

BABY RABBIT AND CARROT

Model: FE4
Modeller: Ray Ayres
Height: 3 ¼", 8.3 cm
Colour: Brown and orange
Issued: 01/83 - 12/85
Series: First Encounters

U.K.: £ 50.00
U.S.: $100.00
Can.: $100.00

BABY ROBIN

Model: WB60
Modeller: Russell Willis
Height: 3", 7.6 cm
Colour: Red, brown, mauve
and green
Issued: 01/93 - 12/97
Series: 1. Miniature Baby Birds
2. Russell Willis Birds

U.K.: £20.00
U.S.: $40.00
Can.: $40.00

BABY ROBINS (Three)
Model: WB21
Modeller: Russell Willis
Height: 3 ½", 8.9 cm
Colour: Brown, red and white
Issued: 07/92 - 12/95
Series: 1. Baby Birds
2. Russell Willis Birds

U.K.: £25.00
U.S.: $50.00
Can.: $50.00

BABY SITTER
(Border collie and lambs)
Model: A8437
Modeller: Unknown
Height: 5 ¼", 13.3 cm
Colour: Black, white, tan
and pale yellow
Issued: 06/07 to the present
Series: James Herriot
Studio Collection

U.K.: £ 55.00
U.S.: $110.00
Can.: $110.00

BABY SQUIRREL
Model: B0937
Modeller: Ray Ayres
Height: 5 ½", 14.0 cm
Colour: Reddish-brown, black
and white
Issued: 01/05 - 12/06
Series: Classic Babies

U.K.: £40.00
U.S.: $80.00
Can.: $80.00

BABY SQUIRREL AND BLUE TIT
Model: FE15A, B
Modeller: Ray Ayres
Height: 5", 12.7 cm
Colour: A. Red squirrel
B. Grey squirrel
Issued: A. 06/91 - 12/97
B. 06/91 - 12/96
Series: First Encounters

U.K.: £40.00
U.S.: $80.00
Can.: $80.00.

BABY TAWNY OWLET
Model: WB62
Modeller: Russell Willis
Height: 2 ¾", 7.0 cm
Colour: Brown, white and
golden
Issued: 01/93 - 12/97
Series: 1. Miniature Baby Birds
2. Russell Willis Birds

U.K.: £20.00
U.S.: $40.00
Can.: $40.00

BABY TAWNY OWLS (Three)
Model: WB25
Modeller: Russell Willis
Height: 6", 15.0 cm
Colour: Cream
Issued: 01/93 - 12/94
Series: 1. Baby Birds
2. Russell Willis Birds

U.K.: £40.00
U.S.: $80.00
Can.: $80.00

BABY WREN
Model: WB63
Modeller: Russell Willis
Height: 2 ½", 6.4 cm
Colour: Light and dark brown
and cream
Issued: 01/93 - 12/97
Series: 1. Miniature Baby Birds
2. Russell Willis Birds

U.K.: £20.00
U.S.: $40.00
Can.: $40.00

BABY WRENS (Four)
Model: WB24
Modeller: Russell Willis
Height: 4", 10.1 cm
Colour: Brown, golden and
white
Issued: 01/93 - 12/95
Series: 1. Baby Birds
2. Russell Willis Birds

U.K.: £25.00
U.S.: $50.00
Can.: $50.00

BACK FROM THE AUCTION
(Jeep, farmer, son and sheep)

Model:	B0976
Modeller:	Ray Ayres
Height:	5" x 14"
	12.7 x 35.5 cm
Colour:	Charcoal, silver, cream, blue, brown and red
Issued:	01/07 in a limited edition of 500
U.K.:	£350.00
U.S.:	$700.00
Can.:	$700.00

BACK SCRATCH
(Piglet)

Model:	JH77A, B
Modeller:	Anne Wall
Height:	3", 7.6 cm
Colour:	A. Pink
	B. Spotted
Issued:	01/93 - 12/94
Series:	Every Living Thing
U.K.:	£20.00
U.S.:	$40.00
Can.:	$40.00

BADGER
Style One

Model:	ML05
Modeller:	Mairi Laing Hunt
Height:	4", 10.1 cm
Colour:	Dark grey and white
Issued:	01/88 - 12/90
Series:	Woodland
U.K.:	£ 65.00
U.S.:	$125.00
Can.:	$125.00

BADGER
Style Two

Model:	M26
Modeller:	David Walton
Height:	3", 7.6 cm
Colour:	Grey, black and white
Issued:	01/93 - 12/94
Series:	Miniature Wildlife
U.K.:	£25.00
U.S.:	$50.00
Can.:	$50.00

BADGER
Style Three

Model:	A6726
Modeller:	Unknown
Height:	3 ¾", 9.5 cm
Colour:	Grey, white and black
Issued:	06/06 to the present
Series:	BFA Pottery Company
U.K.:	£18.00
U.S.:	$35.00
Can.:	$35.00

"BADGER"
(Foal)

Model:	JH17
Modeller:	Ray Ayres
Height:	2 ½", 6.4 cm
Colour:	1. Chestnut
	2. Black
Issued:	01/87 - 12/93
Series:	1. All Creatures Great and Small
	2. James Herriot's Favourite Characters

	Chestnut	Black
U.K.:	£40.	£ 75.
U.S.:	$80.	$150.
Can.:	$80.	$150.

BADGER, Seated, Head Turned

Model:	023
Modeller:	Judy Boyt
Height:	3 ½", 8.9 cm
Colour:	Dark grey and white
Issued:	01/82 - 06/86
Series:	Judy Boyt Woodland
U.K.:	£ 75.00
U.S.:	$150.00
Can.:	$150.00

BADGER AND SQUIRREL

Model:	B0205
Modeller:	David Walton
Height:	5 ¾", 14.6 cm
Colour:	Grey, black, white and reddish-brown
Issued	06/97-06/99
Series:	First Encounters
U.K.:	£ 60.00
U.S.:	$120.00
Can.:	$120.00

BADGER BALL

Model:	A1020
Modeller:	John Brown
Height:	5 ½", 14.0 cm
Colour:	Dark grey, black, white, green, brown, yellow, lilac and rust
Issued:	01/02 - 06/03
Series:	Country Characters
U.K.:	£45.00
U.S.:	$90.00
Can.:	$90.00

BADGER CUB

Model:	B0921
Modeller:	Ray Ayres
Height:	5 ¾", 14.6 cm
Colour:	Black, grey and white
Issued:	06/04 - 12/06
Series:	Classic Babies
U.K.:	£40.00
U.S.:	$80.00
Can.:	$80.00

BADGER CUB AND MOLE

Model:	FE2
Modeller:	Ray Ayres
Height:	3", 7.6 cm
Colour:	Dark grey and white
Issued:	01/83 - 12/85
Series:	First Encounters
U.K.:	£ 65.00
U.S.:	$125.00
Can.:	$125.00

BADGER FAMILY
Style One

Model:	WW13
Modeller:	Richard Wawrzesta
Height:	3 ½", 8.9 cm
Colour:	Grey, white and black
Issued:	01/87 - 12/87
Series:	Family Life (WWF)
U.K.:	£25.00
U.S.:	$50.00
Can.:	$50.00

BADGER FAMILY
Style Two

Model:	B0221
Modeller:	Kirsty Armstrong
Height:	5 ¼", 13.3 cm
Colour:	Grey, black, white and pink
Issued:	01/98 - 12/99
Series:	Wildlife Families
U.K.:	£ 55.00
U.S.:	$110.00
Can.:	$110.00

BADGERS
Style One

Model:	RW3
Modeller:	Richard Wawrzesta
Height:	2 ½", 6.4 cm
Colour:	Dark grey, white and green
Issued:	01/88 - 12/93
Series:	1. WWFN
	2. Wildlife Families (WWF)
U.K.:	£40.00
U.S.:	$80.00
Can.:	$80.00

BADGERS
Style Two

Model:	150
Modeller:	David Walton
Height:	5", 12.7 cm
Colour:	Grey, black and white
Issued:	01/92 - 12/95
U.K.:	£ 75.00
U.S.:	$150.00
Can.:	$150.00

BADGERS
Style Three

Model:	RW31
Modeller:	David Walton
Height:	4 ¼", 10.8 cm
Colour:	Grey, black and white
Issued:	07/93 - 12/96
Series:	Wildlife Families (WWF)
U.K.:	£45.00
U.S.:	$90.00
Can.:	$90.00

BADGERS
(Pair Fighting)

Model: 003
Modeller: Victor Hayton
Height: 4", 10.1 cm
Colour: Grey, black and white
Issued: 01/77 - 12/81
Series: Mammals

U.K.: £225.00
U.S.: $450.00
Can.: $450.00

BALLOON RACE, THE
(Pony and rider)

Model: A5121
Modeller: Unknown
Height: 5 ¾", 14.6 cm
Colour: Chestnut, red, blue, white and green
Issued: 01/05 - 06/06
Series: Hay Days

U.K.: £35.00
U.S.: $70.00
Can.: $70.00

BARN OWL
Style One

Model: M11
Modeller: David Fryer
Height: 4", 10.1 cm
Colour: Golden brown with brown highlights; bronze base
Issued: 07/83 - 12/87
Series: Miniatures on Bronze

U.K.: £125.00
U.S.: $250.00
Can.: $250.00

BARN OWL
Style Two

Model: L67
Modeller: Frank DiVita
Height: 7", 17.8 cm
Colour: Golden brown and fawn
Issued: 01/85 in a limited edition of 950

U.K.: £200.00
U.S.: $400.00
Can.: $400.00

BARN OWL
Style Three

Model: RB15
Modeller: Ray Ayres
Height: 10 ½", 26.7 cm
Colour: Golden brown, white and brown
Issued: 01/90 - 12/96
Series: British Birds

U.K.: £200.00
U.S.: $400.00
Can.: $400.00

BARN OWL
Style Four

Model: M20
Modeller: David Walton
Height: 4 ¼", 10.8 cm
Colour: White, golden, yellow and grey
Issued: 01/92 - 12/95
Series: Miniature Wildlife

U.K.: £30.00
U.S.: $60.00
Can.: $60.00

BARN OWL
Style Five

Model: WB03
Modeller: Russell Willis
Height: 3 ¾", 9.5 cm
Colour: Yellow, cream and white
Issued: 07/92 - 12/97
Series: 1. Owls of the World
2. Russell Willis Birds

U.K.: £25.00
U.S.: $50.00
Can.: $50.00

BARN OWL
Style Six

Model: WB92
Modeller: Russell Willis
Height: 6", 15.0 cm
Colour: Golden and white
Issued: 01/93 - 12/97
Series: 1. Owls of the World
2. Russell Willis Birds

U.K.: £ 70.00
U.S.: $140.00
Can.: $140.00

BARN OWL
Style Seven

Model:	WB07
Modeller:	Russell Willis
Height:	6", 15.0 cm
Colour:	Golden and cream
Issued:	01/95 - 12/97
Series:	1. Owls of the World
	2. Russell Willis Birds
U.K.:	£40.00
U.S.:	$80.00
Can.:	$80.00

BARN OWL
Style Eight

Model:	B0232
Modeller:	Russell Willis
Height:	4", 10.1 cm
Colour:	Golden brown and white
Issued:	07/97 - Unknown
Series:	Russell Willis Collection
U.K.:	£25.00
U.S.:	$50.00
Can.:	$50.00

BARN OWL
Style Nine

Model:	484261
Modeller:	Russell Willis
Height:	3", 7.6 cm
Colour:	Golden brown and white
Issued:	06/98 - 12/02
Series:	Miniature Figurines
U.K.:	£10.00
U.S.:	$20.00
Can.:	$20.00

BARN OWL
Style Ten

Model:	B0502
Modeller:	Ray Ayres
Height:	10 ½", 26.7 cm
Colour:	Bronze patina
Issued:	01/99 in a limited edition of 500
Series:	25th Anniversary
U.K.:	£125.00
U.S.:	$250.00
Can.:	$250.00

BARN OWL
Style Eleven

Model:	A4610
Modeller:	Russell Willis
Height:	4 ½", 11.9 cm
Colour:	Light and dark cream, brown and green
Issued:	01/04 - 12/06
Series:	BFA Pottery Company
U.K.:	£15.00
U.S.:	$30.00
Can.:	$30.00

BARN OWL
Style Twelve

Model:	A6052
Modeller:	Unknown
Height:	4 ¾", 12.1 cm
Colour:	Pale golden brown, and white
Issued:	06/05 to the present
U.K.:	£ 9.95
U.S.:	$20.00
Can.:	$20.00

BARN OWL
(Flying, large)

Model:	A4055
Modeller:	Russell Willis
Height:	8 ¾", 22.2 cm
Colour:	Yellow, white, brown, grey, green, deep pink
Issued:	06/04 -12/05
Series:	Birds by Russell Willis
U.K.:	£ 75.00
U.S.:	$150.00
Can.:	$150.00

BARN OWL
(Flying, small)

Model:	RB18
Modeller:	Ray Ayres
Height:	3 ½", 8.9 cm
Colour:	White, yellow and brown
Issued:	07/90 - 12/92
U.K.:	£ 65.00
U.S.:	$125.00
Can.:	$125.00

BARN OWL
(On a post with rope)

Model:	092/B092
Modeller:	Ray Ayres
Height:	7", 17.8 cm
Colour:	Golden brown and white
Issued:	01/88 - 12/96
U.K.:	£ 80.00
U.S.:	$160.00
Can.:	$160.00

BARN OWL
(On branch)

Model:	A1477
Modeller:	Russell Willis
Height:	5 ½", 14.0 cm
Colour	Yellow, white, green and beige
Issued:	01/02 - 06/06
Series:	Birds by Russell Willis
U.K.:	£32.00
U.S.:	$65.00
Can.:	$65.00

BARN OWL
(On milk can)

Model:	A2324
Modeller:	Russell Willis
Height:	5", 12.7 cm
Colour:	White, yellow, grey, green and pink
Issued:	01/03 - 06/06
Series:	Garden Guests
U.K.:	£24.00
U.S.:	$50.00
Can.:	$50.00

BARN OWL AND BRAMBLES

Model:	484458
Modeller:	Russell Willis
Height:	7 ¾", 19.7 cm
Colour:	Golden brown, white, black and green
Issued:	01/98 - 12/02
Series:	1. Birds of Prey 2. Woodland and Garden
U.K.:	£45.00
U.S.:	$90.00
Can.:	$90.00

BARN OWL AND CHICK
Style One

Model:	WB82
Modeller:	Russell Willis
Height:	6", 15.0 cm
Colour:	Cream and golden
Issued:	01/93 - 12/94
Series:	1. Owls of the World 2. Russell Willis Birds
U.K.:	£ 65.00
U.S.:	$125.00
Can.:	$125.00

BARN OWL AND CHICK
Style Two

Model:	WB71
Modeller:	Russell Willis
Height:	10 ¾", 27.8 cm
Colour:	Yellow and cream
Issued:	01/94 in a limited edition of 1,250
Series:	Russell Willis Birds
U.K.:	£200.00
U.S.:	$400.00
Can.:	$400.00

BARN OWL AND CHICK
Style Three

Model:	650587
Modeller:	Russell Willis
Height:	6", 15.0 cm
Colour:	White, yellow, black, pink and green
Issued:	06/99 - 12/01
Series:	Families
U.K.:	£30.00
U.S.:	$60.00
Can.:	$60.00

BARN OWL AND CHICKS

Model:	A2484
Modeller:	Russell Willis
Height:	8", 20.3 cm
Colour:	White, yellow and brown
Issued:	01/03 - 12/04
Series:	Birds by Russell Willis
U.K.:	£ 60.00
U.S.:	$120.00
Can.:	$120.00

BARN OWL AND YOUNG

Model: A0405
Modeller: Russell Willis
Height: 4", 10.1 cm
Colour: Yellow, cream and
green
Issued: 01/01 - 12/01
Series: Families

U.K.: £15.00
U.S.: $30.00
Can.: $30.00

BARN OWL FAMILY, THE

Model: RB34
Modeller: Ray Ayres
Height: 6 ½", 16.5 cm
Colour: Golden, white and
brown
Issued: 07/92 - 12/97
Series: RSPB Birds of the
Countryside

U.K.: £100.00
U.S.: $200.00
Can.: $200.00

**BARN OWL IN CHURCH
WINDOW**

Model: F1
Modeller: David Burnham Smith
Height: 8 ½", 21.6 cm
Colour: Golden-yellow and
white
Issued: 01/89 -12/91
Series: Finesse Birds

U.K.: £150.00
U.S.: $300.00
Can.: $300.00

BARN OWL ON ROOF BEAMS

Model: RB30
Modeller: Ray Ayres
Height: 7 ¼", 18.4 cm
Colour: White, golden and
brown
Issued: 01/92 - 12/94

U.K.: £ 75.00
U.S.: $150.00
Can.: $150.00

BARN OWL ON WATERPUMP

Model: B0227
Modeller: Russell Willis
Height: 7", 17.8 cm
Colour: Golden brown, white
and grey
Issued: 07/97 - Unknown
Series: Russell Willis Collection

U.K.: £40.00
U.S.: $80.00
Can.: $80.00

BARN OWL ON WHEEL

Model: 484342
Modeller: Russell Willis
Height: 4 ½", 11.9 cm
Colour: Golden brown, white
and brown
Issued: 06/98 - 12/01
Series: Birds And ...

U.K.: £25.00
U.S.: $50.00
Can.: $50.00

BARN OWLETS (Three)

Model: 089
Modeller: Ray Ayres
Height: 3", 7.6 cm
Colour: White and brown
Issued: 01/88 - 12/92
Series: British Birds

U.K.: £40.00
U.S.: $80.00
Can.: $80.00

BARNACLE GEESE

Model: PS05
Modeller: Richard Roberts
Height: 7", 17.8 cm
Colour: Black, white and greys
Issued: 06/91 in a limited
edition of 1,850
Series: Peter Scott Memorial
Appeal (WWF)

U.K.: £250.00
U.S.: $500.00
Can.: $500.00

BARREL OF FUN
(Puppy, kitten, rabbit, lamb)

Model:	A3870
Modeller:	Hans Kendrick
Height:	2 ¾", 7.0 cm
Colour:	Dark brown, golden brown, black and white
Issued:	06/04 - 12/06
Series:	On The Farm
U.K.:	£18.00
U.S.:	$35.00
Can.:	$35.00

BASSET HOUND, Lying
Variation One

Model:	B0016A, B	
Modeller:	Margaret Turner	
Height:	4", 10.1 cm	
Colour:	A. Tricolour	
	B. Tan and white	
Issued:	A. 06/96 - 12/98	
	B. 06/96 - 12/97	
Series:	Dogs Galore	
	B0016A	**B0016B**
U.K.:	£25.	£30.
U.S.:	$50.	$60.
Can.:	$50.	$60.

BASSET HOUND, Lying
Variation Two

Model:	A3051, 3791	
Modeller:	Margaret Turner	
Height:	3 ¾", 9.5 cm	
Colour:	A3051	Tricolour
	A3791	Bicolour
Issued:	A3051	06/03-12/05
	A3791	06/03-12/04
Series:	Dogs and Pups Galore	
U.K.:	£12.00	
U.S.:	$25.00	
Can.:	$25.00	

BASSET HOUND PUP, Seated

Model:	PG10
Modeller:	Margaret Turner
Height:	3", 7.6 cm
Colour:	Tan and white
Issued:	01/94 - 06/01
Series:	Pups Galore
U.K.:	£12.00
U.S.:	$25.00
Can.:	$25.00

BATH TIME
(Boy and Border Collie)

Model:	B0086
Modeller:	Anne Wall
Height:	5 ¼", 13.3 cm
Colour:	Black, white, blue and grey
Issued:	01/97 - 12/99
Series:	J. Herriot Collection
U.K.:	£ 60.00
U.S.:	$120.00
Can.:	$120.00

BE MY FRIEND
(Border Collie Pup)

Model:	B0084/CEV06
Modeller:	Ray Ayres
Height:	3", 7.6 cm
Colour:	Black, white, blue and red
Issued:	01/97 - 12/98
Series:	Event Special
U.K.:	£20.00
U.S.:	$40.00
Can.:	$40.00

Note: One of a set of four.

BEACHCOMBERS
(Two Otter Cubs and Crab)

Model:	CEV02
Modeller:	Ray Ayres
Height:	4 ½", 11.9 cm
Colour:	Brown and stone
Issued:	01/93 - 12/94
Series:	Society Event Figure
U.K.:	£ 65.00
U.S.:	$125.00
Can.:	$125.00

BEAGLE

Model:	UK - DM2
	USA - 225-423
Modeller:	Ray Ayres
Height:	3 ½", 8.9 cm
Colour:	Brown, black and white
Issued:	01/83 - 12/85
Series:	The World of Dogs
U.K.:	£200.00
U.S.:	$400.00
Can.:	$400.00

BEAGLE, Seated

Model:	B0017
Modeller:	Margaret Turner
Height:	4", 10.1 cm
Colour:	White, black and brown
Issued:	06/96 - 12/01
Series:	Dogs Galore

U.K.:	£20.00
U.S.:	$40.00
Can.:	$40.00

**BEAGLE, Standing
Style One**

Model:	072
Modeller:	Ray Ayres
Height:	6", 15.0 cm
Colour:	Black, tan and white
Issued:	01/82 - 06/83

U.K.:	£125.00
U.S.:	$250.00
Can.:	$250.00

**BEAGLE, Standing
Style Two**

Model:	A5181
Modeller:	Margaret Turner
Height:	4 ¾", 12.1 cm
Colour:	White, golden brown and black
Issued:	01/05 to the present
Series:	Dogs and Pups Galore

U.K.:	£21.00
U.S.:	$40.00
Can.:	$40.00

BEAGLE IN JUMPER

Model:	610844
Modeller:	Unknown
Height:	2 ½", 6.4 cm
Colour:	Tan, white and blue
Issued:	01/99 - 12/00
Series:	Puppy Tales

U.K.:	£10.00
U.S.:	$20.00
Can.:	$20.00

BEAR CUB

Model:	FF16
Modeller:	Anne Wall
Height:	2 ½", 6.4 cm
Colour:	Brown
Issued:	01/93 - 12/95
Series:	First Friends

U.K.:	£12.00
U.S.:	$25.00
Can.:	$25.00

**BEARDED COLLIE, Standing
Variaiton One**

Model:	B0313A, B/B0485
Modeller:	Margaret Turner
Height:	4 ¾", 12.1 cm
Colour:	A. Black and white
	B. Fawn and white
	B0485 Bronze
Issued:	B0313A 6/98 - 12/01
	B0313B 6/98 - 06/01
	B0485 6/99 - 06/00
Series:	1. Bronzed
	2. Dogs Galore

U.K.:	£20.00
U.S.:	$40.00
Can.:	£40.00

**BEARDED COLLIE, Standing
Variation Two**

Model:	A1384, 1385
Modeller:	Margaret Turner
Height:	4 ½", 11.9 cm
Colour:	A1384 Black / white
	A1385 Fawn / white
Issued:	A1384 01/02-12/06
	A1385 01/02-12/04
Series:	Dogs and Pups Galore

U.K.:	£15.00
U.S.:	$30.00
Can.:	$30.00

BEHIND THE SCENES

Model:	K41
Designer:	Ben Black
Modeller:	David Geenty
Height:	10 ½", 26.7 cm
Colour:	Blue, purple, red and orange
Issued:	01/88 in a limited edition of 1,850
Series:	Ben Black's Intermission Series

U.K.:	£150.00
U.S.:	$300.00
Can.:	$300.00

BELGIAN BLUE BULL
Style One

Model: B0406
Modeller: Ray Ayres
Height: 7", 17.8 cm
Colour: White and grey-blue
Issued: 01/00 in a limited
edition of 1,250
Series: Agricultural and
Sporting

U.K.: £200.00
U.S.: $400.00
Can.: $400.00

BELGIAN BLUE BULL
Style Two

Model: A0742
Modeller: Lesley McKenzie
Height: 5 ¼", 13.3 cm
Colour: White and grey-blue
Issued: 06/01 - 12/06
Series: Cattle Breeds

U.K.: £40.00
U.S.: $80.00
Can.: $80.00

BELGIAN BLUE
Style Three

	BULL	CALF	COW
Model:	A4579	A4585	A4582
Modeller:	Kirsty Arstrong		
Height:	4 ½'	3"	4 ¼"
	11.9 cm	7.5 cm	10.8 cm
Colour:	White with blue-grey patches		
Issued:	01/04 to the present		
Series:	BFA Pottery Company		
U.K.:	£25.00	£14.95	£25.00
U.S.:	$50.00	$30.00	$50.00
Can.:	$50.00	$30.00	$50.00

BELGIAN BLUE BULL
Style Four

Model: B0833
Modeller: Jack Crewdson
Height: 8 ¾", 22.2 cm
Colour: White with blue-grey
patches
Issued: 06/04 in a limited
edition of 500

U.K.: £220.00
U.S.: $450.00
Can.: $450.00

BELGIAN BLUE COW AND
CALF
Style One

Model: B0590
Modeller: Ray Ayres
Height: 6 ¾", 17.2 cm
Colour: White and grey-blue
Issued: 01/01 in a limited
edition of 1,250
Series: The County Show

U.K.: £150.00
U.S.: $300.00
Can.: $300.00

BELGIAN BLUE COW AND
CALF
Style Two

Model: A1252
Modeller: Lesley McKenzie
Height: 5", 12.7 cm
Colour: White and grey-blue
Issued: 06/02 - 06/06
Series: Cattle Breeds

U.K.: £ 55.00
U.S.: $110.00
Can.: $110.00

BELGIAN BLUE COW AND
CALF
Style Three

Model: B0929
Modeller: Jack Crewdson
Height: 8", 20.3 cm
Colour: Dark grey, white
and green
Issued: 01/05 in a limited
edition of 500

U.K.: £275.00
U.S.: $550.00
Can.: $550.00

BELGIAN BLUE FAMILY

Model: B0771
Modeller: Kirsty Armstrong
Height: 6 ½", 16.5 cm
Colour: White and grey-blue
Issued: 06/02 in a limited edition of 1,250
Series: Classic Collection

U.K.: £250.00
U.S.: $500.00
Can.: $500.00

BENGAL TIGER

Model: L117
Modeller: Richard Roberts
Height: 10 ¾", 27.8 cm
Colour: Golden with dark brown stripes
Issued: 01/92 in a limited edition of 750
Series: WWFN

U.K.: £250.00
U.S.: $500.00
Can.: $500.00

BENGAL TIGRESS AND CUBS

Model: L118
Modeller: Richard Roberts
Height: 5 ½", 14.0 cm
Colour: Golden with dark brown stripes
Issued: 01/92 in a limited edition of 750
Series: WWFN

U.K.: £275.00
U.S.: $550.00
Can.: $550.00

BENGAL TIGRESS AND CUBS, Lying

Model: RW17
Modeller: Richard Wawrzesta
Height: 4", 10.1 cm
Colour: Orange, black and white
Issued: 01/90 - 12/95
Series: Endangered Species (WWF)

U.K.: £ 60.00
U.S.: $120.00
Can.: $120.00

BERNESE MOUNTAIN DOG (Pulling milk churns on cart)

Model: CH1
Modeller: Elizabeth MacAllister
Height: Unknown
Colour: Black, white, grey and brown
Issued: 01/80 - 12/83

U.K.: £400.00
U.S.: $800.00
Can.: $800.00

BERNESE MOUNTAIN DOG (Standing)

Model: A6238
Modeller: Margaret Turner
Height: 6", 15.0 cm
Colour: Black, tan and white
Issued: 01/06 to the present
Series: Dogs and Pups Galore

U.K.: £23.00
U.S.: $45.00
Can.: $45.00

BERRY PICKERS, THE (Two Foxes)

Model: A1490
Modeller: John Brown
Height: 6", 15.0 cm
Colour: Golden brown, white, green and grey
Issued: 01/03 - 12/05
Series: Country Characters

U.K.: £45.00
U.S.: $90.00
Can.: $90.00

BEST AT SHOW, Gold Edition (Clydesdale mare and foal)

Model: B0404A, B, C
Modeller: Anne Wall
Height: 9", 22.9 cm
Colour: A. Bay
B. Strawberry roan
C. Blue roan
Issued: 10/99 in a limited edition of 350
Varieties: B0404 Standard Ed.
Series: Heavy Horse

U.K.: £425.00
U.S.: $850.00
Can.: $850.00

Note: Issued nos. 1-350.

**BEST AT SHOW, Std. Edition
(Clydesdale Mare and Foal)**

Model:	B0404
Modeller:	Anne Wall
Height:	9", 22.9 cm
Colour:	Brown mare, chestnut foal
Issued:	06/00 in a limited edition of 600
Varieties:	Best At Show Gold Ed.
Series:	Agricultural and Sporting
U.K.:	£275.00
U.S.:	$550.00
Can.:	$550.00

Note: Issued nos. 351-950.

**BETSY
(Steam Engine)**

Model:	B0663
Modeller:	Ray Ayres
Size:	6 ½" x 6 ½" x 16 ½", 16.5 x 16.5 x 41.9 cm
Colour:	Green, black, red and stone
Issued:	03/00 in a limited edition of 1,750
Series:	The Fred Dibnah Vintage Steam Engine Collection
U.K.:	£ 600.00
U.S.:	$1,200.00
Can.:	$1,200.00

BETWEEN ACTS

Model:	K44
Designer:	Ben Black
Modeller:	David Geenty
Height:	11", 27.9 cm
Colour:	Green, blue, orange and red
Issued:	01/88 in a limited edition of 1,850
Series:	Ben Black's Intermission Series
U.K.:	£200.00
U.S.:	$400.00
Can.:	$400.00

BICHON FRISE (standing)

Model:	A3841
Modeller:	Margaret Turner
Height:	3 ¼", 8.3 cm
Colour:	White
Issued:	06/04 to the present
Series:	Dogs and Pups Galore
U.K.:	£13.00
U.S.:	$25.00
Can.:	$25.00

**BIRDS OF THE NIGHT
(Screech Owl and Owlet)**

Model:	WB122
Modeller:	Russell Willis
Height:	4 ¼", 10.8 cm
Colour:	Browns and cream
Issued:	01/96 - 12/97
Series:	1. Owls of the World 2. Russell Willis Birds
U.K.:	£35.00
U.S.:	$70.00
Can.:	$70.00

BIRTHDAY SURPRISE

Model:	B0837
Modeller:	Craig Harding
Height:	7 ¼", 18.4 cm
Colour:	Dark blue, red, tan, black, white, grey and green
Issued:	01/04 in a limited edition of 950
Series:	Classic Collection
U.K.:	£175.00
U.S.:	$350.00
Can.:	$350.00

BLACK BEAR AND CUBS

Model:	WW30
Modeller:	David Walton
Height:	2 ¼", 5.7 cm
Colour:	Brownish-red
Issued:	01/95 - 12/96
Series:	Miniature (WWF)
U.K.:	£20.00
U.S.:	$40.00
Can.:	$40.00

BLACK GROUSE (Cock)

Model:	044
Modeller:	David Geenty
Height:	5 ½", 14.0 cm
Colour:	Black and cream
Issued:	01/81 - 06/83
U.K.:	£200.00
U.S.:	$400.00
Can.:	$400.00

BLACK RHINO AND BABY

Model:	A5410
Modeller:	David Mayer
Height:	6", 15.2 cm
Colour:	Dark grey, brown and green
Issued:	06/05 - 12/06
Series:	Wild World
U.K.:	£ 55.00
U.S.:	$110.00
Can.:	$110.00

BLACKBIRD
Style One

Model:	L90
Modeller:	David Burnham Smith
Height:	7", 17.8 cm
Colour:	Black, green and pink
Issued:	01/89 in a limited edition of 1,850
U.K.:	£200.00
U.S.:	$400.00
Can.:	$400.00

BLACKBIRD
Style Two

Model:	RB32
Modeller:	David Walton
Height:	6 ¼", 15.9 cm
Colour:	Black, brown and green
Issued:	01/92 - 12/93
U.K.:	£ 65.00
U.S.:	$125.00
Can.:	$125.00

BLACKBIRD
Style Three

Model:	A0404
Modeller:	Russell Willis
Height:	3 ¼", 8.3 cm
Colour:	Black, pink, green and brown
Issued:	01/01 - 12/04
Series:	1. Feathered Friends 2. Birds by Russell Willis
U.K.:	£12.00
U.S.:	$25.00
Can.:	$25.00

BLACKBIRD WITH NEST

Model:	541664
Modeller:	Russell Willis
Height:	2 ½", 6.4 cm
Colour:	Black, green, pale pink and yellow
Issued:	01/99 - 12/01
Series:	Feathered Friends
U.K.:	£12.00
U.S.:	$25.00
Can.:	$25.00

BLACKCOCK

Model:	A1278
Modeller:	John Brown
Height:	8 ¼", 21.0 cm
Colour:	Black, white, red and green
Issued:	01/02 - 12/03
Series:	Game Birds
U.K.:	£ 65.00
U.S.:	$125.00
Can.:	$125.00

BLACKFACED EWE
Style One

Model:	117
Modeller:	Ray Ayres
Height:	4 ¾", 12.1 cm
Colour:	White and black
Issued:	01/90 - 12/91
Series:	Agricultural and Sporting
U.K.:	£250.00
U.S.:	$500.00
Can.:	$500.00

BLACKFACED	EWE Style Two	LAMB	RAM Style Two
Model:	A4604	A4605	A4603
Modeller:	R. Ayres	L. Mackenzie	R. Ayres
Height:	4"	2 ½"	4"
	10.1 cm	6.3 cm	10.1 cm
Colour:	Cream, white, black and tan		
Issued:	01/05 to the present		
Series:	BFA Pottery Company		
U.K.:	£18.00	£ 9.95	£18.00
U.S.:	$35.00	$20.00	$35.00
Can.:	$35.00	$20.00	$35.00

BLACKFACED EWE AND COLLIE

Model:	B0505
Modeller:	Ray Ayres
Height:	4 ½", 11.9 cm
Colour:	Bronze; gilt
Issued:	01/99 in a limited edition of 500
Series:	25th Anniversary
U.K.:	£ 80.00
U.S.:	$160.00
Can.:	$160.00

BLACKFACED EWE AND BORDER COLLIE

Model:	104/B104
Modeller:	Ray Ayres
Height:	4 ¼", 10.8 cm
Colour:	Black and white
Issued:	01/82 - 12/96
Series:	1. Agricultural and Sporting
	2. Farm Series
	3. The James Herriot Collection
U.K.:	£125.00
U.S.:	$250.00
Can.:	$250.00

Note: This model was combined with 106 to form 105/S1.

BLACKFACED EWE AND COLLIE, AND COLLIE AND SHEPHERD

Model:	105/S1
Modeller:	Ray Ayres
Height:	7 ½", 19.1 cm
Colour:	Black, white, green and brown
Issued:	01/82 - 12/85
Series:	1. Agricultural and Sporting
	2. Farm Series
U.K.:	£300.00
U.S.:	$600.00
Can.:	$600.00

Note: This model is a combination of nos. 104 and 106. It was a sequential number edition.

BLACKFACED EWE AND LAMBS
Style One

Model: L25
Modeller: Mairi Laing Hunt
Height: 4 ½", 11.9 cm
Colour: Grey, white and black
Issued: 01/80 in a limited edition of 750

U.K.: £ 500.00
U.S.: $1,000.00
Can.: $1,000.00

BLACKFACED EWE AND LAMBS
Style Two

Model: 124/B124
Modeller: Ray Ayres
Height: 5", 12.7 cm
Colour: Cream, black and white
Issued: 01/92 - 12/00
Series: Agricultural and Sporting

U.K.: £ 65.00
U.S.: $125.00
Can.: $125.00

BLACKFACED EWE AND LAMBS
Style Three

Model: A1244
Modeller: Lesley McKenzie
Height: 5 ¼", 13.3 cm
Colour: White, brown and black
Issued: 01/02 - 12/04
Series: Sheep Breeds

U.K.: £45.00
U.S.: $90.00
Can.: $90.00

BLACKFACED RAM
Style One

Model: A0734
Modeller: Lesley McKenzie
Height: 5", 12.7 cm
Colour: White, brown and black
Issued: 06/01 - 06/06
Series: Sheep Breeds

U.K.: £30.00
U.S.: $60.00
Can.: $60.00

BLACKFACED TUP
Style One

Model: L15
Modeller: Mairi Laing Hunt
Height: 4", 10.1 cm
Colour: A. Grey and black
        B. Bronze
Issued: 07/78 in a limited edition of 750

	Grey	Bronze
U.K.:	£ 675.	£325.
U.S.:	$1,350.	$650.
Can.:	$1,350	$650.

BLACKFACED TUP
Style Two

Model: 169/B169
Modeller: Anne Wall
Height: 4 ¾", 12.1 cm
Colour: Grey-brown and black
Issued: 09/95 - 12/00
Series: Agricultural and Sporting

U.K.: £ 70.00
U.S.: $140.00
Can.: $140.00

BLACKIE EWE AND LAMB

Model: B0887
Modeller: Ray Ayres
Size: 6 ½" x 8 ¼"
      16.5 x 21.0 cm
Colour: Pale white-grey and black
Issued: 06/04 in a limited edition of 1,250

U.K.: £150.00
U.S.: $300.00
Can.: $300.00

BLACKIE TUP

Model: B0354
Modeller: Ray Ayres
Height: 9", 22.9 cm
Colour: Cream, black and white
Issued: 1999 in a limited edition of 1,750
Series: 1. Agricultural and Sporting
        2. The County Show

U.K.: £150.00
U.S.: $300.00
Can.: $300.00

BLONDE D'AQUITAINE BULL
Style One

Model:	L116
Modeller:	Ray Ayres
Height:	7", 17.8 cm
Colour:	Orange-brown and white
Issued:	07/92 in a limited edition of 500
Series:	Agricultural and Sporting
U.K.:	£ 900.00
U.S.:	$1,750.00
Can.:	$1,750.00

BLONDE D'AQUITANE

		BULL Style Two	CALF	COW
Model:		A5254	A5259	A5256
Modeller:	Ray Ayres			
Height:		5"	3 ¼"	4 ¾"
Colour:		12.7 cm	8.3 cm	12.1 cm
Issued:	Light brown and white			
Series:	BFA Pottery Company			
U.K.:		£25.00	£14.95	£25.00
U.S.:		$50.00	$30.00	$50.00
Can.:		$50.00	$30.00	$50.00

BLONDE D'AQUITAINE COW
AND CALF

Model:	B0353
Modeller:	Kirsty Armstrong
Height:	7", 17.8 cm
Colour:	Tan and white
Issued:	01/99 in a limited edition of 1,250
Series:	1. Agricultural and Sporting
	2. The County Show
U.K.:	£150.00
U.S.:	$300.00
Can.:	$300.00

BLOODHOUND AND
DACHSHUND

Model:	A4672
Modeller:	Janet Miller
Height:	6 ¾", 17.2 cm
Colour:	Light brown, black and reddish brown
Issued:	01/05 - 12/05
Series:	Big Dog, Little Dog
U.K.:	£45.00
U.S.:	$90.00
Can.:	$90.00

BLOWER BENTLEY (c.1930)

Model:	GC2
Modeller:	David Burnham Smith
Height:	5", 12.7 cm
Colour:	Dark green, silver and brown
Issued:	01/92 in a limited edition of 950
Series:	Classic Cars By Gordon-Crosby
U.K.:	£250.00
U.S.:	$500.00
Can.:	$500.00

BLUE AND GOLD MACAWS

Model:	B0327
Modeller:	Richard Roberts
Height:	16", 40.6 cm
Colour:	Blue, yellow and green
Issued:	06/98 in a limited edition of 950
Series:	1. Birds of the World
	2. Exotic Birds
U.K.:	£ 500.00
U.S.:	$1,000.00
Can.:	$1,000.00

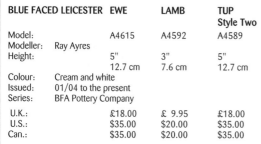

BLUE FACED LEICESTER	EWE	LAMB	TUP Style Two
Model:	A4615	A4592	A4589
Modeller:	Ray Ayres		
Height:	5"	3"	5"
	12.7 cm	7.6 cm	12.7 cm
Colour:	Cream and white		
Issued:	01/04 to the present		
Series:	BFA Pottery Company		
U.K.:	£18.00	£ 9.95	£18.00
U.S.:	$35.00	$20.00	$35.00
Can.:	$35.00	$20.00	$35.00

BLUE FACED LEICESTER EWE AND LAMBS
Style One

Model:	L31
Modeller:	Ray Ayres
Height:	5 ½", 14.0 cm
Colour:	Cream, grey and green
Issued:	01/81 in a limited edition of 850
U.K.:	£ 550.00
U.S.:	$1,100.00
Can.:	$1,100.00

BLUE FACED LEICESTER EWE AND LAMBS
Style Two

Model:	B0741
Modeller:	Ray Ayres
Height:	7", 17.8 cm
Colour:	Cream, white and green
Issued:	06/03 in a limited edition of 950
Series:	Classic Collection
U.K.:	£115.00
U.S.:	$225.00
Can.:	$225.00

BLUE FACED LEICESTER EWE AND LAMBS
Style Three

Model:	A1247
Modeller:	Lesley McKenzie
Height:	6 ¼", 15.9 cm
Colour:	Light brown and white
Issued:	06/03 - 12/03
Series:	Sheep Breeds
U.K.:	£45.00
U.S.:	$90.00
Can.:	$90.00

BLUE FACED LEICESTER RAM

Model:	A0737
Modeller:	Lesley McKenzie
Height:	6 ¼", 15.9 cm
Colour:	Light brown and white
Issued:	06/01 - 12/03
Series:	Sheep Breeds
U.K.:	£30.00
U.S.:	$60.00
Can.:	$60.00

BLUE FACED LEICESTER TUP
Style One

Model:	B0149
Modeller:	Ray Ayres
Height:	7", 17.8 cm
Colour:	Brown and white
Issued:	01/98 in a limited edition of 950
Series:	Agricultural and Sporting
U.K.:	£200.00
U.S.:	$400.00
Can.:	$400.00

BLUE TIT
Style One

Model:	047
Modeller:	Janet Nightingale
Height:	5", 12.7 cm
Colour:	Blue, yellow and green
Issued:	01/81 - 06/83
U.K.:	£ 65.00
U.S.:	$125.00
Can.:	$125.00

BLUE TIT
Style Two

Model:	M13
Modeller:	David Fryer
Height:	3", 7.6 cm
Colour:	Blue, yellow, white and black; bronze base
Issued:	07/83 - 12/87
Series:	Miniatures on Bronze
U.K.:	£ 50.00
U.S.:	$100.00
Can.:	$100.00

BLUE TIT
Style Three

Model:	RB13
Modeller:	Ray Ayres
Height:	4 ¼", 10.8 cm
Colour:	Blue, yellow and white
Issued:	01/90 - 12/92
Series:	British Birds
U.K.:	£35.00
U.S.:	$70.00
Can.:	$70.00

BLUE TIT
Style Four

Model:	M25
Modeller:	David Walton
Height:	3", 7.6 cm
Colour:	Blue, yellow, white and brown
Issued:	01/92 - 12/94
Series:	Miniature Wildlife
U.K.:	£25.00
U.S.:	$50.00
Can.:	$50.00

BLUE TIT
Style Five

Model:	B0022
Modeller:	Russell Willis
Height:	4 ½", 11.9 cm
Colour:	Blue, yellow, white and brown
Issued:	06/96 - 12/97
Series:	Birds by Russell Willis
U.K.:	£40.00
U.S.:	$80.00
Can.:	$80.00

BLUE TIT
Style Six

Model:	484296
Modeller:	Russell Willis
Height:	3", 7.6 cm
Colour:	Blue, yellow, brown and pale green
Issued:	06/98 - 12/05
Series:	Birds by Russell Willis
U.K.:	£10.00
U.S.:	$20.00
Can.:	$20.00

BLUE TIT
Style Seven

Model:	A0407
Modeller:	Russell Willis
Height:	3 ¼", 8.3 cm
Colour:	Blue, yellow, green and brown
Issued:	01/01 - 12/06
Series:	Birds by Russell Willis
U.K.:	£12.00
U.S.:	$25.00
Can.:	$25.00

BLUE TIT
Style Eight

Model:	A1473
Modeller:	Russell Willis
Height:	4 ¼", 10.8 cm
Colour:	Blue, yellow, white, pink and green
Issued:	01/02 - 12/04
Series:	Birds by Russell Willis
U.K.:	£20.00
U.S.:	$40.00
Can.:	$40.00

BLUE TIT
Style Nine

Model:	A2319
Modeller:	Russell Willis
Height:	3 ¾", 9.5 cm
Colour:	Blue, yellow, white, green
Issued:	01/03 - 06/06
Series:	Garden Guests
U.K.:	£15.00
U.S.:	$30.00
Can.:	$30.00

BLUE TIT
Style Ten

Model:	A2323
Modeller:	Russell Willis
Height:	4 ¼", 10.8 cm
Colour:	Blue, yellow, white, pink and brown
Issued:	01/03 - 06/05
Series:	Garden Guests
U.K.:	£15.00
U.S.:	$30.00
Can.:	$30.00

BLUE TIT
Style Eleven

Model:	A4606
Modeller:	Russsell Willis
Height:	3 ¾", 9.5 cm
Colour:	Blue, yellow, white, black, brown, green
Issued:	01/04 - 12/06
Series:	BFA Pottery Company
U.K.:	£15.00
U.S.:	$30.00
Can.:	$30.00

BLUE TIT
Style Twelve

Model:	A6056
Modeller:	Unknown
Height:	5", 12.7 cm
Colour:	Blue, yellow, white, pink and green
Issued:	06/05 to the present
U.K.:	£ 9.95
U.S.:	$20.00
Can.:	$20.00

BLUE TIT AND CHICKS
Style One

Model:	541710
Modeller:	Russell Willis
Height:	3 ¾", 9.5 cm
Colour:	Blue, yellow and lemon
Issued:	01/99 - 06/00
Series:	Families
U.K.:	£25.00
U.S.:	$50.00
Can.:	$50.00

BLUE TIT AND CHICKS
Style Two

Model:	B0344
Modeller:	John Brown
Height:	7 ¼", 18.4 cm
Colour:	Yellow, blue, white and brown
Issued:	01/99 in a limited edition of 1,250
Series:	Border Classic Birds
U.K.:	£100.00
U.S.:	$200.00
Can.:	$200.00

BLUE TIT AND COINS

Model:	B0122
Modeller:	Russell Willis
Height:	5 ½", 14.0 cm
Colour:	Yellow, blue and brown
Issued:	01/97 - 12/97
Series:	Finders Keepers
U.K.:	£40.00
U.S.:	$80.00
Can.:	$80.00

BLUE TIT AND HYDRANGEA

Model:	A0909
Modeller:	David Mayer
Height:	6", 15.0 cm
Colour:	Yellow, blue, white and green
Issued:	06/02 - 12/03
Series:	Garden Guests
U.K.:	£25.00
U.S.:	$50.00
Can.:	$50.00

BLUE TIT AND LOCKET

Model:	484377
Modeller:	Russell Willis
Height:	4", 10.1 cm
Colour:	Blue, yellow, brown and green
Issued:	06/98 - 12/99
Series:	Finders Keepers
U.K.:	£25.00
U.S.:	$50.00
Can.:	$50.00

BLUE TIT AND NEST

Model:	WB35
Modeller:	Russell Willis
Height:	4 ¼", 10.8 cm
Colour:	Yellow, blue, green, white and pink
Issued:	01/93 - 12/94
Series:	1. Birds In Your Garden 2. Russell Willis Birds
U.K.:	£35.00
U.S.:	$70.00
Can.:	$70.00

BLUE TIT FAMILY
Style One

Model:	WB50
Modeller:	Russell Willis
Height:	5 ¾", 14.6 cm
Colour:	Yellow, blue, green, white and pink
Issued:	07/92 - 12/93
Series:	1. Birds In Your Garden 2. Russell Willis Birds
U.K.:	£ 75.00
U.S.:	$150.00
Can.:	$150.00

BLUE TIT FAMILY
Style Two

Model:	B0900
Modeller:	David Mayer
Height:	13 ¼", 33.6 cm
Colour:	Blue, green, yellow, white, grey and red
Issued:	01/04 in a limited edition of 500
Series:	Classic Collection
U.K.:	£250.00
U.S.:	$500.00
Can.:	$500.00

BLUE TIT FLYING

Model:	WB12
Modeller:	Russell Willis
Height:	5 ½", 14.0 cm
Colour:	Yellow, blue, white, black and pink
Issued:	07/92 - 12/93
Series:	Russell Willis Birds
U.K.:	£45.00
U.S.:	$90.00
Can.:	$90.00

BLUE TIT ON COCONUT
Style One

Model:	RB3
Modeller:	Ray Ayres
Height:	3 ¾", 9.5 cm
Colour:	1. Blue, yellow and white 2. Bronze
Issued:	07/83 - 12/93
Series:	1. British Birds 2. RSPB Birds 3. Bronzed

	Blue	Bronze
U.K.:	£40.	£25.
U.S.:	$80.	$50.
Can.:	$80.	$50.

BLUE TIT ON COCONUT
Style Two

Model:	RB46
Modeller:	Ray Ayres
Height:	4", 10.1 cm
Colour:	Blue, yellow, white and brown
Issued:	01/95 - 12/96
Series:	Garden Birds
U.K.:	£40.00
U.S.:	$80.00
Can.:	$80.00

BLUE TIT ON CUP

Model:	WB51
Modeller:	Russell Willis
Height:	3 ¼", 8.3 cm
Colour:	Yellow, blue, green and white
Issued:	01/94 - 12/95
Series:	1. Birds In Your Garden 2. Russell Willis Birds
U.K.:	£30.00
U.S.:	$60.00
Can.:	$60.00

BLUE TIT ON FIELD BINDWEED

Model:	F5
Modeller:	David Burnham Smith
Height:	4", 10.1 cm
Colour:	Yellow, blue, white and black
Issued:	01/89 - 12/91
Series:	Finesse Birds
U.K.:	£ 75.00
U.S.:	$150.00
Can.:	$150.00

BLUE TIT ON FIR CONE

Model: RB47
Modeller: Ray Ayres
Height: 4 ¾", 12.1 cm
Colour: Blue, yellow, white and brown
Issued: 01/95 - 12/98
Series: Garden Birds

U.K.: £ 75.00
U.S.: $150.00
Can.: $150.00

BLUE TIT ON MATCHBOX

Model: WB152
Modeller: Russell Willis
Height: 5", 12.7 cm
Colour: Yellow, blue, green, white and red
Issued: 01/95 - 12/97
Series: 1. Birds In Your Garden
2. Russell Willis Birds

U.K.: £35.00
U.S.: $70.00
Can.: $70.00

BLUE TIT ON MILK BOTTLE

Model: 541583
Modeller: Russell Willis
Height: 3 ½", 8.9 cm
Colour: Blue, yellow, white, green and cream
Issued: 06/99 - 12/01
Series: Birds And ...

U.K.: £15.00
U.S.: $30.00
Can.: $30.00

BLUE TIT ON PEBBLE

Model: WB160
Modeller: Russell Willis
Height: 3 ¾", 9.5 cm
Colour: Yellow, blue, white and black
Issued: 01/95 - 12/97
Series: 1. Pebble Birds
2. Russell Willis Birds

U.K.: £15.00
U.S.: $30.00
Can.: $30.00

BLUE TIT ON TAP

Model: 484326
Modeller: Russell Willis
Height: 3", 7.6 cm
Colour: Blue, yellow, bronze and green
Issued: 06/98 - 12/05
Series: 1. Birds And ...
2. Birds by Russell Willis

U.K.: £20.00
U.S.: $40.00
Can.: $40.00

BLUE TIT WITH APPLE BLOSSOM

Model: WB31
Modeller: Russell Willis
Height: 4 ½", 11.9 cm
Colour: Yellow, blue, green and white
Issued: 07/92 - 12/93
Series: 1. Birds In Your Garden
2. Birds by Russell Willis

U.K.: £40.00
U.S.: $80.00
Can.: $80.00

BLUE TIT WITH NEST

Model: 541672
Modeller: Russell Willis
Height: 3", 7.6 cm
Colour: Blue, yellow, grey and green
Issued: 01/99 - 12/03
Series: 1. Feathered Friends
2. Birds by Russell Willis

U.K.: £12.00
U.S.: $25.00
Can.: $25.00

Note: For the Miniature Blue Tit and Nest, and Miniature Blue Tit on Nest see page 153.

BLUE TITS AND SWEET PEAS (Pair)

Model: A1023
Modeller: David Mayer
Height: 7", 17.8 cm
Colour: Yellow, blue, white, pink and green
Issued: 06/02 - 12/03
Series: Garden Guests

U.K.: £40.00
U.S.: $80.00
Can.: $80.00

BLUE TITS ON NUT FEEDER

Model: 484466
Modeller: Russell Willis
Height: 10", 25.4 cm
Colour: Blue, yellow, brown, pink and green
Issued: 06/98 - 12/01
Series: 1. Birds And ...
2. Woodland and Garden

U.K.: £ 65.00
U.S.: $125.00
Can.: $125.00

BLUE TITS ON OAK BRANCH

Model: RB48
Modeller: Ray Ayres
Height: 5 ¼", 13.3 cm
Colour: Blue, yellow and white
Issued: 01/95 - 12/97
Series: Garden Birds

U.K.: £45.00
U.S.: $90.00
Can.: $90.00

BLUE TITS ON PLATE (Two)

Model: WB55
Modeller: Russell Willis
Height: 4 ¼", 10.8 cm
Colour: Yellow, blue, white, green and pink
Issued: 01/94 - 12/95
Series: 1. Birds In Your Garden
2. Birds by Russell Willis

U.K.: £40.00
U.S.: $80.00
Can.: $80.00

BLUE TITS WITH FORSYTHIA

Model: A3450
Modeller: Russell Willis
Height: 8 ½", 21.6 cm
Colour: Blue, green, yellow, black, white and brown
Issued: 01/04 - 06/05
Series: Birds by Russell Willis

U.K.: £ 80.00
U.S.: $150.00
Can.: $150.00

BLUECOAT REGIMENT OFFICER (ENGLISH CIVIL WAR)

Model: MF03
Modeller: David Burnham Smith
Height: 11 ¼", 28.5 cm
Colour: Blue, brown and white
Issued: 01/92 in a limited edition of 750
Series: The Military Collection

U.K.: £200.00
U.S.: $400.00
Can.: $400.00

BOB (Collie jumping wall)

Model: JH59
Modeller: Anne Butler
Height: 6", 15.0 cm
Colour: Black, white and beige
Issued: 01/91 - 12/97
Series: 1. All Things Wise and Wonderful
2. J. Herriot Collection

U.K.: £ 70.00
U.S.: $140.00
Can.: $140.00

BOB AND SWEEP, On Base (Collies)

Model: JH60
Modeller: Anne Butler
Height: 7", 17.8 cm
Colour: Black, white and beige
Issued: 01/91 - 12/97
Series: 1. All Things Wise and Wonderful
2. J. Herriot Collection

U.K.: £110.00
U.S.: $220.00
Can.: $220.00

Note: This model combines JH58 and JH59.

BOLTED

Model: A1017
Modeller: Unknown
Height: 5 ¼", 13.3 cm
Colour: Black, white, grey, green and brown
Issued: 01/02 - 12/03
Series: The James Herriot Studio Collection

U.K.: £45.00
U.S.: $90.00
Can.: $90.00

BONNIE FISHER LAD, THE

Model: B0931
Modeller: Hans Kendrick
Size: 9 ¾" x 12"
            24.7 x 30.5 cm
Colour: Blue, white, browns and grey
Issued: 06/04 in a limited edition of 500

U.K.:   £195.00
U.S.: $400.00
Can.: $400.00

Note: Approved by The Coble Boat Society,

BORDER COLLIE
Style One

Model: 055
Modeller: Mairi Laing Hunt
Height: 4", 10.1 cm
Colour: Black and white
Issued: 01/80 - 12/92
Series: 1. The World of Dogs
            2. Special Interest

U.K.:   £125.00
U.S.: $250.00
Can.: $250.00

BORDER COLLIE
Style Two

Model: 078
Modeller: Elizabeth Waugh
Height: 5", 12.7 cm
Colour: Black and white
Issued: 01/87 - 12/88
Series: The World of Dogs

U.K.:   £175.00
U.S.: $350.00
Can.: $350.00

BORDER COLLIE
Style Three

Model: B0449A, B
Modeller: Margaret Turner
Height: 5", 12.7 cm
Colour: A. Black and white
            B. Tricolour
Issued: 06/99 - 12/01
Series: Dogs by Margaret
            Turner

U.K.:   £ 65.00
U.S.: $125.00
Can.: $125.00

BORDER COLLIE, Lying

Model: DG14A, B
Modeller: Steve McKeown
Height: 3 ¾", 9.5 cm
Colour: A. Black and white
            B. Tricolour
Issued: 01/91 - 12/96
Series: Dogs Galore

U.K.:   £20.00
U.S.: $40.00
Can.: $40.00

BORDER COLLIE, Seated
Style One

Model: MT07
Modeller: Margaret Turner
Height: 8 ¼", 21.0 cm
Colour: Black and white
Issued: 07/95 - 12/99
Series: Dogs by Margaret
            Turner

U.K.:   £ 75.00
U.S.: $150.00
Can.: $150.00

BORDER COLLIE, Seated
Style Two

Model: B0127/B0468
Modeller: Margaret Turner
Height: 4 ¾", 12.1 cm
Colour: B0127 Black, white
            B0468 Bronze
Issued: B0127 01/97-12/01
            B0468 06/99-06/00
Series: Dogs Galore/Bronzed

U.K.:   £20.00
U.S.: $40.00
Can.: $40.00

**BORDER COLLIE, Seated
Style Three**

Model: A0648
Modeller: Lesley McKenzie
Height: 14 ¾", 37.5 cm
Colour: Black and white
Issued: 01/01 - 06/05
Series: Fireside Dogs

U.K.:   £ 70.00
U.S.: $140.00
Can.: $140.00

**BORDER COLLIE, Seated
Style Four**

Model: A2087, 88
Modeller: Margaret Turner
Height: 4 ¾", 12.1 cm
Colour: A2087   Black/white
            A2088   Tricolour
Issued: 01/03 to the present
Series: Dogs and Pups Galore

	B&W	Tricolour
U.K.:	£19.00	£19.00
U.S.:	$40.00	$40.00
Can.:	$40.00	$40.00

**BORDER COLLIE, Standing
Style One**

Model: A1162, 63
Modeller: Margaret Turner
Height: 5", 12.7 cm
Colour: A1162   Black/white
            A1163   Tricolour
Issued: A1162   06/01-12/06
            A1163   06/01 to the
                    present
Series: Dogs and Pups Galore

	B&W	Tricolour
U.K.:	£19.00	£19.00
U.S.:	$40.00	$40.00
Can.:	$40.00	$40.00

**BORDER COLLIE, Standing
Style Two**

Model: A1865, 2649
Modeller: Margaret Turner
Height: 9 ¾", 24.7 cm
Colour: A1865   Black/white
            A2649   Tricolour
Issued: 01/03 - 12/04

U.K.:   £ 50.00
U.S.: $100.00
Can.: $100.00

**BORDER COLLIE, Standing
Style Three**

Model: A7125
Modeller: Unknown
Height: 3", 7.6 cm
Colour: Black and white
Issued: 01/07 to the present
Series: Dogs and Pups Galore

U.K.:   £21.00
U.S.: $40.00
Can.: $40.00

**BORDER COLLIE AND BORDER
TERRIER PUP**

Model: A4677
Modeller: Anne Wall
Height: 6 ¾", 17.2 cm
Colour: Black, white, brown
            and blue
Issued: 01/05 - 12/05
Series: Big Dog, Little Dog

U.K.:   £35.00
U.S.: $70.00
Can.: $70.00

BORDER COLLIE AND PUP

Model: 137
Modeller: Margaret Turner
Height: 5 ¼", 13.3 cm
Colour: Black and white
Issued: c.1999

U.K.:   £ 50.00
U.S.: $100.00
Can.: $100.00

Note: This model combines B0127
       and B0493.

BORDER COLLIE PUP, Lying

Model: PG08/B0458
Modeller: Margaret Turner
Height: 2 ¾", 7.0 cm
Colour: PG08   Black/white
            B0458   Bronze
Issued: PG08   01/94-05/99
            B0458   06/99-06/00
Series: 1. Pups Galore
            2. Bronzed

U.K.:   £12.00
U.S.: $25.00
Can.: $25.00

BORDER COLLIE PUP, Seated
Model: B0493
Modeller: Margaret Turner
Height: 3 ¾", 9.5 cm
Colour: Black and white
Issued: 06/99 - 12/01
Series: Pups Galore

U.K.: £15.00
U.S.: $30.00
Can.: $30.00

BORDER COLLIE PUPS (Pair)
Model: B0251/B0462
Modeller: Margaret Turner
Height: 3 ¾", 9.5 cm
Colour: B0251 Black/white
        B0462 Bronze
Issued: B0251 01/98-12/01
        B0462 06/99-06/00
Series: B0251 Pups Galore
        B0462 Bronzed

	B&W	Bronze
U.K.:	£25.	£20.
U.S.:	$50.	$40.
Can.:	$50.	$40.

BORDER LEICESTER

	EWE	LAMB	RAM Style Two
Model:	A5240	A5241	A5239
Modeller: Ray Ayres			
Height:	4 ½"	3 ½"	4 ¾"
	11.9 cm	8.9 cm	12.1 cm
Colour: Cream, white black and grey			
Issued: 01/05 to the present			
Series: BFA Pottery Company			
U.K.:	£18.00	£ 9.95	£18.00
U.S.:	$35.00	$20.00	$35.00
Can.:	$35.00	$20.00	$35.00

BORDER LEICESTER EWE AND LAMB
Model: A3226
Modeller: Lesley McKenzie
Height: 6 ¼", 15.9 cm
Colour: Cream, white and green
Issued: 06/03 - 06/06
Series: Sheep Breeds

U.K.: £ 55.00
U.S.: $110.00
Can.: $110.00

BORDER LEICESTER EWE AND LAMBS
Model: B0930
Modeller: Ray Ayres
Size: 6 ½" x 10"
      16.5 x 25.4 cm
Colour: Cream, white, black and green
Issued: 01/05 in a limited edition of 500

U.K.: £145.00
U.S.: $300.00
Can.: $300.00

BORDER LEICESTER RAM Style One
Model: A3225
Modeller: Lesley McKenzie
Height: 6 ¼", 15.9 cm
Colour: Cream, white, green and sandy brown
Issued: 06/04 - 06/06

U.K.: £35.00
U.S.: $70.00
Can.: $70.00

BORDER LEICESTER TUP
Model: L163
Modeller: Ray Ayres
Height: 6 ¾", 17.2 cm
Colour: Cream and white
Issued: 01/96 in a limited edition of 950
Series: Agricultural and Sporting

U.K.: £100.00
U.S.: $200.00
Can.: $200.00

BORDER TERRIER
Model: DS7
Modeller: Ray Ayres
Height: 3 ¼", 8.3 cm
Colour: Brown
Issued: 07/83 - 12/88
Series: The World of Dogs

U.K.:   £40.00
U.S.: $80.00
Can.: $80.00

**BORDER TERRIER, Seated
Style One, First Variation**
Model: DG31/B0472
Modeller: Margaret Turner
Height: 4", 10.1 cm
Colour: DG31   Browns, black
            B0472   Bronze
Issued: DG31   01/95-12/01
            B0472   06/99-06/00
Series: 1. Dogs Galore
            2. Bronzed

U.K.:   £20.00
U.S.: $40.00
Can.: $40.00

**BORDER TERRIER, Seated
Style One, Second Variation**
Model: A2075
Modeller: Margaret Turner
Height: 3 ¾", 9.5 cm
Colour: Brown and black
Issued: c.2001 to the present
Series: Dogs and Pups Galore

U.K.:   £15.00
U.S.: $30.00
Can.: $30.00

**BORDER TERRIER, Seated
Style Two**
Model: A2696
Modeller: Margaret Turner
Height: 12 ¾", 32.4 cm
Colour: Light brown and black
Issued: 06/03 to the present
Series: Fireside Dogs

U.K.:   £ 86.00
U.S.: $175.00
Can.: $175.00

**BORDER TERRIER, Standing
Style One**
Model: A1382
Modeller: Margaret Turner
Height: 4", 10.1 cm
Colour: Brown and black
Issued: 01/02 to the present
Series: Dogs and Pups Galore

U.K.:   £17.00
U.S.: $35.00
Can.: $35.00

**BORDER TERRIER, Standing
Style Two**
Model: A3229
Modeller: Margaret Turner
Height: 6 ¼", 15.9 cm
Colour: Light brown, grey
            and green
Issued: 01/04 - 06/06
Series: Dogs and Pups Galore

U.K.:   £45.00
U.S.: $90.00
Can.: $90.00

**BORDER TERRIER, Standing
Style Three**
Model: A7713
Modeller: Unknown
Height: 3 ¼", 8.3 cm
Colour: Brown and black
Issued: 06/06 to the present
Series: Dogs and Pups Galore

U.K.:   £17.00
U.S.: $35.00
Can.: $35.00

**BORDER TERRIER
(With hedgehog)**
Model: 066
Modeller: David Geenty
Height: 4", 10.1 cm
Colour: Brown, black and
            green
Issued: 01/81 - 12/92
Series: 1. Special Interest
            2. The World of Dogs

U.K.:   £175.00
U.S.: $350.00
Can.: $350.00

BORDER TERRIER AND VIXEN

Model: L35
Modeller: Ray Ayres
Height: 5", 12.7 cm
Colour: Brown and grey
Issued: 07/81 in a limited
             edition of 850

U.K.:   £200.00
U.S.: $400.00
Can.: $400.00

BORDER TERRIER FAMILY GROUP

Model: A5889
Modeller: Anne Wall
Height: 3", 7.6 cm
Colour: Browns
Issued: 06/05 to the present
Series: Dogs & Pups: Family
             Groups

U.K.:   £20.00
U.S.: $40.00
Can.: $40.00

BORDER TERRIER PUPS

Model: A3838
Modeller: Adrian Hughes
Height: 2 ½", 6.4 cm
Colour: Light browns
Issued: 01/04 to the present
Series: Dogs and Pups Galore

U.K.:   £20.00
U.S.: $40.00
Can.: $40.00

BORDER TERRIER PUPPY, Seated

Model: PG12/B0455
Modeller: Margaret Turner
Height: 2 ¾", 7.0 cm
Colour: PG12   Brown/beige
             B0455   Bronze
Issued: PG12   01/95-12/01
             B0455   06/99-06/00
Series: 1. Pups Galore
             2. Bronzed

U.K.:   £12.00
U.S.: $25.00
Can.: $25.00

BOSTON TERRIER, Standing

Model: A4982
Modeller: Margaret Turner
Height: 4 ¾", 12.1 cm
Colour: Dark brown and white
Issued: 01/05 to the present
Series: Dogs and Pups Galore

U.K.:   £20.00
U.S.: $40.00
Can.: $40.00

BOXER

Model: DL7
Modeller: Ray Ayres
Height: 4 ¾", 12.1 cm
Colour: Tan, white and black
Issued: 07/83 - 12/88
Series: The World of Dogs

U.K.:   £ 75.00
U.S.: $150.00
Can.: $150.00

BOXER, Lying

Model: DG13A, B
Modeller: Steve McKeown
Height: 3 ½", 8.9 cm
Colour: A. Reddish-brown
                and white
             B. Brindle
Issued: 01/91 - 12/97
Series: Dogs Galore

U.K.:   £25.00
U.S.: $50.00
Can.: $50.00

**BOXER, Seated
Style One**

Model: MT09
Modeller: Margaret Turner
Height: 9 ¾", 24.7 cm
Colour: Reddish-brown and
             white
Issued: 01/96 - 12/99
Series: Dogs by Margaret
             Turner

U.K.:   £100.00
U.S.: $200.00
Can.: $200.00

BOXER, Seated
Style Two, First Variation

Model:	B0247A, B/B0466
Modeller:	Margaret Turner
Height:	5 ½", 14.0 cm
Colour:	B02474A – Tan/white
	B02472B – Brindle
	B0466 – Bronze
Issued:	B02474A/B
	01/98-12/01
	B0466 06/99-06/00
Series:	1. Dogs Galore
	2. Bronzed
U.K.:	£25.00
U.S.:	$50.00
Can.:	$50.00

BOXER, Seated
Style Two, Second Variation

Model:	A2078, 79
Modeller:	Margaret Turner
Height:	5 ½", 14.0 cm
Colour:	A2078 Brindle
	A2079 Tan and white
Issued:	06/02 to the present
Series:	Dogs and Pups Galore
U.K.:	£21.00
U.S.:	$40.00
Can.:	$40.00

BOXER, Seated
Style Three

Model:	A1257, 1899	
Modeller:	Margaret Turner	
Height:	17 ½", 44.5 cm	
Colour:	A1257	Brindle
	A1899	Fawn / white
Issued	A1257	01/03-06/05
	A1899	06/02-12/04
Series:	Fireside Dogs	
U.K.:	£ 75.00	
U.S.:	$150.00	
Can.:	$150.00	

BOXER, Standing
Style One

Model:	A1261, 1262	
Modeller:	Margaret Turner	
Height:	5 ½", 14.0 cm	
Colour:	A1261	Tan and white
	A1262	Brindle
Issued:	A1261	01/02-06/06
	A1262 01/02 to the present	
Series:	Dogs and Pups Galore	
U.K.:	£23.00	
U.S.:	$45.00	
Can.:	$45.00	

BOXER, Standing
Style Two

Model:	A3038, 3789	
Modeller:	Margaret Turner	
Height:	9 ½", 24.0 cm	
Colour:	A3038	Brindle
	A3789	Fawn
Issued:	06/03 - 12/04	
Series:	Dogs and Pups Galoren	
U.K.:	£ 75.00	
U.S.:	$150.00	
Can.:	$150.00	

BOXER, Standing
Style Three

Model:	A3836, 3883	
Modeller:	Margaret Turner	
Height:	5 ½", 14.0 cm	
Colour:	A3836	Brindle
	A3883	Fawn
Issued:	1. 01/04 to the present	
	2. 12/05 - 06/06	
Series:	Dogs and Pups Galore	
U.K.:	£23.00	
U.S.:	$45.00	
Can.:	$45.00	

BOXER AND POODLE

Model:	A4675
Designer:	Toni Goffe
Modeller:	Anne Wall
Height:	8 ½", 21.6 cm
Colour:	Browns, white and red
Issued:	01/05 - 12/05
Series:	Big Dog, Little Dog
U.K.:	£25.00
U.S.:	$50.00
Can.:	$50.00

BOXER AND PUPS

Model:	B0654
Modeller:	Margaret Turner
Height:	8 ¾", 22.2 cm
Colour:	Tan, white and blue
Issued:	01/01 in a limited
	edition of 950
Series:	Dogs by Margaret
	Turner
U.K.:	£125.00
U.S.:	$250.00
Can.:	$250.00

BOXER IN BOX
Model: 484075
Modeller: Unknown
Height: 3", 7.6 cm
Colour: Tan, white, fawn and red
Issued: 06/98 - 12/00
Series: Puppy Tales

U.K.: £12.00
U.S.: $25.00
Can.: $25.00

BOXER PUP, Lying
Model: PG05/B0452
Modeller: Margaret Turner
Height: 2 ¾", 7.0 cm
Colour: PG05 Red-brown
B0452 Bronze
Issued: PG05 01/93-12/01
B0452 06/99-06/00
Series: 1. Pups Galore
2. Bronzed

U.K.: £12.00
U.S.: $25.00
Can.: $25.00

BOXING DAY MEET
(Horse, huntsman and hounds)
Model: B0876/876A
Modeller: Anne Wall
Size: 9" x 13 ½"
22.9 x 34.3 cm
Colour: B0876 Bay horse
B0876A Grey horse
Issued: 06/04 in a limited edition of 950

U.K.: £295.00
U.S.: $600.00
Can.: $600.00

BOXING RING THE
(Two hares)
Model: A0459
Modeller: John Brown
Height: 7", 17.8 cm
Colour: Browns, grey, tan and green
Issued: 01/01 - 12/02
Series: Country Characters

U.K.: £45.00
U.S.: $90.00
Can.: $90.00

BRAVE BOYS
(Border collie pups and ram)
Model: A6863
Modeller: Unknown
Size: 4 ½" a 12"
11.4 x 30.5 cm
Colour: Cream, black, white and green
Issued: 06/06 to the present
Series: James Herriot Studio Collection

U.K.: £ 65.00
U.S.: $125.00
Can.: $125.00

BREAKING COVER
(Fox)
Model: B0839
Modeller: Ray Ayres
Size: 8" x 13 ¼"
20.3 x 33.6 cm
Colour: Reddish brown, black, green and brown
Issued: 06/04 in a limited edition of 750

U.K.: £275.00
U.S.: $550.00
Can.: $550.00

BREAKING THE ICE
(Farmer, cow and sheep)
Model: A2682
Modeller: Hans Kendrick
Height: 5", 12.7 cm
Colour: White, brown, black, grey and green
Issued: 01/04 - 12/05
Series: James Herriot Studio Collection

U.K.: £100.00
U.S.: $200.00
Can.: $200.00

BRIDE, THE
Model: B0739
Modeller: Craig Harding
Height: 6 ¼" 15.9 cm
Colour: Dark brown and black horse; blue and yellow cart; black and white dog; borwn clothing and pink pig
Issued: 01/03 in a limited edition of 1,500
Series: James Herriot Classic Collection

U.K.: £250.00
U.S.: $500.00
Can.: $500.00

BRIGHT EYES
(Rabbit)
Model: B0256
Modeller: Ray Ayres
Height: 2 ¾", 7.0 cm
Colour: Brown, yellow and grey
Issued: 06/98 - 05/99
Series: Membership Gift

U.K.: £15.00
U.S.: $30.00
Can.: $30.00

BRINGING IN
(Holstein Friesian dairy cows and border collie)
Model: B1049
Modeller: Hans Kendrick
Size: 5 ¾" x 11 ½"
14.6 x 29.2 cm
Colour: Black, white, browns, green and grey
Issued: 01/07 in a limited edition of 600

U.K.: £299.00
U.S.: $600.00
Can.: $600.00

BRINGING IN THE HARVEST
Model: B0735
Modeller: Ray Ayres
Height: 6 ¾", 17.2 cm
Colour: Red, black, grey, yellow, white, brown
Issued: 01/02 in a limited edition of 850
Series: Classic Collection

U.K.: £ 550.00
U.S.: $1,100.00
Can.: $1,100.00

BROWN BEAR AND CUB
Model: RW24
Modeller: Richard Wawrzesta
Height: 5", 12.7 cm
Colour: Reddish-brown
Issued: 07/92 - 12/95
Series: Endangered Species (WWF)

U.K.: £40.00
U.S.: $80.00
Can.: $80.00

BROWN SITE DEVELOPMENT
(JCB Mark I Major Loader)
Model: B1003
Modeller: Ray Ayres
Size: 8 ¼" x 15"
21.0 x 38.1 cm
Colour: Red, blue, brown and black
Issued: 06/06 in a limited edition of 500

U.K.: £395.00
U.S.: $800.00
Can.: $800.00

BUCKET OF BUNNIES
Model: A5628
Modeller: Anne Wall
Height: 3 ¾", 9.5 cm
Colour: Silver, green, yellow, black, brown and white
Issued: 01/05 - 12/06
Series: On The Farm

U.K.: £16.00
U.S.: $30.00
Can.: $30.00

BUCKET OF JOY
(Kitten, rabbit and hampster)
Model: A3871
Modeller: Hans Kendrick
Height: 3 ½", 9.5 cm
Colour: Silver, brown, white, black, orange and red
Issued: 04/04 - 12/06
Series: On The Farm

U.K.: £15.00
U.S.: $30.00
Can.: $30.00

BUDGERIGAR
Model: RB24A, B
Modeller: Richard Roberts
Height: 9", 22.9 cm
Colour: A. Blue
B. Green
Issued: 01/91 - 12/92

U.K.: £125.00
U.S.: $250.00
Can.: $250.00

BUDGERIGARS

Model: L96
Modeller: Richard Roberts
Height: 21", 53.3 cm
Colour: Blue, green, yellow
           and black
Issued: 01/90 in a limited
           edition of 950

U.K.:   £350.00
U.S.: $700.00
Can.: $700.00

BUGATTI (c.1930)

Model: GC1
Modeller: David Burnham Smith
Height: 5", 12.7 cm
Colour: Blue, white and brown
Issued: 01/92 in a limited
           edition of 950
Series: Classic Cars By
           Gordon-Crosby

U.K.:   £250.00
U.S.: $500.00
Can.: $500.00

BUILDING BRITAIN

Model: B0737
Modeller: Ray Ayres
Height: 6 ½", 16.5 cm
Colour: Yellow, red, browns,
           black, red-brown
           and blue
Issued: 06/02 in a limited
           edition of 950
Series: Classic Collection

U.K.:   £ 550.00
U.S.: $1,100.00
Can.: $1,100.00

BULL AFRICAN ELEPHANT

Model: L98
Modeller: Richard Roberts
Height: 8", 20.3 cm
Colour: Grey and white
Issued: 1990 in a limited
           edition of 750
Series: WWFN

U.K.:   £175.00
U.S.: $300.00
Can.: $300.00

BULLDOG, Standing
Style One

Model: UK - 057
           USA - 225-120
Modeller: David Geenty
Height: 4 ½", 11.9 cm
Colour: White and tan
Issued: 01/80 - 12/82

U.K.:   £100.00
U.S.: $200.00
Can.: $200.00

BULLDOG, Standing
Style Two

Model: A4983
Modeller: Margaret Turner
Height: 4 ¼", 10.8 cm
Colour: Golden brown, black
           and white
Issued: 01/05 - 06/07
Series: Dogs and Pups Galore

U.K.:   £23.00
U.S.: $45.00
Can.: $45.00

BULLFINCH

Model: A7149
Modeller: Unknown
Height: 4 ¼", 10.8 cm
Colour: Pink, grey, black, white,
           brown and green
Issued: 06/06 to the present

U.K.:   £ 9.95
U.S.: $20.00
Can.: $20.00

BUNNY RABBIT

Model: B0920
Modeller: Ray Ayres
Size: 6 ¾" x 3 ½"
           17.2 x 8.9 cm
Colour: Brown
Issued: 06/04 - 12/06
Series: Classic Babies

U.K.:   £35.00
U.S.: $70.00
Can.: $70.00

BUSTER THE PLAYFUL KITTEN

Model:	B0200
Modeller:	Kirsty Armstrong
Height:	3 ½", 8.9 cm
Colour:	Dark and light brown and red
Issued:	06/97 - 25/99
Series:	James Herriot's Cat Stories
U.K.:	£25.00
U.S.:	$50.00
Can.:	$50.00

**BUTTERCUP
(Calf)**

Model:	JH25
Modeller:	Richard Roberts
Height:	2 ½", 6.4 cm
Colour:	1. Black
	2. Brown
Issued:	01/88 - 12/92
Series:	1. All Creatures Great and Small
	2. James Herriot's Favourite Characters
U.K.:	£25.00
U.S.:	$50.00
Can.:	$50.00

BUZZARD

Model:	B0867
Modeller:	Richard Roberts
Height:	19 ½", 49.4 cm
Colour:	Brown, white, black, grey, green and yellow
Issued:	01/04 in a limited edition of 500
U.K.:	£ 500.00
U.S.:	$1,000.00
Can.:	$1,000.00

CAIRN, Seated

Model:	DG20
Modeller:	Margaret Turner
Height:	4 ½", 11.9 cm
Colour:	Creamy-yellow
Issued:	01/93 - 12/95
Series:	Dogs Galore
U.K.:	£20.00
U.S.:	$40.00
Can.:	$40.00

**CAIRN TERRIER, Standing
Style One**

Model:	DS4
Modeller:	Ray Ayres
Height:	3", 7.6 cm
Colour:	Black, beige and cream
Issued:	01/83 - 12/92
Series:	1. The World of Dogs
	2. Special Interest
U.K.:	£45.00
U.S.:	$90.00
Can.:	$90.00

**CAIRN TERRIER, Standing
Style Two**

Model:	B0245
Modeller:	Margaret Turner
Height:	7 ¼", 18.4 cm
Colour:	Wheaten
Issued:	01/98 - 12/99
Series:	Dogs by Margaret Turner
U.K.:	£ 75.00
U.S.:	$150.00
Can.:	$150.00

**CALF, Lying
Style One**

Model:	M8
Modeller:	David Geenty
Height:	2 ½", 6.4 cm
Colour:	Dark brown and white
Issued:	07/80 - 12/80
Series:	Beginners, Please
U.K.:	£ 75.00
U.S.:	$150.00
Can.:	$150.00

**CALF, Lying
Style Two**

Model:	FF13A, B
Modeller:	Anne Wall
Height:	2", 5.0 cm
Colour:	A. Black and white
	B. Cream
Issued:	01/93 - 12/95
Series:	First Friends
U.K.:	£12.00
U.S.:	$25.00
Can.:	$25.00

CALF AND WELLIES

Model: A0168, 69
Modeller: Anne Wall
Height: 2 ½", 6.4 cm
Colour: A0168   White
            A0169   Black / white
Issued: 06/00 - 12/04
Series: On The Farm

U.K.:   £15.00
U.S.: $30.00
Can.: $30.00

CALL OF THE FALCON
(Peregrine Falcon and Chicks)

Model: L162
Modeller: Ray Ayres
Height: 25", 63.5 cm
Colour: Blue-grey, white and
            black
Issued: 01/96 in a limited
            edition of 200
Series: Masterpiece

U.K.:   £1,750.00
U.S.: $3,500.00
Can.: $3,500.00

Note: Issued with a book.

CALL OF THE WILD
(Wolf, howling)

Model: STW03
Modeller: Richard Roberts
Height: 10 ½", 26.7 cm
Colour: Blue-grey, white, tan
            and black
Issued: 07/95 in a limited
            edition of 2,500
Series: Spirit of the Wolf

U.K.:   £150.00
U.S.: $300.00
Can.: $300.00

CALVES

Model: B0216A,B
Modeller: Kirsty Armstrong
Height: 4 ¾", 12.1 cm
Colour: A. Dairy
            B. Ayrshire
Issued: 01/98 - 12/99
Series: Agricultural and
            Sporting

U.K.:   £100.00
U.S.: $200.00
Can.: $200.00

CAMBERWELL BEAUTY
(Butterfly)

Model: B3
Modeller: Ray Ayres
Height: 3 ¼", 8.3 cm
Colour: Purple, yellow and
            pink
Issued: Without antenae:
            07/80 - 12/85
Re-issued: With antenae
            07/90 - 12/91
Series: British Butterflies

U.K.:   £ 65.00
U.S.: $125.00
Can.: $125.00

Note: Domes were optional with
all butterflies.

CANADA GEESE

Model: PS06
Modeller: Richard Roberts
Height: 6 ¾", 17.2 cm
Colour: Black, white and greys
Issued: 06/91 in a limited
            edition of 1,500
Series: Peter Scott Memorial
            Appeal (WWF)

U.K.:   £225.00
U.S.: $450.00
Can.: $450.00

CANADA GOOSE AND
GOSLINGS
Style One

Model: RW9
Modeller: Richard Wawrzesta
Height: 4", 10.1 cm
Colour: Brown, grey and black
Issued: 01/89 - 12/92
Series: 1. Special Interest
            2. Wildlife Families
               (WWF)

U.K.:   £35.00
U.S.: $70.00
Can.: $70.00

CANADA GOOSE AND
GOSLINGS
Style Two

Model: PS11
Modeller: Richard Roberts
Height: 3 ¼", 8.3 cm
Colour: Black, white, grey
            and yellow
Issued: 01/92 - 12/93
Series: Peter Scott Memorial
            Appeal (WWF)

U.K.:   £45.00
U.S.: $90.00
Can.: $90.00

CANADA GOOSE AND GOSLINGS
Style Three

Model: B0882
Modeller: Jack Crewdson
Height: 11 ¾", 29.8 cm
Colour: Black, white, brown,
           grey, beige, green and
           yellow
Issued: 01/04 in a limited
           edition of 500
Series: Classic Collection

U.K.:   £275.00
U.S.: $550.00
Can.: $550.00

CANTERING DOWN
(Racehorse)

Model: UK# L16A, B
           USA# 225-170
Modeller: Anne Wall
Height: 9", 22.9 cm
Colour: A. Bay horse; multi-
              coloured silks
           B. Bronze
Issued: 06/78 in a limited
           edition of 850

	Brown	Bronze
U.K.:	£450.	£175.
U.S.:	$900.	$350.
Can.:	$900.	$350.

CARRIAGE HORSE, THE

Model: L94
Modeller: Elizabeth MacAllister
Height: 12", 30.5 cm
Colour: Brown
Issued: 01/90 in a limited
           edition of 100

U.K.:   £ 675.00
U.S.: $1,350.00
Can.: $1,350.00

CARRYING BURDENS
(Pony, rider and border collies)

Model: B0892
Modeller: Hans Kendrick
Size: 7 ¼" x 11"
           18.4 x 27.9 cm
Colour: Black, yellow, grey,
           white, green, brown
Issued: 01/05 in a limited
           edition of 950

U.K.:   £225.00
U.S.: $450.00
Can.: $450.00

CASHMERE GOAT

Model: CG1
Modeller: Ray Ayres
Height: Unknown
Colour: Creamy white
Issued: 01/80 - Unknown

U.K.:   £200.00
U.S.: $400.00
Can.: $400.00

Note: Commissioned by retailer.

CAT, Circling

Model: A1563, 64, 65
Modeller: Richard Roberts
Height: 9", 22.9 cm
Colour: A1563 Slate blue
           A1564 Walnut
           A1565 Stone
Issued: 01/02 - 12/03
Series: Cubist Cats and Kittens

U.K.:   £35.00
U.S.: $70.00
Can.: $70.00

CAT, Eyes Forward

Model: CL9A, B, C
Modeller: David Burnham Smith
Height: 5", 12.7 cm
Colour: A. Black and white
           B. Ginger
           C. Grey tabby
Issued: 06/91 - 12/92
Series: Special Interest

U.K.:   £45.00
U.S.: $90.00
Can.: $90.00

CAT, Eyes Up

Model: CL8A, B, C
Modeller: David Burnham Smith
Height: 5", 12.7 cm
Colour: A. Black and white
           B. Ginger
           C. Grey tabby
Issued: 06/91 - 12/92
Series: Special Interest

U.K.:   £45.00
U.S.: $90.00
Can.: $90.00

CAT, Laying

Model:	B0689 (A1543);
	B0690 (A1542);
	B0691 (A1541)
Modeller:	Richard Roberts
Height:	3 ¼", 8.3 cm
Colour:	B0689 Stone
	B0690 Walnut
	B0691 Slate blue
Issued:	01/01 - 12/03
Series:	Cubist Cats and Kittens
U.K.:	£40.00
U.S.:	$80.00
Can.:	$80.00

CAT, Laying Back

Model:	541494; 541508 (A1519); 541516;		
	638366 (A1517); B0566 (A1518); B0573		
Modeller:	Richard Roberts		
Height:	3", 7.6 cm		
Colour /	541494	Graphite	01/99 - 12/99
Issued:	541508	Stone	12/99 - 12/03
	541516	Verdigris	01/99 - 06/00
	638366	Slate blue	12/99 - 12/03
	B0566	Walnut	01/00 - 12/03
	B0573	Pumice	06/00 - 12/00
Series:	Cubist Cats and Kittens		
U.K.:	£40.00		
U.S.:	$80.00		
Can.:	$80.00		

CAT, Lying
Style One

Model:	CL7A, B, C
Modeller:	David Burnham Smith
Height:	3", 7.6 cm
Colour:	A. Black and white
	B. Ginger
	C. Grey tabby
Issued:	06/91 - 12/92
Series:	Special Interest
U.K.:	£45.00
U.S.:	$90.00
Can.:	$90.00

CAT, Lying
Style Two

Model:	CG11A, B, C
Modeller:	Anne Wall
Height:	2 ½", 6.4 cm
Colour:	A. Grey and white
	B. Ginger and white
	C. Black and white
Issued:	01/95 - 12/95
Series:	Cats Galore
U.K.:	£15.00
U.S.:	$30.00
Can.:	$30.00

CAT, Lying
Style Three

Model:	A1170, 71, 72, 73	
Modeller:	John Brown	
Height:	6 ¼", 15.9 cm	
Colour:	A1170	Black / white
	A1171	Ginger tabby
	A1172	Brown tabby
	A1173	Silver tabby
Issued:	A1170, 71, 73	
	06/01 - 06/04	
	A1172 06/01 - Current	
Series:	1. Cats by John Brown	
	2. Cats, Kittens Galore	
U.K.:	£35.00	
U.S.:	$70.00	
Can.:	$70.00	

CAT, Lying
Style Four

Model:	A1458, 2012, 2013	
Modeller:	Barry Snelson	
Height:	2 ½', 6.4 cm	
Size:	Small	
Colour:	A1458	Ginger tabby
	A2012	Black / white
	A2013	Silver tabby
Issued:	06/02	06/02-06/04
Series:	Cats and Kittens Galore	
U.K.:	£12.00	
U.S.:	$25.00	
Can.:	$25.00	

CAT, Lying
Style Five

Model:	A2643, 2644
Modeller:	Richard Roberts
Height:	3 ½", 8.9 cm
Colour:	A2643 - Stone
	A2644 - Slate Blue
Issued:	01/03 - 12/03
Series:	Cubist Cats and Kittens
U.K.:	£20.00
U.S.:	$40.00
Can.:	$40.00

CAT, Lying
Style Six

Model: A7365, 7366
Modeller: Unknown
Height: 3", 7.6 cm
Colour: A7365 Grey / white
A7366 Ginger tabby
Issued: 06/06 to the present
Series: Cats and Kittens Galore

U.K.: £14.00
U.S.: $28.00
Can.: $28.00

CAT, Lying, Licking Paw

Model: A1883, 2652, 2653
Modeller: Unknown
Height: 2", 5.0 cm
Colour: A1883 Ginger tabby
A2652 Black / white
A2653 Silver tabby
Issued: 01/03 01/03-06/04
Series: Cats and Kittens Galore

U.K.: £12.00
U.S.: $25.00
Can.: $25.00

CAT, Reaching, Style One

Model:	Colour:	Issued:
638412 (A1532)	Slate Blue	01/99-12/03
638420	Graphite	01/99-12/99
638439	Verdigris	01/99-06/00
638447 (A1534)	Stone	01/99-12/03
B0569 (A1533)	Walnut	01/00-12/03
B0576	Pumice	06/00-12/00

Modeller: Richard Roberts
Height: 11 ¼", 28.5 cm
Series: Cubist Cats and Kittens

U.K.: £40.00
U.S.: $80.00
Can.: $80.00

CAT, Reaching
Style Two

Model: A4682, 4688
Modeller: Unknown
Height: 11 ¾", 29.8 cm
Colour: A4682 Rouge
A4688 Granite
Issued: 01/04 - 06/05
Series: Contemporary Cats

U.K.: £45.00
U.S.: $90.00
Can.: $90.00

CAT, Reposed

Model: B0721 (A1552);
B0722 (A1551);
B0723 (A1550)
Modeller: Richard Roberts
Height: 4 ½", 11.9 cm
Colour: B0721 Stone
B0722 Walnut
B0723 Slate blue
Issued: 06/01 - 12/03
Series: Cubist Cats and Kittens

U.K.: £40.00
U.S.: $80.00
Can.: $80.00

CAT, Scratching

Model: B0725 (A1546);
B0726 (A1545);
B0727 (A1544)
Modeller: Richard Roberts
Height: 6 ¼", 15.9 cm
Colour: B0725 Stone
B0726 Walnut
B0727 Slate blue
Issued: 06/01 - 12/03
Series: Cubist Cats and Kittens

U.K.: £30.00
U.S.: $60.00
Can.: $60.00

CAT, Seated
Style One
First Version - Tail up

Model: CL4
Modeller: Judy Boyt
Height: 4 ½", 11.9 cm
Colour: A. Ginger
B. Grey (Burmese)
Issued: 01/84 - Unknown
Series: A Cat Around the
House

U.K.: £45.00
U.S.: $90.00
Can.: $90.00

CAT, Seated
Style One
Second Version - Tail down

Model: CL4
Modeller: Judy Boyt
Height: 4 ½", 11.9 cm
Colour: A. Pale ginger and
stone grey
B. Grey (Burmese)
Issued: Unknown - 12/86
Series: A Cat Around the
House

U.K.: £45.00
U.S.: $90.00
Can.: $90.00

CAT, Seated
Style Two

Model: CL6A, B, C/130-125
Modeller: David Burnham Smith
Height: 5", 12.7 cm
Colour: A. Black and white
B. Ginger
C. Grey tabby
Issued: 06/91 - 12/92
Series: Special Interest

U.K.: £45.00
U.S.: $90.00
Can.: $90.00

CAT, Seated,
Style Three

Model: 463469; 463523; 463590 (A1525); 638382 (A1523);
B0570 (A1524); B0577
Modeller: Richard Roberts
Height: 6 ¾", 17.2 cm
Colour / 463469 Graphite 01/98 - 12/99
Issued: 463523 Verdigris 01/99 - 06/00
463590 Stone 01/98 - 12/03
638382 Slate blue 01/99 - 12/03
B0570 Walnut 01/00 - 12/03
B0577 Pumice 06/00 - 12/00
Series: Cubist Cats and Kittens

U.K.: £30.00
U.S.: $60.00
Can.: $60.00

CAT, Seated
Style Four

Model: A1166, 67, 68, 69
Modeller: John Brown
Height: 9 ¾", 24.7 cm
Colour: A1166 Black / white
A1167 Ginger tabby
A1168 Brown tabby
A1169 Silver tabby
Issued: A1166, 67,69
06/01-06/03
A1168 06/01-12/01
Series: 1. Cats by John Brown
2. Cats / Kittens Galore

U.K.: £40.00
U.S.: $80.00
Can.: $80.00

CAT, Seated
Style Five

Model: A1457, 2010, 2011
Modeller: Barry Snelson
Height: 3 ½", 8.9 cm
Size: Small
Colour: A1457 Ginger tabby
A2010 Black / white
A2011 Silver tabby
Issued: 06/02 - 06/04
Series: Cats and Kittens Galore

U.K.: £12.00
U.S.: $25.00
Can.: $25.00

CAT, Seated
Style Six

Model: A2641, 42
Modeller: Richard Roberts
Height: 6 ¾", 17.2 cm
Colour: A2641 Stone
A2642 Slate blue
Issued: 01/03 - 12/03
Series: Cubist Cats and Kittens

U.K.: £25.00
U.S.: $50.00
Can.: $50.00

CAT, Seated
Style Seven

Model: A4679, 4685
Modeller: Unknown
Height: 6 ¾", 17.2 cm
Colour: A4679 Rouge
A4685 Granite
Issued: 01/04 - 06/05
Series: Contemporary Cats

U.K.: £30.00
U.S.: $60.00
Can.: $60.00

52

CAT, Seated
Style Eight
Model: A5261, 7362
Modeller: Unknown
Height: 5", 12.7 cm
Colour: A5261   Black / white
           A7362   Ginger tabby
Issued: 06/06 to the present

U.K.:   £14.00
U.S.: $28.00
Can.: $28.00

CAT, Snoozing
Model: CL2
Modeller: Judy Boyt
Height: 3", 7.6 cm
Colour: Ginger tabby
Issued: 01/84 - 12/86
Series: A Cat Around the
           House

U.K.   £40.00
U.S. $80.00
Can. $80.00

CAT, Stalking
Style One
Model: None
Modeller: Anne Wall
Height: 3", 7.6 cm
Colour: A. Browns
           B. Bronze
Issued: 07/78 - 06/79
Series: Mammals

	Browns	Bronze
U.K.	£ 65.	£40.
U.S.	$125.	$80.
Can.	$125.	$80

CAT, Stalking
Style Two
Model: CL3
Modeller: Judy Boyt
Height: 3 ¼", 8.3 cm
Colour: 1. Black and white
           2. Silver tabby
Issued: 01/84 - 12/86
Series: A Cat Around the
           House

U.K.   £35.00
U.S. $70.00
Can. $70.00

CAT, Standing
Model: A1267, 68, 70
Modeller: Unknown
Height: 13", 33.0 cm
Colour: A 1267   Black / white
           A1268   Ginger tabby
           A1270   Silver tabby
Issued: 01/02 - 06/03
Series: Cats and Kittens Galore

U.K.   £ 50.00
U.S. $100.00
Can. $100.00

CAT, Stretching
Style One
Model: 463477; 463531; 463604 (A1528); 638390 (A1526);
           B0568 (A1527); B0575
Modeller: Richard Roberts
Height: 7", 17.8 cm
Colour /   463477   Graphite   01/98 - 12/99
Issued: 463531   Verdigris   01/98 - 06/00
           463604   Stone   01/98 - 12/03
           638390   Slate blue 01/99 - 12/03
           B0568   Walnut   01/00 - 06/02
           B0575   Pumice   06/00 - 12/00
Series: Cubist Cats and Kittens

U.K.:   £40.00
U.S.: $80.00
Can.: $80.00

CAT, Stretching
Style Two
Model: A1271, 72, 74
Modeller: Unknown
Height: 12 ¾", 32.4 cm
Size: Large
Colour: A1271   Black / white
           A1272   Ginger tabby
           A1274   Silver tabby
Issued: 01/02 - 06/04
Series: Cats and Kittens Galore

U.K.:   £ 50.00
U.S.: $100.00
Can.: $100.00

CAT, Stretching
Style Three

Model:	A4678, 4684
Modeller:	Unknown
Height:	6 ¾", 17.2 cm
Colour:	A4678 Rouge
	A4684 Granite
Issued:	01/04 - 06/05
Series:	Contemporary Cats

U.K.:	£35.00
U.S.:	$70.00
Can.:	$70.00

CAT, Stretching
Style Four

Model:	A1459, 2014, 2015
Modeller:	Barry Snelson
Height:	3 ½", 8.9 cm
Size:	Small
Colour:	A1459 Ginger tabby
	A2014 Black / white
	A2015 Silver tabby
Issued:	06/02 - 06/04
Series:	Cats and Kittens Galore

U.K.:	£12.00
U.S.:	$25.00
Can.:	$25.00

CAT, Striding

Model:	CL5
Modeller:	Judy Boyt
Height:	3 ¼", 8.3 cm
Colour:	Light and dark brown
	and white
Issued:	01/84 - 12/86
Series:	A Cat Around the
	House

U.K.	£ 50.00
U.S.	$100.00
Can.	$100.00

CAT, Walking, Style One

Model:	B0577 Salte blue
Colour:	B0560 Walnut
	B0562 Verdigris
	B0564 Stone
	B0628 Pumice
Modeller:	Richard Roberts
Height:	9", 22.9 cm
Issued:	B0557 01/00-12/03
Issued	B0560 01/00-12/03
	B0562 01/00-06/00
	B0564 01/00-12/03
	B0628 06/00-12/00
Series:	Cubist Cats and Kittens

U.K.	£40.00
U.S.	$80.00
Can.	$80.00

CAT, Walking
Style Two

Model:	A1456, 2008, 2009
Modeller:	Barry Snelson
Height:	4 ¼", 10.8 cm
Size:	Small
Colour:	A1456 Ginger tabby
	A2008 Black / white
	A2009 Silver tabby
Issued:	06/02 - 06/04
Series:	Cats and Kittens Galore

U.K.:	£12.00
U.S.:	$25.00
Can.:	$25.00

CAT, Walking
Style Three

Model:	A4681, 4687
Modeller:	Unknown
Height:	9 ½", 24.0 cm
Colour:	A4681 Rouge
	A4687 Granite
Issued:	01/04 - 06/05
Series:	Contemporary Cats

U.K.:	£40.00
U.S.:	$80.00
Can.:	$80.00

CAT, Walking
Style Four

Model:	A7363, 7364
Modeller:	Unknown
Height:	5 ¼", 13.3 cm
Colour:	A7363 Silver tabby
	A7364 Tortoiseshell
Issued:	06/06 to the present

U.K.:	£18.00
U.S.:	$35.00
Can.:	$35.00

CAT, Washing

Model:	B0559 Slate Blue
Colour:	B0561 Walnut
	B0563 Verdigris
	B0565 Stone
	B0629 Pumice
Modeller:	Richard Roberts
Height:	6", 15.0 cm
Issued:	B0559 01/00-12/03
	B0561 01/00-12/03
	B0563 01/00-06/00
	B0565 01/00-12/03
	B0629 06/00-12/00

U.K.:	£30.00
U.S.:	$60.00
Can.:	$60.00

**CAT AND GOLDFISH BOWL
"CAT FISH"**

Model: C17
Modeller: Ray Ayres
Height: 5", 12.7 cm
Colour: Grey and red
Issued: 01/91 - 12/93
Series: A Cat Around the House

U.K.:   £40.00
U.S.: $80.00
Can.: $80.00

**CAT AND KITTENS
"CAT WALK"**

Model: C6
Modeller: Judy Boyt
Height: 2 ½", 6.4 cm
Colour: A. Brown, black, white
               and ginger
           B. Black and white
Issued: 01/83 - 12/84
Series: A Cat Around the House

U.K.:   £ 50.00
U.S.: $100.00
Can.: $100.00

**CAT AND MIRROR
"COPY CAT"**

Model: C8
Modeller: Judy Boyt
Height: 4", 10.1 cm
Colour: Ginger, white and
               brown
Issued: 01/83 - 12/87
Series: A Cat Around the House

U.K.:   £35.00
U.S.: $70.00
Can.: $70.00

CAT AND ONE KITTEN

Model: CG13A, B, C
Modeller: Unknown
Height: 3 ¾", 9.5 cm
Colour: A. Black, white,
               tortoiseshell
           B. Ginger, white, grey
           C. Tabby, white, ginger
Issued: 01/95 - 12/95
Series: Cats Galore

U.K.:   £20.00
U.S.: $40.00
Can.: $40.00

**CAT AND STOOL
"HAPPY CAT"**

Model: C7
Modeller: Judy Boyt
Height: 4", 10.1 cm
Colour: Grey, brown and green
Issued: 01/83 - 12/85
Series: A Cat Around the House

U.K.:   £35.00
U.S.: $70.00
Can.: $70.00

**CAT AND STREET SIGN
"CAT WALK"**

Model: C18
Modeller: Ray Ayres
Height: 3 ½", 8.9 cm
Colour: A. Ginger
           B. Black and white
Issued: 01/91 - 12/92
Series: A Cat Around the House

U.K.:   £30.00
U.S.: $60.00
Can.: $60.00

CAT AND THREE KITTENS

Model: CG12A, B, C
Modeller: Unknown
Height: 2 ½", 6.4 cm
Colour: A. Tortoiseshell cat
           B. Ginger and white cat
           C. Tabby and white cat
Issued: 01/95 - 12/95
Series: Cats Galore

U.K.:   £25.00
U.S.: $50.00
Can.: $50.00

CAT AND TOP HAT "TOP CAT"

Model: C16
Modeller: Ray Ayres
Height: 3", 7.6 cm
Colour: Grey cat, black top hat
Issued: 01/90 - 12/91
Series: A Cat Around the House

U.K.:   £25.00
U.S.: $50.00
Can.: $50.00

CAT IN BASKET "CATNAP"
First Version - Without kittens
Model: C9
Modeller: Judy Boyt
Height: 1 ½", 3.8 cm
Colour: Black, white and brown
Issued: 07/83 - 12/83
Series: A Cat Around the House

U.K.:   £20.00
U.S.: $40.00
Can.: $40.00

CAT IN BASKET "CATNAP"
Second Version - With kittens
Model: C9
Modeller: Judy Boyt
Height: 1 ½", 3.8 cm
Colour: Black, white, lilac and
            pale golden brown
Issued: 01/84 - 12/87
Series: A Cat Around the House

U.K.:   £15.00
U.S.: $30.00
Can.: $30.00

CAT LICKING KITTEN
"CATLICK"
Model: C13
Modeller: Ray Ayres
Height: 3", 7.6 cm
Colour: White, black and grey
Issued: 01/89 - 12/91
Series: A Cat Around the House

U.K.:   £25.00
U.S.: $50.00
Can.: $50.00

CAT LICKING PAW
Model: B0717 (A1549);
            B0718 (A1548);
            B0719 (A1547)
Modeller: Unknown
Height: 5 ¼", 13.3 cm
Colour: B0717   Stone
            A1548   Walnut
            A1549   Slate blue
Issued: 06/01 - 12/03
Series: Cubist Cats and Kittens

U.K.:   £25.00
U.S.: $50.00
Can.: $50.00

CAT LYING DOWN
Model: 541524; 541532 (A1522); 541540; 638374 (A1520);
            B0567 (A1521); B0574
Modeller: Richard Roberts
Height: 3", 7.6 cm
Issued: 541524   Graphite   01/99-12/99
Issued: 541532   Stone   01/99-12/03
            541540   Verdigris   01/99-06/00
            638374   Slate Blue   01/99-12/03
            B0567   Walnut   01/00-12/03
            B0574   Pumice   06/00-12/00
Series: Cubist Cats and Kittens

U.K.:   £25.00
U.S.: $50.00
Can.: $50.00

CAT ON BOOKS "WISE CAT"
Style One - Closed books
Model: C10
Modeller: Judy Boyt
Height: 2 ¾", 7.0 cm
Colour: Grey, white, blue and
            red
Issued: 07/83 - 12/83
Series: A Cat Around the House

U.K.   £ 65.00
U.S. $125.00
Can. $125.00

CAT ON BOOKS "WISE CAT"
Style Two - Open books
Model: C10
Modeller: Judy Boyt
Height: 2 ¾", 7.0 cm
Colour: Black, white, blue and
            red
Issued: 01/84 - 12/92
Series: A Cat Around the House

U.K.   £25.00
U.S. $50.00
Can. $50.00

CAT ON FENCE "CATERWAUL"
Model: C19
Modeller: Ray Ayres
Height: 6", 15.0 cm
Colour: Black and white
Issued: 01/91 - 12/92
Series: A Cat Around the House

U.K. £30.00
U.S. $60.00
Can. $60.00

**CAT ON FOOTSTOOL
"COMFY CAT"**
Model: C14
Modeller: Ray Ayres
Height: 4", 10.1 cm
Colour: White and browns
Issued: 01/89 - 12/91
Series: A Cat Around the House

U.K. £30.00
U.S. $60.00
Can. $60.00

CAT ON POST "POLE-CAT"
Model: C5
Modeller: Judy Boyt
Height: 5", 12.7 cm
Colour: Ginger, white and brown
Issued: 01/83 - 12/93
Series: A Cat Around the House

U.K. £40.00
U.S. $80.00
Can. $80.00

**CAT ON STEPS
"CATASTROPHE"**
Model: C12
Modeller: Judy Boyt
Height: 4", 10.1 cm
Colour: Ginger and white
Issued: 07/83 - 12/85
Series: A Cat Around the House

U.K. £45.00
U.S. $90.00
Can. $90.00

**CAT SCRATCHING "SCRATCH"
First Version - Square base**
Model: C11
Modeller: Judy Boyt
Height: 2 ¾", 7.0 cm
Colour: Grey, white and sandy brown
Issued: 07/83 - 12/83
Series: A Cat Around the House

U.K. £45.00
U.S. $90.00
Can. $90.00

**CAT SCRATCHING "SCRATCH"
Second Version - Round base**
Model: C11
Modeller: Judy Boyt
Height: 2 ¾", 7.0 cm
Colour: Black, white and red
Issued: 01/84 - 12/91
Series: A Cat Around the House

U.K. £30.00
U.S. $60.00
Can. $60.00

CAT SCRATCHING EAR
Model: A1882, 2650, 2651
Modeller: Unknown
Height: 3 ¼", 8.3 cm
Colour: A1882 Ginger tabby
A2650 Black / white
A2651 Silver tabby
Issued: 01/03 - 06/04
Series: Cats and Kittens Galore

U.K.: £12.00
U.S.: $25.00
Can.: $25.00

CAT, SHELF
Model: 470856 Graphite
470864 Verdigris
470872 Stone
638404 Slate bllue
B0571 Walnut
B0578 Pumice
Modeller: Richard Roberts
Height: 6 ¾", 17.2 cm
Issued: 470856 01/98-12/99
Issued: 470864 01/98-06/00
470872 01/98-12/03
638404 01/99-12/03
B0571 01/00-12/03
B0578 06/00-12/00
Series: Cubist Cats and Kittens

U.K. £40.00
U.S. $80.00
Can. $80.00

CAT WITH PAW UP, Style One

Model /	541451	Graphite
Colour:	541478	Stone
	541486	Verdigris
	638358	Slate
	B0572	Walnut
	B0679	Pumice
Modeller:	Richard Roberts	
Height:	6 ¾", 17.2 cm	
Issued:	541451	01/99-12/99
	541478	01/99-12/03
	541486	01/99-06/00
	638358	01/99-12/03
	B0572	01/00-12/03
	B0679	06/00-12/03
Series:	Cubist Cats and Kittens	
U.K.:	£40.00	
U.S.:	$75.00	
Can.:	$75.00	

CAT WITH PAW UP
Style Two

Model:	A4683, 4689
Modeller:	Unknown
Height:	7 ¼", 18.4 cm
Colour:	A4683 Rouge
	A4689 Granite
Issued:	01/04 - 06/05
Series:	Contemporary Cats
U.K.:	£37.00
U.S.:	$70.00
Can.:	$70.00

CATS IN WASHING
"CAT PLAY"

Model:	C2
Modeller:	Judy Boyt
Height:	1 ½", 3.8 cm
Colour:	Black, white, grey
	and brown
Issued:	01/83 - 12/85
Series:	A Cat Around the House
U.K.:	£35.00
U.S.:	$70.00
Can.:	$70.00

CAUGHT IN THE ACT
Three Fox Cubs

Model:	L48
Modeller:	Ray Ayres
Height:	3 ¾", 9.5 cm
Colour:	Red, white and black
Issued:	01/83 in a limited
	edition of 1,500
U.K.:	£45.00
U.S.:	$90.00
Can.:	$90.00

CAUGHT NAPPING

Model:	B0972 Standard
	B972A Bespoke
Modeller:	Ray Ayres
Height:	7 ½" x 6 ¼"
	19.1 x 15.9 cm
Colour:	Black, white, browns,
	green and blue
Issued:	01/06 - 12/06
Series:	Membership Figurine
U.K.:	£150.00
U.S.:	$300.00
Can.:	$300.00

Note: Bespoke version can have the dog painted another colour and the name added to the back of the model.

CAUSING A STIR
(Otter and grebe)

Model:	B0893
Modeller:	Ray Ayres
Height:	16 ½" x 8",
	41.9 x 20.3 cm
Colour:	Browns, green,
	white and red
Issued:	06/04 in a limited
	edition of 950
Series:	Above and Below
U.K.:	£195.00
U.S.:	$400.00
Can.:	$400.00

CAVALIER KING CHARLES
SPANIEL, Seated
Style One

Model:	DS12
Modeller:	Elizabeth MacAllister
Height:	4", 10.1 cm
Colour:	Brown and white
Issued:	01/87 - 12/92
Series:	The World of Dogs
U.K.:	£35.00
U.S.:	$70.00
Can.:	$70.00

CAVALIER KING CHARLES
SPANIEL, Seated
Style Two

Model:	DG06A, B, C, D
Modeller:	Steve McKeown
Height:	3 ¾", 9.5 cm
Colour:	A. Tricolour
	B. Blenheim
	C. Black and tan
	D. Ruby
Issued:	01/91 - 12/95
Series:	Dogs Galore
U.K.	£20.00
U.S.	$40.00
Can.	$40.00

58

CAVALIER KING CHARLES SPANIEL, Seated
Style Three
Model: A2093, 2640
Modeller: Margaret Turner
Height: 3 ¾", 9.5 cm
Colour: A2093   Blenheim
               A2640   Tricolour
Issued: 01/03 to the present
Series: Dogs and Pups Galore

U.K.:   £16.00
U.S.: $30.00
Can.: $30.00

CAVALIER KING CHARLES SPANIEL, Seated
Style Four
Model: A5180, 5622
Modeller: Unknown
Height: 10 ½", 26.7 cm
Colour: A5180   Tricolour
               A5622   Blenheim
Issued: 01/05 - 12/06
Series: Fireside Dogs

U.K.:   £ 65.00
U.S.: $125.00
Can.: $125.00

CAVALIER KING CHARLES SPANIEL, Standing
Model: A1159, 1201
Modeller: Unknown
Height: 4", 10.1 cm
Colour: A1159   Tricolour
               A1201   Blenheim
Issued: 2003 to the present
Series: Dogs and Pups Galore

U.K.:   £18.00
U.S.: $35.00
Can.: $35.00

CHAFFINCH
Style One
Model: RB4
Modeller: Ray Ayres
Height: 3 ½", 8.9 cm
Colour: Pale brown, blue
               and black
Issued: 06/83 - 12/85
Series: RSPB Birds

U.K.:   £30.00
U.S.: $60.00
Can.: $60.00

CHAFFINCH
Style Two
Model: M14
Modeller: David Fryer
Height: 3", 7.6 cm
Colour: Orange and blue;
               bronze base
Issued: 07/83 - 06/86
Series: Miniatures on Bronze

U.K.:   £ 65.00
U.S.: $125.00
Can.: $125.00

CHAFFINCH
Style Three
Model: A7150
Modeller: Unknown
Height: 4 ¾", 12.1 cm
Colour: Pink, black, white,
               brown and green
Issued: 06/06 to the present

U.K.:   £ 9.95
U.S.: $20.00
Can.: $20.00

CHAMPION AT THE HOLM
(Shepherd and Sheep)
Model: L141
Modeller: Anne Wall
Height: 5 ¾", 14.6 cm
Colour: White and pale green
Issued: 08/93 in a limited
               edition of 250

U.K.:   £150.00
U.S.: $300.00
Can.: $300.00

CHAMPION MARE AND FOAL
(Shire Mare and Foal, Gold Edition)
Model: B0334
Modeller: Anne Wall
Height: 8 ½", 21.6 cm
Colour: A. Bay
               B. Grey
               C. Black (deeper red
               base)
Issued: Autumn 1998 in a
               limited edition of 350
Series: Heavy Horse Collection

U.K.:   £450.00
U.S.: $850.00
Can.: $850.00

Note: Issued nos. 1-350.

CHAMPION MARE AND FOAL
(Shire Mare and Foal, Std. Edition)

Model: B0334A
Modeller: Anne Wall
Height: 8 ½", 21.6 cm
Colour: Bay
Issued: 01/00 in a limited
           edition of 600
Series: Agricultural and
           Sporting

U.K.:   £325.00
U.S.: $650.00
Can.: $650.00

Note: Issued nos. 351-950.

CHAMPION OF CHAMPIONS SHIRE STALLION
(American Std. Edition)

Model: L142A
Modeller: Anne Wall
Height: 9 ½", 24.0 cm
Colour: A. Bay
           B. Grey
Issued: 01/94 in a limited
           edition of 500
Series: Heavy Horse

	Bay	Grey
U.K.:	£350.	£450.
U.S.:	$700.	$900.
Can.:	$700.	$900.

CHAMPION OF CHAMPIONS SHIRE STALLION
(Gold Edition)

Model: L140
Modeller: Anne Wall
Height: 10 ¼", 26.0 cm
Colour: A. Bay
           B. Grey
           C. Black
Issued: 01/94 Ltd. ed. of 350
Series: Heavy Horse

	Bay	Grey	Black
U.K.:	£ 550.	600.	550.
U.S.:	$1,100.	1,200.	1,100.
Can.:	$1,100.	1,200.	1,100.

Note: Issued nos. 1-350.

(Standard Edition)

Model: L140A
Modeller: Anne Wall
Height: 9 ½", 24.0 cm
Colour: Bay
Issued: 01/94 Ltd. ed. of 600
Series: Heavy Horse

U.K.:   £425.00
U.S.: $850.00
Can.: $850.00

Note: Issued nos. 351-950.

CHAMPION SHIRE, THE

Model: B0888, 0888A
Modeller: Anne Wall
Size: 14 ¾" x 18 ¼"
           37.5 x 46.3 cm
Colour: B0888 Bay horse,
           red / blue ribbons
           B0888A Grey horse,
           yellow / black ribbons
Issued: 06/04 in a limited
           edition of 500

U.K.:   £495.00
U.S.: $950.00
Can.: $950.00

CHANGING TIMES
(Ford Ferguson 9N)

Model: B0912
Modeller: Ray Ayres
Height: 4 ¾" x 10 ¾"
           12.1 x 27.8 cm
Colour: Grey, brown, cream,
           black and white
Issued: 01/05 - 12/05
Series: Classic Member-only
           Tractor Figurine

U.K.:   £225.00
U.S.: $450.00
Can.: $450.00

Note: Ford Ferguson is a registered
      trademark owned and licensed
      by Ford Motor Company.

CHARLIE'S RETREAT

Model: L69
Modeller: Elizabeth MacAllister
Height: 6 ½", 16.5 cm
Colour: Tricolour dog, reddish
           brown fox
Issued: 01/85 in a limited
           edition of 500

U.K.:   £300.00
U.S.: $600.00
Can.: $600.00

CHARMER, THE

Model: A7324, 7603
Modeller: Unknown
Height: 7", 17.8 cm
Colour: A7324 Grey
           A7603 Siamese
Issued: 06/06 to the present
Series: Feline Fun

U.K.:   £ 9.95
U.S.: $20.00
Can.: $20.00

CHAROLAIS BULL
Style One

Model:	L112
Modeller:	Ray Ayres
Height:	7 ¼", 18.4 cm
Colour:	Cream
Issued:	09/91 in a limited edition of 1,500
Series:	Agricultural and Sporting
U.K.:	£ 625.00
U.S.:	$1,250.00
Can.:	$1,250.00

CHAROLAIS BULL
Style Two

Model:	B0587
Modeller:	Jack Crewdson
Height:	9 ½", 24.0 cm
Colour:	Cream
Issued:	06/00 in a limited edition of 950
Series:	Agricultural and Sporting
U.K.:	£250.00
U.S.:	$500.00
Can.:	$500.00

CHAROLAIS BULL
Style Three

Model:	A0738
Modeller:	Lesley McKenzie
Height:	5 ¾", 14.6 cm
Colour:	Cream
Issued:	06/01 - 12/04
Series:	Cattle Breeds
U.K.:	£40.00
U.S.:	$80.00
Can.:	$80.00

CHAROLAIS BULL
Style Five

Model:	B1075
Modeller:	Kirst Armstrong
Size:	8" x 10 ½" 20.3 x 26.7 cm
Colour:	Creamy white
Issued:	06/07 in a limited edition of 500
U.K.:	£199.00
U.S.:	$400.00
Can.:	$400.00

CHAROLAIS	BULL Style Four	CALF	COW
Model:	A4598	A4602	A4599
Modeller:	Kirsty Armstrong		
Height:	5" 12.7 cm	3 ½" 8.9 cm	5 ½" 14.0 cm
Colour:	Creamy white		
Issued:	01/04 to the present		
Series:	BFA Pottery Company		
U.K.:	£25.00	£14.95	£25.00
U.S.:	$50.00	$30.00	$50.00
Can.:	$50.00	$30.00	$50.00

CHAROLAIS BULL, Lying

Model:	A4246
Modeller:	Lesley McKenzie
Height:	4 ¼", 10.8 cm
Colour:	White, red, brown and golden brown
Issued:	06/04 - 12/06
U.K.:	£ 60.00
U.S.:	$120.00
Can.:	$120.00

CHAROLAIS CALVES (Pair)
Style One

Model:	B0272
Modeller:	Kirsty Armstrong
Height:	4 ¾", 12.1 cm
Colour:	Cream, brown and green
Issued:	01/98 - 12/00
Series:	Agricultural and Sporting
U.K.:	£ 55.00
U.S.:	$110.00
Can.:	$110.00

CHAROLAIS CALVES
Style Two
Model: A5275
Modeller: Lelsey Mackenzie
Height: 5", 12.7 cm
Colour: Creamy white
Issued: 06/05 - 12/06

U.K.: £38.00
U.S.: $75.00
Can.: $75.00

CHAROLAIS COW AND CALF
Style One
Model: L137
Modeller: Ray Ayres
Height: 7 ¼", 18.4 cm
Colour: Cream
Issued: 07/93 in a limited
edition of 1,500
Series: Agricultural and
Sporting

U.K.: £475.00
U.S.: $950.00
Can.: $950.00

CHAROLAIS COW AND CALF
Style Two
Model: A1249
Modeller: Lesley McKenzie
Height: 5 ½", 14.0 cm
Colour: Cream
Issued: 01/02 - 06/04
Series: Cattle Breeds

U.K.: £45.00
U.S.: $90.00
Can.: $90.00

CHAROLAIS COW AND CALF
Style Three
Model: B0742
Modeller: Jack Crewdson
Height: 9 ¼", 23.5 cm
Size: Large
Colour: Cream
Issued: 01/02 in a limited
edition of 750
Series: Classic Collection

U.K.: £250.00
U.S.: $500.00
Can.: $500.00

CHAROLAIS EWE AND LAMBS
Model: L121
Modeller: Ray Ayres
Height: 5 ½", 14.0 cm
Colour: Cream
Issued: 09/92 in a limited
edition of 750
Series: Special Interest

U.K.: £475.00
U.S.: $950.00
Can.: $950.00

CHAROLAIS FAMILY GROUP
Model: B0184
Modeller: Kirsty Armstrong
Height: 6 ½", 16.5 cm
Colour: Cream
Issued: 06/97 in a limited
edition of 1,250
Series: Agricultural and
Sporting

U.K.: £250.00
U.S.: $500.00
Can.: $500.00

CHAROLAIS RAM
Model: B0774
Modeller: Ray Ayres
Height: 6", 15.0 cm
Colour: Cream, white and green
Issued: 06/02 in a limited
edition of 750
Series: Classic Collection

U.K.: £ 75.00
U.S.: $150.00
Can.: $150.00

CHASE, THE
(Austin Seven Ruby and
Collies)
Model: B0444
Modeller: Ray Ayres
Height: 4 ½", 11.9 cm
Colour: Green, black, white,
brown and grey
Issued: 01/00 - 12/01
Series: The James Herriot
Collection

U.K.: £175.00
U.S.: $350.00
Can.: $350.00

CHASER, THE
Model: L50
Modeller: David Geenty
Height: 8 ½", 21.6 cm
Colour: Multicoloured
Issued: 01/83 - 12/95
Series: 1. Race Horses
2. Special Interest

U.K.: £425.00
U.S.: $850.00
Can.: $850.00

Note: This model was individually hand-painted to order.

CHEETAH
Style One
Model: L132
Modeller: Richard Roberts
Height: 10", 25.4 cm
Colour: Golden, brown, white and black
Issued: 01/93 in a limited edition of 750
Series: WWFN

U.K.: £300.00
U.S.: $600.00
Can.: $600.00

CHEETAH
Style Two
Model: A3780
Modeller: David Mayer
Height: 5 ¼", 13.3 cm
Colour: Golden brown, cream, black and grey
Issued: 01/05 - 12/06
Series: Wild World

U.K.: £ 70.00
U.S.: $140.00
Can.: $140.00

CHEETAH AND CUBS
Model: L133
Modeller: Richard Roberts
Height: 8", 20.3 cm
Colour: Golden, brown, white and black
Issued: 01/93 in a limited edition of 750
Series: WWFN

U.K.: £300.00
U.S.: $600.00
Can.: $600.00

CHEQUERED SKIPPER
(Butterflies)
Model: B7
Modeller: Ray Ayres
Height: 2 ¾", 7.0 cm
Colour: Black, yellow, brown and green
Issued: 01/81 - 12/85
Series: British Butterflies

U.K.: £ 75.00
U.S.: $150.00
Can.: $150.00

Note: Original models were issued without antenae. Domes were optional with all butterflies.

CHESTERTON
Model: LA11
Designer: Lesley Anne Ivory
Modeller: Anne Butler
Height: 4 ½", 11.9 cm
Colour: Black and white
Issued: 01/92 - 12/93
Varieties: LAM2 (Musical)
Series: Ivory Cats

U.K.: £35.00
U.S.: $70.00
Can.: $70.00

CHESTERTON (Musical)
Model: LAM2
Designer: Lesley Anne Ivory
Modeller: Anne Butler
Height: 6 ½", 16.5 cm
Colour: Black and white
Issued: 01/92 - 12/93
Varieties: LA11 Chesterton
Series: Ivory Cats (Musical)

U.K.: £45.00
U.S.: $90.00
Can.: $90.00

CHEVIOT EWE AND LAMBS
Model: Unknown
Modeller: Mairi Laing Hunt
Height: 5", 12.7 cm
Colour: Grey and white
Issued: 01/77 in a limited edition of 250

U.K.: £1,250.00
U.S.: $2,500.00
Can.: $2,500.00

CHEVIOT RAM

Model: L39
Modeller: Ray Ayres
Height: 5", 12.7 cm
Colour: Beige and white
Issued: 01/82 in a limited
edition of 850

U.K.: £450.00
U.S.: $900.00
Can.: $900.00

CHEWING THE CUD

Model: A0904
Modeller: Craig Harding
Height: 3 ¾", 9.5 cm
Colour: Black and white
Issued: 06/01 - 06/04
Series: James Herriot
Studio Collection

U.K.: £45.00
U.S.: $90.00
Can.: $90.00

CHICK

Model: FF10A, B
Modeller: Anne Wall
Height: 2", 5.0 cm
Colour: A. Yellow
B. Yellow flecked,
mottled
Issued: 01/92 - 12/94
Series: First Friends

U.K.: £12.00
U.S.: $25.00
Can.: $25.00

CHICKEN

Model: A5251, A6126
Modeller: Russell Willis
Height: 4 ¾", 12.1 cm
Colour: 1. Rhode Island Red
2. Light Sussex
Issued: 01/06 to the present
Series: BFA Pottery Company

U.K.: £16.00
U.S.: $32.00
Can.: $32.00

CHICKENING OUT
(Border Collie and Cockerel)

Model: A0189
Modeller: Anne Wall
Height: 3 ¼", 8.3 cm
Colour: Reddish-brown, black,
white and stone
Issued: 01/01 - 12/05
Series: James Herriot
Studio Collection

U.K.: £20.00
U.S.: $40.00
Can.: $40.00

CHIHUAHUA, Standing

Model: A4981
Modeller: Margaret Turner
Height: 3", 7.6 cm
Colour: Golden brown and
white
Issued: 01/05 to the present
Series: Dogs and Pups Galore

U.K.: £14.00
U.S.: $28.00
Can.: $28.00

CHIPMUNK (Eastern)

Model: Unknown
Modeller: Anne Wall
Height: 3 ¼", 8.3 cm
Colour: Brown, black, white
and green
Issued: 1978-Unknown

U.K.: £45.00
U.S.: $90.00
Can.: $90.00

CHIPMUNKS

Model: ED4
Modeller: Judy Boyt
Height: 2 ¼", 5.7 cm
Colour: Brown, black and white
Issued: 07/82 - 12/82
Series: Early Days

U.K.: £45.00
U.S.: $90.00
Can.: $90.00

CLEAN SWEEP, A

Gold Edition

Model: B0591
Modeller: Ray Ayres
Height: 6", 15.0 cm
Colour: Unknown
Issued: 06/02 in a limited
edition of 350
Series: Classic Collection

U.K.: £400.00
U.S.: $800.00
Can.: $800.00

Standard Edition

Model: B0591A
Modeller: Ray Ayres
Height: 6", 15.0 cm
Colour: Black, brown, white
green and beige
Issued: 06/02 in a limited
edition of 600
Series: Classic Collection

U.K.: £300.00
U.S.: $600.00
Can.: $600.00

Numbered 1 to 350.   Numbered 351 to 950.

CLEARING OUT
(Country Ploughman 55)

Model: A6343
Modeller: Unknown
Size: 6 ¾" x 12 ¾"
17.2 x 32.4 cm
Colour: Blue, red, brown,
green, black and white
Issued: 06/07 to the presemt
Series: Tractors

U.K.: £130.00
U.S.: $250.00
Can.: $250.00

CLEARING THE WAY
© 2006 Land Rover

Model: B0945
Modeller: Ray Ayres
Size: 4 ½" x 12 ¼"
11.9 x 31.1 cm
Colour: Dark green, browns,
black, white and blue
Issued: 01/05 in a limited
edition of 750

U.K.: £225.00
U.S.: $450.00
Can.: $450.00

CLEVELAND BAY STALLION
"FOREST FOREMAN"

Model: L63
Modeller: Judy Boyt
Height: 9 ½", 24.0 cm
Colour: Bay
Issued: 01/85 in a limited
edition of 200
Series: Special Interest

U.K.: £2,250.00
U.S.: $4,500.00
Can.: $4,500.00

CLOUDED YELLOW
(Butterfly)

Model: B1
Modeller: Anne Wall
Height: 2 ½", 6.4 cm
Colour: Yellow, green and
deep purple
Issued: 07/80 - 12/85
Series: British Butterflies

U.K.: £ 65.00
U.S.: $125.00
Can.: $125.00

Note: Original models were issued
with antenae. Domes were
optional with all butterflies.

CLOVER HILL FARM

Model: JH50
Modeller: Richard Young
Height: 4", 10.1 cm
Colour: Grey, brown, yellow
and green
Issued: 01/89 - 09/90
Series: James Herriot's
Yorkshire

U.K.: £ 60.00
U.S.: $120.00
Can.: $120.00

CLOVER'S NEW CALF

Model: A6519
Modeller: Unknown
Height: 4 ¾", 12.1 cm
Colour: White, brown, straw
yellow and silver
Issued: 01/07 to the present
Series: James Herriot
Studio Collection

U.K.: £39.00
U.S.: $80.00
Can.: $80.00

CLYDESDALE MARE AND FOAL

Model:	A0187
Modeller:	Anne Wall
Height:	6 ¾", 17.2 cm
Colour:	Browns, white and green
Issued:	06/00 - 12/05
Series:	Horse Breeds

U.K.:	£ 50.00
U.S.:	$100.00
Can.:	$100.00

CLYDESDALE STALLION
Style One

Model:	A0732
Modeller:	Anne Wall
Height:	6 ½", 16.5 cm
Colour:	Brown and white; green base
Issued:	06/01 - 12/04
Series:	Horse Breeds

U.K.:	£40.00
U.S.:	$80.00
Can.:	$80.00

CLYDESDALE STALLION
Style Two

Model:	A4594
Modeller:	Anne Wall
Height:	6 ¾, 17.2 cm
Colour:	Brown, black and white
Issued:	06/04 to the present
Series:	BFA Pottery Company

U.K.:	£35.00
U.S.:	$70.00
Can.:	$70.00

COAL TIT

Model:	L60
Modeller:	Frank DiVita
Height:	6 ½", 16.5 cm
Colour:	Brown, white and yellow
Issued:	01/84 in a limited edition of 950

U.K.:	£150.00
U.S.:	$300.00
Can.:	$300.00

COB TYPE FOAL

Model:	A6544
Modeller:	Unknown
Height:	5", 12.7 cm
Colour:	Brown and white
Issued:	06/06 to the present
Series:	BFA Pottery Company

U.K.:	£17.00
U.S.:	$35.00
Can.:	$35.00

COCK AND HEN PHEASANTS
AND CHICKS

Model:	RB23
Modeller:	Ray Ayres
Height:	5 ½", 14.0 cm
Colour:	Browns, black and red
Issued:	01/91 - 12/93

U.K.:	£125.00
U.S.:	$250.00
Can.:	$250.00

Note: This is a combination of model RB21 and RB22.

COCK PHEASANT

Model:	RB21
Modeller:	Ray Ayres
Height:	5", 12.7 cm
Colour:	Brown, black and red
Issued:	01/91 - 12/93

U.K.:	£ 65.00
U.S.:	$125.00
Can.:	$125.00

Note: This model was combined with RB22 to form RB23.

COCKATOO

Model:	L84
Modeller	Richard Roberts
Height:	20", 50.8 cm
Colour:	White, black and yellow
Issued:	01/88 in a limited edition of 950
Series:	Exotic Birds

U.K.:	£300.00
U.S.:	$600.00
Can.:	$600.00

COCKER SPANIEL

Model:	UK: 062
	USA: 225-130
Modeller:	Ray Ayres
Height:	6 ½", 16.5 cm
Colour:	Black and white
Issued:	07/81 - 12/91
Series:	Special Interest
U.K.:	£ 80.00
U.S.:	$160.00
Can.:	$160.00

COCKER SPANIEL, Seated Style One

Model:	DG05A, B, C
Modeller:	Steve McKeown
Height:	4 ¼", 10.8 cm
Colour:	A. Golden
	B. Black
	C. Black and white
Issued:	01/91 - 12/96
Series:	Dogs Galore
U.K.:	£20.00
U.S.:	$40.00
Can.:	$40.00

COCKER SPANIEL, Seated Style Two

Model:	B0015A, B/B0480
Modeller:	Margaret Turner
Height:	4 ½", 11.9 cm
Colour:	A. Blue roan
	B. Golden
	B0480 Bronze
Issued:	A/B. 06/96-12/01
	C 06/99-12/01
Series:	1. Dogs Galore
	2. Bronzed
U.K.:	£20.00
U.S.:	$40.00
Can.:	$40.00

COCKER SPANIEL, Standing Style One

Model:	A1265, 66
Modeller:	Margaret Turner
Height:	4 ¼", 10.8 cm
Colour:	A1265 Golden
	A1266 Blue Roan
Issued:	A1265 01/02-06/06
	A1266 01/02 to the
	present
Series:	Dogs and Pups Galore
U.K.:	£20.00
U.S.:	$40.00
Can.:	$40.00

COCKER SPANIEL, Standing Style Two

Model:	A3827, 4447
Modeller:	Adrian Hughes
Height:	13 ½", 34.3 cm
Colour:	A3827 Black
	A4447 Blue Roan
Issued:	01/04 - 06/05
Series:	Fireside Dogs
U.K.:	£ 80.00
U.S.:	$150.00
Can.:	$150.00

COCKER SPANIEL, Standing Style Three

Model:	A7121, 8305
Modeller:	Unknown
Height:	4 ½", 11.4 cm
Colour:	A7121 Blue Road
	A8305 Golden
Issued:	01/07 to the present
Series:	Dogs and Pups Galore
U.K.:	£19.00
U.S.:	$40.00
Can.:	$40.00

COCKER SPANIEL AND PUP

Model:	B0105A, B
Modeller:	Margaret Turner
Height:	5", 12.7 cm
Colour:	A. Blue roan
	B. Golden
Issued:	06/96 - 12/98
Series:	Dogs Galore
U.K.:	£40.00
U.S.:	$80.00
Can.:	$80.00

COCKER SPANIEL AND PUPS

Model:	B0312A, B	
Modeller:	Margaret Turner	
Height:	7", 17.8 cm	
Colour:	B0312A Blue roan	
	B0312B Golden	
Issued:	06/98 - 12/99	
Series:	Dogs by Margaret Turner	
	Blue	**Golden**
U.K.:	£150.	£125.
U.S.:	$300.	$250.
Can.:	$300.	$250.

COCKER SPANIEL AND THREE PUPS

Model: A5212, 5863
Modeller: Kerry Bell
Height: 3 ¼", 8.3 cm
Colour: A5212   Black
            A5863   Blue Roan
Issued: 01/05 - 12/06
Series: Dogs and Pups Galore:
            Family Groups

U.K.:   £26.00
U.S.: $50.00
Can.: $50.00

COCKER SPANIEL IN TRUG

Model: 656739
Modeller: Unknown
Height: 2 ¾", 7.0 cm
Colour: Reddish-brown and
            fawn
Issued: 06/99 - 12/00
Series: Puppy Tales

U.K.:   £12.00
U.S.: $25.00
Can.: $25.00

COCKER SPANIEL PUP, Seated

Model: PG03A, B, C/B0457
Modeller: Margaret Turner
Height: 2 ½", 6.4 cm
Colour: A. Golden and white
            B. Black
            C. Blue roan
            B0457   Bronze
Issued: A-C. 01/92 - 12/01
            B0457   06/99-06/00
Series: 1. Pups Galore
            2. Bronzed

U.K.:   £12.00
U.S.: $25.00
Can.: $25.00

COCKER SPANIEL PUPS

Model: A3837, 4240
Modeller: Adrian Hughes
Height: 2 ½", 6.4 cm
Colour: A3837   Black
            A4240   Blue Roan
Issued: A3837   01/04-06/06
            A4240   01/04 to the
                    present
Series: Dogs and Pups Galore

U.K.:   £20.00
U.S.: $40.00
Can.: $40.00

COCKEREL
Style One

Model: UK: 038
            USA: 225-062
Modeller: David Geenty
Height: 7", 17.8 cm
Colour: Red, yellow and black
Issued: 06/79 - 12/81

U.K.:   £175.00
U.S.: $350.00
Can.: $350.00

COCKEREL
Style Two

Model: 739448, 739456
Modeller: Russell Willis
Height: 11 ¾", 29.8 cm
Colour: 739448   White
            739456   Brown
Issued: 739448 01/00-12/03
            739456 01/00-06/03
Series: 1. Birds And ...
            2. Farmyard Friends

U.K.:   £ 75.00
U.S.: $150.00
Can.: $150.00

COCKEREL
Style Three

Model: A1672
Modeller: Unknown
Height: 12 ¾", 32.4 cm
Colour: Black, yellow, red,
            brown and green
Issued: 01/02 - 12/03
Series: Farmyard Friends

U.K.:   £ 75.00
U.S.: $150.00
Can.: $150.00

COCKEREL
Style Four

Model: A4597
Modeller: Russell Willis
Height: 5 ¼", 13.3 cm
Colour: Red, yellow, orange
            and green
Issued: 06/04 to the present
Series: BFA Pottery Company

U.K.:   £20.00
U.S.: $40.00
Can.: $40.00

COCKEREL AND PIGLET AT WATERER

Model:	A3702
Modeller:	Kerry Bell
Height:	5", 12.7 cm
Colour:	Pale pink, silver, black, red, orange and green
Issued:	01/04 - 12/06
Series:	James Herriot Studio Collection
U.K.:	£30.00
U.S.:	$60.00
Can.:	$60.00

COLLECTING THE HOUNDS
(Huntsman and two hounds)

Model:	L125
Modeller:	Anne Wall
Height:	8", 20.3 cm
Colour:	Brown, black and red
Issued:	01/93 in a limited edition of 950
Series:	Agricultural and Sporting
U.K.:	£250.00
U.S.:	$500.00
Can.:	$500.00

COLLIE AND SHEPHERD

Model:	106
Modeller:	Ray Ayres
Height:	7 ½", 19.1 cm
Colour:	Green, brown, black and white
Issued:	01/82 - 12/86
Series:	1. Agricultural and Sporting
	2. The Farm Series
U.K.:	£100.00
U.S.:	$200.00
Can.:	$200.00

Note: This model was combined with 104 to form 105/S1.

COLLIE AND THREE PUPS

Model:	A5209, 5658
Modeller:	Kerry Bell
Height:	4", 10.1 cm
Colour:	A5209 Black / white
	A5658 Tricolour
Issued:	01/05 - 12/06
Series:	Dogs and Pups Galore: Family Groups
U.K.:	£30.00
U.S.:	$60.00
Can.:	$60.00

COLLIE IN COAL BUCKET

Model:	484091
Modeller:	Unknown
Height:	2 ½", 6.4 cm
Colour:	Black, white and brown
Issued:	06/98 - 12/00
Series:	Puppy Tales
U.K.:	£12.00
U.S.:	$25.00
Can.:	$25.00

COLLIE PUP

Model:	B0944
Modeller:	Ray Ayres
Height:	6", 15.0 cm
Colour:	Black, white and fawn
Issued:	01/05 - 12/06
Series:	Classic Babies
U.K.:	£40.00
U.S.:	$80.00
Can.:	$80.00

COLLIE PUP IN BREAD BIN

Model:	A3867
Modeller:	Janet Miller
Height:	2", 5.0 cm
Colour:	Black, white, blue and tan
Issued:	01/04 to the present
Series:	On The Farm
U.K.:	£15.00
U.S.:	$30.00
Can.:	$30.00

COLLIE PUPS FOR SALE

Model:	JH67
Modeller:	Anne Wall
Height:	3", 7.6 cm
Colour:	Black and white
Issued:	01/92 - 12/96
Series:	All Things Wise and Wonderful
U.K.:	£100.00
U.S.:	$200.00
Can.:	$200.00

COLOURED MARE AND FOAL

Model: A0729
Modeller: Anne Wall
Height: 5 ¾", 14.6 cm
Colour: Mare: Black and white;
Foal: brown, white and
black
Issued: 06/01 - 06/05
Series: Horse Breeds

U.K.: £ 65.00
U.S.: $125.00
Can.: $125.00

COLOURED STALLION

Model: A0733
Modeller: Anne Wall
Height: 6 ¾", 17.2 cm
Colour: Black and white;
green base
Issued: 06/01 - 12/04
Series: Horse Breeds

U.K.: £40.00
U.S.: $80.00
Can.: $80.00

COME BY SHEP!
(Boy and sheep dog)

Model: B0296
Modeller: Anne Wall
Height: 6 ¾", 17.2 cm
Colour: Browns, green, black
and white
Issued: 06/98 - 06/00
Series: 1. Every Living Thing
2. J. Herriot Collection

U.K.: £ 65.00
U.S.: $125.00
Can.: $125.00

COME NO CLOSER
(Sheep and border collies)

Model: A5914
Modeller: Unknown
Height: 3 ¾", 9.5 cm
Colour: Cream, black, brown
and green
Issued: 06/05 to the present
Series: James Herriot
Studio Collection

U.K.: £ 55.00
U.S.: $110.00
Can.: $110.00

COMING HOME
(Two heavy horses)

Model: JH9A, B
Modeller: Judy Boyt
Height: 7 ¾", 19.7 cm
Colour: A. Bay and black
B. Grey and bay
Issued: 01/85 - 12/93
Series: All Creatures Great and Small

	Bay/black	Grey/bay
U.K.:	£400.00	425.00
U.S.:	$800.00	850.00
Can.:	$800.00	850.00

COMMON BLUE ON APPLE BLOSSOM

Model: A5903
Modeller: Kerry Bell
Height: 5 ¼", 13.3 cm
Colour: Pale blue, fawn, pink,
green and brown
Issued: 01/06 to the present
Series: Butterflies

U.K.: £20.00
U.S.: $40.00
Can.: $40.00

COMMON TEAL

Model: Unknown
Modeller: Victor Hayton
Height: 7", 17.8 cm
Colour: Brown, green, grey
and orange
Issued: 01/77 in a limited
edition of 250

U.K.: £400.00
U.S.: $800.00
Can.: $800.00

CONNEMARA MARE AND FOAL

Model: A5055
Modeller: Anne Wall
Height: 5 ¼", 13.3 cm
Colour: Light dapple grey, chestnut and green
Issued: 01/05 - 06/06
Series: Mares and Foals

U.K.: £ 60.00
U.S.: $120.00
Can.: $120.00

CONNEMARA PONY

Model: NP4
Modeller: Judy Boyt
Height: 6", 15.0 cm
Colour: Grey
Issued: 01/82 - 12/84
Series: Native Ponies of Britain

U.K.: £ 500.00
U.S.: $1,000.00
Can.: $1,000.00

CONTEMPLATION

Model: K231
Designer: Ben Black
Modeller: David Geenty
Height: 4 ¾", 12.1 cm
Colour: White, yellow and orange
Issued: 01/88 in a limited edition of 950
Series: Ben Black's Garden of Clowns

U.K.: £200.00
U.S.: $400.00
Can.: $400.00

CONTENTED
(Piglets)

Model: A5905
Modeller: Unknown
Height: 3 ¼", 8.3 cm
Colour: Pink, black and light brown
Issued: 06/05 to the present
Series: James Herriot Studio Collection

U.K.: £22.00
U.S.: $45.00
Can.: $45.00

COOL RECEPTION
(Dog and Vixen Fox in Winter)

Model: B0092
Modeller: David Walton
Height: 6 ¼", 15.9 cm
Colour: A. Brown, white, grey
B. Orange, white, black
Issued: 01/97 in a limited edition of 2,500
Series: Fox Tales

U.K.: £125.00
U.S.: $250.00
Can.: $250.00

COOLING HIS HEELS

Model: B0770
Modeller: Ray Ayres
Height: 7", 17.8 cm
Colour: Reddish-brown, brown, white, green and grey
Issued: 06/02 in a limited edition of 1,500
Series: The James Herriot Classic Collection

U.K.: £175.00
U.S.: $350.00
Can.: $350.00

CORGI, Standing
First Variation

Model: B0317/B0481
Modeller: Margaret Turner
Height: 3 ½", 8.9 cm
Colour: B0317 Brown/white
B0481 Bronze
Issued: B0317 06/98-12/01
B0481 06/99-06/00
Series: 1. Dogs Galore
2. Bronzed

	Brown	Bronze
U.K.:	£15.	£12.
U.S.:	$30.	$25.
Can.:	$30.	$25.

CORGI, Standing
Second Variation

Model: A1383
Modeller: Margaret Turner
Height: 3 ½", 8.9 cm
Colour: Yellowish-brown and white
Issued: 01/02 to the present
Series: Dogs and Pups Galore

U.K.: £17.00
U.S.: $35.00
Can.: $35.00

CORONATION 1953, THE
(Gold State Coach)

Model:	B0810
Modeller:	Ray Ayres
Size:	6 ¾" x 29 ½", 17.0 x 75.0 cm
Colour:	Gold, white, red, black and yellow
Issued:	2003 in a limited edition of 350
Series:	Golden Anniversary Celebration
U.K.:	£1,050.00
U.S.:	$3,000.00
Can.:	$3,000.00

COSY
(Cat on cushion)

Model:	A6895
Modeller:	Andrew Edwards
Height:	2 ½", 6.4 cm
Colour:	White, turquoise, brown and black
Issued:	06/06 to the present
Series:	Cat Round the House
U.K.:	£17.00
U.S.:	$35.00
Can.:	$35.00

COUNT RAGGI'S BIRD OF PARADISE

Model:	B0400
Modeller:	Richard Roberts
Height:	12 ¼", 31.1 cm
Colour:	Brown, red, yellow and green
Issued:	01/99 in a limited edition of 950
Series:	1. Exotic Birds
	2. Birds of the World
U.K.:	£350.00
U.S.:	$700.00
Can.:	$700.00

COUNTRY DOCTOR, THE
(Man and Gig)

Model:	JH63
Modeller:	Ray Ayres
Height:	8", 20.3 cm
Colour:	Bay, black, brown and green
Issued:	01/92 in a limited edition of 1,250
Series:	All Things Wise and Wonderful
U.K.:	£1,250.00
U.S.:	$2,500.00
Can.:	$2,500.00

COURTING GREBES

Model:	WW3
Modeller:	Ray Ayres
Height:	9 ¾", 24.7 cm
Colour:	Grey, black and white
Issued:	01/86 - 12/92
Series:	1. The Wetlands (WWF)
	2. WWFN
U.K.:	£275.00
U.S.:	$550.00
Can.:	$550.00

COW AND CALF AFRICAN ELEPHANTS

Model:	L99
Modeller:	Richard Roberts
Height:	8", 20.3 cm
Colour:	Grey and white
Issued:	01/90 in a limited edition of 750
Series:	WWFN
U.K.:	£150.00
U.S.:	$300.00
Can.:	$300.00

CRESTED TIT

Model:	RB39
Modeller:	Ray Ayres
Height:	5 ¼", 13.3 cm
Colour:	Brown, yellow, white and black
Issued:	01/93 - 12/95
Series:	RSPB Birds of the Countryside
U.K.:	£45.00
U.S.:	$90.00
Can.:	$90.00

CROSS-COUNTRY

Model:	B0319
Modeller:	Rob Donaldson
Height:	9", 22.9 cm
Colour:	Brown, blue, red and white
Issued:	06/98 in a limited edition of 850
Series:	1. Agricultural and Sporting
	2. Three-Day Eventing
U.K.:	£275.00
U.S.:	$550.00
Can.:	$550.00

CROSSER, THE
(Labrador)

Model:	B0983, A, B
Modeller:	Paul Back
Height:	13 ¼" x 7 ¾"
	33.6 x 19.7 cm
Colour:	B0983 Yellow
	B0983A Black
	B0983B Chocolate
Issued:	01/06 to the present
U.K.:	£195.00
U.S.:	$400.00
Can.:	$400.00

CROSSING, THE
(Shepherd, sheep and collie)

Model:	B0013
Modeller:	Ray Ayres
Height:	6 ¾", 17.2 cm
Colour:	Brown, blue, green, cream black and white
Issued:	06/96 in a limited edition of 1,750
Series:	1. Every Living Thing
	2. The James Herriot Collection
U.K.:	£400.00
U.S.:	$800.00
Can.:	$800.00

CUBIST KITTEN

Model:	A4692, 4695
Modeller:	Unknown
Height:	2", 5.0 cm
Colour:	A4692 Rouge
	A4695 Granite
Issued:	06/04 - 06/05
Series:	Contemporary Kittens
U.K.:	£ 7.95
U.S.:	$15.00
Can.:	$15.00

CUBIST KITTENS

Model:	A4690, 4693
Modeller:	Unknown
Height:	3 ¾", 9.5 cm
Colour:	A4690 Rouge
	A4693 Granite
Issued:	06/04 - 06/05
Series:	Contemporary Cats
U.K.:	£19.95
U.S.:	$40.00
Can.:	$40.00

CUBS' CORNER

Model:	A0725
Modeller:	John Brown
Height:	4 ¼", 10.8 cm
Colour:	Red-brown, beige, green, pink and black
Issued:	06/01 - 12/03
Series:	1. Young Ones by John Brown
	2. Country Characters
U.K.:	£35.00
U.S.:	$70.00
Can.:	$70.00

CUMBRIAN FELL PONY

Model:	B0812
Modeller:	Kirsty Armstrong
Height:	8 ¼", 21.0 cm
Colour:	Black
Issued:	01/04 in a limited edition of 750
Series:	Classic Collection
U.K.:	£ 85.00
U.S.:	$175.00
Can.:	$175.00

CURIOSITY
(Shire foal and cat)

Model:	JH81
Modeller:	Anne Wall
Height:	4", 10.1 cm
Colour:	Chestnut and white; black and white
Issued:	01/93 - 12/97
Series:	1. Every Living Thing
	2. The James Herriot Collection
U.K.:	£ 55.00
U.S.:	$110.00
Can.:	$110.00

CURIOSITY
(Owl and two squirrels)

Model:	A1282
Modeller:	John Brown
Height:	6", 15.0 cm
Colour:	White, cream, brown, red-brown, yellow and grey
Issued:	01/02 - 12/05
Series:	Country Characters
U.K.:	£35.00
U.S.:	$70.00
Can.:	$70.00

CUT AND CRATED
(Allis Chalmers Tractor)

Model:	B0649
Modeller:	Ray Ayres
Height:	6 ½", 16.5 cm
Colour:	Red, browns, greens and blue
Issued:	01/01 in a limited edition of 2,001
U.K.:	£425.00
U.S.:	$850.00
Can.:	$850.00

CUTE PUPS (Collies)

Model:	A4065
Modeller:	Kerry Bell
Height:	3 ½", 8.9 cm
Colour:	Brown, grey, black and white
Issued:	06/04 to the present
Series:	On The Farm
U.K.:	£40.00
U.S.:	$80.00
Can.:	$80.00

CUTE PUPS (Labradors)

Model:	A4245
Modeller:	Kerry Bell
Height:	4 ¼", 10.8 cm
Colour:	Brown, grey, black and yellow
Issued:	06/04 - 12/06
Series:	On The Farm
U.K.:	£40.00
U.S.:	$80.00
Can.:	$80.00

DACHSHUND, Seated

Model:	DG22
Modeller:	Margaret Turner
Height:	3 ½", 8.9 cm
Colour:	Black and tan
Issued:	01/93 - 12/00
Series:	Dogs Galore
U.K.:	£20.00
U.S.:	$40.00
Can.:	$40.00

DACHSHUND (Long-haired)
Seated

Model:	A3829, 4247
Modeller:	Margaret Turner
Height:	2 ¼", 5.7 cm
Colour:	A3829 Black / tan
	A4247 Red
Issued:	01/04 - 06/06
Series:	Dogs and Pups Galore
U.K.:	£16.00
U.S.:	$30.00
Can.:	$30.00

DACHSHUND (Long-haired)
Standing

Model:	076	
Modeller:	Margaret Turner	
Length:	10 ¼", 26.0 cm	
Colour:	1. Reddish-brown	
	2. Black and tan	
Issued:	01/86 - 12/88	
Series:	Special Interest	
	Brown	**Black/tan**
U.K.:	£ 75.	£ 65.
U.S.:	$150.	$125.
Can.:	$150.	$125.

DACHSHUND (Short-haired),
Seated

Model:	A3878
Modeller:	Margaret Turner
Height:	3 ½", 8.9 cm
Colour:	Black and tan
Issued:	01/04 to the present
Series:	Dogs and Pups Galore
U.K.:	£17.50
U.S.:	$35.00
Can.:	$35.00

DACHSHUND (Smooth-haired)
Style One
Model: UK# DS3
USA # 225-425
Modeller: Ray Ayres
Height: 2 ¾", 7.0 cm
Colour: Black and golden brown
Issued: 01/83 - 12/87
Series: The World of Dogs

U.K.: £35.00
U.S.: $70.00
Can.: $70.00

DACHSHUND (Smooth-haired)
Style Two
Model: 074
Modeller: Margaret Turner
Length: 8 ½", 21.6 cm
Colour: Tan
Issued: 01/86 - 12/88
Series: Special Interest

U.K.: £ 65.00
U.S.: $125.00
Can.: $125.00

DACHSHUND (Wire-haired),
Seated
Model: B0246
Modeller: Margaret Turner
Height: 3 ½", 8.9 cm
Colour: Grey-brown
Issued: 01/98 - 06/00
Series: Dogs Galore

U.K.: £20.00
U.S.: $40.00
Can.: $40.00

DACHSHUND (Wire-haired),
Standing
Model: 075
Modeller: Margaret Turner
Length: 9 ¼", 23.5 cm
Colour: Light brown
Issued: 01/86 - 12/88
Series: Special Interest

U.K.: £ 75.00
U.S.: $150.00
Can.: $150.00

DACHSHUND IN BAG
Model: 484105
Modeller: Unknown
Height: 3 ¼", 8.3 cm
Colour: Black, tan, blue and brown
Issued: 06/98 - 12/00
Series: Puppy Tales

U.K.: £12.00
U.S.: $25.00
Can.: $25.00

DACHSHUND PUP
(Long-Haired)
Model: B0248
Modeller: Margaret Turner
Height: 2 ¼", 5.7 cm
Colour: Reddish-brown
Issued: 01/98 - 06/99
Series: Pups Galore

U.K.: £12.00
U.S.: $25.00
Can.: $25.00

DAILY DELIVERY
(Milkman with horse-drawn cart)
Model: JH103
Modeller: Ray Ayres
Height: 7 ½", 19.1 cm
Colour: Dark brown, blue, cream and white
Issued: 01/95 in a limited edition of 1,500
Series: 1. Every Living Thing
2. The James Herriot Collection

U.K.: £475.00
U.S.: $950.00
Can.: $950.00

DAIRY BULL
Model: 163/B163
Modeller: Anne Butler
Height: 4 ¼", 10.8 cm
Colour: Black and white
Issued: 07/93 - 12/96
Series: Agricultural and Sporting

U.K.: £ 65.00
U.S.: $125.00
Can.: $125.00

Photograph not
available
at press time

DALES
(Horse)

Model:	A6533
Modeller:	Unknown
Height:	5 ½", 14.0 cm
Colour:	Black
Issued:	06/06 to the present
Series:	BFA Pottery Company
U.K.:	£20.00
U.S.:	$40.00
Can.:	$40.00

DALES PONY MARE AND FOAL

Model:	A5054
Modeller:	Anne Wall
Height:	6 ¾", 17.2 cm
Colour:	Black, brown and green
Issued:	01/05 - 06/06
Series:	Mares and Foals
U.K.:	£ 60.00
U.S.:	$120.00
Can.:	$120.00

DALMATIAN (Pair)

Model:	079
Modeller:	Margaret Turner
Height:	7 ½", 19.1 cm
Colour:	Black and white
Issued:	01/87 - 12/91
Series:	Special Interest
U.K.:	£125.00
U.S.:	$250.00
Can.:	$250.00

Note: Models 079A and 079B combine to make model 079.

DALMATIAN, Standing

Model:	A3842
Modeller:	Margaret Turner
Height:	5 ¾", 14.6 cm
Colour:	Black and white
Issued:	06/04 to the present
Series:	Dogs and Pups Galore
U.K.:	£23.00
U.S.:	$45.00
Can.:	$45.00

DALMATIAN BITCH

Model:	079B
Modeller:	Margaret Turner
Height:	6 ½", 16.5 cm
Colour:	Black and white
Issued:	01/87 - 12/91
Series:	Special Interest
U.K.:	£ 75.00
U.S.:	$150.00
Can.:	$150.00

DALMATIAN DOG

Model:	079A
Modeller:	Margaret Turner
Height:	7 ½", 19.1 cm
Colour:	Black and white
Issued:	01/87 - 12/91
Series:	Special Interest
U.K.:	£ 75.00
U.S.:	$150.00
Can.:	$150.00

DALMATIAN PUP
(Seated, Mouth Open)

Model:	B0074
Modeller:	Margaret Turner
Height:	3", 7.6 cm
Colour:	White and black
Issued:	06/96 - 12/01
Series:	Pups Galore
U.K.:	£12.00
U.S.:	$25.00
Can.:	$25.00

DALMATIAN READY TO
POUNCE

Model:	B0117
Modeller:	Margaret Turner
Height:	2 ¾", 7.0 cm
Colour:	White and black
Issued:	01/97 - 06/01
Series:	Pups Galore
U.K.:	£12.00
U.S.:	$25.00
Can.:	$25.00

DALMATIAN UNDER BLANKET

Model:	B0116
Modeller:	Margaret Turner
Height:	1 ½", 3.8 cm
Colour:	White, black and cream
Issued:	01/97 - 06/01
Series:	Pups Galore
U.K.:	£12.00
U.S.:	$25.00
Can.:	$25.00

DALMATIANS
(Three puppies on plinth)

Model:	B0107
Modeller:	Margaret Turner
Height:	3 ½", 8.9 cm
Colour:	White and black
Issued:	06/96 - 12/98
Series:	Dogs Galore
U.K.:	£35.00
U.S.:	$70.00
Can.:	$70.00

DEER

Model:	RW7
Modeller:	Richard Wawrzesta
Height:	5", 12.7 cm
Colour:	Reddish-brown and green
Issued:	01/88 - 12/93
Series:	1. WWFN
	2. Wildlife Families (WWF)
U.K.:	£40.00
U.S.:	$80.00
Can.:	$80.00

DEFENDING THE HERD
(Elephant)

Model:	B0125
Modeller:	Richard Roberts
Height:	10 ½", 26.7 cm
Colour:	Grey
Issued:	01/97 in a limited edition of 850
Series:	An African Safari
U.K.:	£200.00
U.S.:	$400.00
Can.:	$400.00

DELIVERED WARM
(Horse-drawn baker's van)

Model:	B0040
Modeller:	Ray Ayres
Height:	9 ½", 24.0 cm
Colour:	Dark brown, yellow, blue, white and black
Issued:	01/97 in a limited edition of 1,500
Series:	1. Every Living Thing
	2. The James Herriot Collection
U.K.:	£425.00
U.S.:	$850.00
Can.:	$850.00

DELIVERING THE MILK
(Donkey cart)

Model:	AG01
Modeller:	Ray Ayres
Height:	6 ¼", 15.9 cm
Colour:	Grey, brown, black, white and silver
Issued:	1998 in a limited edition of 950
U.K.:	£250.00
U.S.:	$500.00
Can.:	$500.00

DEN MOTHER
(Wolf and three cubs)

Model:	STW06
Modeller:	Richard Roberts
Height:	7 ¼", 18.4 cm
Colour:	Blue-grey, white, tan and black
Issued:	07/95 in a limited edition of 2,500
Series:	Spirit of the Wolf
U.K.:	£200.00
U.S.:	$400.00
Can.:	$400.00

Note: This order could be custom-painted. The model illustrated is a grey pony, with a name on the trap.

DERBY, THE
(Four lambs)

Model: A0906
Modeller: Ray Ayres
Height: 5", 12.7 cm
Colour: Black, white, green and brown
Issued: 06/01 - 12/03
Series: James Herriot Studio Collection

U.K.: £40.00
U.S.: $80.00
Can.: $80.00

DEXTER COW AND CALF

Model: B0974
Modeller: Ray Ayres
Size: 6" x 10"
15.0 x 25.4 cm
Colour: Black, green and fawn
Issued: 01/06 in a limited edition of 500

U.K.: £165.00
U.S.: $325.00
Can.: $325.00

DILYS AND HER DUCKLINGS
(Duck and ducklings)

Model: JH86
Modeller: Anne Wall
Height: 3 ¼", 8.3 cm
Colour: White and yellow
Issued: 01/94 - 12/95
Series: Every Living Thing

U.K.: £30.00
U.S.: $60.00
Can.: $60.00

DINNER GUEST
(Siamese cat)

Model: A7616
Modeller: Andrew Edwards
Height: 5 ¼", 13.3 cm
Colour: Cream, black, green and gold
Issued: 06/06 to the present
Series: Cats Round the House

U.K.: £22.00
U.S.: $45.00
Can.: $45.00

DIPPER
Style One

Model: 040
Modeller: Ray Ayres
Height: 4", 10.1 cm
Colour: Dark brown and white
Issued: 01/80 - 06/86

U.K.: £45.00
U.S.: $90.00
Can.: $90.00

DIPPER
Style Two

Model: RB37
Modeller: Ray Ayres
Height: 5 ¾", 14.6 cm
Colour: Black, white and green
Issued: 07/92 - 12/95
Series: RSPB Birds of the Countryside

U.K.: £45.00
U.S.: $90.00
Can.: $90.00

DISCOVERY
(Badger and Fox cubs)

Model: A1283
Modeller: Unknown
Height: 4 ½", 11.9 cm
Colour: Red-brown, grey, white and black
Issued: 01/02 - 12/05
Series: Country Characters

U.K.: £30.00
U.S.: $60.00
Can.: $60.00

DISTURBING THE PEACE
(Labrador and Mallards)

Model: L80
Modeller: Ray Ayres
Height: 6 ½", 16.5 cm
Colour: A. Golden Labrador
B. Black Labrador
Issued: 01/88 in a limited edition of 1,500
Series: Special Interest

U.K.: £200.00
U.S.: $400.00
Can.: $400.00

DIVING KINGFISHER
Model: A0656
Modeller: Russell Willis
Height: 4 ¼", 10.8 cm
Colour: Blue-green, white and
            brown
Issued: 01/01 - 06/03
Series: 1. Birds And ...
            2. Birds by Russell
               Willis

U.K.:   £25.00
U.S.: $50.00
Can.: $50.00

DOBERMAN, Seated
Style One
Model: A1255
Modeller: Margaret Turner
Height: 18 ½", 47.0 cm
Colour: Black and tan
Issued: 06/02 - 06/05
Series: Fireside Dogs

U.K.:   £ 75.00
U.S.: $150.00
Can.: $150.00

DOBERMAN, Seated
Style Two
Model: A2090
Modeller: Margaret Turner
Height: 6", 15.0 cm
Colour: Black and tan
Issued: 01/03 - 12/05
Series: Dogs and Pups Galore

U.K.:   £15.00
U.S.: $30.00
Can.: $30.00

DOBERMAN, Standing
Style One
Model: A1259
Modeller: Margaret Turner
Height: 5 ¾", 14.6 cm
Colour: Black and tan
Issued: 01/02 - 12/05
Series: Dogs and Pups Galore

U.K.:   £15.00
U.S.: $30.00
Can.: $30.00

DOBERMAN, Standing
Style Two
Model: A3036
Modeller: Margaret Turner
Height: 10", 25.4 cm
Colour: Black and tan
Issued: 06/03 - 12/05

U.K.:   £ 65.00
U.S.: $125.00
Can.: $125.00

DOBERMAN AND CUSHION
Model: 610828
Modeller: Unknown
Height: 1 ½", 3.9 cm
Colour: Black, tan, pink, orange
            and yellow
Issued: 01/99 - 12/00
Series: Puppy Tales

U.K.:   £12.00
U.S.: $25.00
Can.: $25.00

DOBERMAN PINSCHER, Action
Model: EW4
Modeller: Elizabeth Waugh
Height: 9", 22.9 cm
Colour: A. Dark brown and tan
            B. Pink ears
Issued: 01/87 in a limited
            edition of 500
Series: Special Interest

U.K.:   £125.00
U.S.: $250.00
Can.: $250.00

DOBERMAN PINSCHER Seated
Model: DG26/B0477
Modeller: Margaret Turner
Height: 6", 15.0 cm
Colour: DG26   Black and tan
            B0477   Bronze
Issued: DG26   01/94-12/01
            B0477   06/99-06/00
Series: 1. Dogs Galore
            2. Bronzed

U.K.:   £20.00
U.S.: $40.00
Can.: $40.00

DOBERMAN PINSCHER, Standing

Model: DL2
Modeller: Ray Ayres
Height: 5 ½", 14.0 cm
Colour: Black and golden
Issued: 01/83 - 12/92
Series: 1. The World of Dogs
2. Special Interest

U.K.: £ 65.00
U.S.: $125.00
Can.: $125.00

DOE'SI DOE (Rabbits)

Model: A1021
Modeller: John Brown
Height: 4 ¼", 10.8 cm
Colour: Light brown, brown, white, green, grey and pink
Issued: 01/02 - 06/03
Series: Country Characters

U.K.: £30.00
U.S.: $60.00
Can.: $60.00

DOG, Lying

Model: NM01A, B
Modeller: Anne Butler
Height: 1", 2.5 cm
Colour: A. Brown
B. Black
Issued: 06/91 - 12/92
Series: It's a Dogs Life

U.K.: £15.00
U.S.: $30.00
Can.: $30.00

DOG, Scratching

Model: NM02A, B
Modeller: Anne Butler
Height: 2 ½", 6.4 cm
Colour: A. Brown
B. Black
Issued: 06/91 - 12/92
Series: It's a Dogs Life

U.K.: £15.00
U.S.: $30.00
Can.: $30.00

DOG, Seated

Model: NM03A, B
Modeller: Anne Butler
Height: 2 ½", 6.4 cm
Colour: A. Brown
B. Black
Issued: 06/91 - 12/92
Series: It's a Dogs Life

U.K.: £20.00
U.S.: $40.00
Can.: $40.00

DOG BATH

Model: A5029
Modeller: Paul Back
Height: 5", 12.7 cm
Colour: Green, silver, black, white, red, dark blue
Issued: 01/05 - 06/06
Series: Young Farmers

U.K.: £40.00
U.S.: $80.00
Can.: $80.00

DOG WITH STICK

Model: NM04A, B
Modeller: Anne Butler
Height: 1 ½", 3.8 cm
Colour: A. Brown
B. Black
Issued: 06/91 - 12/92
Series: It's a Dogs Life

U.K.: £20.00
U.S.: $40.00
Can.: $40.00

DOGGING 'EM UP
First Version - Spaniels

Model: 112A, B
Modeller: Ray Ayres
Height: 8", 20.3 cm
Colour: A. Liver and white
B. Black and white
Issued: 01/88 - 12/92
Series: 1. Agricultural and Sporting
2. Special Interest

U.K.: £200.00
U.S.: $400.00
Can.: $400.00

DOGGING 'EM UP
Second Version - Labradors
Model: 114A, B
Modeller: Ray Ayres
Height: 8", 20.3 cm
Colour: A. Black
B. Yellow
Issued: 01/88 - 12/92
Series: 1. Agricultural and
Sporting
2. Special Interest

U.K.: £200.00
U.S.: $400.00
Can.: $400.00

DOING THE BOOKS
(Puppies)
Model: A6226
Modeller: Unknown
Height: 3", 7.6 cm
Colour: Grey, golden, black,
white and red
Issued: 01/06 - 12/06
Series: On The Farm

U.K.: £18.00
U.S.: $35.00
Can.: $35.00

DOLPHIN AND BABY
Model: RW20
Modeller: Richard Wawrzesta
Height: 5", 12.7 cm
Colour: Blue, cream and white
Issued: 01/91 - 12/95
Series: Endangered Species
(WWF)

U.K.: £ 50.00
U.S.: $100.00
Can.: $100.00

DOLPHIN AND YOUNG
Model: WW22
Modeller: David Walton
Height: 2 ¾", 7.0 cm
Colour: Black, cream and blue
Issued: 07/94 - 12/95
Series: Miniature (WWF)

U.K.: £25.00
U.S.: $50.00
Can.: $50.00

DONKEY
Model: A2714
Modeller: Anne Wall
Height: 6 ¼", 15.9 cm
Colour: Brown, fawn, cream
and black
Issued: 01/05 to the present
Series: BFA Pottery Company

U.K.: £30.00
U.S.: $60.00
Can.: $60.00

DONKEY FOAL
Model: 071
Modeller: Anne Wall
Height: 5", 12.7 cm
Colour: Grey-brown with
seashore base
Issued: 07/80 - 12/82
Series: Mammals

U.K.: £200.00
U.S.: $400.00
Can.: $400.00

DONKEY JENNY AND FOAL
Model: A3699
Modeller: Anne Wall
Height: 8 ½", 21.6 cm
Colour: Browns and green
Issued: 01/04 - 12/06
Series: Horse Breeds

U.K.: £ 75.00
U.S.: $150.00
Can.: $150.00

DORMICE
Model: L07
Modeller: Victor Hayton
Height: 11 ½", 29.2 cm
Colour: A. Golden brown and
grey
B. Bronze
Issued: 01/77 in a limited
edition of 500

	Brown	Bronze
U.K.:	£275.	£100.
U.S.:	$550.	$200.
Can.:	$550.	$200.

DORMOUSE

Model:	UK# 011
	USA# 225-056
Modeller:	Anne Wall
Height:	3", 7.6 cm
Colour:	Reddish-brown
Issued:	06/79 - 12/81
Series:	Mammals
U.K.:	£ 65.00
U.S.:	$125.00
Can.:	$125.00

DOUBLE TAKE
(Ewe and two lambs)

Model:	JH108
Modeller:	David Walton
Height:	4 ¾", 12.1 cm
Colour:	Cream, black and white
Issued:	01/96 - 12/00
Series:	1. All Creatures Great and Small
	2. The James Herriot Collection
U.K.:	£ 55.00
U.S.:	$110.00
Can.:	$110.00

DOUBLE TAWNY OWLETS

Model:	A5206
Modeller:	Russell Willis
Height:	6 ½", 16.5 cm
Colour:	Cream, brown, green and grey
Issued:	01/05 - 06/06
Series:	Birds by Russell Willis
U.K.:	£ 50.00
U.S.:	$100.00
Can.:	$100.00

DOVES WITH BLOSSOM

Model:	WB34
Modeller:	Russell Willis
Height:	5 ¼", 13.3 cm
Colour:	White, pink and brown
Issued:	01/93 - 12/97
Series:	1. Birds In Your Garden
	2. Russell Willis Birds
U.K.:	£35.00
U.S.:	$70.00
Can.:	$70.00

DOWN FROM THE HILLS
(Shepherd, sheep and collie)

Model:	JH18
Modeller:	Elizabeth MacAllister
Height:	6 ½", 16.5 cm
Colour:	Cream, black, white and grey
Issued:	01/87 in a limited edition of 1,500
Series:	All Creatures Great and Small
U.K.:	£450.00
U.S.:	$900.00
Can.:	$900.00

DOWN TO THE START
(Horse and jockey)

Model:	B0965, 0965A
Modeller:	Anne Wall
Height:	8 ¾" x 11 ½" 22.2 x 29.2 cm
Colour:	B0965 Bay horse B0965A Grey horse
Issued:	06/06 in a limited edition of 750
U.K.:	£225.00
U.S.:	$450.00
Can.:	$450.00

DOWNLAND PARTNERS

Model:	B0336
Modeller:	Kirsty Armstrong
Height:	6 ½", 16.5 cm
Colour:	White, black, cream, brown and cream
Issued:	01/98 in a limited edition of 1,250
U.K.:	£225.00
U.S.:	$450.00
Can.:	$450.00

DRAGOON OFFICER
(WATERLOO)

Model:	MF06
Modeller:	David Burnham Smith
Height:	12 ½", 31.7 cm
Colour:	Red jacket
Issued:	01/92 in a limited edition of 750
Series:	The Military Collection
U.K.:	£200.00
U.S.:	$400.00
Can.:	$400.00

DREAMER, THE

Model: A7610, 7622
Modeller: Unknown
Height: 8 ½", 21.6 cm
Colour: A7610 Black and tan
A7622 Tan and white
Issued: 06/06 to the present
Series: Canine Capers

U.K.: £18.00
U.S.: $35.00
Can.: $35.00

DRESSAGE

Model: B0278
Modeller: Rob Donaldson
Height: 9 ½", 24.0 cm
Colour: Dark bay
Issued: 01/98 in a limited
edition of 850
Series: 1. Agricultural and
Sporting
2. Three-Day Eventing

U.K.: £350.00
U.S.: $700.00
Can.: $700.00

Note: Portrait model featured.

DRIFT, THE
(New Forest ponies)

Model: A3876
Modeller: Anne Wall
Height: 6 ¾", 17.2 cm
Colour: White, brown, blue,
black, green and lilac
Issued: 01/04 in a limited
edition of 750
Series: Horse Breeds

U.K.: £150.00
U.S.: $300.00
Can.: $300.00

DROVERS' ARMS

Model: JH55
Modeller: Richard Young
Height: 3 ½", 8.9 cm
Colour: White, black, red,
brown and grey
Issued: 01/89 - 09/90
Series: James Herriot's
Yorkshire

U.K.: £ 65.00
U.S.: $125.00
Can.: $125.00

DRUMMER (MARLBOROUGH)

Model: MF02
Modeller: David Burnham Smith
Height: 11", 27.9 cm
Colour: Grey, red and beige
Issued: 01/92 in a limited
edition of 750
Series: The Military Collection

U.K.: £200.00
U.S.: $400.00
Can.: $400.00

DUCK AND DUCKLINGS

Model: M3
Modeller: David Geenty
Height: 1 ½", 3.8 cm
Colour: White and yellow
Issued: 07/80 - 12/80
Series: Beginners, Please

U.K.: £40.00
U.S.: $80.00
Can.: $80.00

DUCK FEEDING

Model: B0640/B0641/B0642
Modeller: Russell Willis
Height: 2", 5.0 cm
Colour: B0640 Gold
B0641 Silver
B0642 Slate blue
Issued: 06/00 - 06/01
Series: Cubist Ducks

U.K.: £10.00
U.S.: $20.00
Can.: $20.00

DUCK PREENING

Model: B0634/B0635/B0636
Modeller: Russell Willis
Height: 3 ½", 8.9 cm
Colour: B0634 Gold
B0635 Silver
B0636 Slate blue
Issued: 06/00 - 06/01
Series: Cubist Ducks

U.K.: £10.00
U.S.: $20.00
Can.: $20.00

DUCK PREENING, Large

Model:	B0643/B0644/B0645
Modeller:	Russell Willis
Height:	7 ¾", 19.7 cm
Colour:	B0643 Gold
	B0644 Silver
	B0645 Slate blue
Issued:	06/00 - 06/01
Series:	Cubist Ducks
U.K.:	£30.00
U.S.:	$60.00
Can.:	$60.00

DUCK, Sleeping

Model:	B0637/B0638/B0639
Modeller:	Russell Willis
Height:	1 ¼", 3.1 cm
Colour:	B0637 Gold
	B0638 Silver
	B0639 Slate Blue
Issued:	06/00 - 06/01
Series:	Cubist Ducks
U.K.:	£10.00
U.S.:	$20.00
Can.:	$20.00

DUCKLING

Model:	FF12A, B
Modeller:	Anne Wall
Height:	2 ¼", 5.7 cm
Colour:	A. Yellow
	B. Yellow and brown
Issued:	01/92 - 12/95
Series:	First Friends
U.K.:	£12.00
U.S.:	$25.00
Can.:	$25.00

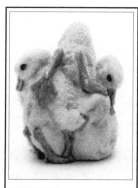

DUCKLINGS
Style One

Model:	ED10
Modeller:	Judy Boyt
Height:	2 ¾", 7.0 cm
Colour:	Yellow
Issued:	01/84 - 12/84
Series:	Early Days
U.K.:	£40.00
U.S.:	$80.00
Can.:	$80.00

DUCKLINGS
Style Two

Model:	A0127
Modeller:	Russell Willis
Height:	4 ¾", 12.1 cm
Colour:	Yellow, brown, orange
	and green
Issued:	06/00 - 12/01
Series:	Farmyard Friends
U.K.:	£30.00
U.S.:	$60.00
Can.:	$60.00

DUCKLINGS IN HAT

Model:	A5623
Modeller:	Kerry Bell
Height:	1 ¾", 4.4 cm
Colour:	Yellow, orange,
	cream and green
Issued:	01/05 to the present
Series:	On The Farm
U.K.:	£20.00
U.S.:	$40.00
Can.:	$40.00

DUKE AND DUCHESS
(Fox and vixen)

Model:	FT05
Modeller:	David Walton
Height:	6 ½", 16.5 cm
Colour:	Reddish-brown, white
	and black
Issued:	07/95 in a limited
	edition of 2,500
Series:	Fox Tales
U.K.:	£100.00
U.S.:	$200.00
Can.:	$200.00

EAGER TO LEARN
(Border collie pups)

Model:	B0589
Modeller:	Margaret Turner
Height:	5 ¾", 14.6 cm
Colour:	Black, white, tan
	and grey
Issued:	06/00 - 12/02
Series:	Dogs by Margaret
	Turner
U.K.:	£ 75.00
U.S.:	$150.00
Can.:	$150.00

EARLY HARVEST
(Harvest mouse on corn)

Model:	BCM03
Modeller:	Ray Ayres
Height:	4 ¼", 10.8 cm
Colour:	Golden brown and green
Issued:	01/91 - 12/93
Series:	The Country Mouse
U.K.:	£ 65.00
U.S.:	$125.00
Can.:	$125.00

EARLY LAMBS, LATE SNOW
(Sheep and lambs)

Model:	113
Modeller:	Ray Ayres
Height:	5 ½", 14.0 cm
Colour:	Cream, black and brown
Issued:	01/88 - 12/89
Series:	1. Agricultural and Sporting
	2. Farm Series
U.K.:	£250.00
U.S.:	$500.00
Can.:	$500.00

EARLY LEARNING
(Border collie and toy lamb)

Model:	A0165
Modeller:	Anne Wall
Height:	2 ¾", 7.0 cm
Colour:	Black, white, cream and brown
Issued:	01/01 - 12/04
Series:	The James Herriot Studio Collection
U.K.:	£20.00
U.S.:	$40.00
Can.:	$40.00

EARLY MORNING
(Otter)

Model:	B0704
Modeller:	Ray Ayres
Height:	11 ¾", 29.8 cm
Colour:	Black, brown, white, green, grey andyellow
Issued:	01/02 in a limited edition of 1,750
Series:	Classic Collection
U.K.:	£175.00
U.S.:	$350.00
Can.:	$350.00

EARLY MORNING CALL
(Cockerel)

Model:	JH43A, B, C
Modeller:	Anne Butler
Height:	4 ¼", 10.8 cm
Colour:	A. Light Sussex
	B. Buff Orpington
	C. Rhode Island Red
Issued:	A. 07/90 - 12/93
	B. 07/90 - 12/93
	C. 07/90 - 12/94
Series:	All Creatures Great and Small

	JH43A	JH43B	JH43C
U.K.	£ 50.00	£ 50.00	£ 50.00
U.S.	$100.00	$100.00	$100.00
Can.	$100.00	$100.00	$100.00

EASY RIDERS
(Man, dog and vehicle)

Model:	153
Modeller:	David Walton
Height:	6", 15.0 cm
Colour:	Green, red, blue, black and white
Issued:	01/93 - 12/95
Series:	Agricultural and Sporting
U.K.:	£225.00
U.S.:	$450.00
Can.:	$450.00

EBB AND FLOW
(Pair of otters)

Model:	B0187
Modeller:	Ray Ayres
Height:	9 ¾", 24.7 cm
Colour:	Brown, white and green
Issued:	07/97 in a limited edition of 2,500
Series:	Masters of the River
U.K.:	£100.00
U.S.:	$200.00
Can.:	$200.00

EBB TIDE
(Three dunlin, two black godwit and one shelduck)

Model:	BS4
Modeller:	Richard Roberts
Height:	4 ½", 11.9 cm
Colour:	Brown, white, grey and cream
Issued:	01/87 - 12/88
Series:	Birds of the Seashore

U.K.:	£125.00
U.S.:	$250.00
Can.:	$250.00

EGG MONEY
(Farmer's wife and hens)

Model:	JH71A, B
Modeller:	Anne Butler
Height:	5 ½", 14.0 cm
Colour:	A. Blonde
	B. Brunette
Issued:	01/93 - 12/94
Series:	All Things Wise and Wonderful

U.K.:	£ 75.00
U.S.:	$150.00
Can.:	$150.00

EGGS FOR SALE
(Hens and ducks)

Model:	A3707
Modeller:	Kerry Bell
Height:	6", 15.0 cm
Colour:	Brown, red, white and green
Issued:	01/04 - 12/06
Series:	James Herriot Studio Collection

U.K.:	£35.00
U.S.:	$70.00
Can.:	$70.00

EGGSTRA TREAT
(Border collie and hen)

Model:	A7938
Modeller:	Unknown
Height:	4 ¼", 10.8 cm
Colour:	Black, white, brown and red
Issued:	01/07 to the present
Series:	James Herriot Studio Collection

U.K.:	£24.00
U.S.:	$50.00
Can.:	$50.00

ELEGANCE IN THE FIELD
(Rider and horse)

Model:	L126
Modeller:	Anne Wall
Height:	8", 20.3 cm
Colour:	Chestnut, black and white
Issued:	01/93 in a limited edition of 950
Series:	Agricultural and Sporting

U.K.:	£250.00
U.S.:	$500.00
Can.:	$500.00

ELEMENT OF SURPRISE
(Collie and sheep)

Model:	B0089
Modeller:	Ray Ayres
Height	6 ½", 16.5 cm
Colour:	Browns, black and white
Issued:	01/97 - 12/97
Series:	1. Annual Figurine (1997)
	2. Every Living Thing

U.K.:	£200.00
U.S.:	$400.00
Can.:	$400.00

ELEPHANT

Model:	B0675, 76, 77
Modeller:	Richard Roberts
Height:	4", 10.1 cm
Colour:	B0675 Slate blue
	B0676 Stone
	B0677 Gold
Issued:	01/01 - 12/01
Series:	Cubist Africa

U.K.:	£35.00
U.S.:	$70.00
Can.:	$70.00

ELEPHANT AND CALF
Style One

Model:	WW20
Modeller:	David Walton
Height:	2 ½", 6.4 cm
Colour:	Grey-brown
Issued:	07/94 - 12/96
Series:	Miniature (WWF)

U.K.:	£20.00
U.S.:	$40.00
Can.:	$40.00

ELEPHANT AND CALF
Style Two
Model: A5409
Modeller: David Mayer
Height: 6", 15.0 cm
Colour: Dark grey, green and fawn
Issued: 01/05 - 12/06
Series: Wild World

U.K.: £ 65.00
U.S.: $130.00
Can.: $130.00

EMERGENCY RATIONS
(Horse, farmer and sheep)
Model: A2140
Modeller: Ray Ayres
Height: 8 ¾", 22.2 cm
Colour: Dark brown horse, white, yellow-green hay, cream and black sheep; blue coat, red scarf; black and white dog
Issued: 06/02 - 12/05
Series: James Herriot Studio Collection

U.K.: £150.00
U.S.: $300.00
Can.: $300.00

EMILY
(Kitten)
Model: A6511
Modeller: Ray Ayres
Height: 2 ½", 6.4 cm
Colour: Ginger, white, brown, blue and green
Issued: 01/06 to the present
Series: James Herriot Studio Collection

U.K.: £13.00
U.S.: $25.00
Can.: $25.00

EMILY AND HER KITTEN
Model: B0178
Modeller: Kirsty Armstrong
Height: 2 ¾", 7.0 cm
Colour: Black, grey, green and brown
Issued: 06/97 - 06/99
Series: James Herriot's Cat Stories

U.K.: £20.00
U.S.: $40.00
Can.: $40.00

EMILY'S JOY
(Goat and kid)
Model: JH84A, B
Modeller: Anne Wall
Height: 3 ½", 8.9 cm
Colour: A. Brown
        B. White
Issued: 01/94 - 12/96
Series: 1. Every Living Thing
        2. The James Herriot Collection

U.K.: £40.00
U.S.: $80.00
Can.: $80.00

EMPEROR PENGUIN
Model: RB2
Modeller: Ray Ayres
Height: 6", 15.0 cm
Colour: Black, cream and grey
Issued: 07/83 - 12/85
Series: Birds of the World

U.K.: £ 50.00
U.S.: $100.00
Can.: $100.00

END OF AN ERA?
(Huntsman and hounds)
Model: B0881
Modeller: David Mayer
Height: 11" x 9 ½"
        27.9 x 24.0 cm
Colour: Red, beige, black, tan and white
Issued: 01/05 in a limited edition of 500

U.K.: £200.00
U.S.: $400.00
Can.: $400.00

ENGLISH BULL TERRIER, Lying (Head Up)

Model:	DG08
Modeller:	Steve McKeown
Height:	3 ¾", 9.5 cm
Colour:	White
Issued:	01/91 - 12/96
Series:	Dogs Galore

U.K.:	£20.00
U.S.:	$40.00
Can.:	$40.00

ENGLISH BULL TERRIER, Seated, Style One

Model:	B0190 - White
	B0190A - White eye patch
	B0479 - Bronze
Modeller:	Margaret Turner
Height:	5 ¼", 13.3 cm
Colour:	See above
Issued:	B0190 06/97-12/01
	B0190A 06/98-12/01
	B0479 06/99-06/00
Series:	1. Dogs Galore
	2. Bronzed

U.K.:	£20.00
U.S.:	$40.00
Can.:	$40.00

ENGLISH BULL TERRIER, Seated Style Two

Model:	A2091, 92
Modeller:	Margaret Turner
Height:	5 ¼", 13.3 cm
Colour:	A2091 White
	A2092 Brindle
Issued:	A2091 01/03-06/06
	A2902 01/03 to the present
Series:	Dogs and Pups Galore

U.K.:	£17.00
U.S.:	$35.00
Can.:	$35.00

ENGLISH BULL TERRIER, Standing Style One

Model:	A1263, 1264
Modeller:	Margaret Turner
Height:	5 ¼", 13.3 cm
Colour:	A1263 White with black patch
	A-1264 White
Issued:	01/02 to the present
Series:	Dogs and Pups Galore

U.K.:	£21.00
U.S.:	$40.00
Can.:	$40.00

ENGLISH BULL TERRIER, Standing Style Two

Model:	A5179, 5862
Modeller:	Adrian Hughes
Height:	15", 38.1 cm
Colour:	A5179 Brindle
	A5862 White
Issued:	01/05 - 12/06
Series:	Fireside Dogs

U.K.:	£ 90.00
U.S.:	$175.00
Can.:	$175.00

ENGLISH POINTER

Model:	B1050, 1050A
Modeller:	Margaret Turner
Height:	10" x 12 ¼"
	25.4 x 31.1 cm
Colour:	A1050 Black/white
	A1050A Orange/white
Issued:	01/07 in a limited edition of 500

U.K.:	£199.00
U.S.:	$400.00
Can.:	$400.00

ENGLISH POINTERS

Model:	L03
Modeller:	Victor Hayton
Height:	5 ½", 14.0 cm
Colour:	A. Liver and white
	B. Tan and white
	C. Bronze
Issued:	01/77 in a limited edition of 500

	Liver	Tan	Bronze
U.K.:	£200.	£200.	£100.
U.S.:	$400.	$400.	$200.
Can.:	$400.	$400.	$200.

ENGLISH SETTER

Model:	UK # 051
	USA# 225-124
Modeller:	Anne Wall
Height:	5", 12.7 cm
Colour:	Grey and white
Issued:	07/78 - 12/82

U.K.:	£350.00
U.S.:	$700.00
Can.:	$700.00

ENGLISH SETTER
(Lying, curled with head up)

Model:	DG16
Modeller:	Margaret Turner
Height:	3 ¾", 9.5 cm
Colour:	White and pale grey
Issued:	01/92 - 12/95
Series:	Dogs Galore
U.K.:	£25.00
U.S.:	$50.00
Can.:	$50.00

ENGLISH SETTER, Seated
Style One

Model:	B0315A, B/B0484
Modeller:	Margaret Turner
Height:	6", 15.0 cm
Colour:	A. Blue roan
	B. Liver roan
	B0484 Bronze
Issued:	A. 06/98 12/01
	B. 06/98 06/01
	B0484 06/99-06/00
Series:	1. Dogs Galore
	2. Bronzed
U.K.:	£30.00
U.S.:	$60.00
Can.:	$60.00

ENGLISH SETTER, Seated
Style Two

Model:	A3057, 3787
Modeller:	Margaret Turner
Height:	6", 15.0 cm
Colour:	A3057 Blue Belton
	A3787 Orange Belton
Issued:	06/03 - 12/04
Series:	Dogs and Pups Galore
U.K.:	£20.00
U.S.:	$40.00
Can.:	$40.00

ENGLISH SETTER, Standing

Model:	A1395, 96
Modeller:	Margaret Turner
Height:	6", 15.0 cm
Colour:	A1395 Blue Belton
	A1396 Orange Belton
Issued:	01/02 - 12/04
Varieties:	Also called Irish Setter, standing (A1394)
Series:	Dogs and Pups Galore
U.K.:	£20.00
U.S.:	$40.00
Can.:	$40.00

ENGLISH SPRINGER SPANIEL,
Action

Model:	DM3A, B
Modeller:	Ray Ayres
Height:	3 ¼", 8.3 cm
Colour:	A. Liver and white
	B. Black and white
Issued:	01/83 - 12/92
Series:	1. The World of Dogs
	2. Special Interest
U.K.:	£ 65.00
U.S.:	$125.00
Can.:	$125.00

ENGLISH SPRINGER SPANIEL,
Lying
Style One

Model:	B0499A, B
Modeller:	Margaret Turner
Height:	3 ¼, 8.3 cm
Colour:	A. Liver and white
	B. Black and white
Issued:	A. 06/99 - 12/01
	B. 06/99 - 06/01
Series:	Dogs Galore
U.K.:	£20.00
U.S.:	$40.00
Can.:	$40.00

ENGLISH SPRINGER SPANIEL,
Lying
Style Two

Model:	A3040, 41
Modeller:	Margaret Turner
Height:	3 ½", 8.9 cm
Colour:	A3040 Black / white
	A3041 Liver / white
Issued:	A3040 06/03-06/06
	A3041 06/03 to the present
Series:	Dogs and Pups Galore
U.K.:	£19.00
U.S.:	$40.00
Can.:	$40.00

ENGLISH SPRINGER SPANIEL,
Seated
Style One

Model:	UK# 058A, B
	USA# 225-065
Modeller:	David Geenty
Height:	6", 15.0 cm
Colour:	A. Liver and white
	B. Black and white
Issued:	01/80 - 12/86
Series:	The World of Dogs
U.K.:	£40.00
U.S.:	$80.00
Can.:	$80.00

ENGLISH SPRINGER SPANIEL,
Seated
Style Two

Model:	MT03A, B
Modeller:	Margaret Turner
Height:	8 ½", 21.6 cm
Colour:	A. Black and white
	B. Liver and white
Issued:	A. 01/94 - 12/96
	B. 01/94 - 12/98
Series:	Dogs by Margaret
	Turner

	Black	Liver
U.K.:	£ 80.	£ 60.
U.S.:	$160.	$120.
Can.:	$160.	$120.

ENGLISH SPRINGER SPANIEL,
Seated
Style Three

Model:	A2094, 95
Modeller:	Margaret Turner
Height:	5 ¼". 13.3 cm
Colour:	A2094 Black and white
	A2095 Liver and white
Issued:	01/03 to the present
Series:	Dogs and Pups Galore

U.K.:	£19.00
U.S.:	$40.00
Can.:	$40.00

ENGLISH SPRINGER SPANIEL
Seated
Style Four

Model:	A3828, 4446
Modeller:	Adrian Hughes
Height:	15 ½", 39.4 cm
Colour:	A3828 Liver / white
	A4446 Black / white
Issued:	01/04 - 06/06
Series:	Fireside Dogs

U.K.:	£ 90.00
U.S.:	$175.00
Can.:	$175.00

ENGLISH SPRINGER SPANIEL,
Seated
(One Paw Up)

Model:	DG33A, B/B0469
Modeller:	Margaret Turner
Height:	5 ½", 14.0 cm
Colour:	A. Liver and white
	B. Black and white
	B0469 - Bronze
Issued:	A.-B. - 07/95-05/99
	B0469 - 06/99-06/00
Series:	1. Dogs Galore
	2. Bronzed

U.K.:	£25.00
U.S.:	$50.00
Can.:	$50.00

ENGLISH SPRINGER SPANIEL
(Standing)
Style One

Model:	A1160, 61
Modeller:	Margaret Turner
Height:	5 ¼", 13.3 cm
Colour:	A1160 Liver / white
	A1161 Black / white
Issued:	A1160 06/01-06/06
	A1161 06/01-12/04
Series:	Dogs and Pups Galore

U.K.:	£20.00
U.S.:	$40.00
Can.:	$40.00

ENGLISH SPRINGER SPANIEL
(Standing)
Style Two

Model:	A7111, 7801
Modeller:	Unknown
Height:	5 ¼", 13.3 cm
Colour:	A7111 Black / white
	A7801 Liver / white
Issued:	06/06 to the present
Series:	Dogs and Pups Galore

U.K.:	£23.00
U.S.:	$45.00
Can.:	$45.00

ENGLISH SPRINGER SPANIEL
AND PHEASANT

Model:	L42
Modeller:	Ray Ayres
Height:	4 ½", 11.9 cm
Colour:	Liver and white, brown
Issued:	07/82 in a limited
	edition of 1,500

U.K.:	£175.00
U.S.:	$350.00
Can.:	$350.00

ENGLISH SPRINGER SPANIEL
AND PUP

Model:	B0104A, B
Modeller:	Margaret Turner
Height:	5 ¾", 14.6 cm
Colour:	A. Liver and white
	B. Black and white
Issued:	A. 06/96 - 12/98
	B. 06/96 - 12/97
Series:	Dogs Galore

	Liver	Black
U.K.:	£40.	£ 50.
U.S.:	$80.	$100.
Can.:	$80.	$100.

ENGLISH SPRINGER SPANIEL AND PUPS

Model:	B0533A, B
Modeller:	Margaret Turner
Height:	8 ½", 21.6 cm
Colour:	A. Liver and white
	B. Black and white
Issued:	01/00 in a limited edition of 950
Series:	Dogs by Margaret Turner
U.K.:	£100.00
U.S.:	$200.00
Can.:	$200.00

ENGLISH SPRINGER SPANIEL PUP, Lying

Model:	B0494A, B
Modeller:	Margaret Turner
Height:	2 ¾", 7.0 cm
Colour:	A. Liver and white
	B. Black and white
Issued:	A. 06/99 - 12/01
	B. 06/99 - 06/01
Series:	Pups Galore
U.K.:	£15.00
U.S.:	$30.00
Can.:	$30.00

ENGLISH SPRINGER SPANIEL PUPPY, Seated

Model:	B0019A, B/B0459
Modeller:	Margaret Turner
Height:	3 ¼", 8.3 cm
Colour:	A. Liver and white
	B. Black and white
	B0459 Bronze
Issued:	A. 06/96 - 12/01
	B. 06/96 - 06/01
	B0459 06/99-06/00
Series:	1. Pups Galore
	2. Bronzed
U.K.:	£12.00
U.S.:	$25.00
Can.:	$25.00

ENGLISH SPRINGER SPANIEL PUPS (Pair)

Model:	B0252A, B/B0453
Modeller:	Margaret Turner
Height:	3 ¼", 8.3 cm
Colour:	A. Liver and white
	B. Black and white
	B0453 Bronze
Issued:	A. 01/98 - 12/01
	B. 01/98 - 12/99
	B0453 06/99-06/00
Series:	1. Pups Galore
	2. Bronzed
U.K.:	£20.00
U.S.:	$40.00
Can.:	$40.00

ENGLISH SPRINGER SPANIELS Style One

Model:	L04	
Modeller:	Victor Hayton	
Height:	5 ½", 14.0 cm	
Colour:	A. Browns and white	
	B. Bronze	
Issued:	1977 in a limited edition of 500	
	Browns	**Bronze**
U.K.:	£200.	£100.
U.S.:	$400.	$200.
Can.:	$400.	$200.

ENGLISH SPRINGER SPANIELS Style Two

Model:	B0699A, B
Modeller:	Margaret Turner
Height:	8 ¼", 21.0 cm
Colour:	A. Liver and white
	B. Black and white
Issued:	01/01 - 12/02
Series:	Dogs by Margaret Turner
U.K.:	£100.00
U.S.:	$200.00
Can.:	$200.00

ESSENTIAL REPAIRS (Workman with JCB back hoe)

Model:	B0652
Modeller:	Ray Ayres
Height:	5 ¾", 14.6 cm
Colour:	Yellow, black, red and white
Issued:	01/01 in a limited edition of 1,750
U.K.:	£350.00
U.S.:	$700.00
Can.:	$700.00

EVENING FLIGHT (Barn owl in flight)

Model:	L107
Modeller:	Ray Ayres
Height:	10 ½", 26.7 cm
Colour:	Golden, white, brown and green
Issued:	01/91 in a limited edition of 1,250
Series:	Nature's Kingdom
U.K.:	£350.00
U.S.:	$700.00
Can.:	$700.00

EVENING RISE
(Salmon)

Model: A3070
Modeller: Adrian Hughes
Height: 7 ½", 19.1 cm
Colour: Silvery grey, sandy
brown, black, grey
and green
Issued: 06/04 in a limited
edition of 950
Series: Wildlife

U.K.: £ 75.00
U.S.: $150.00
Can.: $150.00

EVENING SHADOWS
(Female badger and three
cubs)

Model: SOC7
Modeller: Ray Ayres
Height: 5 ¾", 14.6 cm
Colour: Black, white and brown
Issued: 06/94 - 05/95
Series: Annual Society Figurine
(1994/95)

U.K.: £150.00
U.S.: $300.00
Can.: $300.00

EVENING VIGIL

Model: B0039
Modeller: Kirsty Armstrong
Height: 2 ¾", 7.0 cm
Colour: Browns and grey
Issued: 1996
Series: Special Offer

U.K.: £15.00
U.S.: $30.00
Can.: $30.00

Note: Available for £19.95 or when
£65.00 was spent on BFA
products.

EVER ALERT

Model: B0451
Modeller: Ray Ayres
Height: 2 ¼", 5.7 cm
Colour: Browns and grey
Issued: 06/99 - 12/00
Series: Special Offer

U.K.: £20.00
U.S.: $40.00
Can.: $40.00

Note: Available for £19.95 or when
£65.00 was spent on BFA
products.

EWEDINI
(Sheep)

Model: A0907
Modeller: Craig Harding
Height: 5", 12.7 cm
Colour: Black, white, green
and brown
Issued: 06/01 - 06/04
Series: The James Herriot
Studio Collection

U.K.: £45.00
U.S.: $90.00
Can.: $90.00

EXHILARATION

Model: K230
Designer: Ben Black
Modeller: David Geenty
Height: 9 ¾", 24.7 cm
Colour: White, purple and
orange
Issued: 01/88 in a limited
edition of 950
Series: Ben Black's
Garden of Clowns

U.K.: £225.00
U.S.: $450.00
Can.: $450.00

EXMOOR PONY MARE AND
FOAL

Model: A3257
Modeller: Anne Wall
Height: 5", 12.7 cm
Colour: Dark brown, light
brown, white and green
Issued: 06/03 - 12/05
Series: Horse Breeds

U.K.: £40.00
U.S.: $80.00
Can.: $80.00

EXMOOR STALLION

Model: A4058
Modeller: Anne Wall
Height: 5 ¾", 14.6 cm
Colour: Brown, black and
greem
Issued: 06/04 - 06/06
Series: Horse Breeds

U.K.: £20.00
U.S.: $40.00
Can.: $40.00

EXPECTING RAIN
(Friesian calf and rabbit)

Model:	JH109
Modeller:	David Walton
Height:	3", 7.6 cm
Colour:	Black, white, brown and green
Issued:	01/96 - 05/99
Series:	1. Every Living Thing
	2. The James Herriot Collection
U.K.:	£40.00
U.S.:	$80.00
Can.:	$80.00

FAITHFUL FRIENDS
(Horse and puppy)

Model:	B0942, 0942A
Modeller:	Anne Wall
Height:	12 ¾" x 14 ¼" 32.4 x 36.2 cm
Colour:	B0942 Bay horse
	B0942A Grey horse
Issued:	06/05 in a limited edition of 500
Series:	Classic Collection
U.K.:	£275.00
U.S.:	$550.00
Can.:	$550.00

FALLOW BUCK
Style One

Model:	L73
Modeller:	James Harvey
Height:	8", 20.3 cm
Colour:	Tan and cream
Issued:	01/86 in a limited edition of 850
Series:	Special Interest
U.K.:	£250.00
U.S.:	$500.00
Can.:	$500.00

FALLOW BUCK
Style Two

Model:	B0329
Modeller:	Jack Crewdson
Height:	12 ¾", 32.4 cm
Colour:	Reddish-brown and cream
Issued:	06/98 - 12/99
U.K.:	£200.00
U.S.:	$400.00
Can.:	$400.00

FAMILIES WELCOME
(Border collie and pups)

Model:	B0181
Modeller:	Anne Wall
Height:	5 ½", 14.0 cm
Colour:	Black and white
Issued:	06/97 - 05/98
Series:	Special Offer
U.K.:	£ 65.00
U.S.:	$125.00
Can.:	$125.00

Note: Purchased on points system.

FAMILY FORAGE

Model:	B0332
Modeller:	Kirsty Armstrong
Height:	5", 12.7 cm
Colour:	Tan, white and black
Issued:	Autumn 1998 in a limited edition of 1,250
U.K.:	£ 75.00
U.S.:	$150.00
Can.:	$150.00

FAMILY HOME
(Field mice)

Model:	B0188
Modeller:	Anne Wall
Height:	5 ½", 14.0 cm
Colour:	Reddish-brown, white green and red
Issued:	06/97 - 12/98
Series:	The Country Mouse
U.K.:	£ 65.00
U.S.:	$125.00
Can.:	$125.00

FAMILY OUTING
(Vixen and five cubs)

Model:	FT07
Modeller:	David Walton
Height:	8", 20.3 cm
Colour:	Reddish-brown, white and green
Issued:	07/95 in a limited edition of 1,950
Series:	Fox Tales
U.K.:	£225.00
U.S.:	$450.00
Can.:	$450.00

FAMILY PORTRAIT
(Vixen and cubs)

Model:	B0038
Modeller:	David Walton
Height:	4 ½", 11.9 cm
Colour:	Red, white and black
Issued:	06/96 - 05/97
Series:	Special Offer
U.K.:	£40.00
U.S.:	$80.00
Can.:	$80.00

Note: Purchased on points system.

FANCY DRESS PARADE
(Rider and pony)

Model:	A5120
Modeller:	Anne Wall
Height:	6 ½", 16.5 cm
Colour:	Grey, yellow, black, orange, white, green
Issued:	01/05 - 06/06
Series:	Hay Days
U.K.:	£37.00
U.S.:	$65.00
Can.:	$65.00

FANTAIL DOVES (Pair)

Model:	WB73
Modeller:	Russell Willis
Height:	10 ½", 26.7 cm
Colour:	White, pink, green and brown
Issued:	01/95 in a limited edition of 750
Series:	Russell Willis Birds
U.K.:	£175.00
U.S.:	$350.00
Can.:	$350.00

FARM MEETING
(Cattle, geese and kitten)

Model:	A8434, 8976
Modeller:	Unknown
Height:	5", 12.7 cm
Colour:	A8434 Black / white A8976 Brown / white
Issued:	06/07 to the present
Series:	James Herriot Studio Collection
U.K.:	£ 55.00
U.S.:	$110.00
Can.:	$110.00

FARMYARD DUCK

Model:	A0126
Modeller:	Russell Willis
Height:	11 ¼", 28.5 cm
Colour:	White, orange and green
Issued:	06/00 - 12/01
Series:	Farmyard Friends
U.K.:	£ 65.00
U.S.:	$125.00
Can.:	$125.00

FAWN
Style One

Model:	UK# 016 USA# 225-054
Modeller:	Anne Wall
Height:	3 ½", 8.9 cm
Colour:	Brown, white, green
Issued:	07/80 - 12/81
Series:	Mammals
U.K.:	£100.00
U.S.:	$200.00
Can.:	$200.00

Note: USA model named White-tailed Deer.

FAWN
Style Two

Model:	B0943
Modeller:	Ray AYres
Height:	5 ½", 14.0 cm
Colour:	Fawn, black and white
Issued:	01/05 - 12/06
Series:	Classic Babies
U.K.:	£40.00
U.S.:	$75.00
Can.:	$75.00

FEARLESS
(Puppy and Kennel)

Model:	A7048
Modeller:	Barry Snelson
Height:	5", 12.7 cm
Colour:	Brown, charcoal and pink
Issued:	06/06 - 06/07
Series:	Puppy Trouble
U.K.:	£22.00
U.S.:	$45.00
Can.:	$45.00

FEED TIME
(Piglet)
Model: B0006
Modeller: Kirsty Armstrong
Height: 2 ½", 6.4 cm
Colour: Pink pig; white and
            blue dish
Issued: 06/96 - 12/00
Series: 1. Every Living Thing
            2. J. Herriot Collection

U.K.:   £15.00
U.S.: $30.00
Can.: $30.00

FEEDING PIGLETS
Model: A5030
Modeller: Paul Back
Height: 6", 15.2 cm
Colour: Blue, yellow, pink,
            silver and green
Issued: 06/05 - 06/06
Series: Young Farmers

U.K.:   £40.00
U.S.: $80.00
Can.: $80.00

FEEDING TIME
(Farmer feeding Queenie and piglets)
Model: JH107
Modeller: Anne Wall
Height: 4 ¾", 12.1 cm
Colour: Pink, green, yellow,
            and blue
Issued: 01/96 in a limited
            edition of 1,750
Series: 1. All Creatures Great
               and Small
            2. The James Herriot
               Collection

U.K.:   £150.00
U.S.: $300.00
Can.: $300.00

FELL HOUND AND TERRIERS
Model: B0885
Modeller: Anne Wall
Height: 8 ¾", 22.2 cm
Colour: Black, white, tan, grey,
            beige and green
Issued: 01/04 in a limited
            edition of 950

U.K.:   £125.00
U.S.: $250.00
Can.: $250.00

FELL HOUND WITH LAKELAND TERRIER
Model: L92
Modeller: Mairi Laing Hunt
Height: 6 ½", 16.5 cm
Colour: A. White, black and tan
               hound; light brown
               terrier
            B. Lemon and white
               hound; black terrier
Issued: 01/90 in a limited
            edition of 750
Series: Special Interest

U.K.:   £ 750.00
U.S.: $1,500.00
Can.: $1,500.00

FELL MARE AND FOAL
Model: B0971
Modeller: Anne Wall
Height: 7 ¼" x 9 ¼"
            18.4 x 23.5 cm
Colour: Black, brown
            and green
Issued: 01/06 in a limited
            edition of 750

U.K.:   £195.00
U.S.: $400.00
Can.: $400.00

FELL PONY
Model: NP3
Modeller: Judy Boyt
Height: 5 ½", 14.0 cm
Colour: Black
Issued: 01/82 - 12/84
Series: Native Ponies of Britain

U.K.:   £300.00
U.S.: $600.00
Can.: $600.00

FELLING THE FURROW
(Clydesdale ploughing the stubble in Autumn)
Model: L57
Modeller: Judy Boyt
Height: 4 ½" x 15",
            11.9 x 38.1 cm
Colour: Brown, green and grey
Issued: 01/84 in a limited
            edition of 350

U.K.:   £ 950.00
U.S.: $1,900.00
Can.: $1,900.00

FERGIE, THE
(Tractor Ploughing)

Model:	JH64
Modeller:	Ray Ayres
Height:	6", 15.0 cm
Colour:	Grey, brown, black and green
Issued:	01/92 in a limited edition of 1,250
Series:	All Creatures Great and Small
U.K.:	£2,000.00
U.S.:	$4,000.00
Can.:	$4,000.00

FERRETS

Model:	A7116
Modeller:	Unknown
Height:	5 ¾", 14.6 cm
Colour:	Browns and green
Issued:	06/06 to the present
U.K.:	£ 50.00
U.S.:	$100.00
Can.:	$100.00

FIELD MICE

Model:	RW5
Modeller:	Richard Wawrzesta
Height:	4", 10.1 cm
Colour:	Tan, white and pink
Issued:	01/88 - 12/92
Series:	1. Special Interest
	2. WWFN
	3. Wildlife Families (WWF)
U.K.:	£40.00
U.S.:	$80.00
Can.:	$80.00

FIELD STUDY
(Rabbit)

Model:	B1056
Modeller:	Ray Ayres
Height:	3 ¼", 8.3 cm
Colour:	Brown and green
Issued:	06/06 - 05/07
Series:	Membership Gift
U.K.:	£20.00
U.S.:	$40.00
Can.:	$40.00

FIELDMOUSE FAMILY

Model:	WW16
Modeller:	Richard Wawrzesta
Height:	3 ½", 8.9 cm
Colour:	Tan and white
Issued:	01/87 - 12/87
Series:	Family Life (WWF)
U.K.:	£40.00
U.S.:	$80.00
Can.:	$80.00

FINAL FURLONG, THE
(Two racehorses)

Model:	L109
Modeller:	Anne Wall
Height:	9 ¼", 23.5 cm
Colour:	Dark brown and chestnut
Issued:	01/92 in a limited edition of 950
Series:	Agricultural and Sporting
U.K.:	£ 650.00
U.S.:	$1,300.00
Can.:	$1,300.00

FINAL HURDLE, THE
(Hurdler)

Model:	L156
Modeller:	Anne Wall
Height:	8", 20.3 cm
Colour:	Grey, pink, yellow and white
Issued:	06/95 in a limited edition of 1,850
Series:	Agricultural and Sporting
U.K.:	£275.00
U.S.:	$550.00
Can.:	$550.00

FINISH, THE

Model:	L52
Modeller:	David Geenty
Height:	9", 22.9 cm
Colour:	Multicoloured
Issued:	01/83 - 12/95
Series:	1. Race Horses
	2. Special Interest
U.K.:	£425.00
U.S.:	$850.00
Can.:	$850.00

Note: This model was individually hand-painted to order.

FINISHING OFF
(Horse and blacksmith)

Model:	B0947
Modeller:	Hans Kendrick
Height:	6 ¼" x 10 ¼"
	15.9 x 26.0 cm
Colour:	Light grey, browns,
	black, white and red
Issued:	01/05 in a limited
	edition of 750
U.K.:	£225.00
U.S.:	$450.00
Can.:	$450.00

FIRST CUT, THE
(David Brown cropmaster)

Model:	JH70
Modeller:	Ray Ayres
Height:	5 ¾", 14.6 cm
Colour:	Red, green, black and grey
Issued:	Jan. 1993 in a limited
	edition of 1,500
Series:	All Creatures Great and Small
U.K.:	£1,500.00
U.S.:	$3,000.00
Can.:	$3,000.00

FIRST LESSON
(Collie pups and ducks)

Model:	JH38
Modeller:	David Walton
Height:	3 ¾", 9.5 cm
Colour:	Black, white and yellow
Issued:	01/90 - 12/95
Series:	All Things Wise and
	Wonderful
U.K.:	£45.00
U.S.:	$90.00
Can.:	$90.00

FIRST ONE IN
(Swan and cygnets)

Model:	B0189
Modeller:	Ray Ayres
Height:	7 ½", 19.1 cm
Colour:	White, grey and green
Issued:	06/97 - 05/98
Series:	Annual Society Figurine
	(1997/98)
U.K.:	£150.00
U.S.:	$300.00
Can.:	$300.00

FIRST OUTING
(Hen and chicks)

Model:	JH44A, B, C
Modeller:	Anne Butler
Height:	2 ¾", 7.0 cm
Colour:	A. Light Sussex
	B. Buff Orpington
	C. Rhode Island Red
Issued:	A. 07/90 - 12/92
	B. 07/90 - 12/92
	C. 07/90 - 12/94
Series:	All Creatures Great
	and Small
U.K.	£45.00
U.S.	$90.00
Can.	$90.00

FIRST OUTING
(Otter)

Model:	MTR01
Modeller:	Ray Ayres
Height:	2 ½", 6.4 cm
Colour:	Brown and white
Issued:	01/95 - 12/00
Series:	Masters of the River
U.K.:	£15.00
U.S.:	$30.00
Can.:	$30.00

FIRST PRIZE
(Pony and girl)

Model:	A3781
Modeller:	Anne Wall
Height:	4 ¼", 10.8 cm
Colour:	Grey, black, blue,
	yellow, and sandy
	yellow
Issued:	06/04 - 06/06
Series:	Hay Days
U.K.:	£25.00
U.S.:	$50.00
Can.:	$50.00

FIRST TIME OUT
(Three fox cubs)

Model:	BFA206
Modeller:	Ray Ayres
Height:	4 ½", 11.9 cm
Colour:	Reddish-brown
Issued:	01/94 - 12/94
Series:	20th Anniversary

U.K.:	£ 55.00
U.S.:	$110.00
Can.:	$110.00

FIRST TIME OUT
(Pony and rider)

Model:	A4699
Modeller:	Anne Wall
Height:	6", 15.0 cm
Colour:	Bay, white, black and green
Issued:	01/05 - 06/06
Series:	Hay Days

U.K.:	£35.00
U.S.:	$70.00
Can.:	$70.00

FIRST TIME OUT
(Wolf cub)

Model:	STW01
Modeller:	Richard Roberts
Height:	3 ½", 8.9 cm
Colour:	Blue-grey, white, tan and black
Issued:	07/95 - 12/97
Series:	Spirit of the Wolf

U.K.:	£25.00
U.S.:	$50.00
Can.:	$50.00

FLASH AND LIGHTNING
(Shepherd and border collies)

Model:	B0668
Modeller:	Ray Ayres
Height:	9 ¾", 24.7 cm
Colour:	Brown, grey, black, white and orange
Issued:	10/00 in a limited edition of 1,250
Varieties:	A Moment To Reflect (B0516)
Series:	The James Herriot Classic Collection

U.K.:	£175.00
U.S.:	$350.00
Can.:	$350.00

FLAT REFUSAL
(Friesian/Holstein Cows)

Model:	B0650/B0650A
Modeller:	Kirsty Armstrong
Height:	6 ½", 16.5 cm
Colour:	Black, white, browns, cream, blue, grey and yellow
Issued:	01/02 in a limited edition of 1,500
Series:	Classic Collection

U.K.:	£350.00
U.S.:	$700.00
Can.:	$700.00

Note: Also available as Dairy Shorthorn, B0650A.

FLOPSY
(Rabbit)

Model:	JH23
Modeller:	Richard Roberts
Height:	3 ¾", 9.5 cm
Colour:	Brown and white
Issued:	01/88 - 12/92
Series:	1. All Creatures Great and Small
	2. James Herriot's Favourite Characters

U.K.:	£20.00
U.S.:	$40.00
Can.:	$40.00

FLY FISHING

Model:	110
Modeller:	David Geenty
Height:	8 ½", 21.6 cm
Colour:	Greens and browns
Issued:	01/86 - 12/92
Series:	1. Agricultural and Sporting
	2. Special Interest

U.K.:	£225.00
U.S.:	$450.00
Can.:	$450.00

FLYING BARN OWL

Model:	B0908
Modeller:	Russell Willis
Height:	12 ¾", 32.4 cm
Colour:	White, cream, brown, black, green and pale yellow
Issued:	01/04 in a limited edition of 500
Series:	Birds by Russell Willis

U.K.:	£325.00
U.S.:	$650.00
Can.:	$650.00

FLYING EAGLE

Model: A1277
Modeller: Russell Willis
Height: 15 ½", 39.4 cm
Colour: Dark and light brown, yellow, pink, grey and green
Issued: 01/02 - 06/03
Series: Birds of Prey

U.K.: £ 75.00
U.S.: $150.00
Can.: $150.00

FLYING KESTREL

Model: A1275
Modeller: Russell Willis
Height: 12 ¼", 31.1 cm
Colour: Cream, browns, yellow, white and green
Issued: 01/02 - 06/03
Series: Birds of Prey

U.K.: £ 75.00
U.S.: $150.00
Can.: $150.00

FLYING PEREGRINE

Model: A1276
Modeller: Russell Willis
Height: 13 ½", 34.3 cm
Colour: Greys, cream, browns, red and green
Issued: 01/02 - 06/03
Series: Birds of Prey

U.K.: £ 75.00
U.S.: $150.00
Can.: $150.00

FLYING TAWNY OWL

Model: B0909
Modeller: Russell Willis
Height: 16 ¼", 41.2 cm
Colour: Light reddish-brown, white, dark grey, green, yellow and lilac
Issued: 01/04 - 12/05
Series" Birds by Russell Willis

U.K.: £375.00
U.S.: $750.00
Can.: $750.00

FOAL

Model: FF7A, B
Modeller: Anne Wall
Height: 2 ¼", 5.7 cm
Colour: A. Grey
B. Bay
Issued: 07/90 - 12/95
Series: First Friends

U.K.: £12.00
U.S.: $25.00
Can.: $25.00

FOAL (Fore-leg up)

Model: M9A, B
Modeller: David Geenty
Height: 5", 12.7 cm
Colour: A. Grey
B. Bay
Issued: 07/80 - 12/82
Series: Beginners, Please

U.K.: £125.00
U.S.: $250.00
Can.: $250.00

FOAL (Scratching)

Model: M7A, B
Modeller: David Geenty
Height: 4", 10.1 cm
Colour: A. Grey
B. Bay
Issued: 07/80 - 12/80
Series: Beginners, Please

U.K.: £125.00
U.S.: $250.00
Can.: $250.00

FOAL WITH RIDING BOOTS

Model: A0166, 67
Modeller: Anne Wall
Height: 2 ¾", 7.0 cm
Colour: A0166 Brown
A0167 Black / white
Issued: 06/00 - 12/04
Series: On the Farm

U.K.: £15.00
U.S.: $30.00
Can.: $30.00

FOLLOW MY LEADER
(Three elephants)

Model: BFA203
Modeller: Richard Roberts
Height: 8", 20.3 cm
Colour: Grey
Issued: 01/94 in a limited
edition of 950
Series: 1. 20th Anniversary
2. WWFN

U.K.: £300.00
U.S.: $600.00
Can.: $600.00

FOLLOWING TO HOUNDS

Model: B0951, 951A
Modeller: Anne Wall
Height: 7 ¾" x 10 ¾"
19.7 x 27.8 cm
Colour: B0951 Bay horse
B0951A Grey horse
Issued: 01/06 in a limited
edition of 750

U.K.: £250.00
U.S.: $500.00
Can.: $500.00

FOOTBALLER

Model: BB03
Modeller: John Warren
Height: 6 ½", 16.5 cm
Colour: Bronze
Issued: 01/88 - 12/89
Series: Studio Bronze

U.K.: £ 65.00
U.S.: $125.00
Can.: $125.00

FORBIDDEN FRUIT
(Border collies and rabbit)

Model: B0928
Modeller: Craig Harding
Height: 2 ¾ x 7"
7.0 x 17.8 cm
Colour: Black, white, golden
brown and green
Issued: 01/05 - 12/05
Series: Classic Event Figure

U.K.: £ 50.00
U.S.: $100.00
Can.: $100.00

FOREST FAMILY
(Badger mother and young)

Model: A0403
Modeller: John Brown
Height: 6", 15.0 cm
Colour: Grey, black, and white
Issued: 01/01 - 12/05
Series: Secret Places

U.K.: £40.00
U.S.: $80.00
Can.: $80.00

FOREST FRIENDS
(Badgers)

Model: PRO2
Modeller: David Walton
Height: 2 ½", 6.4 cm
Colour: Grey, black and white
Issued: 01/96 - 12/96
Series: Special Offer

U.K.: £25.00
U.S.: $50.00
Can.: $50.00

Note: Available for £19.95 or when
£65.00 was spent on BFA.

FORRARD AWAY
(Three hounds chasing a fox)

Model: L64
Modeller: Elizabeth Waugh
Height: 7", 17.8 cm
Colour: Dogs: Black, tan and white
Fox: Reddish-brown
Issued: 01/85 in a limited edition of 1,500
Series: Special Interest

U.K.: £400.00
U.S.: $800.00
Can.: $800.00

Note: Two pieces make up L64, Hounds and Fox on separate plinths.

FOSTER PARENTS
(Rooster, hen and ducklings)

Model:	A3706
Modeller:	Kerry Bell
Height:	4", 10.1 cm
Colour:	White, yellow, orange, red, black and green
Issued:	01/04 - 06/06
Series:	James Herriot Studio Collection
U.K.:	£35.00
U.S.:	$70.00
Can.:	$70.00

FOUND SAFE
(Border collie and lamb)

Model:	A0602
Modeller:	Kirsty Armstrong
Height:	5 ½", 14.0 cm
Colour:	Black, white, cream, brown and green
Issued:	01/01 to the present
Series:	The James Herriot Studio Collection
U.K.:	£46.00
U.S.:	$90.00
Can.:	$90.00

FOUR FAULTS?
(Horse and rider)

Model:	B0964, 0964A
Modeller:	Anne Wall
Height:	10 ½" x 11 ½" 26.7 x 29.2 cm
Colour:	B0964 Bay horse B0964A Grey horse
Issued:	01/06 in a limited edition of 400
U.K.:	£295.00
U.S.:	$575.00
Can.:	$575.00

FOX

Model:	RW1
Modeller:	Richard Wawrzesta
Height:	4", 10.1 cm
Colour:	Reddish-brown and green
Issued:	01/88 - 12/92
Series:	1. Special Interest 2. WWFN 3. Wildlife Families (WWF)
U.K.:	£35.00
U.S.:	$70.00
Can.:	$70.00

FOX
(Curled, in front of Log)

Model:	142
Modeller:	David Walton
Height:	3", 7.6 cm
Colour:	Reddish-brown, browns and green
Issued:	01/91 - 12/92
U.K.:	£45.00
U.S.:	$90.00
Can.:	$90.00

FOX, Lying

Model:	A5890
Modeller:	Unknown
Height:	5 ¾" x 16 ¼" 14.6 x 41.2 cm
Colour:	Reddish-brown
Issued:	06/06 to the present
Series:	Fireside Models
U.K.:	£ 99.00
U.S.:	$200.00
Can.:	$200.00

FOX, Seated
Style One

Model:	021
Modeller:	Judy Boyt
Height:	5 ¾", 14.6 cm
Colour:	Reddish-brown, white and black
Issued:	01/82 - 12/87
Series:	Judy Boyt Woodland
U.K.:	£ 75.00
U.S.:	$150.00
Can.:	$150.00

FOX, Seated
Style Two

Model:	146
Modeller:	David Walton
Height:	5 ½", 14.0 cm
Colour:	Reddish-brown and white
Issued:	06/91 - 12/95
U.K.	£ 55.00
U.S.	$110.00
Can.	$110.00

FOX, Seated
Style Three

Model: A5891
Modeller: Adiran Hughes
Height: 16 ½", 41.9 cm
Colour: Reddish-brown
Issued: 06/05 - 06/06
Series: 1. Fireside
            2. Wildlife

U.K.:   £100.00
U.S.: $200.00
Can.: $200.00

FOX, Seated
Style Four

Model: A6724
Modeller: Unknown
Height: 5 ¼", 13.3 cm
Colour: Reddish-brown,
            black and white
Issued: 06/06 to the present
Series: BFA Pottery Company

U.K.:   £18.00
U.S.: $35.00
Can.: $35.00

FOX, Standing
Style One

Model: ML01
Modeller: Mairi Laing Hunt
Height: 5 ½", 14.0 cm
Colour: Reddish-brown and
            white
Issued: 01/88 - 12/90
Series: Woodland

U.K.:   £110.00
U.S.: $225.00
Can.: $225.00

FOX, Standing
Style Two

Model: M21
Modeller: David Walton
Height: 3", 7.6 cm
Colour: Reddish-brown and
            black
Issued: 01/92 - 12/95
Series: Miniature Wildlife

U.K.:   £40.00
U.S.: $80.00
Can.: $80.00

FOX AND CUB

Model: WW24
Modeller: David Walton
Height: 3", 7.6 cm
Colour: Reddish-brown
Issued: 07/94 - 12/96
Series: Miniature (WWF)

U.K.:   £30.00
U.S.: $60.00
Can.: $60.00

FOX AND FAMILY

Model: L53
Modeller: David Geenty
Height: 6", 15.0 cm
Colour: Reddish-brown and
            white
Issued: 01/83 in a limited
            edition of 1,500

U.K.:   £150.00
U.S.: $300.00
Can.: $300.00

FOX CUB
Style One

Model: FF1
Modeller: Ray Ayres
Height: 2", 5.0 cm
Colour: Reddish-brown, white
            and black
Issued: 01/89 - 12/93
Series: First Friends

U.K.:   £12.00
U.S.: $25.00
Can.: $25.00

FOX CUB
Style Two

Model: B0919
Modeller: Ray Ayres
Height: 6 ½" x 4 ½"
            16.5 x 11.9 cm
Colour: Reddish-brown
            and white
Issued: 06/04 - 12/06
Series: Classic Babies

U.K.:   £40.00
U.S.: $75.00
Can.: $75.00

FOX CUB
Style Three

Model:	A7678
Modeller:	Unknown
Height:	3 ¼", 8.3 cm
Colour:	Reddish-brown,white, black, grey and green
Issued:	01/07 to the present
Series:	Wildlife
U.K.:	£15.00
U.S.:	$30.00
Can.:	$30.00

FOX CUB AND HEDGEHOG

Model:	FE1
Modeller:	Ray Ayres
Height:	3 ¼", 8.3 cm
Colour:	Reddish-brown and brown
Issued:	01/83 - 12/97
Series:	First Encounters
U.K.:	£40.00
U.S.:	$80.00
Can.:	$80.00

FOX CUB AND OWLET

Model:	B0207
Modeller:	David Walton
Height:	5 ½", 14.0 cm
Colour:	Reddish-brown, white and green
Issued:	06/97 - 05/99
Series:	First Encounters
U.K.:	£ 50.00
U.S.:	$100.00
Can.:	$100.00

FOX FAMILY
Style One

Model:	WW11
Modeller:	Richard Wawrzesta
Height:	3 ½", 8.9 cm
Colour:	Red, white and black
Issued:	01/87 - 12/87
Series:	Family Life (WWF)
U.K.:	£35.00
U.S.:	$70.00
Can.:	$70.00

FOX FAMILY
Style Two

Model:	RW25
Modeller:	David Walton
Height:	5", 12.7 cm
Colour:	Reddish-brown, white and black
Issued:	01/93 - 12/96
Series:	Endangered Species (WWF)
U.K.:	£ 65.00
U.S.:	$125.00
Can.:	$125.00

FOX TALES POINT OF SALE
(Fox and logo)

Model:	FTP01
Modeller:	David Walton
Height:	2 ¾", 7.0 cm
Colour:	Reddish-brown and grey
Issued:	07/95 - 12/97
Series:	Fox Tales
U.K.:	£25.00
U.S.:	$50.00
Can.:	$50.00

FOX TROT
(Two Foxes)

Model:	A1019
Modeller:	John Brown
Height:	6 ¼", 15.9 cm
Colour:	Red-brown, white, brown, grey, green and yellow
Issued:	01/02 - 12/03
Series:	Country Characters
U.K.:	£40.00
U.S.:	$80.00
Can.:	$80.00

FOX WITH RABBIT

Model:	UK# 010
	USA# 225-051
Modeller:	Mairi Laing
Height:	5 ½", 14.0 cm
Colour:	Reddish-brown, black, white and brown
Issued:	06/79 - 12/87
Series:	Mammals
U.K.:	£ 75.00
U.S.:	$150.00
Can.:	$150.00

FOXES

Model: Unknown
Modeller: Victor Hayton
Height: 3 ½", 8.9 cm
Colour: Reddish-brown
Issued: 01/77 - 06/78

U.K.: £ 75.00
U.S.: $150.00
Can.: $150.00

FOXHOUND, Stalking

Model: 050
Modeller: Victor Hayton
Height: 4 ½", 11.9 cm
Colour: Browns and white
Issued: 01/77 - 12/80

U.K.: £150.00
U.S.: $300.00
Can.: $300.00

**FOXHOUND, Standing
Style One**

Model: L22
Modeller: David Geenty
Height: 8 ½", 21.6 cm
Colour: Browns and white
Issued: 01/80 in a limited
edition of 850

U.K.: £200.00
U.S.: $400.00
Can.: $400.00

**FOXHOUND, Standing
Style Two**

Model: B0733
Modeller: Margaret Turner
Height: 7 ¾", 19.5 cm
Colour: White, black, tan,
grey, and green
Issued: 06/01 in a limited
edition of 950
Series: Dogs by Margaret
Turner

U.K.: £100.00
U.S.: $200.00
Can.: $200.00

**FOXHOUND, Standing
Style Three**

Model: B1011
Modeller: Margaret Turner
Height: 10", 25.4 cm
Colour: White, tan, black
and green
Issued: 06/06 in a limited
edition of 500

U.K.: £175.00
U.S.: $350.00
Can.: $350.00

**FREE LUNCH
(Pig and piglets)**

Model: JH79A, B
Modeller: Anne Wall
Height: 2 ½", 6.4 cm
Colour: A. Pink
B. Spotted
Issued: 01/93 - 12/94
Series: Every Living Thing

U.K.: £30.00
U.S.: $60.00
Can.: $60.00

**FREE SPIRITS
(Wolf and two cubs)**

Model: STW08
Modeller: Richard Roberts
Height: 8 ¼", 21.0 cm
Colour: Blue-grey, white,
tan and black
Issued: 07/95 in a limited
edition of 1,500
Series: Spirit of the Wolf

U.K.: £225.00
U.S.: $450.00
Can.: $450.00

**FRIEND OR FOE?
(Badger and kingfisher)**

Model: B0986
Modeller: Ray Ayres
Height: 8 ¾" x 10"
22.2 x 25.4 cm
Colour: Brown, grey,
turquoise and orange
Issued: 2006 in a limited
edition of 500

U.K.: £195.00
U.S.: $400.00
Can.: $400.00

FRIENDS
(Border terrier and hedgehog)

Model:	JH75
Modeller:	Anne Butler
Height:	2 ½", 6.4 cm
Colour:	Brown, grey and white
Issued:	01/93 - 05/99
Series:	1. Every Living Thing
	2. The James Herriot
	Collection

U.K.:	£40.00
U.S.:	$80.00
Can.:	$80.00

FRIESIAN COW

Model:	100
Modeller:	Ray Ayres
Height:	6", 15.0 cm
Colour:	Black and white
Issued:	01/81 - 12/82
Series:	Farm Series

U.K.:	£100.00
U.S.:	$200.00
Can.:	$200.00

FRIESIAN COW AND CALF
Style One

Model:	L34
Modeller:	Ray Ayres
Height:	6", 15.0 cm
Colour:	Black and white
Issued:	July 1981 in a limited
	edition of 850

U.K.:	£450.00
U.S.:	$900.00
Can.:	$900.00

FRIESIAN COW AND CALF,
Style Two /
AYRSHIRE COW AND CALF

Model:	160/B160A, B
Modeller:	Ray Ayres
Height:	4 ½", 11.9 cm
Colour:	A. Black and white
	B. Brown and white
Issued:	A. 07/92 - 12/00
	B. 01/93 - 12/95
Series:	Agricultural and
	Sporting

	Black	Brown
U.K.:	£45.	£ 65.
U.S.:	$90.	$125.
Can.:	$90.	$125.

FRISK
(Kitten)

Model:	A6512
Modeller:	Ray Ayres
Height:	3", 7.6 cm
Colour:	Black, white and
	light brown
Issued:	01/06 to the present
Series:	James Herriot
	Studio Collection

U.K.:	£13.00
U.S.:	$25.00
Can.:	$25.00

FRISK, THE CAT WITH MANY
LIVES

Model:	B0185
Modeller:	Kirsty Armstrong
Height:	2 ½", 6.4 cm
Colour:	Black, white and
	mustard
Issued:	06/97 - 12/99
Series:	James Herriot's Cat
	Stories

U.K.:	£15.00
U.S.:	$30.00
Can.:	$30.00

FROG

Model:	FF15
Modeller:	Anne Wall
Height:	1 ¾", 4.4 cm
Colour:	Brown and yellow
Issued:	01/93 - 12/95
Series:	First Friends

U.K.:	£12.00
U.S.:	$25.00
Can.:	$25.00

FROG AND DUCKLING

Model:	FE10
Modeller:	Ray Ayres
Height:	3", 7.6 cm
Colour:	Brown, white and green
Issued:	01/84 - 12/91
Series:	First Encounters

U.K.:	£40.00
U.S.:	$80.00
Can.:	$80.00

BFA CLASSIC COLLECTION - Birds

Canada Goose and Goslings, Style Three (B0882)

Grebe and Chicks (B0973)

Kestral, Style Four (B0869)

More Up Than Down [Swans] (B0923)

Puffins (B0991)

Greylags Rising (B1059)

BFA CLASSIC COLLECTION

Guinness Dray (B0838)

Back From the Auction (B0976)

Tipping Turnips (B1037)

BFA CLASSIC COLLECTION

The Last Laugh (B0946)

Lacking Horse Power (B0985)

Warm Work on a Cold Day (B1028)

BFA CLASSIC COLLECTION - Cattle

Belgian Blue Cow and Calf, Style Three (B0929)

Belgian Blue Bull, Style Four (B0833)

Dexter Cow and Calf (B0974)

Longhorn Cow and Calf (B0993)

Limousin Family (B0855)

Charolais Bull, Style Five (B1075)

BFA CLASSIC COLLECTION - Sheep

Lleyn Ewe and Lambs (B0975)

Suffolf Ewe and Lambs, Style Three (B0778)

Texel Ewe and Lambs, Style Four (B1054)

Border Leicester Ewe and Lambs (B0930)

Blue Faced Leicester Ewe and Lambs,
Style Two (B0741)

Blackie Ewe and Lambs (B0887)

BFA CLASSIC COLLECTION - Horses

Welsh Cob, Style Four (B1035)

Hackney, Action, Style Two (B1010)

The Champion Shire (B0888A)

Faithful Friend (B0942A)

Welsh Cob Mare and Foal, Style Two (B0906)

Fell Mare and Foal (B0971)

BFA CLASSIC COLLECTION - Dogs

Terriers Ratting (B0884)

Spade Work (B1034)

Lurcher, Standing, Style Three (B1053)

Three Muskateers (B0990)

Foxhound, Standing, Style Three (B1011)

English Pointer (B1050A)

BFA CLASSIC COLLECTION - Farm Life

Weighing Up The Problem (B1014)

Awkward Cow (B0891)

Homeward Bound (B1029)

Having 10 (B1079)

Carrying Burdens (B0892)

Bringing In (B1049)

FROG FAMILY

Model: RW10
Modeller: Richard Wawrzesta
Height: 4", 10.1 cm
Colour: Green, yellow and grey
Issued: 01/89 - 12/93
Series: 1. Wildlife Families (WWF)
2. Special Interest

U.K.: £40.00
U.S.: $80.00
Can.: $80.00

FROGS

Model: ED11
Modeller: Judy Boyt
Height: 2 ¾", 7.0 cm
Colour: Green and yellow
Issued: 01/84 - 12/84
Series: Early Days

U.K.: £40.00
U.S.: $80.00
Can.: $80.00

FRONTIERS OF FARMING
(Fastrac JCB)

Model: B0273
Modeller: Kirsty Armstrong
Height: 6", 15.0 cm
Colour: Yellow, black, red, grey and green
Issued: 06/97 in a limited edition of 1,000

U.K.: £300.00
U.S.: $600.00
Can.: $600.00

Note: Fastrac© is a copyright of JCB©.

FROSTY MORNING
(Fergie TE20)

Model: B0343
Modeller: Ray Ayres
Height: 7", 17.8 cm
Colour: Grey, beige, brown, black and white
Issued: 01/99 in a limited edition of 1,750
Series: The James Herriot Collection

U.K.: £475.00
U.S.: $950.00
Can.: $950.00

FULL CRY
(Foxhunter scene)

Model: UK# L23
USA# 225-151
Modeller: David Geenty
Height: 8 ¾" x 13 ½"
22.2 x 34.3 cm
Colour: Grey, red, black, brown and green
Issued: 01/80 in a limited edition of 300

U.K.: £ 750.00
U.S.: $1,500.00
Can.: $1,500.00

Note: This model is also seen with a bay horse.

FULL STRETCH
(Racehorse)

Model: L82
Modeller: David Geenty
Height: 8", 20.3 cm
Colour: Chocolate, blue, yellow and white
Issued: 01/88 in a limited edition of 1,500

U.K.: £275.00
U.S.: $550.00
Can.: $550.00

Note: Custom painted, also made in Bronze.

FUTURE STARS
(Pair of border collie pups)

Model: B0103/B0359
Modeller: Ray Ayres
Height 2 ½", 6.4 cm
Colour: Black and white
Issued: 06/99 - 06/00
Series: Membership Gift

U.K.: £15.00
U.S.: $30.00
Can.: $30.00

GALLOWAY/BELTED GALLOWAY BULL
Style One

Model: L33
Modeller: Ray Ayres
Height: 6 ½", 16.5 cm
Colour: A. Black (Galloway)
B. Black and white (Belted)
Issued: 01/81 in a limited edition of 850
Series: Special Interest

U.K.: £ 500.00
U.S.: $1,000.00
Can.: $1,000.00

**GALLOWAY/BELTED
GALLOWAY BULL
Style Two**

Model:	A2692, 4891
Modeller:	Lesley McKenzie
Height:	5 ½", 14.0 cm
Colour:	A2692 Black
	A4891 Belted
Issued:	06/04 - 06/06
U.K.:	£45.00
U.S.:	$90.00
Can.:	$90.00

GALLOWAY/BELTED

		BULL **Style Three**	**CALF**	**COW**
Model / Colour:	Black	A5253	A5258	A5255
	Belted	A6746	A6865	A6747
Modeller:	Lesley McKenzie			
Height:		5"	3 ¼"	4 ¾"
		12.7 cm	8.3 cm	12.1 cm
Colour:	See above			
Issued:	01/06 to the present			
Series:	BFA Pottery Company			
U.K.:		£25.00	£14.95	£25.00
U.S.:		$50.00	$30.00	$50.00
Can.:		$50.00	$30.00	$50.00

**GALLOWAY/BELTED COW
AND CALF
Style One**

Model:	B0005A, B
Modeller:	Anne Wall
Height:	4 ¾", 12.1 cm
Colour:	A. Black
	B. Black and white
Issued:	06/96 - 12/97
Series:	Agricultural and
	Sporting
U.K.:	£110.00
U.S.:	$225.00
Can.:	$225.00

**GALLOWAY/BELTED COW
AND CALF
Style Two**

Model:	A2693, 3790
Modeller:	Lesley McKenzie
Height:	6", 15.0 cm
Colour:	A2693 Belted
	A3790 Black
Issued:	06/03 - 06/06
Series:	Cattle Breeds
U.K.:	£ 55.00
U.S.:	$110.00
Can.:	$110.00

**GARDEN GUESTS
(House mice)**

Model:	B0199
Modeller:	Anne Wall
Height:	6 ¼", 15.9 cm
Colour:	Brown, white and
	green
Issued:	06/97 - 12/98
Series:	The Country Mouse
U.K.:	£ 65.00
U.S.:	$125.00
Can.:	$125.00

**GARDENER, THE
(Rabbit)**

Model:	A0129
Modeller:	Ray Ayres
Height:	4 ¾", 12.1 cm
Colour:	Brown and orange
Issued:	06/00 - 12/01
Series:	Country Characters
U.K.:	£25.00
U.S.:	$50.00
Can.:	$50.00

**GARDENER'S FRIEND, THE
(Robin)**

Model:	SRE6
Modeller:	Ray Ayres
Height:	2 ½", 6.4 cm
Colour:	Red, brown and grey
Issued:	06/95 - 05/96
Series:	Membership Gift
U.K.:	£25.00
U.S.:	$50.00
Can.:	$50.00

GATHERING IN THE STRAYS
(Sheep and collie)

Model:	JH28
Modeller:	Ray Ayres
Height:	5 ¼", 13.3 cm
Colour:	Cream, black and white
Issued:	01/89 in a limited edition of 2,500
Series:	All Creatures Great and Small
U.K.:	£ 600.00
U.S.:	$1,200.00
Can.:	$1,200.00

GAZELLES

Model:	A5408
Modeller:	David Mayer
Height:	6 ¾", 17.2 cm
Colour:	Golden brown, black, white and greeb
Issued:	06/05 - 12/06
Series:	Wild World
U.K.:	£ 55.00
U.S.:	$110.00
Can.:	$110.00

GENTLE GIANT (Tetley'sDrays)
Gold Edition

Model:	PJ02
Modeller:	Ray Ayres
Height:	9" x 15", 22.9 x 38.1 cm
Colour:	White horses, gold-plated rosettes; blue cart; hardwood base; brass plaque
Issued:	10/92 in a limited edition of 150
Varieties:	PJ01 Standard Ed.
U.K.:	£ 800.00
U.S.:	$1,600.00
Can.:	$1,600.00

Standard Edition

Model:	PJ01
Modeller:	Ray Ayres
Height:	9" x 15", 22.9 x 38.1 cm
Colour:	White horses, blue cart
Issued:	10/92 in a limited edition of 750
Varieties:	PJ02 Gold Ed.
U.K.:	£ 775.00
U.S.:	$1,550.00
Can.:	$1,550.00

GENTLY GRAZING
(Shire Mare and Foal)

Model:	JH33A
Modeller:	Ray Ayres
Height:	6", 15.0 cm
Colour:	Grey and chestnut
Issued:	04/93 in a limited edition of 350
Varieties:	JH33 Summer Days
Series:	All Creatures Great and Small
U.K.:	£225.00
U.S.:	$450.00
Can.:	$450.00

GERMAN SHEPHERD
(Crouching, in action)

Model:	B0532
Modeller:	Margaret Turner
Height:	5 ½", 14.0 cm
Colour:	Black and tan
Issued:	01/00 - 12/02
Series:	Dogs by Margaret Turner
U.K.:	£ 65.00
U.S.:	$125.00
Can.:	$125.00

**GERMAN SHEPHERD, Lying
First Variation**

Model: DG34/B0465
Modeller: Margaret Turner
Height: 4 ¾", 12.1 cm
Colour: DG34   Black and tan
              B0465   Bronze
Issued: DG34   07/95-05/99
              B0465   06/99-06/00
Series: 1. Dogs Galore
              2. Bronzed

	Black/tan	Bronze
U.K.:	£25.	£20.
U.S.:	$50.	$40.
Can.:	$50.	$40.

**GERMAN SHEPHERD, Lying
Second Variation**

Model: A3042
Modeller: Margaret Turner
Height: 5", 12.7 cm
Colour: Black and tan
Issued: 06/03 to the present
Series: Dogs and Pups Galore

U.K.:   £21.00
U.S.: $40.00
Can.: $40.00

**GERMAN SHEPHERD, Seated
Style One**

Model: DG15
Modeller: Margaret Turner
Height: 6 ¾", 17.2 cm
Colour: Black and tan
Issued: 01/92 - 09/95
Series: Dogs Galore

U.K.:   £30.00
U.S.: $60.00
Can.: $60.00

**GERMAN SHEPHERD, Seated
Style Two**

Model: B0501/MT06
Modeller: Margaret Turner
Height: 8 ¾", 22.2 cm
Colour: B0501   Bronze
              MT06   Black and tan
Issued: B0501   01/99 in a
                        ltd. ed. of 500
              MT06   01/95-12/02
Series: 1. Dogs by M. Turner
              2. 25th Anniversary

U.K.:   £125.00
U.S.: $250.00
Can.: $250.00

**GERMAN SHEPHERD, Seated
Style Three**

Model: B0496
Modeller: Margaret Turner
Height: 7", 17.8 cm
Colour: Black and tan
Issued: 06/99 - 12/01
Series: Dogs Galore

U.K.:   £40.00
U.S.: $80.00
Can.: $80.00

**GERMAN SHEPHERD, Seated
Style Four**

Model: A0647
Modeller: Lesley McKenzie
Height: 19", 48.0 cm
Colour: Black and tan
Issued: 01/01 - 12/04
Series: Fireside Dogs

U.K.:   £ 90.00
U.S.: $175.00
Can.: $175.00

**GERMAN SHEPHERD, Seated
Style Five**

Model: A2082
Modeller: Margaret Turner
Height: 6 ¾", 17.2 cm
Colour: Black and tan
Issued: 06/02 to the present
Series: Dogs and Pups Galore

U.K.:   £23.00
U.S.: $45.00
Can.: $45.00

**GERMAN SHEPHERD, Standing
Style One**

Model: UK# L29
              USA# 225-125
Modeller: David Geenty
Height: 7 ½", 19.1 cm
Colour: Black and tan
Issued: 01/81 in a limited
              edition of 850

U.K.:   £125.00
U.S.: $250.00
Can.: $250.00

GERMAN SHEPHERD, Standing Style Two

Model:	UK# DL3
	USA# 225-420
Modeller:	Ray Ayres
Height:	5 ½", 14.0 cm
Colour:	Black and golden
Issued:	01/83 - 12/92
Series:	1. The World of Dogs
	2. Special Interest
U.K.:	£ 75.00
U.S.:	$150.00
Can.:	$150.00

GERMAN SHEPHERD, Standing Style Three

Model:	A1164
Modeller:	Margaret Turner
Height:	6 ½", 16.5 cm
Colour:	Black and tan
Issued:	06/01 - 06/06
Series:	Dogs and Pups Galore
U.K.:	£25.00
U.S.:	$50.00
Can.:	$50.00

GERMAN SHEPHERD, Standing Style Four

Model:	A1863
Modeller:	Margaret Turner
Height:	11", 27.9 cm
Colour:	Black and tan
Issued:	01/03 - 06/06
U.K.:	£ 70.00
U.S.:	$140.00
Can.:	$140.00

GERMAN SHEPHERD, Standing Style Five

Model:	A7112
Modeller:	Unknown
Height:	6 ½", 15.9 cm
Colour:	Brown and black
Issued:	06/06 to the present
Series:	Dogs and Pups Galore
U.K.:	£29.00
U.S.:	$60.00
Can.:	$60.00

GERMAN SHEPHERD AND BOOT

Model:	610771
Modeller:	Unknown
Height:	2 ¼", 5.7 cm
Colour:	Black and tan
Issued:	01/99 - 12/00
Series:	Puppy Tales
U.K.:	£12.00
U.S.:	$25.00
Can.:	$25.00

GERMAN SHEPHERD AND PUP Style One

Model:	203
Modeller:	Ray Ayres
Height:	4 ½", 11.9 cm
Colour:	Brown and black
Issued:	01/89 - 12/92
Series:	1. The World of Dogs
	2. Special Interest
U.K.:	£ 75.00
U.S.:	$150.00
Can.:	$150.00

GERMAN SHEPHERD AND PUP Style Two

Model:	DPG03
Modeller:	Margaret Turner
Height:	6", 15.0 cm
Colour:	Brown, black and white
Issued:	01/96 - 12/98
Series:	Dogs Galore
U.K.:	£ 50.00
U.S.:	$100.00
Can.:	$100.00

Note: This model combines DPG03 and PG06.

GERMAN SHEPHERD AND PUPS

Model:	B0351
Modeller:	Margaret Turner
Height:	10", 25.4 cm
Colour:	Black and tan
Issued:	01/99 - 06/03
Series:	Dogs by Margaret
	Turner
U.K.:	£175.00
U.S.:	$350.00
Can.:	$350.00

GERMAN SHEPHERD AND THREE PUPS

Model: A5211
Modeller: Kerry Bell
Height: 5 ¼", 13.3 cm
Colour: Black, brown and cream
Issued: 01/05 - 06/06
Series: Dogs and Pups Galore: Family Groups

U.K.: £35.00
U.S.: $70.00
Can.: $70.00

GERMAN SHEPHERD AND WEST HIGHLAND TERRIER

Model: A4676
Modeller: Anne Wall
Height: 5 ¼", 13.3 cm
Colour: Tan, black, white and grey
Issued: 01/05 - 12/05
Series: Big Dog, Little Dog

U.K.: £35.00
U.S.: $70.00
Can.: $70.00

GERMAN SHEPHERD PUP, Seated

Model: PG06/B0460
Modeller: Margaret Turner
Height: 4 ½", 11.9 cm
Colour: PG06 Black and tan
         B0460 Bronze
Issued: PG06 01/93-12/01
         B0460 06/99-06/00
Series: 1. Pups Galore
         2. Bronzed

U.K.: £20.00
U.S.: $40.00
Can.: $40.00

GERMAN SHEPHERD PUPS (Three)

Model: A3845
Modeller: Adrian Hughes
Height: 2 ½", 6.4 cm
Colour: Black, tan and blue
Issued: 06/04 to the present
Series: Dogs and Pups Galore

U.K.: £20.00
U.S.: $40.00
Can.: $40.00

GERMAN SHORT-HAIRED POINTER, Standing Style One

Model: 053
Modeller: Mairi Laing Hunt
Height: 5", 12.7 cm
Colour: Chocolate brown and white
Issued: 06/79 - 12/84

U.K.: £275.00
U.S.: $550.00
Can.: $550.00

GERMAN SHORT-HAIRED POINTER, Standing Style Two

Model: A7114
Modeller: Unknown
Height: 6", 15.0 cm
Colour: Dark brown
Issued: 06/06 to the present
Series: Dogs and Pups Galore

U.K.: £23.00
U.S.: $45.00
Can.: $45.00

GETTING READY FOR SMITHFIELD

Model: A2143
Modeller: Ray Ayres
Height: 5 ½", 14.0 cm
Colour: Red, white, black, dark blue and browns
Issued: 01/03 - 06/04
Series: Tractors

U.K.: £125.00
U.S.: $250.00
Can.: $250.00

GETTING READY FOR THE SHOW

Model: B0861
Modeller: Craig Harding
Height: 7", 17.8 cm
Colour: Reddish-brown, white, blue, green, beige and black
Issued: 01/04 in a limited edition of 950
Series: Classic Collection

U.K.: £175.00
U.S.: $350.00
Can.: $350.00

GIANT PANDA AND CUB

Model:	RW19
Modeller:	Richard Wawrzesta
Height:	5", 12.7 cm
Colour:	Black and white
Issued:	01/90 - 12/93
Series:	Endangered Species (WWF)

U.K.:	£40.00
U.S.:	$80.00
Can.:	$80.00

GIRAFFE

Model:	B0678, 79, 80	
Modeller:	Richard Roberts	
Height:	6 ¾", 17.2 cm	
Colour:	B0678	Slate blue
	B0679	Stone
	B0680	Gold
Issued:	01/01 - 12/01	
Series:	Cubist Africa	

U.K.:	£30.00
U.S.:	$60.00
Can.:	$60.00

GIRAFFE AND CALF
Style One

Model:	WW28
Modeller:	David Walton
Height:	3 ½", 8.9 cm
Colour:	Brown, yellow and white
Issued:	01/95 - 12/95
Series:	Miniature (WWF)

U.K.:	£25.00
U.S.:	$50.00
Can.:	$50.00

GIRAFFE AND CALF
Style Two

Model:	A5407
Modeller:	David Mayer
Height:	11 ¾", 29.8 cm
Colour:	Golden brown, cream, green and fawn
Issued:	01/05 - 12/06
Series:	Wild World

U.K.:	£ 90.00
U.S.:	$175.00
Can.:	$175.00

GIRL ON PONY

Model:	165/B165
Modeller:	Anne Wall
Height:	5 ½", 14.0 cm
Colour:	Brown, black and beige
Issued:	07/93 - 12/96
Series:	Agricultural and Sporting

U.K.:	£ 80.00
U.S.:	$160.00
Can.:	$160.00

Note: The model illustrated is a portrait piece.

GLAD YOU'RE MINE
(Horse and Girl)

Model:	A0539
Modeller:	Anne Wall
Height:	4", 10.1 cm
Colour:	Dark brown, yellow and cream
Issued:	01/01 - 12/04
Series:	Hay Days

U.K.:	£25.00
U.S.:	$50.00
Can.:	$50.00

GOAT

Model:	A4596
Modeller:	Lesley McKenzie
Height:	5", 12.7 cm
Colour:	White and pink
Issued:	06/04 to the present
Series:	BFA Pottery Company

U.K.:	£18.00
U.S.:	$35.00
Can.:	$35.00

GOAT KID

Model:	M5
Modeller:	David Geenty
Height:	4", 10.1 cm
Colour:	White
Issued:	07/80 - 12/80
Series:	Beginners, Please

U.K.:	£ 80.00
U.S.:	$160.00
Can.:	$160.00

GOING FOR THE POST
(Three Racehorses)

Model:	L83
Modeller:	David Geenty
Height:	8", 20.3 cm
Colour:	Brown, chestnut, blue, yellow, green, red and white
Issued:	01/88 in a limited edition of 250
U.K.:	£ 700.00
U.S.:	$1,400.00
Can.:	$1,400.00

Note: Custom painted.

GOLDCREST

Model:	A7151
Modeller:	Unknown
Height:	5", 12.7 cm
Colour:	Green, black and brown
Issued:	06/06 to the present
U.K.:	£ 9.95
U.S.:	$20.00
Can.:	$20.00

GOLDEN EAGLE
Style One

Model:	RB40
Modeller:	Ray Ayres
Height:	7 ¼", 18.4 cm
Colour:	Brown, golden and grey
Issued:	01/93 - 12/95
Series:	RSPB Birds of the Countryside
U.K.:	£100.00
U.S.:	$200.00
Can.:	$200.00

GOLDEN EAGLE
Style Two

Model:	A0658
Modeller:	Russell Willis
Height:	10 ½", 26.7 cm
Colour:	Browns, golden, black and stone
Issued:	01/01 - 06/03
Series:	Birds of Prey
U.K.:	£ 75.00
U.S.:	$150.00
Can.:	$150.00

GOLDEN MEMORIES
(Ferguson 35)

Model:	B0799
Modeller:	Ray Ayres
Height:	7" x 9", 17.8 x 22.9 cm
Colour:	Slate-grey, grey, brown, black, white, blue, green and beige
Issued:	01/03 - 12/03
Series:	Classic Member-only Tractor figurine
U.K.:	£225.00
U.S.:	$450.00
Can.:	$450.00

GOLDEN RETRIEVER, Lying
Style One

Model:	MT08
Modeller:	Margaret Turner
Height:	6 ¾", 17.2 cm
Colour:	Pale golden brown
Issued:	01/96 - 12/98
Series:	Dogs by Margaret Turner
U.K.	£100.00
U.S.	$200.00
Can.	$200.00

GOLDEN RETRIEVER, Lying
Style Two

Model:	B0438
Modeller:	Margaret Turner
Height:	2", 5.0 cm
Colour:	Pale golden brown
Issued:	01/99 - 12/01
Series:	Pups Galore
U.K.:	£12.00
U.S.:	$25.00
Can.:	$25.00

GOLDEN RETRIEVER, Lying
Style Three

Model:	B0439
Modeller:	Margaret Turner
Height:	3 ¾", 9.5 cm
Colour:	Pale golden brown
Issued:	01/99 - 12/01
Series:	Dogs Galore
U.K.:	£25.00
U.S.:	$50.00
Can.:	$50.00

GOLDEN RETRIEVER, Lying Style Four

Model: A3047
Modeller: Margaret Turner
Height: 2 ½", 6.4 cm
Colour: Yellow
Issued: 06/03 - 12/05
Series: Dogs and Pups Galore

U.K.: £20.00
U.S.: $40.00
Can.: $40.00

GOLDEN RETRIEVER, Seated Style One

Model: DG12
Modeller: Steve McKeown
Height: 5 ¾", 14.6 cm
Colour: Pale golden brown
Issued: 01/91 - 12/94
Series: Dogs Galore

U.K.: £30.00
U.S.: $60.00
Can.: $60.00

GOLDEN RETRIEVER, Seated Style Two

Model: DG29, B0467
Modeller: Margaret Turner
Height: 5 ½", 14.0 cm
Colour: DG29 Yellow
          B0467 Bronze
Issued: DG29 01/95-12/01
          B0467 06/99-06/00
Series: 1. Dogs Galore
          2. Bronzed

U.K.: £25.00
U.S.: $50.00
Can.: $50.00

GOLDEN RETRIEVER, Seated Style Three

Model: A1256
Modeller: Margaret Turner
Height: 18", 46.0 cm
Colour: Pale golden brown
Issued: 01/03 - 06/05
Series: Fireside Dogs

U.K.: £ 75.00
U.S.: $150.00
Can.: $150.00

GOLDEN RETRIEVER, Seated Style Four

Model: A2089
Modeller: Margaret Turner
Height: 5 ¾", 14.6 cm
Colour: Yellow
Issued: 01/03 to the present
Series: Dogs and Pups Galore

U.K.: £21.00
U.S.: $40.00
Can.: $40.00

GOLDEN RETRIEVER, Standing Style One

Model: A1165
Modeller: Margaret Turner
Height: 5 ½", 14.0 cm
Colour: Yellow
Issued: 06/01 - 06/06
Series: Dogs and Pups Galore

U.K.: £20.00
U.S.: $40.00
Can.: $40.00

GOLDEN RETRIEVER, Standing Style Two

Model: A7123
Modeller: Unknown
Height: 5 ¾", 14.6 cm
Colour: Pale golden brown
Issued: 01/07 to the present
Series: Dogs and Pups Galore

U.K.: £21.00
U.S.: $40.00
Can.: $40.00

GOLDEN RETRIEVER, Walking Style One

Model: UK# 056
          USA# 225-122
Modeller: David Geenty
Height: 6", 15.0 cm
Colour: Pale golden brown
Issued: 01/80 - 12/82

U.K.: £125.00
U.S.: $250.00
Can.: $250.00

GOLDEN RETRIEVER, Walking Style Two

Model:	UK# DL1
	USA# 225-422
Modeller:	Ray Ayres
Height:	4 ½", 11.9 cm
Colour:	Pale golden brown
Issued:	01/83 - 12/92
Series:	The World of Dogs
U.K.:	£ 65.00
U.S.:	$125.00
Can.:	$125.00

GOLDEN RETRIEVER AND PUP, Seated

Model:	DPG02
Modeller:	Margaret Turner
Height:	6 ½", 16.5 cm
Colour:	Yellow
Issued:	01/96 - 06/00
Series:	Dogs Galore
U.K.:	£35.00
U.S.:	$70.00
Can.:	$70.00

GOLDEN RETRIEVER AND PUPS

Model:	202
Modeller:	Ray Ayres
Height:	4 ¾", 12.1 cm
Colour:	Pale golden brown
Issued:	01/89 - 12/92
Series:	1. The World of Dogs
	2. Special Interest
U.K.:	£ 65.00
U.S.:	$125.00
Can.:	$125.00

GOLDEN RETRIEVER AND SLIPPER

Model:	610798
Modeller:	Unknown
Height:	2 ¾", 7.0 cm
Colour:	Golden brown and brown
Issued:	01/99 - 12/00
Series:	Puppy Tales
U.K.:	£12.00
U.S.:	$25.00
Can.:	$25.00

GOLDEN RETRIEVER AND THREE PUPS

Model:	A5210
Modeller:	Kerry Bell
Height:	4 ¼", 10.8 cm
Colour:	Pale golden brown
Issued:	01/05 - 06/06
Series:	Dogs and Pups Galore: Family Groups
U.K.:	£30.00
U.S.:	$60.00
Can.:	$60.00

GOLDEN RETRIEVER PUP, Seated

Model:	PG04/B0461
Modeller:	Margaret Turner
Height:	2 ¾", 7.0 cm
Colour:	PG04 Yellow
	B0461 Bronze
Issued:	PG04 01/92-12/01
	B0461 06/99-06/00
Series:	1. Pups Galore
	2. Bronze
U.K.:	£12.00
U.S.:	$25.00
Can.:	$25.00

GOLDENEYE DRAKE

Model:	PS14
Modeller:	Richard Roberts
Height:	2 ½", 6.4 cm
Colour:	Black and white
Issued:	01/92 - 12/93
Series:	Peter Scott Memorial Appeal (WWF)
U.K.:	£ 50.00
U.S.:	$100.00
Can.:	$100.00

GOLDFINCH ON THISTLE Style One

Model:	F7
Modeller:	David Burnham Smith
Height:	8 ½", 21.6 cm
Colour:	Brown, white, black and red
Issued:	01/90 - 12/91
Series:	Finesse Birds
U.K.:	£110.00
U.S.:	$220.00
Can.:	$220.00

GOLDFINCH ON THISTLE
Style Two
Model:	RB35
Modeller:	Ray Ayres
Height:	6 ½", 16.5 cm
Colour:	Yellow, black and white
Issued:	07/92 - 12/93
Series:	RSPB Birds of the Countryside
U.K.:	£ 75.00
U.S.:	$150.00
Can.:	$150.00

GOLFER
Model:	BB01
Modeller:	John Warren
Height:	8", 20.3 cm
Colour:	Bronze
Issued:	01/88 - 12/89
Series:	1. Special Interest
	2. Studio Bronze
U.K.:	£ 65.00
U.S.:	$125.00
Can.:	$125.00

GONE AWAY
(Mounted huntsman and four hounds)
Model:	L71
Modeller:	David Geenty
Height:	9", 22.9 cm
Colour:	Browns, black and red
Issued:	07/85 in a limited edition of 750
U.K.:	£ 725.00
U.S.:	$1,450.00
Can.:	$1,450.00

GONE FISHING
(Boy and Border Collie)
Model:	B0520
Modeller:	Anne Wall
Height:	5 ¼", 13.3 cm
Colour:	Cream, blue, black and white
Issued:	01/00 - 06/01
Series:	The James Herriot Collection
U.K.:	£ 65.00
U.S.:	$125.00
Can.:	$125.00

Note: Promotional figure has red shorts.

GOOD FOR THE GOOSE
(Two Geese)
Model:	A0450
Modeller:	Anne Wall
Height:	4 ¼", 10.8 cm
Colour:	White, silver, green and orange
Issued:	01/01 - 12/02
Series:	The James Herriot Studio Collection
U.K.:	£25.00
U.S.:	$50.00
Can.:	$50.00

GOOD SAMARITAN, THE
(Border collie)
Model:	A6127
Modeller:	Hans Kendrick
Height:	6 ¾", 17.2 cm
Colour:	Black, white and grey
Issued:	01/06 to the present
Series:	Border Collie Collection
U.K.:	£ 60.00
U.S.:	$120.00
Can.:	$120.00

GOOSE
Style One
Model:	A0125
Modeller:	Russell Willis
Height:	13", 33.0 cm
Colour:	White, orange and green
Issued:	06/00 - 12/01
Series:	Farmyard Friends
U.K.:	£ 75.00
U.S.:	$150.00
Can.:	£150.00

GOOSE
Style Two
Model:	A5252
Modeller:	Russell Willis
Height:	5 ¼", 13.3 cm
Colour:	White, orange, green
Issued:	01/06 to the present
Series:	BFA Pottery Company
U.K.:	£16.00
U.S.:	$30.00
Can.:	$30.00

GORDON SETTER

Model:	L17
Modeller:	Ray Ayres
Height:	5", 12.7 cm
Colour:	A. Chocolate brown and tan
	B. Bronze
Issued:	01/79 in a limited edition of 500
Series:	1. Dogs Galore
	2. Bronze

	Brown	Bronze
U.K.:	£300.	£100.
U.S.:	$600.	$200.
Can.:	$600.	$200.

GRACEFUL SWANS

Model:	A0190
Modeller:	Russell Willis
Height:	7 ¼", 18.4 cm
Colour:	White
Issued:	06/00 - 12/01
Series:	1. British Favourites
	2. Families
U.K.:	£ 75.00
U.S.:	$150.00
Can.:	$150.00

GRAND PARADE
(Pony, sheep, cow, and pig at the Royal Welsh Show)

Model:	A3563
Modeller:	David Mayer
Height:	5", 12.7 cm
Colour:	Black, chestnut, white and pink
Issued:	2004 in a limited edition of 1,250
U.K.:	£150.00
U.S.:	$300.00
Can.:	$300.00

Note: Produced for the Royal Welsh Agricultural Society.

GREAT DANE
(Bitch, Seated)

Model:	DG23
Modeller:	Margaret Turner
Height:	7", 17.8 cm
Colour:	1. Golden brown
	2. Harlequin
Issued:	07/93 - 12/00
Series:	Dogs Galore

	Golden	Harlequin
U.K.:	£30.	£ 50.
U.S.:	$60.	$100.
Can.:	$60.	$100.

GREAT DANE
(Dog, Seated)

Model:	DG25, B0487
Modeller:	Margaret Turner
Height:	7", 17.8 cm
Colour:	DG25 Golden brown
	B0487 Bronze
Issued:	DG25 01/94-12/00
	B0487 06/99-06/00
Series:	1. Dogs Galore
	2. Bronzed
U.K.:	£25.00
U.S.:	$50.00
Can.:	$50.00

GREAT DANE
(Lying, Curled Up)

Model:	077
Modeller:	Elizabeth Waugh
Height:	4", 10.1 cm
Colour:	Light brown
Issued:	01/86 - 12/92
Series:	1. Special Interest
	2. The World of Dogs
U.K.:	£125.00
U.S.:	$250.00
Can.:	$250.00

Note: Custom painted.

GREAT DANE, Seated

Model:	A3831, 3880
Modeller:	Margaret Turner
Height:	6 ¾", 17.2 cm
Colour:	A3831 Fawn
	A3880 Harlequin
Issued:	01/04 - 06/06
Series:	Dogs and Pups Galore
U.K.:	£25.00
U.S.:	$50.00
Can.:	$50.00

GREAT DANE, Standing

Model:	A2645, 3810
Modeller:	Margaret Turner
Height:	6 ¾", 17.2 cm
Colour:	A2645 Fawn
	A3810 Harlequin
Issued:	06/03 - 12/05
Series:	Dogs and Pups Galore
U.K.:	£25.00
U.S.:	$50.00
Can.:	$50.00

GREAT DANE AND PUPS

Model: B0653
Modeller: Margaret Turner
Height: 6", 15.0 cm
Colour: Light brown and black
Issued: 01/01 in a limited edition of 950
Series: Dogs by Margaret Turner

U.K.: £175.00
U.S.: $350.00
Can.: $350.00

GREAT DANE IN DRAWER

Model: 656720
Modeller: Unknown
Height: 2 ¾", 7.0 cm
Colour: Tan, brown and blue
Issued: 06/99 - 12/00
Series: Puppy Tales

U.K.: £12.00
U.S.: $25.00
Can.: $25.00

GREAT ESCAPE, THE
(Piglets)

Model: B0087
Modeller: Kirsty Armstrong
Height: 5 ¼", 13.3 cm
Colour: Pink, grey and brown
Issued: 01/97 - 12/99
Series: 1. Every Living Thing
2. The James Herriot Collection

U.K.: £ 65.00
U.S.: $125.00
Can.: $125.00

GREAT HORNED OWL

Model: WB06
Modeller: Russell Willis
Height: 4 ¼", 10.8 cm
Colour: Browns and cream
Issued: 07/92 - 12/94
Series: 1. Owls of the World
2. Russell Willis Birds

U.K.: £30.00
U.S.: $60.00
Can.: $60.00

GREAT SPOTTED
WOODPECKER

Model: A0409
Modeller: Russell Willis
Height: 3 ¼", 8.3 cm
Colour: Black, white, brown and green
Issued: 01/01 - 12/04
Series: 1. Feathered Friends
2. Birds by Russell Willis

U.K.: £15.00
U.S.: $30.00
Can.: $30.00

GREAT TIT ON BUTTON BOX

Model: WB153
Modeller: Russell Willis
Height: 5", 12.7 cm
Colour: Yellow, green, black, white, gold and blue
Issued: 01/95 - 12/96
Series: 1. Birds In Your Garden
2. Russell Willis Birds

U.K.: £40.00
U.S.: $80.00
Can.: $80.00

GREAT TIT ON COCONUT

Model: RB17
Modeller: Ray Ayres
Height: 5", 12.7 cm
Colour: Yellow, black, white and brown
Issued: 07/90 - 12/92

U.K.: £ 65.00
U.S.: $125.00
Can.: $125.00

GREATER FLAMINGOS

Model: PS01
Modeller: Richard Roberts
Height: 12 ¼", 31.1 cm
Colour: Pink, white and black
Issued: 01/91 in a limited edition of 950
Series: Peter Scott Memorial Appeal (WWF)

U.K.: £350.00
U.S.: $700.00
Can.: $700.00

GREBE AND CHICKS
Model: B0973
Modeller: Ray Ayres
Size: 8" x 8 ½"
20.3 x 21.6 cm
Colour: Grey, browns, white, orange, green, black
Issued: 01/06 in a limited edition of 500

U.K.: £145.00
U.S.: $275.00
Can.: $275.00

GREY WAGTAIL
Model: 034
Modeller: Mairi Laing Hunt
Height: 5 ½", 14.0 cm
Colour: Blue, yellow and brown
Issued: 07/78 - 06/86

U.K.: £ 65.00
U.S.: $125.00
Can.: $125.00

GREYHOUND, Lying
Model: 064A, B
Modeller: David Geenty
Height: 4 ½", 11.9 cm
Colour: A. Tan
B. Black and white
Issued: 07/81 - 12/85

U.K.: £150.00
U.S.: $300.00
Can.: $300.00

GREYHOUND, Seated
Style One
Model: DG30A, B, C; B0470
Modeller: Margaret Turner
Height: 6 ½", 16.5 cm
Colour: A. Black/white
B. Brindle/white
C.Tan and white
B0470 Bronze
Issued: A.-C. 01/95-12/01
B0470 06/99-06/00
Series: 1. Dogs Galore
2. Bronzed

U.K.: £30.00
U.S.: $60.00
Can.: $60.00

GREYHOUND, Seated
Style Two
Model: A2080, 81
Modeller: Margaret Turner
Height: 6 ½", 16.5 cm
Colour: A2080 Brindle
A2081 Black / white
Issued: 06/02 to the present
Series: Dogs and Pups Galore

U.K.: £21.00
U.S.: $40.00
Can.: $40.00

GREYHOUND, Standing
Model: A1397, 98
Modeller: Margaret Turner
Height: 6", 15.0 cm
Colour: A1397 Black / white
A1398 Brindle
Issued: A1397 01/02-06/06
A1398 01/02 to the present
Series: Dogs and Pups Galore

U.K.: £21.00
U.S.: $40.00
Can.: $40.00

GREYHOUND (Young, walking)
Model: B0348A, B
Modeller: Margaret Turner
Height: 6 ¾", 17.2 cm
Colour: A. Brindle and white
B. Black and white
Issued: 01/99 - 06/01
Series: Dogs by Margaret Turner

U.K.: £ 75.00
U.S.: $150.00
Can.: $150.00

GREYHOUNDS COURSING
Model: EW2
Modeller: Elizabeth Waugh
Height: 6 ½", 16.5 cm
Colour: 1. Black and white
2. Tan and white
3. Bronze
Issued: 01/86 in a limited edition of 250
Series: Special Interest

U.K.: £350.00
U.S.: $700.00
Can.: $700.00

GREYLAG GEESE

Model: L93
Modeller: Ray Ayres
Height: 6", 15.0 cm
Colour: Grey, white and green
Issued: 01/90 in a limited
edition of 950

U.K.: £175.00
U.S.: $350.00
Can.: $350.00

GREYLAGS RISING

Model: B1059
Modeller: Ray Ayres
Size: 8 ½" x 9 ½"
21.6 x 24.0 cm
Colour: Browns, grey, orange
and green
Issued: 04/07 in a limited
edition of 500

U.K.: £200.00
U.S.: $400.00
Can.: $400.00

GROOMER, THE

Model: A7599, 7605
Modeller: Unknown
Height: 4", 10.1 cm
Colour: A7559 Grey
A7605 Ginger
Issued: 06/06 to the present
Series: Feline Fun

U.K.: £ 9.95
U.S.: $20.00
Can.: $20.00

GUINNESS DRAY

Model: B0838, 0838A
Modeller: Ray Ayres
Height: 6 ¼", 15.9 cm
Colour: B0838 Brown horse
B0838A Grey horse
Issued: 06/03 in a limited
edition of 1,250
Series: Classic Collection

U.K.: £425.00
U.S.: $850.00
Can.: $850.00

GYP
(Collie Pup)
Style One

Model: JH15
Modeller: Richard Roberts
Height: 2 ½", 6.4 cm
Colour: Black and white
Issued: 01/87 - 12/93
Series: 1. All Creatures Great
and Small
2. James Herriot's
Favourite Characters

U.K.: £20.00
U.S.: $40.00
Can.: $40.00

GYP
(Collie Pup)
Style Two

Model: A6509
Modeller: Kerry Bell
Height: 3", 7.6 cm
Colour: Black, white and
light brown
Issued: 01/06 to the present
Series: James Herriot
Studio Collection

U.K.: £13.00
U.S.: $25.00
Can.: $25.00

HACKNEY
Style One

Model: L14A, B
Modeller: Anne Wall
Height: 7 ½", 19.1 cm
Colour: A. Bay
B. Bronze
Issued: 07/78 in a limited
edition of 650

	Bay	Bronze
U.K.:	£325.	£150.
U.S.:	$650.	$300.
Can.:	$650.	$300.

HACKNEY
Style Two

Model: 128A, B
Modeller: Anne Wall
Height: 4 ½", 11.9 cm
Colour: A. Bay
B. Black
Issued: 07/92 - 12/94
Series: Agricultural and
Sporting

U.K.: £ 60.00
U.S.: $120.00
Can.: $120.00

HACKNEY, Action
Style One
Model: B0791
Modeller: Anne Wall
Height: 10", 25.4 cm
Colour: Bay horse; black harness
Issued: 01/03 in a limited edition of 950
Series: Classic Collection

U.K.: £200.00
U.S.: $400.00
Can.: $400.00

HACKNEY, Action
Style Two
Model: B1010
Modeller: David Mayer
Size: 17 ¾" x 14 ½"
45.0 x 36.2 cm
Colour: Bay horse, green base
Issued: 06/06 in a limited edition og 150

U.K.: £1,000.00
U.S.: $2,000.00
Can.: $2,000.00

HALCYON DAYS
(Kingfishers)
Model: L115
Modeller: Ray Ayres
Height: 20 ½", 52.1 cm
Colour: Blue, orange, brown and green
Issued: 01/92 in a limited edition of 750
Series: Nature's Kingdom

U.K.: £ 500.00
U.S.: $1,000.00
Can.: $1,000.00

HALLOA AWAY
(Jumping huntsman and three hounds)
Model: L104
Modeller: Anne Wall
Height: 11 ½", 29.2 cm
Colour: Bay and red
Issued: Autumn 1990 in a limited edition of 500

U.K.: £ 800.00
U.S.: $1,600.00
Can.: $1,600.00

HAPPY DAYS
(Field mice)
Model: BCM04
Modeller: Ray Ayres
Height: 3 ¼", 8.3 cm
Colour: Brown, beige and green
Issued: 01/91 - 12/95
Series: The Country Mouse

U.K.: £ 65.00
U.S.: $125.00
Can.: $125.00

HARBOUR LIFE
(Great black-backed gull, herring gull, cormorant, goldeneye drake and redshank)
Model: BS3
Modeller: Richard Roberts
Height: 6 ½", 16.5 cm
Colour: Black, white and beige
Issued: 01/87 - 12/88
Series: Birds of the Seashore

U.K.: £100.00
U.S.: $200.00
Can.: $200.00

HARD TIMES
(Vole in the snow)
Model: BCM01
Modeller: Ray Ayres
Height: 5", 12.7 cm
Colour: Light brown and pink
Issued: 01/91 - 12/92
Series: The Country Mouse

U.K.: £ 50.00
U.S.: $100.00
Can.: $100.00

HARE
Style One
Model: 002
Modeller: Ray Ayres
Height: 4", 10.1 cm
Colour: Brown and white
Issued: 07/78 - 12/82
Series: Mammals

U.K.: £ 75.00
U.S.: $150.00
Can.: $150.00

HARE
Style Two

Model:	JB2
Modeller:	Judy Boyt
Height:	7", 17.8 cm
Colour:	Brown
Issued:	07/83 - 12/85
Series:	Judy Boyt Woodland

U.K.:	£ 75.00
U.S.:	$150.00
Can.:	$150.00

HARE
Style Three

Model:	ML03
Modeller:	Mairi Laing Hunt
Height:	6 ¼", 15.9 cm
Colour:	Brown
Issued:	01/88 - 12/90
Series:	Woodland

U.K.:	£ 65.00
U.S.:	$125.00
Can.:	$125.00

HARE, Running

Model:	144
Modeller:	David Walton
Height:	6", 15.0 cm
Colour:	Reddish-brown
Issued:	01/91 - 12/92

U.K.:	£ 75.00
U.S.:	$150.00
Can.:	$150.00

HARMONY

Model:	K232
Designer:	Ben Black
Modeller:	David Geenty
Height:	11", 27.9 cm
Colour:	White, yellow and red
Issued:	01/88 in a limited edition of 950
Series:	Ben Black's Garden of Clowns

U.K.:	£225.00
U.S.:	$450.00
Can.:	$450.00

HARVEST HOME

Model:	B0661
Modeller:	Kirsty Armstrong
Height:	17 ¼", 44.0 cm
Colour:	Golden brown, brown, reddish-brown, white, yellow, green and blue
Issued:	06/01 - 05/02
Series:	Annual BFA Society Member-only Figurine

U.K.:	£125.00
U.S.:	$250.00
Can.:	$250.00

HARVEST MOUSE

Model:	027
Modeller:	Ray Ayres
Height:	2 ¾", 7.0 cm
Colour:	Golden brown and white
Issued:	01/83 - 12/84
Series:	Mice by Ray Ayres

U.K.:	£100.00
U.S.:	$200.00
Can.:	$200.00

HARVEST PEACE

Model:	B0103
Modeller:	Ray Ayres
Height:	2 ¼", 5.7 cm
Colour:	Golden brown, white, red, green and brown
Issued:	06/02
Series:	Instant Membership Kit

U.K.:	£12.00
U.S.:	$25.00
Can.:	$25.00

HARVESTING

Model:	L62
Modeller:	Judy Boyt
Height:	8", 20.3 cm
Colour:	Brown, tan, yellow and red
Issued:	01/84 in a limited edition of 350

U.K.:	£1,250.00
U.S.:	$2,500.00
Can.:	$2,500.00

HAULING OUT
(Field marshall tractor)

Model:	JH98
Modeller:	Ray Ayres
Height:	7", 17.8 cm
Colour:	Green, black, browns, blue and silver
Issued:	01/95 in a limited edition of 1,500
Series:	All Creatures Great and Small
U.K.:	£1,000.00
U.S.:	$2,000.00
Can.:	$2,000.00

HAVING 10
(Shepherd, collie and bearded collie)

Model:	B1079
Modeller:	Hans Kendrick
Size:	6 ¾" x 8 ¼" 17.2 x 21.0 cm
Colour:	Black, white, grey and green
Issued:	06/07 in a limited edition of 950
U.K.:	£180.00
U.S.:	$350.00
Can.:	$350.00

HAWAIIAN OR NE-NE GOOSE AND GOSLINGS

Model:	PS02
Modeller:	Richard Roberts
Height:	9", 22.9 cm
Colour:	Brown, grey, white and black
Issued:	01/91 in a limited edition of 1,850
Series:	Peter Scott Memorial Appeal (WWF)
U.K.:	£200.00
U.S.:	$400.00
Can.:	$400.00

HAY BALING

Model:	B0738
Modeller:	Ray Ayres
Height:	8 ½" x 24", 21.6 x 61.0 cm
Colour:	Blue, black, red, yellow and green
Issued:	01/02 in a limited edition of 2,002
Series:	Classic Collection
U.K.:	£425.00
U.S.:	$850.00
Can.:	$850.00

HAY BOGIE

Model:	B0698A
Modeller:	Ray Ayres
Size:	9" x 15" 22.9 x 38.1 cm
Colour:	Black horse, white legs
Issued:	06/04 in a limited edition of 950
U.K.:	£375.00
U.S.:	$750.00
Can.:	$750.00

Note: Gold ed. nos. 1-350
Standard ed. nos 351-950

HAY CUTTING STARTS TODAY
(Gold Edition)

Model:	B0405
Modeller:	Ray Ayres
Height:	5 ¼", 13.3 cm
Colour:	Light brown, black, white, tan, red and green
Issued:	09/99 in a limited edition of 350
Varieties:	Standard Edition B0405A
U.K.:	£375.00
U.S.:	$750.00
Can.:	$750.00

Note: Issued nos. 1-350.

(Standard Edition)

Model:	B0405A
Modeller:	Ray Ayres
Height:	5 ¼", 13.3 cm
Colour:	Brown, black, white, tan and green
Issued:	06/00 in a limited edition of 600
Varieties:	Gold Edition B0405
U.K.:	£350.00
U.S.:	$700.00
Can.:	$700.00

Note: Issued nos. 351-950.

HAY TURNING
(Massey Ferguson Tractor and Wuffler)

Model:	JH110
Modeller:	Ray Ayres
Height:	6 ¼", 15.9 cm
Colour:	Red, amber, black and white
Issued:	01/96 in a limited edition of 1,750
Series:	1. All Creatures Great and Small 2. J. Herriot Collection
U.K.:	£ 625.00
U.S.:	$1,250.00
Can.:	$1,250.00

HAYWAIN (THE)
(Haymaking)

Model:	JH73
Modeller:	Anne Wall
Height:	6 ½", 16.5 cm
Colour:	Grey, yellow, white and black
Issued:	01/93 in a limited edition of 1,500
Series:	All Things Wise and Wonderful
U.K.:	£ 500.00
U.S.:	$1,000.00
Can.:	$1,000.00

HEAD TO HEAD
(Lambs)

Model:	JH106A, B, C, D
Modeller:	David Walton
Height:	2 ¼", 5.7 cm
Colour:	A. Black-faced
	B. White-faced
	C. Herdwick
	D. Suffolk
Issued:	01/96 - 12/97
Series:	1. Every Living Thing
	2. J. Herriot Collection
U.K.:	£35.00
U.S.:	$70.00
Can.:	$70.00

HEDGE LAYING

Model:	JH65
Modeller:	Ray Ayres
Height:	7", 17.8 cm
Colour:	Blue, white, brown and black
Issued:	01/92 in a limited edition of 1,750
Series:	All Creatures Great and Small
U.K.:	£250.00
U.S.:	$500.00
Can.:	$500.00

HEDGEHOG
Style One

Model:	004
Modeller:	Anne Wall
Height:	3 ½", 8.9 cm
Colour:	Browns
Issued:	01/77 - 12/82
Series:	Mammals
U.K.:	£30.00
U.S.:	$60.00
Can.:	$60.00

HEDGEHOG
Style Two

Model:	JB1
Modeller:	Judy Boyt
Height:	3", 7.6 cm
Colour:	Brown
Issued:	07/83 - 12/85
Series:	Judy Boyt Woodland
U.K.:	£40.00
U.S.:	$80.00
Can.:	$80.00

HEDGEHOG
Style Three

Model:	ML04
Modeller:	Mairi Laing Hunt
Height:	3", 7.6 cm
Colour:	Brown, green and red
Issued:	01/88 - 12/90
Series:	Woodland
U.K.:	£ 55.00
U.S.:	$110.00
Can.:	$110.00

HEDGEHOG
Style Four

Model:	148/B148
Modeller:	David Walton
Height:	3 ¾", 9.5 cm
Colour:	Browns, green and white
Issued:	01/92 - 12/97
U.K.:	£30.00
U.S.:	$60.00
Can.:	$60.00

HEDGEHOG
Style Five

Model:	M28
Modeller:	David Walton
Height:	2 ¾", 7.0 cm
Colour:	Browns
Issued:	01/93 - 12/95
Series:	Miniature Wildlife
U.K.:	£25.00
U.S.:	$50.00
Can.:	$50.00

HEDGEHOG AND PLATE

Model:	Unknown
Modeller:	Victor Hayton
Height:	3 ½", 8.9 cm
Colour:	Brown and off-white
Issued:	01/77 - 06/78

U.K.:	£ 90.00
U.S.:	$175.00
Can.:	$175.00

HEDGEHOG AND WREN

Model:	B0206
Modeller:	David Walton
Height:	5", 12.7 cm
Colour:	Browns, red and green
Issued:	06/97 - 06/99
Series:	First Encounters

U.K.:	£40.00
U.S.:	$80.00
Can.:	$80.00

HEDGEHOG AND YOUNG

Model:	WW25
Modeller:	David Walton
Height:	2", 5.0 cm
Colour:	Browns
Issued:	07/94 - 12/96
Series:	Miniature (WWF)

U.K.:	£15.00
U.S.:	$30.00
Can.:	$30.00

HEDGEHOG FAMILY
Style One

Model:	WW12
Modeller:	Richard Wawrzesta
Height:	3 ½", 8.9 cm
Colour:	Browns, grey, cream and green
Issued:	01/87 - 12/87
Series:	Family Life (WWF)

U.K.:	£35.00
U.S.:	$70.00
Can.:	$70.00

HEDGEHOG FAMILY
Style Two

Model:	B0222
Modeller:	Kirsty Armstrong
Height:	4 ¼", 10.8 cm
Colour:	Brown, cream and green
Issued:	01/98 - 12/99
Series:	Wildlife Families (WWF)

U.K.:	£ 65.00
U.S.:	$125.00
Can.:	$125.00

HEDGEHOGS
(Adult and Three Young)
Style One

Model:	143
Modeller:	David Walton
Height:	3 ¾", 9.5 cm
Colour:	Browns and greens
Issued:	01/91 - 12/94

U.K.:	£ 65.00
U.S.:	$125.00
Can.:	$125.00

HEDGEHOGS
(Adult and Three Young)
Style Two

Model:	RW33
Modeller:	David Walton
Height:	3 ½", 8.9 cm
Colour:	Browns
Issued:	07/93 - 12/95
Series:	Wildlife Families (WWF)

U.K.:	£35.00
U.S.:	$70.00
Can.:	$70.00

HEDGEROW ADVENTURE
(Hedgehogs)

Model:	B0949
Modeller:	Ray Ayres
Size:	7" x 9 ¼" 17.8 x 23.5 cm
Colour:	Browns, yellow and green
Issued:	06/05 - 05/06
Series:	Annual BFA Society Member-only Figurine

U.K.:	£150.00
U.S.:	$300.00
Can.:	$300.00

HELPING OUT
(Border Collie Pups)

Model: B0202
Modeller: Anne Wall
Height: 6 ¼", 15.9 cm
Colour: Black, white, orange, green and brown
Issued: 06/97 in a limited edition of 1,500
Series: 1. Every Living Thing
2. J. Herriot Collection

U.K.: £125.00
U.S.: $250.00
Can.: $250.00

HEN AND CHICKS

Model: 739464, 739472, A0162
Modeller: Russell Willis
Height: 9", 22.9 cm
Colour: 739464 White and tan
739472 Brown
A0162 Black / white
Issued: 739464 01/00-12/02
739472 01/00-12/02
A0162 06/00-12/02
Series: 1. Birds And ...
2. Farmyard Friends

U.K.: £ 75.00
U.S.: $150.00
Can.: $150.00

HEN PHEASANT AND CHICKS

Model: RB22
Modeller: Ray Ayres
Height: 2 ½", 6.4 cm
Colour: Browns
Issued: 01/91 - 12/93

U.K.: £40.00
U.S.: $80.00
Can.: $80.00

Note: Model RB22 was combined with RB21 to form RB23.

HERBERT
(Lamb)
Style One

Model: JH14
Modeller: Richard Roberts
Height: 2", 5.0 cm
Colour: White and black
Issued: 01/87 - 12/92
Series: 1. All Creatures Great and Small
2. James Herriot's Favourite Characters

U.K.: £25.00
U.S.: $50.00
Can.: $50.00

HERBERT
(Lamb)
Style Two

Model: A6515, 6738
Modeller: Unknown
Height: 3 ¼", 8.3 cm
Colour: A6515 White
A6738 White / black
Issued: 01/06 to the present
Series: James Herriot Studio Collection

U.K.: £13.00
U.S.: $25.00
Can.: $25.00

HERD BULL

Model: B0004
Modeller: Richard Roberts
Height: 8", 20.3 cm
Colour: Grey
Issued: 01/97 in a limited edition of 1,250
Series: An African Safari

U.K.: £ 75.00
U.S.: $150.00
Can.: $150.00

HERDWICK EWE

Model: 118
Modeller: Ray Ayres
Height: 4", 10.1 cm
Colour: Brown and white
Issued: 01/90 - 12/91
Series: Agricultural and Sporting

U.K.: £225.00
U.S.: $450.00
Can.: $450.00

HERDWICK EWE AND LAMB
Style One

Model: L79
Modeller: Ray Ayres
Height: 7", 17.8 cm
Colour: Dark grey and white
Issued: 01/87 in a limited edition of 500
Series: Special Interest

U.K.: £ 500.00
U.S.: $1,000.00
Can.: $1,000.00

HERDWICK EWE AND LAMB
Style Two
Model:	A1888
Modeler:	Lesley McKenzie
Height:	4 ¾", 12.1 cm
Colour:	Black and white
Issued:	06/02 - 12/03
Series:	Sheep Breeds
U.K.:	£45.00
U.S.:	$90.00
Can.:	$90.00

HERDWICK EWE AND LAMBS
Model:	125
Modeller:	Ray Ayres
Height:	4", 10.1 cm
Colour:	Brown-grey, black and white
Issued:	01/92 - 12/93
Series:	Agricultural and Sporting
U.K.:	£225.00
U.S.:	$450.00
Can.:	$450.00

HERDWICK RAM
Model:	A1887
Modeller:	Lesley McKenzie
Height:	5", 12.7 cm
Colour:	Black and white
Issued:	06/02 - 12/03
Series:	Sheep Breeds
U.K.:	£30.00
U.S.:	$60.00
Can.:	$60.00

HERDWICK TUP
Model:	B0705
Modeller:	Ray Ayres
Height:	7", 17.8 cm
Colour:	Black, cream, white, green and grey
Issued:	01/02 in a limited edition of 750
Series:	Classic Collection
U.K.:	£125.00
U.S.:	$250.00
Can.:	$250.00

HEREFORD BULL
Style One
Model:	L41
Modeller:	Ray Ayres
Height:	6 ¼", 15.9 cm
Colour:	Reddish-brown and white
Issued:	07/82 in a limited edition of 1,500
U.K.:	£475.00
U.S.:	$950.00
Can.:	$950.00

HEREFORD BULL
Style Two
Model:	B0772
Modeller:	Ray Ayres
Height:	6 ½", 16.5 cm
Colour:	Reddish-brown and white
Issued:	06/02 in a limited edition of 950
Series:	Classic Collection
U.K.:	£125.00
U.S.:	$250.00
Can.:	$250.00

HEREFORD
Style Three

		BULL	CALF	COW
Model:		A4580	A4586	A4583
Modeller:	Ray Ayres			
Height:		5" 12.7 cm	3 ¼" 8.3 cm	4 ½" 11.9 cm
Colour:	Reddish-brown and white			
Issued:	01/04 to the present			
Series:	BFA Pottery Company			
U.K.:		£25.00	£14.95	£25.00
U.S.:		$50.00	$30.00	$50.00
Can.:		$50.00	$30.00	$50.00

HEREFORD COW AND CALF

Model: B0835
Modeller: Ray Ayres
Height: 6", 15.0 cm
Colour: Reddish-brown, white and green
Issued: 01/04 in a limited edition of 950
Series: Classic Collection

U.K.: £125.00
U.S.: $250.00
Can.: $250.00

HERON

Model: A0007
Modeller: Richard Roberts
Height: 9", 22.9 cm
Colour: White, black, orange, yellow and green
Issued: 01/00 - 06/03
Series: Reflections

U.K.: £ 50.00
U.S.: $100.00
Can.: $100.00

HIDDEN TREASURES
(Badger and squirrels

Model: B1026
Modeller: Ray Ayres
Size: 9 ½" x 10 ½" 24.0 x 26.7 cm
Colour: Grey, white, browns and green
Issued: 01/07 in a limited edition of 350

U.K.: £195.00
U.S.: $400.00
Can.: $400.00

HIDING PLACE (THE)
(Cock and Hen Pheasant)

Model: L128
Modeller: Frank DiVita
Height: 11 ½", 29.2 cm
Colour: Reddish-brown, browns and beige
Issued: 01/93 in a limited edition of 250
Series: Masterpiece

U.K.: £ 750.00
U.S.: $1,500.00
Can.: $1,500.00

HIGH AND DRY
(Otter and Two Cubs)

Model: MTR09
Modeller: Ray Ayres
Height: 6 ½", 16.5 cm
Colour: Brown and white
Issued: 01/96 in a limited edition of 2,500
Series: Masters of the River

U.K.: £ 75.00
U.S.: $150.00
Can.: $150.00

HIGH BROWSERS
(Giraffe and Calf)

Model: L139
Modeller: Richard Roberts
Height: 15 ¾", 40.0 cm
Colour: Light and dark brown and white
Issued: 01/94 in a limited edition of 850
Series: WWFN

U.K.: £300.00
U.S.: $600.00
Can.: $600.00

HIGHLAND (Pony)
Style Two

Model: A6535
Modeller: Unknown
Height: 5 ¼", 13.3 cm
Colour: Grey
Issued: 06/06 to the present

U.K.: £20.00
U.S.: $40.00
Can.: $40.00

Note: For Style One see page 129.

HIGHLAND BULL
Style One

Model: L78
Modeller: Elizabeth Waugh
Height: 7", 17.8 cm
Colour: Reddish-brown
Issued: 01/87 in a limited edition of 950
Series: Special Interest

U.K.: £400.00
U.S.: $800.00
Can.: $800.00

HIGHLAND BULL
Style Two

Model:	A2311
Modeller:	Lesley McKenzie
Height:	5 ½", 14.0 cm
Colour:	Reddish-brown and light brown
Issued:	01/03 - 12/06
Series:	Cattle Breeds
U.K.:	£40.00
U.S.:	$80.00
Can.:	$80.00

HIGHLAND BULL
Style Three

Model:	B0808
Modeller:	Jack Crewdson
Height:	8 ¾", 22.2 cm
Colour	Reddish-brown, white and green
Issued:	06/03 in a limited edition of 500
Series:	Classic Collection
U.K.:	£200.00
U.S.:	$400.00
Can.:	$400.00

HIGHLAND		BULL	CALF	COW
		Style Four		
Model:		A5233	A5236	A5276
Modeller:	Lelsey Mackenzie			
Height:		4 ¼"	3"	4"
		10.8 cm	7.6 cm	10.1 cm
Colour:	Reddish brown and cream			
Issued:	01/05 to the present			
Series:	BFA Pottery Company			
U.K.:		£25.00	£14.95	£25.00
U.S.:		$50.00	$30.00	$50.00
Can.:		$50.00	$30.00	$50.00

HIGHLAND BULL, Lying

Model:	A4068
Modeller:	Lesley McKenzie
Height:	4 ¼", 10.8 cm
Colour:	Reddish-brown, cream, grey and green
Issued:	06-04 - 12/06
U.K.:	£ 60.00
U.S.:	$120.00
Can.:	$120.00

HIGHLAND CHALLENGE
(Pair of stags fighting)

Model:	L127
Modeller:	Mairi Laing Hunt
Height:	6", 15.0 cm
Colour:	Reddish-brown, black and grey
Issued:	01/93 in a limited edition of 500
U.K.:	£ 500.00
U.S.:	$1,000.00
Can.:	$1,000.00

Photograph not
available
at press time

HIGHLAND CHALLENGE
(Stags in Combat)

Model:	L86
Modeller:	Mairi Laing Hunt
Height:	9", 22.9 cm
Colour:	Bronze
Issued:	01/88 in a limited edition of 200
Series:	Studio Bronze
U.K.:	£ 500.00
U.S.:	$1,000.00
Can.:	$1,000.00

Note: Resin model.

HIGHLAND CHASE
(Deer)

Model:	B0958
Modeller:	Richard Roberts
Height:	11 ½" x 12 ½"
	29.2 x 31.7 cm
Colour:	Reddish-brown, grey, browns and green
Issued:	06/05 in a limited edition of 500
Series:	Classic Collection
U.K.:	£295.00
U.S.:	$600.00
Can.:	$600.00

HIGHLAND COW AND CALF
Style One
Model:	167/B167
Modeller:	Anne Wall
Height:	5 ¼", 13.3 cm
Colour:	Reddish-brown and pale brown
Issued:	07/95 - 12/00
Series:	Agricultural and Sporting
U.K.:	£100.00
U.S.:	$200.00
Can.:	$200.00

HIGHLAND COW AND CALF
Style Two
Model:	A2312
Modeller:	Lesley McKenzie
Height:	5 ¾", 14.6 cm
Colour:	Reddish-brown and light brown
Issued:	01/03 - 06/06
Series:	Cattle Breeds
U.K.:	£ 50.00
U.S.:	$100.00
Can.:	$100.00

HIGHLAND FAMILY
(Red Deer Hind and Calf)
Model:	B0306
Modeller:	Richard Roberts
Height:	9 ¾", 24.7cm
Colour:	Reddish-brown, mauve and green
Issued:	06/98 - 12/99
U.K.:	£225.00
U.S.:	$450.00
Can.:	$450.00

HIGHLAND MAJESTY
(Red Stag)
Model:	B0220
Modeller:	Richard Roberts
Height:	12", 30.5 cm
Colour:	Reddish-brown, mauve and green
Issued:	01/98 to the present
U.K.:	£210.00
U.S.:	$425.00
Can.:	$425.00

HIGHLAND MARE AND FOAL
Model:	A2691
Modeller:	Anne Wall
Height:	6", 15.0 cm
Colour:	Dun mare, chestnut foal, green base
Issued:	01/04 - 06/06
Series:	Horse Breeds
U.K.:	£40.00
U.S.:	$80.00
Can.:	$80.00

HIGHLAND PONY
Style One
Model:	NP2
Modeller:	Judy Boyt
Height:	5 ½", 14.0 cm
Colour:	Dun
Issued:	01/82 - 12/84
Series:	Native Ponies of Britain
U.K.:	£425.00
U.S.:	$850.00
Can.:	$850.00

Note: For Style Two see page 127.

HIGHLAND SECRET
(Scottish wildcat)
Model:	B0948
Modeller:	Ray Ayres
Height:	6", 15.0 cm
Colour:	Grey, black, brown, green and purple
Issued:	01/05 in a limited edition of 250
Series:	Classic Event Figurine
U.K.:	£150.00
U.S.:	$300.00
Can.:	$300.00

HIGHLAND STALLION
Model:	A4069
Modeller:	Anne Wall
Height:	6 ¼, 15.9 cm
Colour:	Light dapple grey and green
Issued:	01/05 - 06/06
Series:	Stallions
U.K.:	£40.00
U.S.:	$80.00
Can.:	$80.00

HIPPO

Model:	B0672, B0673, B0674
Modeller:	Richard Roberts
Height:	4", 10.1 cm
Colour:	B0672 Slate blue
	B0673 Stone
	B0674 Gold
Issued:	01/01 - 12/01
Series:	Cubist Africa
U.K.:	£30.00
U.S.:	$60.00
Can.:	$60.00

HIPPO AND BABY
Style One

Model:	RW22
Modeller:	Richard Wawrzesta
Height:	3 ¾", 9.5 cm
Colour:	Blue-grey
Issued:	01/92 - 12/95
Series:	Endangered Species
	(WWF)
U.K.:	£40.00
U.S.:	$80.00
Can.:	$80.00

HIPPO AND BABY
Style Two

Model:	A2741
Modeller:	David Mayer
Height:	4 ¼", 10.8 cm
Colour:	Dark grey, brown
	and green
Issued:	06/05 - 12/06
Series:	Wild World
U.K.:	£ 50.00
U.S.:	$100.00
Can.:	$100.00

HOBBY

Model:	A1470
Modeller:	Russell Willis
Height:	5 ½", 14.0 cm
Colour:	Blue-grey, white, black,
	yellow and green
Issued:	01/02 - 12/04
Series:	Birds of Prey
U.K.:	£30.00
U.S.:	$60.00
Can.:	$60.00

HOBBY AND DRAGONFLY

Model:	RB33
Modeller:	David Burnham Smith
Height:	12", 30.5 cm
Colour:	Grey-brown, rust
	and white
Issued:	01/92 - 12/93
U.K.:	£250.00
U.S.:	$500.00
Can.:	$500.00

HOG HEAVEN
(Sow and Piglets)

Model:	A1015
Modeller:	Kirsty Armstrong
Height:	5", 12.7 cm
Colour:	Pink, white, black,
	green and brown
Issued:	01/03 - 06/05
Series:	James Herriot
	Studio Collection
U.K.:	£40.00
U.S.:	$80.00
Can.:	$80.00

HOG WASH

Model:	JH56A, B
Modeller:	Anne Butler
Height:	4 ¼", 10.8 cm
Colour:	A. Gloucester Old Spot
	B. Landrace
Issued:	A. 01/91 - 12/94
	B. 01/91 - 12/92
Series:	All Creatures Great
	and Small

	Gloucester	Landrace
U.K.:	£45.	£ 55.
U.S.:	$90.	$110.
Can.:	$90.	$110.

HOLDING HER GROUND
(Ewe, lamb and border collie)

Model:	B0198
Modeller:	Ray Ayres
Height:	6 ¾", 15.9 cm
Colour:	Cream, black, white,
	mauve and grey
Issued:	06/97 in a limited
	edition of 2,500
Series:	1. Every Living Thing
	2. J. Herriot Collection
U.K.:	£125.00
U.S.:	$250.00
Can.:	$250.00

HOLSTEIN BULL

Model: B0308
Modeller: Kirsty Armstrong
Height: 7", 17.8 cm
Colour: White and black
Issued: 06/98 in a limited
        edition of 1,750
Series: 1. Agricultural and
           Sporting
        2. The County Show

U.K.: £125.00
U.S.: $250.00
Can.: $250.00

HOLSTEIN COW

Model: B1072
Modeller: Kirsty Armstrong
Size: 7" x 8 ¾"
      17.8 x 22.2 cm
Colour: Black, white and green
Issued: 04/07 in a limited
        edition of 750

U.K.: £150.00
U.S.: $300.00
Can.: $300.00

HOLSTEIN FRIESIAN

	CALF	COW
Model:	A4601	A4600
Modeller:	L. Mackenzie	K. Armstrong
Height:	3 ¼", 8.3 cm	4 ¼", 10.8 cm
Colour:	Black and white	
Issued:	06/04 to the present	
Series:	BFA Pottery Company	
U.K.:	£14.95	£25.00
U.S.:	$30.00	$50.00
Can.:	$30.00	$50.00

HOLSTEIN FRIESIAN COW AND CALF

Model: B0309
Modeller: Kirsty Armstrong
Height: 6 ¼", 15.9 cm
Colour: Black and white
Issued: 06/98 - in a limited
        edition of 1,750
Series: 1. Agricultural and
           Sporting
        2. The County Show

U.K.: £150.00
U.S.: $300.00
Can.: $300.00

HOLSTEIN FRIESIAN COW AND NEW CALF

Model: A1466
Modeller: Lesley McKenzie
Height: 5 ½", 14.0 cm
Colour: Black, white and green
Issued: 01/03 - 06/06
Series: Cattle Breeds

U.K.: £ 55.00
U.S.: $110.00
Can.: $110.00

HOLSTEIN FRIESIAN COW, Lying

Model: A5273
Modeller: Lesley McKenzie
Height: 4", 10.1 cm
Colour: Black, white, green,
        yellow and fawn
Issued: 01/05 - 12/06

U.K.: £ 65.00
U.S.: $130.00
Can.: $130.00

HOME COMFORTS
(Hen house, hen and chicks)

Model: A1016
Modeller: Kirsty Armstrong
Height: 3 ¼", 8.3 cm
Colour: White, black, yellow
        and green
Issued: 01/02 - 06/05
Series: James Herriot
        Studio Collection

U.K.: £20.00
U.S.: $40.00
Can.: $40.00

HOME FROM SCHOOL
(Boy on Clydesdale)

Model: B0403
Modeller: Ray Ayres
Height: 8", 20.3 cm
Colour: Brown, white, black,
            grey and green
Issued: 1999 in a limited
            edition of 500

U.K.:   £250.00
U.S.: $500.00
Can.: $500.00

HOMEWARD BOUND
(Clydesdale horses)

Model: B1029
Modeller: Anne Wall
Size: 6 ¾" x 13 ½"
            17.2 x 34.3 cm
Colour: Grey, brown, white
            and black
Issued: 04/07 in a limited
            edition of 650

U.K.:   £295.00
U.S.: $600.00
Can.: $600.00

HORSE GALLOPING

Model: B0624, 25, 26, 27
Modeller: Richard Roberts
Height: 13 ½", 34.3 cm
Colour: B0624   Walnut
            B0625   Stone
            B0626   Slate blue
            B0627   Gold
Issued: 06/00 - 12/01
Series: Cubist Horses

U.K.:   £ 65.00
U.S.: $125.00
Can.: $125.00

HORSE LYING

Model: B0620, 21, 22, 23
Modeller: Richard Roberts
Height: 5 ½", 14.0 cm
Colour: B0620   Walnut
            B0621   Stone
            B0622   Slate blue
            B0623 - Gold
Issued: 06/00 - 12/01
Series: Cubist Horses

U.K.:   £40.00
U.S.: $80.00
Can.: $80.00

HORSE REARING

Model: B0616, 17, 18, 19
Modeller: Richard Roberts
Height: 13 ½", 34.3 cm
Colour: B0616   Walnut
            B0617   Stone
            B0618   Slate blue
            B0619   Gold
Issued: 06/00 - 12/01
Series: Cubist Horses

U.K.:   £ 65.00
U.S.: $125.00
Can.: $125.00

HOT WORK
(Shepherd Clipping)

Model: JH95
Modeller: Anne Butler
Height: 6", 15.0 cm
Colour: White, blue, brown
            and black
Issued: 01/94 - 12/95
Series: All Creatures Great
            and Small

U.K.:   £ 80.00
U.S.: $160.00
Can.: $160.00

HOUNDS AWAY
(Huntsman, horse and hounds)

Model: B1070, 1070A
Modeller: Anne Wall
Height: 10" x 14 ½"
            25.4 x 36.8 cm
Colour: B1070   Bay horse
            B1070A Grey horse
Issued: 01/07 in a limited
            edition of 950

U.K.:   £350.00
U.S.: $700.00
Can.: $700.00

HOUSEMOUSE ON TRAP

Model: None
Modeller: Victor Hayton
Height: 3 ½", 8.9 cm
Colour: 1. Browns
            2. Bronze
Issued: 01/77 in a limited
            edition of 500

	Browns	Bronze
U.K.:	£175.	£ 80.
U.S.:	$350.	$160.
Can.:	$350.	$160.

HUNGRY MOUTHS TO FEED
(Blue Tits)

Model: CEV01
Modeller: Ray Ayres
Height: 3", 7.6 cm
Colour: Blue, yellow, white,
brown and green
Issued: 03/92 - 12/94
Series: Event Special

U.K.: £35.00
U.S.: $70.00
Can.: $70.00

HURDLER, THE

Model: L51
Modeller: David Geenty
Height: 8 ½", 21.6 cm
Colour: Multicoloured
Issued: 01/83 - 12/95
Series: 1. Race Horses
2. Special Interest

U.K.: £425.00
U.S.: $850.00
Can.: $850.00

Note: This model was individually
hand-painted to order.

HUSSAR OFFICER
(WATERLOO)

Model: MF04
Modeller: David Burnham Smith
Height 13", 33.0 cm
Colour: Blue, white and black
Issued: 01/92 in a limited
edition of 750
Series: The Military Collection

U.K.: £225.00
U.S.: $450.00
Can.: $450.00

I'M HUNGRY
(Horse and Rider)

Model: A0537
Modeller: Anne Wall
Height: 4 ½", 11.9 cm
Colour: Brown, white, black
and cream
Issued: 01/01 - 12/05
Series: Hay Days

U.K.: £25.00
U.S.: $50.00
Can.: $50.00

I'M SO STUBBORN
(Horse and Rider)

Model: A1242
Modeller: Anne Wall
Height: 5 ¼", 13.3 cm
Colour: Brown, white, red,
cream, blue and green
Issued: 01/02 - 06/06
Series: Hay Days

U.K.: £25.00
U.S.: $50.00
Can.: $50.00

IN A FLAP
(Hen and border collie pup)

Model: A5915
Modeller: Unknown
Height: 4", 10.1 cm
Colour: Black, white, brown,
yellow and red
Issued: 06/05 - 06/07
Series: James Herriot
Studio Collection

U.K.: £32.00
U.S.: $65.00
Can.: $65.00

IN A SUNNY GLADE
(Roe Deer Doe and Two Fawns)

Model: B0255
Modeller: Ray Ayres
Height: 6", 15.0 cm
Colour: Red-brown, grey-white
Issued: 06/98 - 05/99
Series: Annual Society Figurine
(1998/99)

U.K.: £100.00
U.S.: $200.00
Can.: $200.00

IN CLOVER
(Pig and piglet)

Model: A3705
Modeller: Kerry Bell
Height: 4 ½", 11.9 cm
Colour: Pink, brown, black,
green and red
Issued: 01/04 - 06/07
Series: James Herriot
Studio Collection

U.K.: £40.00
U.S.: $80.00
Can.: $80.00

IN FROM THE COLD
(Collies and Cooking Range)

Model: JH62
Modeller: David Walton
Height: 6 ½", 16.5 cm
Colour: Black, white, cream and golden-brown
Issued: 09/91 - 12/97
Series: 1. All Things Wise and Wonderful
2. J. Herriot Collection

U.K.: £125.00
U.S.: $250.00
Can.: $250.00

IN THE POTTING SHED
(Robin Nesting in Old Paint Tin)

Model: B0045
Modeller: Ray Ayres
Height: 7", 17.8 cm
Colour: Red, brown and grey
Issued: 06/97 in a limited edition of 1,500
Series: Border Classic Birds

U.K.: £ 75.00
U.S.: $150.00
Can.: $150.00

IN THE SHADE
(Border Collie Pups)

Model: B0275
Modeller: Ray Ayres
Height: 7 ¾", 19.7 cm
Colour: Black, white and grey
Issued: 01/98 - 12/00
Varieties: In the Shade (Lamp) B0218
Series: All Creatures Great and Small

U.K.: £125.00
U.S.: $250.00
Can.: $250.00

IN THE SHADE (Lamp)
(Border Collie Pups)

Model: B0218
Modeller: Ray Ayres
Height: 18", 45.7 cm
Colour: Black, white and grey
Issued: 01/98 - 12/99
Varieties: In the Shade (Figure) B0275
Series: All Creatures Great and Small

U.K.: £175.00
U.S.: $350.00
Can.: $350.00

Note: Only available in U.K.

IN THE WINGS

Model: K39
Designer: Ben Black
Modeller: David Geenty
Height: 11 ½", 29.2 cm
Colour: White, pink and yellow
Issued: 01/88 in a limited edition of 3,500
Series: Ben Black's intermission Series

U.K.: £150.00
U.S.: $300.00
Can.: $300.00

INFANTRY MAN OF THE LINE
(WATERLOO)

Model: MF05
Modeller: David Burnham Smith
Height: 12", 30.5 cm
Colour: Red, grey and white
Issued: 01/92 in a limited edition of 750
Series: The Military Collection

U.K.: £200.00
U.S.: $400.00
Can.: $400.00

INQUISITIVE
(Cat)

Model: A6890
Modeller: Andrew Edwards
Height: 3", 7.6 cm
Colour: Grey, white, silver and orange
Issued: 06/06 to the present
Series: Cats Round the House

U.K.: £22.00
U.S.: $45.00
Can.: $45.00

INTERLUDE

Model: K42
Designer: Ben Black
Modeller: David Geenty
Height: 4", 10.1 cm
Colour: Multicoloured
Issued: 01/88 in a limited edition of 2,500
Series: Ben Black's Intermission Series

U.K.: £150.00
U.S.: $300.00
Can.: $300.00

IRISH SETTER
(Puppy, Seated)

Model:	PG14
Modeller:	Margaret Turner
Height:	4", 10.1 cm
Colour:	Reddish-brown
Issued:	01/95 - 12/00
Series:	Pups Galore
U.K.:	£15.00
U.S.:	$30.00
Can.:	$30.00

IRISH SETTER, Seated
Style One

Model:	DG24/B0478	
Modeller:	Margaret Turner	
Height:	5 ¾", 14.6 cm	
Colour:	DG24	Red-brown
	B0478	Bronze
Issued:	DG24	07/93-12/01
	B0478	06/99-06/00
Series:	DG24	Dogs Galore
	B0478	Bronze
U.K.:	£25.00	
U.S.:	$50.00	
Can.:	$50.00	

IRISH SETTER, Seated
Style Two

Model:	A3832
Modeller:	Margaret Turner
Height:	6", 15.0 cm
Colour:	Reddish-brown
Issued:	01/04 - 06/06
Series:	Dogs and Pups Galore
U.K.:	£18.00
U.S.:	$35.00
Can.:	$35.00

IRISH SETTER, Standing
Style One

Model:	UK# 059
	USA# 225-127
Modeller:	David Geenty
Height:	6 ½", 16.5 cm
Colour:	Reddish-brown
Issued:	01/80 - 12/82
U.K.:	£100.00
U.S.:	$200.00
Can.:	$200.00

IRISH SETTER, Standing
Style Two

Model:	A1394
Modeller:	Margaret Turner
Height:	6", 15.0 cm
Colour:	Reddish-brown
Issued:	01/02 - 12/05
Varieties:	Also called English Setter (A1395, 96)
Series:	Dogs and pups Galore
U.K.:	£20.00
U.S.:	$40.00
Can.:	$40.00

IRISH SETTER, Trotting

Model:	DL4
Modeller:	Ray Ayres
Height:	4 ¾", 12.1 cm
Colour:	Reddish-brown
Issued:	01/83 - 12/87
Series:	The World of Dogs
U.K.:	£ 75.00
U.S.:	$150.00
Can.:	$150.00

IRISH WOLFHOUND, Seated
Style One

Model:	B0602
Modeller:	Margaret Turner
Height:	6 ¼", 15.9 cm
Colour:	Grey
Issued:	06/00 - 12/01
Series:	Dogs Galore
U.K.:	£30.00
U.S.:	$60.00
Can.:	$60.00

IRISH WOLFHOUND, Seated
Style Two

Model:	A3835
Modeller:	Margaret Turner
Height:	6 ¼", 15.9 cm
Colour:	Shades of light brown and grey
Issued:	01/04 - 06/06
Series:	Dogs and Pups Galore
U.K.:	£25.00
U.S.:	$50.00
Can.:	$50.00

ITCHING TO SCRATCH
(Calf)
Model: JH101A, B, C
Modeller: David Walton
Height: 2 ½", 6.4 cm
Colour: A. Friesian
B. Simmental
C. Charolais
Issued: 01/95 - 12/97
Series: 1. Every Living Thing
2. J. Herriot Collection

U.K.: £25.00
U.S.: $50.00
Can.: $50.00

IT'S MINE
(Golden retreiver puppies)
Model: A7046
Modeller: Barry Snelson
Height: 2 ¾", 7.0 cm
Colour: Yellow, browns,
pink and blue
Issued: 06/06 - 06/07
Series: Puppy Trouble

U.K.: £20.00
U.S.: $40.00
Can.: $40.00

JACK
(Jack Russell terrier)
Model: A6507
Modeller: Kerry Bell
Height: 2 ¼", 5.7 cm
Colour: White, black, tan
and green
Issued: 01/06 to the present
Series: James Herriot
Studio Collection

U.K.: £15.00
U.S.: $30.00
Can.: $30.00

JACK RUSSELL
Model: A6545, 7470, 7471
Modeller: Unknown
Height: 4 ¼", 10.8 cm
Colour: A6545 Black /white
A7470 Tan / white
A7471 Tricolour
Issued: 06/06 - 12/06
Series: BFA Pottery Company

U.K.: £15.00
U.S.: $30.00
Can.: $30.00

JACK RUSSELL FAMILY GROUP
Model: A5887
Modeller: Anne Wall
Height: 2 ¾", 7.0 cm
Colour: Black, white and brown
Issued: 06/05 to the present
Series: Dogs and Pups Galore,
Family Groups

U.K.: £17.50
U.S.: $35.00
Can.: $35.00

JACK RUSSELL TERRIER, Lying
Style One
First Version - Front Paws
Crossed
Model: DG04A
Modeller: Steve McKeown
Height: 3 ¾", 9.5 cm
Colour: A. Tricolour
B. Black and white
C. Brown and white
Issued: 01/91 - 12/94
Series: Dogs Galore

U.K.: £20.00
U.S.: $40.00
Can.: $40.00

JACK RUSSELL TERRIER, Lying
Style One
Second Version - Front Paws
Side by Side
Model: DG04B
Modeller: Steve McKeown
Height: 3 ¾", 9.5 cm
Colour: A. Tricolour
B. Black and white
C. Brown and white
Issued: 01/91 - 12/94
Series: Dogs Galore

U.K.: £20.00
U.S.: $40.00
Can.: $40.00

JACK RUSSELL TERRIER, Lying
Style Two
Model: 208A, B
Modeller: Anne Butler
Height: 2 ½", 6.4 cm
Colour: A. Brown and white
B. Black and white
Issued: 01/92 - 12/93
Series: The World of Dogs

U.K.: £35.00
U.S.: $70.00
Can.: $70.00

JACK RUSSELL TERRIER, Lying Style Three

Model: B0495A, B, C
Modeller: Margaret Turner
Height: 2 ¼, 5.0 cm
Colour: A. Tricolour
B. Black and white
C. Brown and white
Issued: A. 06/99 -12/01
B.-C. 06/99 - 06/01
Series: Pups Galore

U.K.: £12.00
U.S.: $25.00
Can.: $25.00

JACK RUSSELL TERRIER, Lying Style Four

Model: B0498A, B, C
Modeller: Margaret Turner
Height: 2 ½, 5.7 cm
Colour: A. Tricolour
B. Black and white
C. Brown and white
Issued: A. 06/99 - 12/01
B. 06/99 - 06/01
C. 06/99 - 06/01
Series: Dogs Galore

U.K.: £20.00
U.S.: $40.00
Can.: $40.00

JACK RUSSELL TERRIER, Lying Style Five

Model: A3044, 45, 46
Modeller: Unknown
Height: 2 ¼", 5.7 cm
Colour: A3044   Black / white
A3045   Tan / white
A3046   Tricolour
Issued: A3044/45
06/03-12/04
A3046 06/03-12/05
Series: Dogs and Pups Galore

U.K.: £12.00
U.S.: $25.00
Can.: $25.00

JACK RUSSELL TERRIER, Seated (Bitch) Style One

Model: MT05A, B, C
Modeller: Margaret Turner
Height: 5 ½", 14.0 cm
Colour: A. Black and white
B. Brown and white
C. Tricolour
Issued: A. 01/94 - 12/96
B. 01/94 - 12/96
C. 01/94 - 12/98
Series: Dogs by M. Turner

U.K.: £ 50.00
U.S.: $100.00
Can.: $100.00

JACK RUSSELL TERRIER, Seated (Dog) Style Two

Model: MT04A, B, C
Modeller: Margaret Turner
Height: 5 ½", 14.0 cm
Colour: A. Black and white
B. Brown and white
C. Tricolour
Issued: A. 01/94 - 12/96
B. 01/94 - 12/96
C. 01/94 - 12/98
Series: Dogs by M. Turner

U.K.: £ 50.00
U.S.: $100.00
Can.: $100.00

JACK RUSSELL TERRIER, Seated Style Three

Model: DG28A, B, C/B0486
Modeller: Margaret Turner
Height: 3 ¼", 8.3 cm
Colour: A. Tricolour
B. Black and white
C. Brown and white
B0486 Bronze
Issued: A, C.01/95-05/99
B   01/95-12/97
B0486 06/99-06/00
Series: Dogs Galore / Bronzed

	Coloured	Bronzed
U.K.:	£25.00	£15.00
U.S.:	$50.00	$30.00
Can.:	$50.00	$30.00

JACK RUSSEL TERRIER, Seated Style Four

Model: A2697, 3550
Modeller: Unknown
Height: 11 ½", 29.2 cm
Colour: A2697   Black / white
A3550   Tricolour
Issued: A2697   06/03-12/04
A350   06/03 to the
present
Series: Fireside Dogs

U.K.: £ 70.00
U.S.: $140.00
Can.: $140.00

JACK RUSSELL TERRIER, Seated, Style Five

Model: A3834, 3881, 3882
Modeller: Margaret Turner
Height: 3 ¼", 8.3 cm
Colour: A3834   Black / white
A3881   Tan / white
A3882   Tricolour
Issued: A3834 01/04-06/06
A3881, 3882
01/04 to the present
Series: Dogs and Pups Galore

U.K.: £13.00
U.S.: $25.00
Can.: $25.00

JACK RUSSELL TERRIER,
Standing, Style One

Model:	DS5A, B
Modeller:	Ray Ayres
Height:	3", 7.6 cm
Colour:	A. Brown and white
	B. Black and white
Issued:	01/83 - 12/91
Series:	1. The World of Dogs
	2. Special Interest
U.K.:	£40.00
U.S.:	$80.00
Can.:	$80.00

JACK RUSSELL TERRIER,
Standing, Style Two

Model:	A1400, 1, 2
Modeller:	Margaret Turner
Height:	2 ½", 6.4 cm
Colour:	A1400 Tricolour
	A1401 Brown / white
	A1402 Black / white
Issued:	01/02 to the present
Series:	Dogs and Pups Galore
U.K.:	£17.50
U.S.:	$35.00
Can.:	$35.00

JACK RUSSELL TERRIER,
Standing, Style Three

Model:	A3037, 3786, 3792
Modeller:	Margaret Turner
Height:	6", 15.0 cm
Colour:	A3037 Tan / white
	A3786 Tricolour
	A3792 Black / white
Issued:	06/03 - 12/04
Series:	Dogs and Pups Galore
U.K.:	£40.00
U.S.:	$80.00
Can.:	$80.00

JACK RUSSELL TERRIER,
Standing, Style Four

Model:	A7126, 8975
Modeller:	Unknown
Height:	3", 7.6 cm
Colour:	A7126 Tricolour
	A8975 Brown / white
Issued:	06/07 to the present
Series:	Dogs and Pups Galore
U.K.:	£15.00
U.S.:	$30.00
Can.:	$30.00

JACK RUSSELL TERRIER AND
KITTENS

Model:	A1439
Modeller:	Unknown
Height:	3 ½", 8.9 cm
Colour:	Tricolour
Issued:	01/02 - 12/04
Series:	Action Dogs
U.K.:	£35.00
U.S.:	$70.00
Can.:	$70.00

JACK RUSSELL TERRIER AND
PUP

Model:	DPG04A, B, C
Modeller:	Margaret Turner
Height:	4", 10.1 cm
Colour:	A. Tricolour
	B. Black and white
	C. Brown and white
Issued:	A. 01/96 - 12/98
	B. 01/96 - 12/97
	C. 06/95 - 12/98
Series:	Dogs Galore

	Tri.	B&W	Brown
U.K.:	£35.	£40.	£35.
U.S.:	$70.	$80.	$70.
Can.:	$70.	$80.	$70.

JACK RUSSELL TERRIER PUP,
Seated

Model:	PG15A, B, C
Modeller:	Margaret Turner
Height:	2 ½", 6.4 cm
Colour:	A. Tricolour
	B. Black and white
	C. Brown and white
Issued:	A. 07/95 - 05/99
	B. 07/95 - 05/99
	C. 07/95 - 12/97
Series:	Pups Galore

	Tri.	B&W	Brown
U.K.:	£12.	£15.	£15.
U.S.:	$25.	$30.	$30.
Can.:	$25.	$30.	$30.

JACK RUSSELL TERRIER PUPS
(Pair)

Model:	B0250A, B, C
Modeller:	Margaret Turner
Height:	2 ¾", 7.0 cm
Colour:	A. Tricolour
	B. Black and white
	C. Brown and white
Issued:	A. 01/98 - 12/01
	B. 01/98 - 06/99
	C. 01/98 - 06/99
Series:	Pups Galore
U.K.:	£20.00
U.S.:	$40.00
Can.:	$40.00

JACOB SHEEP
(Four-Horned)
Model:	B0352
Modeller:	Ray Ayres
Height:	7 ½", 19.1 cm
Colour:	White and black
Issued:	1999 in a limited edition of 750
Series:	1. Agricultural and Sporting
	2. The County Show
U.K.:	£125.00
U.S.:	$250.00
Can.:	$250.00

JACOB SHEEP
(Two-Horned)
Model:	B0367
Modeller:	Ray Ayres
Height:	6 ½", 16.5 cm
Colour:	White and black
Issued:	1999 in a limited edition of 750
Series:	1. Agricultural and Sporting
	2. The County Show
U.K.:	£125.00
U.S.:	$250.00
Can.:	$250.00

JAKE
(Lurcher)
Model:	JH35
Modeller:	Elizabeth Waugh
Height:	5 ½", 14.0 cm
Colour:	Brown and white
Issued:	01/90 - 12/92
Series:	All Creatures Great and Small
U.K.:	£225.00
U.S.:	$450.00
Can.:	$450.00

JASMINE COTTAGE
Model:	JH53
Modeller:	Richard Young
Height:	3 ½", 8.9 cm
Colour:	Grey and green
Issued:	01/89 - 09/90
Series:	James Herriot's Yorkshire
U.K.:	£40.00
U.S.:	$80.00
Can.:	$80.00

JENNY AND PENNY
(Donkey and Foal)
Model:	JH85
Modeller:	Anne Wall
Height:	3 ¾", 9.5 cm
Colour:	Brown, white and black
Issued:	01/94 - 12/00
Series:	1. Every Living Thing
	2. The James Herriot Collection
U.K.:	£40.00
U.S.:	$80.00
Can.:	$80.00

JENNY WREN
(Wren)
Model:	B1108
Modeller:	Ray Ayres
Height:	2 ½", 6.4 cm
Colour:	Brown, white, red and green
Issued:	06/07 - 05/08
Series:	Society Symbol of Membership
U.K.:	£22.00
U.S.:	$45.00
Can.:	$45.00

JERSEY COW
Model:	A5257
Modeller:	Ray Ayres
Height:	4 ¾", 12.1 cm
Colour:	Light brown
Issued:	01/06 to the present
Series:	BFA Pottery Company
U.K.:	£25.00
U.S.:	$50.00
Can.:	$50.00

JERSEY COW
(Horned)
Model:	L111
Modeller:	Ray Ayres
Height:	6 ¾", 17.2 cm
Colour:	Orange-brown
Issued:	07/91 in a limited edition of 1,250
Varieties:	Polled (L110)
Series:	Agricultural and Sporting
U.K.:	£325.00
U.S.:	$650.00
Can.:	$650.00

JERSEY COW
(Polled)

Model:	L110
Modeller:	Ray Ayres
Height:	6 ¾", 17.2 cm
Colour:	Orange-brown
Issued:	07/91 in a limited edition of 1,250
Varieties:	Horned (L111)
Series:	Agricultural and Sporting
U.K.:	£325.00
U.S.:	$650.00
Can.:	$650.00

JERSEY COW AND NEW CALF

Model:	A1465
Modeller:	Lesley McKenzie
Height:	5 ¼", 13.3 cm
Colour:	Golden brown
Issued:	01/03 - 12/04
Series:	Cattle Breeds
U.K.:	£ 50.00
U.S.:	$100.00
Can.:	$100.00

JESS
(Collie)

Model:	JH20
Modeller:	Ray Ayres
Height:	3 ¾", 9.5 cm
Colour:	Black and white
Issued:	01/88 - 12/00
Series:	1. All Creatures Great and Small
	2. The James Herriot Collection
U.K.:	£30.00
U.S.:	$60.00
Can.:	$60.00

JESTER, THE
(Cat)

Model:	A7606, 7600
Modeller:	Unknown
Height:	2 ¾", 7.0 cm
Colour:	A7006 Ginger
	A7600 Black/ white
Issued:	06/06 to the present
Series:	Feline Fun
U.K.:	£ 9.95
U.S.:	$20.00
Can.:	$20.00

JEWEL OF THE EAST
(Ceremonial Indian Elephant)

Model:	L152
Modeller:	Richard Roberts
Height	17 ½", 44.5 cm
Colour:	Multicoloured
Issued:	01/95 in a limited edition of 350
Series:	Masterpiece
U.K.:	£ 625.00
U.S.:	$1,250.00
Can.:	$1,250.00

JOCK'S PRIDE
(Sheepdog and pups)

Model:	JH5
Modeller:	Ray Ayres
Height:	4 ¾", 12.1 cm
Colour:	Black, white and beige
Issued:	01/85 - 12/98
Series:	All Creatures Great and Small
U.K.:	£125.00
U.S.:	$250.00
Can.:	$250.00

JOCK'S PRIDE (Bronzed)
(Sheepdog and pups)

Model:	B0504
Modeller:	Ray Ayres
Height:	5 ½", 14.0 cm
Colour:	Bronze, patina
Issued:	01/99 in a limited edition of 500
Series:	1. The James Herriot Collection
	2. 25th Anniversary
U.K.:	£100.00
U.S.:	$200.00
Can.:	$200.00

JOKER, THE
(Dog)

Model:	A7330, 7612
Modeller:	Unknown
Height:	3 ¼", 8.3 cm
Colour:	A7330 Black / tan
	A7612 Tan / white
Issued:	06/06 to the present
Series:	Canine Capers
U.K.:	£18.00
U.S.:	$35.00
Can.:	$35.00

JOYS OF SPRING, THE
(Two robins nest in teapot)

Model:	SOC2
Modeller:	Ray Ayres
Height:	6 ½", 16.5 cm
Colour:	Red, brown and white
Issued:	06/90 - 05/91
Series:	Annual Society Figurine (1990/91)
U.K.:	£225.00
U.S.:	$450.00
Can.:	$450.00

JUNGLE QUEEN

Model:	FC4, 5, 6
Designer:	Fleur Cowles
Modeller:	Richard Roberts
Height:	9 ¾", 24.7 cm
Colour:	White
Issued:	FC4 1987 Ltd. ed. 500
	FC5 1987 Ltd. ed. 300
	FC6 1987 Ltd. ed. 300
Series:	The Imagined World of Fleur Cowles
U.K.:	£250.00
U.S.:	$500.00
Can.:	$500.00

JUST ABOUT FRIENDS
(Collie and Cat)

Model:	JH87
Modeller:	Anne Wall
Height:	3 ¼", 8.3 cm
Colour:	Black and white; ginger and white
Issued:	01/94 - 05/99
Series:	1. Every Living Thing
	2. J. Herriot Collection
U.K.:	£30.00
U.S.:	$60.00
Can.:	$60.00

JUST MARRIED

Model:	B0883
Modeller:	Ray Ayres
Height:	6 ¾", 17.2 cm
Colour:	Dark brown, black, blue, white, grey, beige and green
Issued:	01/04 in a limited edition of 950
Series:	Classic Collection
U.K.:	£225.00
U.S.:	$450.00
Can.:	$450.00

KEEPING CLOSE
(Otters)

Model:	B0795
Modeller:	Ray Ayres
Height:	7 ¾", 19.7 cm
Colour:	Black, brown, white, grey and yellow
Issued:	01/03 in a limited edition of 1,750
Series:	Classic Collection
U.K.:	£200.00
U.S.:	$400.00
Can.:	$400.00

KEEPING HIS FEET DRY
(Dog Fox)

Model:	B0225
Modeller:	Richard Roberts
Height:	5 ¼", 13.3 cm
Colour:	Reddish-brown, white and beige
Issued:	01/98 in a limited edition of 2,500
Series:	Nature's Kingdom
U.K.:	£100.00
U.S.:	$200.00
Can.:	$200.00

KEEPING UP
(Otters)

Model:	B0333
Modeller:	Ray Ayres
Height:	5 ¼", 13.3 cm
Colour:	Brown, white, grey and green
Issued:	01/99 in a limited edition of 1,750
Series:	Masters of the River
U.K.:	£125.00
U.S.:	$250.00
Can.:	$250.00

KEEPING WATCH
(Border Collie)

Model:	A7127
Modeller:	Unknown
Height:	7 ½", 19.1 cm
Colour:	Black, white, grey, green, sandy brown
Issued:	01/07 to the present
Series:	Border Collie Collection
U.K.:	£ 60.00
U.S.:	$120.00
Can.:	$120.00

KESTREL
Style One

Model:	UK# 032B
	USA# 225-070
Modeller:	David Geenty
Height:	8 ½", 21.6 cm
Colour:	Brown, white, grey
	and yellow
Issued:	01/77 - 12/82
U.K.:	£125.00
U.S.:	$250.00
Can.:	$250.00

KESTREL
Style Two

Model:	WB83
Modeller:	Russell Willis
Height:	7 ½", 19.1 cm
Colour:	Browns, blue and green
Issued:	01/94 - 12/96
Series:	1. Birds In Your Garden
	2. Russell Willis Birds
U.K.:	£ 65.00
U.S.:	$125.00
Can.:	$125.00

KESTREL
Style Three

Model:	739480
Modeller:	Russell Willis
Height:	10 ¾", 27.8 cm
Colour:	Brown, grey and cream
Issued:	01/01 - 12/02
Series:	Birds of Prey
U.K.:	£ 50.00
U.S.:	$100.00
Can.:	$100.00

KESTREL
Style Four

Model:	B0869
Modeller:	Richad Roberts
Size:	13 ½" x 9"
	34.3 x 22.9 cm
Colour:	Brown, black, grey,
	green, white and yellow
Issued:	01/05 in a limited
	edition of 350
U.K.:	£350.00
U.S.:	$700.00
Can.:	$700.00

KESTREL AND MOUSE

Model:	032A
Modeller:	Victor Hayton
Height:	8 ½", 21.6 cm
Colour:	Browns and cream
Issued:	01/77 - 12/79
U.K.:	£425.00
U.S.:	$850.00
Can.:	$850.00

KESTREL ON A POST

Model:	A0655
Modeller:	Russell Willis
Height:	5 ½", 14.0 cm
Colour:	Browns, cream and
	green
Issued:	01/01 - 12/01
Series:	Birds And ...
U.K.:	£35.00
U.S.:	$70.00
Can.:	$70.00

KESTRELS, THE

Model:	L100/LH100
Modeller:	David Burnham Smith
Height:	17", 43.2 cm
Colour:	Reddish-brown,
	blue-grey, cream
	and yellow
Issued:	01/90 in a limited
	edition of 950
Series:	Nature's Kingdom
U.K.:	£ 550.00
U.S.:	$1,100.00
Can.:	$1,100.00

KICK START
(David Brown Cropmaster
Tractor, Farmer and Collie)

Model:	B0541
Modeller:	Ray Ayres
Height:	6", 15.0 cm
Colour:	Red, browns, black,
	white and stone
Issued:	06/00 - 05/01
Series:	Annual Society Figurine
	(2000/01)
U.K.:	£300.00
U.S.:	$600.00
Can.:	$600.00

KIDS IN MILK
(Kid goats)

Model:	A5627
Modeller:	Anne Wall
Height:	3 ¼", 8.3 cm
Colour:	Brown, white, green and silver
Issued:	01/05 to the present
Series:	On The Farm
U.K.:	£24.00
U.S.:	$50.00
Can.:	$50.00

KING

Model:	FC7, 8, 9
Designer:	Fleur Cowles
Modeller:	Richard Roberts
Height:	6 ½", 16.5 cm
Colour:	White
Issued:	FC7 1987 Ltd. ed. 500
	FC8 1987 Ltd. ed. 300
	FC9 1987 Ltd. ed. 300
Series:	The Imagined World of Fleur Cowles
U.K.:	£250.00
U.S.:	$500.00
Can.:	$500.00

KING BIRD OF PARADISE

Model:	B0326
Modeller:	Richard Roberts
Height:	12 ½", 31.7 cm
Colour:	Red, white, green and brown
Issued:	07/98 in a limited edition of 950
Series:	1. Exotic Birds
	2. Birds of the World
U.K.:	£225.00
U.S.:	$450.00
Can.:	$450.00

KING CHARLES CAVALIER
SPANIEL, Seated

Model:	DG36A, B, C, D, B0482
Modeller:	Margaret Turner
Height:	3 ¾", 9.5 cm
Colour:	A. Tricolour
	B. Blenheim
	C. Black and tan
	D. Ruby
	B0482 Bronze
Issued:	A.-B. 01/96-12/01
	C.-D. 01/96-12/97
	B0482 06/99-06/00
Series:	Dogs Galore/Bronzed
U.K.	£25.00
U.S.	$50.00
Can.	$50.00

KING CHARLES CAVALIER
SPANIEL, Standing
Style One

Model:	061
Modeller:	David Geenty
Height:	5 ½", 14.0 cm
Colour:	Tan and white
Issued:	07/80 - 12/85
U.K.:	£ 60.00
U.S.:	$120.00
Can.:	$120.00

KING CHARLES CAVALIER
SPANIEL, Standing
Style Two

Model:	B0126/B0126A
Modeller:	Margaret Turner
Height:	6", 15.0 cm
Colour:	B0126 Blenheim
	B0126A Tricolour
Issued:	B0126 01/97-12/99
	B0126A 06/97-12/99
Series:	Dogs by Margaret Turner
U.K.:	£ 60.00
U.S.:	$120.00
Can.:	$120.00

KING CHARLES CAVALIER
SPANIEL, Standing
Style Three

Model:	A1159, 1201
Modeller:	Margaret Turner
Height:	4", 10.1 cm
Colour:	A1159 Tricolour
	A1201 Blenheim
Issued:	06/01 to the present
Series:	Dogs and Pups Galore
U.K.:	£21.00
U.S.:	$40.00
Can.:	$40.00

KING CHARLES CAVALIER
SPANIEL PUP, Seated

Model:	PG09A, B
Modeller:	Margaret Turner
Height:	3", 7.6 cm
Colour:	A. Tricolour
	B. Blenheim
Issued:	01/94 - 12/01
Series:	Pups Galore
U.K.:	£15.00
U.S.:	$30.00
Can.:	$30.00

KING OF THE CASTLE
(Black-faced Ewe and Lambs)

Model:	JH37
Modeller:	David Walton
Height:	4 ¼", 10.8 cm
Colour:	Cream, black and green
Issued:	01/90 - 12/98
Series:	1. All Things Wise and Wonderful
	2. J. Herriot Collection

U.K.:	£ 50.00
U.S.:	$100.00
Can.:	$100.00

KING OF THE RIVER
(Salmon)

Model:	A1480
Modeller:	John Brown
Height:	10 ½", 26.7 cm
Colour:	Silver, grey, green and light brown
Issued:	01/03 in a limited edition of 950
Series:	Studio Limited Editions

U.K.:	£ 75.00
U.S.:	$150.00
Can.:	$150.00

KINGFISHER
Style One

Model:	043
Modeller:	Ray Ayres
Height:	7", 17.8 cm
Colour:	Blue, orange and beige
Issued:	01/81 - 12/87

U.K.:	£ 65.00
U.S.:	$125.00
Can.:	$125.00

KINGFISHER
Style Two

Model:	M17
Modeller:	David Fryer
Height:	3", 7.6 cm
Colour:	Blue, salmon and white; bronze base
Issued:	07/83 - 12/87
Series:	Miniatures on Bronze

U.K.:	£ 65.00
U.S.:	$125.00
Can.:	$125.00

KINGFISHER
Style Three

Model:	RB1
Modeller:	Ray Ayres
Height:	7", 17.8 cm
Colour:	Blue, orange and brown
Issued:	07/83 - 12/91
Series:	1. RSPB Birds
	2. British Birds

U.K.:	£ 80.00
U.S.:	$160.00
Can.:	$160.00

KINGFISHER
Style Four

Model:	RB10
Modeller:	Ray Ayres
Height:	5 ½", 14.0 cm
Colour:	Blue, orange, beige and green
Issued:	01/90 - 12/93
Series:	British Birds

U.K.:	£ 65.00
U.S.:	$125.00
Can.:	$125.00

KINGFISHER
Style Five

Model:	M24
Modeller:	David Walton
Height:	3 ¾", 9.5 cm
Colour:	Blue, orange and black
Issued:	01/92 - 12/95
Series:	Miniature Wildlife

U.K.:	£40.00
U.S.:	$80.00
Can.:	$80.00

KINGFISHER
Style Six

Model:	RB41
Modeller:	Ray Ayres
Height:	5 ¾", 14.6 cm
Colour:	Blue-green, orange and white
Issued:	01/93 - 12/94
Series:	RSPB Birds of the Countryside

U.K.:	£100.00
U.S.:	$200.00
Can.:	$200.00

KINGFISHER
Style Seven

Model:	WB72
Modeller:	Russell Willis
Height:	9 ½", 24.0 cm
Colour:	Blue, orange, green and yellow
Issued:	01/95 in a limited edition of 1,250
Series:	Russell Willis Birds
U.K.:	£125.00
U.S.:	$250.00
Can.:	$250.00

KINGFISHER
Style Eight

Model:	B0024
Modeller:	Russell Willis
Height:	5 ¼", 13.3 cm
Colour:	Blue, orange, grey and brown
Issued:	06/96 - 12/97
Series:	Russell Willis Birds
U.K.:	£40.00
U.S.:	$80.00
Can.:	$80.00

KINGFISHER
Style Nine

Model:	484253
Modeller:	Russell Willis
Height:	2 ¾", 7.0 cm
Colour:	Turquoise, orange, green and fawn
Issued:	06/98 - 12/02
Series:	Miniature Figurines
U.K.:	£20.00
U.S.:	$40.00
Can.:	$40.00

KINGFISHER
Style Ten

Model:	484334
Modeller:	Russell Willis
Height:	4 ½", 11.9 cm
Colour:	Turquoise, orange, green and brown
Issued:	06/98 - 12/00
Series:	Birds And ...
U.K.:	£25.00
U.S.:	$50.00
Can.:	$50.00

KINGFISHER
Style Eleven

Model:	A0005
Modeller:	Richard Roberts
Height:	11 ½", 29.2 cm
Colour:	Turquoise, orange, green and brown
Issued:	01/00 - 06/03
Series:	Reflections
U.K.:	£40.00
U.S.:	$80.00
Can.:	$80.00

KINGFISHER
Style Twelve

Model:	A0653
Modeller:	Russell Willis
Height:	3 ¾", 9.5 cm
Colour:	Turquoise, orange, black and brown
Issued:	01/01 - 12/02
Series:	Feathered Friends
U.K.:	£20.00
U.S.:	$40.00
Can.:	$40.00

KINGFISHER
Style Thirteen

Model:	A1889
Modeller:	Russell Willis
Height:	5 ¼", 13.3 cm
Colour:	Blue, yellow, white and green
Issued:	06/02 - 12/03
Series:	Birds by Russell Willis
U.K.:	£30.00
U.S.:	$60.00
Can.:	$60.00

KINGFISHER
Style Fourteen

Model:	A2321
Modeller:	Russell Willis
Height:	3 ¾", 9.5 cm
Size:	Small
Colour:	Blue, yellow, white, green and red
Issued:	01/03 - 06/06
Series:	Garden Guests
U.K.:	£15.00
U.S.:	$30.00
Can.:	$30.00

KINGFISHER
Style Fifteen

Model:	A2325
Modeller:	Russell Willis
Height:	3 ½", 8.9 cm
Size:	Medium
Colour:	Blue, yellow, white, green and brown
Issued:	01/03 - 06/06
Series:	Garden Guests
U.K.:	£25.00
U.S.:	$50.00
Can.:	$50.00

KINGFISHER
Style Sixteen

Model:	A3459
Modeller:	Russell Willis
Height:	11 ½", 29.2 cm
Colour:	Turquoise, orange, white, green, brown
Issued:	01/04 - 12/05
Series:	Birds By Russell Willis
U.K.:	£25.00
U.S.:	$50.00
Can.:	$50.00

KINGFISHER
Style Seventeen

Model:	A4609
Modeller:	Russell Willis
Height:	4 ¼", 10.8 cm
Colour:	Turquoise, orange, white, black, green and pale brown
Issued:	01/04 - 12/06
Series:	BFA Pottery Company
U.K.:	£15.00
U.S.:	$30.00
Can.:	$30.00

KINGFISHER
Style Eighteen

Model:	A6057
Modeller:	Unknown
Height:	5", 12.7 cm
Colour:	Turquoise, orange, white, black and grey
Issued:	06/05 to the present
U.K.:	£ 9.95
U.S.:	$20.00
Can.:	$20.00

KINGFISHER AND FISHING REEL

Model:	484385
Modeller:	Russell Willis
Height:	4 ½", 11.9 cm
Colour:	Turquoise, orange, brown and green
Issued:	06/98 - 12/00
Series:	Finders Keepers
U.K.	£25.00
U.S.	$50.00
Can.	$50.00

KINGFISHER AND YOUNG
Style One

Model:	EG04
Modeller:	Richard Roberts
Height:	8", 20.3 cm
Colour:	Blue, orange and brown
Issued:	07/90 in a limited edition of 950
U.K.	£200.00
U.S.	$400.00
Can.	$400.00

KINGFISHER AND YOUNG
Style Two

Model:	484415
Modeller:	Russell Willis
Height:	5", 12.7 cm
Colour:	Turquoise, orange, fawn, green and white
Issued:	06/98 - 06/00
Series:	Families
U.K.	£35.00
U.S.	$70.00
Can.	$70.00

KINGFISHER FLYING

Model:	WB14
Modeller:	Russell Willis
Height:	5 ½", 14.0 cm
Colour:	Blue, orange, turquoise, browns, yellow and green
Issued:	07/92 - 12/93
Series:	Russell Willis Birds
U.K.	£ 50.00
U.S.	$100.00
Can.	$100.00

**KINGFISHER ON
"NO FISHING" SIGN**
Model: 541613
Modeller: Russell Willis
Height: 4", 10.1 cm
Colour: Turquoise, orange,
            green, yellow and fawn
Issued: 06/99 - 12/00
Series: Birds And ...

U.K.   £20.00
U.S. $40.00
Can. $40.00

KINGFISHER ON REEDS
Model: F6
Modeller: David Burnham Smith
Height: 7 ¾", 19.7 cm
Colour: Blue-green, salmon
            and white
Issued: 01/89 - 12/91
Series: Finesse Birds

U.K.   £125.00
U.S. $250.00
Can. $250.00

**KINGFISHER WITH FISHING
TACKLE**
Model: B0121
Modeller: Russell Willis
Height: 5", 12.7 cm
Colour: Blue, orange, browns
            and silver
Issued: 01/97 - 12/97
Series: Finders Keepers

U.K.   £45.00
U.S. $90.00
Can. $90.00

KINGFISHER WITH WATER LILY
Model: WB32
Modeller: Russell Willis
Height: 5", 12.7 cm
Colour: Blue, orange, brown,
            pink and green
Issued: 01/93 - 12/95
Series: 1. Birds In Your Garden
            2. Russell Willis Birds

U.K.   £35.00
U.S. $70.00
Can. $70.00

**KINGFISHERS WITH YELLOW
FLAGS**
Model: A3449
Modeller: Russell Willis
Height: 10', 25.4 cm
Colour: Turquoise, orange,
            white, green, yellow
            and grey
Issued: 01/04 - 12/05
Series: Birds by Russell Willis

U.K.:   £ 80.00
U.S.: $150.00
Can.: $150.00

**KITTEN, Crouching
Style One**
Model: B0762 (A1559)
            B0763 (A1560)
            B0764 (A1561)
Modeller: Richard Roberts
Height: 2 ½", 6.4 cm
Colour: A1559   Slate Blue
            A1560   Walnut
            A1561   Stone
Issued: 06/01 - 12/03
Series: Cubist Cats and Kittens

U.K.:   £ 7.00
U.S.: $15.00
Can.: $15.00

**KITTEN, Crouching
Style Two**
Model: A1566, 67, 68
Modeller: Richard Roberts
Height: 1 ¾", 4.4 cm
Colour: A1566   Slate blue
            A1567   Walnut
            A1568   Stone
Issued: 01/02 - 12/03
Series: Cubist Cats and Kittens

U.K.:   £10.00
U.S.: $20.00
Can.: $20.00

**KITTEN, Lying
(With ball of wool)
Style One**
Model: M4
Modeller: David Geenty
Height: 2 ½", 6.4 cm
Colour: Grey and yellow
Issued: 07/80 - 12/80
Series: Beginners, Please

U.K.   £30.00
U.S. $60.00
Can. $60.00

**KITTEN, Lying
(With ball of wool)
Style Two**

Model: FF11A, B
Modeller: Anne Wall
Height: 1 ¾", 4.4 cm
Colour: A. Black, white, purple
B. Unknown
Issued: 01/92 - 12/95
Series: First Friends

U.K. £12.00
U.S. $25.00
Can. $25.00

**KITTEN, Seated
Style One**

Model: KG1A, B, C, D, E
Modeller: Anne Wall
Height: 2 ¼", 5.7 cm
Colour: A. White
B. Grey and white
C. Black and white
D. White and ginger
E. Tabby
Issued: 07/94 - 12/95
Series: Kittens Galore

U.K. £12.00
U.S. $25.00
Can. $25.00

**KITTEN, Seated
Style Two**

Model: B0962, 0962A
Modeller: Ray Ayres
Height: 6¼", 15.9 cm
Colour: B0962 Grey / white
B0962A Black / white
Issued: 06/05 - 12/06
Series: Classic Babies

U.K.: £39.00
U.S.: $80.00
Can.: $80.00

**KITTEN, Seated
(On cushion)**

Model: FF3A, B, C
Modeller: Ray Ayres
Height: 2 ¼", 5.7 cm
Colour: A. Black and white;
pink cushion
B. Ginger and white;
green cushion
C. White; blue cushion
Issued: 01/89 - 12/95
Series: First Friends

U.K. £12.00
U.S. $25.00
Can. $25.00

**KITTEN AND CLOCKWORK
MOUSE**

Model: FE5
Modeller: Ray Ayres
Height: 3", 7.6 cm
Colour: Ginger and red
Issued: 01/83 - 12/84
Series: First Encounters

U.K. £ 50.00
U.S. $100.00
Can. $100.00

KITTEN AND MILK JUG

Model: A3869
Modeller: Janet Miller
Height: 3", 7.6 cm
Colour: Ginger striped kitten,
white and blue milk jug
Issued: 01/04 - 12/06
Series: On The Farm

U.K.: £13.00
U.S.: $25.00
Can.: $25.00

**KITTEN AND RADIO
"FAMILY FAVOURITE"**

Model: C15
Modeller: Ray Ayres
Height: 3", 7.6 cm
Colour: White cat, brown radio
Issued: 01/90 - 12/91
Series: A Cat Around the House

U.K.: £25.00
U.S.: $50.00
Can.: $50.00

KITTEN CAPERS

Model: A2681
Modeller: Hans Kendrick
Height: 6 ½", 16.5 cm
Colour: Browns, white, red,
ginger and green
Issued: 06/03 - 12/05
Series: James Herriot
Studio Collection

U.K.: £35.00
U.S.: $70.00
Can.: $70.00

KITTEN IN A BASKET
Model: CC01
Modeller: Anne Butler
Height: 3", 7.6 cm
Colour: Grey and brown
Issued: 01/92 - 12/95
Series: The Kittens

U.K.: £15.00
U.S.: $30.00
Can.: $30.00

KITTEN IN BOBBLE HAT
Model: 484040
Modeller: Unknown
Height: 1 ¾", 4.4 cm
Colour: Ginger and blue
Issued: 06/98 - 12/00
Series: Kitten Tales

U.K. £10.00
U.S. $20.00
Can. $20.00

KITTEN IN BOOT
Model: CC07
Modeller: Anne Butler
Height: 2 ¾", 7.0 cm
Colour: White, yellow and brown
Issued: 01/93 - 12/95
Series: The Kittens

U.K. £15.00
U.S. $30.00
Can. $30.00

KITTEN IN BOWL
Model: CC09
Modeller: Anne Butler
Height: 2 ½", 6.4 cm
Colour: White, tan and beige
Issued: 01/93 - 12/94
Series: The Kittens

U.K. £15.00
U.S. $30.00
Can. $30.00

KITTEN IN CAT BED
Model: CC10
Modeller: Anne Butler
Height: 2 ½", 6.4 cm
Colour: Light brown and pink
Issued: 01/93 - 12/94
Series: The Kittens

U.K. £15.00
U.S. $30.00
Can. $30.00

KITTEN IN FLOWER BASKET
Model: CC08
Modeller: Anne Butler
Height: 2 ½", 6.4 cm
Colour: Blue-grey and brown
Issued: 01/93 - 12/94
Series: The Kittens

U.K.: £15.00
U.S.: $30.00
Can.: $30.00

KITTEN IN FLOWER POT
Style One
Model: CC02
Modeller: Anne Butler
Height: 2 ¼", 5.7 cm
Colour: Grey, white and brown
Issued: 01/92 - 12/95
Series: The Kittens

U.K.: £15.00
U.S.: $30.00
Can.: $30.00

KITTEN IN FLOWER POT
Style Two
Model: 483990
Modeller: Unknown
Height: 2 ½", 6.4 cm
Colour: Black, white and reddish-brown
Issued: 06/98 - 12/00
Series: Kitten Tales

U.K.: £10.00
U.S.: $20.00
Can.: $20.00

KITTEN IN HANDBAG

Model:	483966
Modeller:	Unknown
Height:	2 ½", 6.4 cm
Colour:	Ginger and black
Issued:	06/98 - 12/00
Series:	Kitten Tales
U.K.:	£10.00
U.S.:	$20.00
Can.:	$20.00

KITTEN IN HAT

Model:	CC04
Modeller:	Anne Butler
Height:	2 ¼", 5.7 cm
Colour:	Black, white, brown and red
Issued:	01/92 - 12/94
Series:	The Kittens
U.K.:	£15.00
U.S.:	$30.00
Can.:	$30.00

KITTEN IN KNITTING BAG

Model:	CC06
Modeller:	Anne Butler
Height:	1 ¾", 4.4 cm
Colour:	White, green and brown
Issued:	01/92 - 12/94
Series:	The Kittens
U.K.:	£15.00
U.S.:	$30.00
Can.:	$30.00

KITTEN IN RIDING HAT

Model:	656062
Modeller:	Unknown
Height:	2 ½", 6.4 cm
Colour:	Ginger and black
Issued:	06/99 - 12/00
Series:	Kitten Tales
U.K.:	£10.00
U.S.:	$20.00
Can.:	$20.00

KITTEN IN SATCHEL

Model:	484016
Modeller:	Unknown
Height:	2 ¾", 7.0 cm
Colour:	Black, white and brown
Issued:	06/98 - 12/00
Series:	Kitten Tales
U.K.:	£10.00
U.S.:	$20.00
Can.:	$20.00

KITTEN IN SHOPPING BAG

Model:	CC05
Modeller:	Anne Butler
Height:	2 ½", 6.4 cm
Colour:	White, grey and brown
Issued:	01/92 - 12/95
Series:	The Kittens
U.K.:	£15.00
U.S.:	$30.00
Can.:	$30.00

KITTEN IN SLIPPER

Model:	483982
Modeller:	Unknown
Height:	1 ½", 3.9 cm
Colour:	Black, white and pink
Issued:	06/98 - 12/00
Series:	Kitten Tales
U.K.:	£10.00
U.S.:	$20.00
Can.:	$20.00

KITTEN IN SWEATER

Model:	483974
Modeller:	Unknown
Height:	2 ¼", 5.7 cm
Colour:	Black, white, red and blue
Issued:	06/98 - 12/00
Series:	Kitten Tales
U.K.:	£10.00
U.S.:	$20.00
Can.:	$20.00

KITTEN IN TEAPOT
Model: CC03
Modeller: Anne Butler
Height: 3", 7.6 cm
Colour: Ginger, white and blue
Issued: 01/92 - 12/95
Series: The Kittens

U.K.: £15.00
U.S.: $30.00
Can.: $30.00

KITTEN IN TOTE BAG
Model: 652032
Modeller: Unknown
Height: 3 ¼", 8.3 cm
Colour: Ginger and black
Issued: 06/99 - 12/00
Series: Kitten Tales

U.K.: £10.00
U.S.: $20.00
Can.: $20.00

KITTEN IN WALKING BOOT
Model: 483958
Modeller: Unknown
Height: 3 ¼", 8.3 cm
Colour: White and brown
Issued: 06/98 - 12/00
Series: Kitten Tales

U.K. £10.00
U.S. $20.00
Can. $20.00

KITTEN IN WATERING CAN
Model: 484059
Modeller: Unknown
Height: 3 ¼", 8.3 cm
Colour: Black, tan, and grey
Issued: 06/98 - 12/00
Series: Kitten Tales

U.K. £10.00
U.S. $20.00
Can. $20.00

KITTEN IN WHEELBARROW
Model: 655716
Modeller: Unknown
Height: 2 ½", 6.4 cm
Colour: Fawn and white
Issued: 06/99 - 12/00
Series: Kitten Tales

U.K. £10.00
U.S. $20.00
Can. $20.00

KITTEN LICKING PAW
Model: KG3A, B, C, D, E
Modeller: Anne Wall
Height: 2 ¾", 7.0 cm
Colour: A. White
B. Grey and white
C. Black and white
D. White and ginger
E. Tabby
Issued: 07/94 - 12/95
Series: Kittens Galore

U.K. £12.00
U.S. $25.00
Can. $25.00

KITTEN ON FLAT CAP
Model: 484032
Modeller: Unknown
Height: 1 ½", 3.9 cm
Colour: Grey, black and white
Issued: 06/98 - 12/00
Series: Kitten Tales

U.K.: £10.00
U.S.: $20.00
Can.: $20.00

KITTEN ON HOT WATER BOTTLE
Model: 484008
Modeller: Unknown
Height: 1 ¾", 4.4 cm
Colour: Grey, white and blue
Issued: 06/98 - 12/00
Series: Kitten Tales

U.K.: £10.00
U.S.: $20.00
Can.: $20.00

KITTEN PAWING

Model: A1572, 73, 74
Modeller: Richard Roberts
Height: 3", 7.6 cm
Colour: A1572   Slate blue
            A1573   Walnut
            A1574   Stone
Issued: 01/02 - 12/03
Series: Cubist Cats and Kittens

U.K.:   £10.00
U.S.: $20.00
Can.: $20.00

KITTEN POUNCING

Model: A1569, 70, 71
Modeller: Richard Roberts
Height: 3", 7.6 cm
Colour: A1569   Slate blue
            A1570   Walnut
            A1571   Stone
Issued: 01/02 - 12/03
Series: Cubist Cats and Kittens

U.K.:   £10.00
U.S.: $20.00
Can.: $20.00

KITTEN UNDER SOU'WESTER

Model: 483931
Modeller: Unknown
Height: 1 ¾", 4.4 cm
Colour: Cream, brown and
            yellow
Issued: 06/98 - 12/00
Series: Kitten Tales

U.K.:   £10.00
U.S.: $20.00
Can.: $20.00

KITTENS (Two)
Style One

Model: 085
Modeller: Anne Wall
Height: 4", 10.1 cm
Colour: Browns and black
Issued: 01/82 - 12/82

U.K.:   £ 65.00
U.S.: $125.00
Can.: $125.00

KITTENS (Two)
Style Two

Model: KG4A, B, C
Modeller: Anne Wall
Height: 2", 5.0 cm
Colour: A. Black, white and
               tortoiseshell
            B. Grey, white, ginger
            C. Ginger, white, tabby
Issued: 07/94 - 12/95
Series: Kittens Galore

U.K.:   £15.00
U.S.: $30.00
Can.: $30.00

KITTENS (Two)
Style Three

Model: KG5A, B, C
Modeller: Anne Wall
Height: 2 ½", 6.4 cm
Colour: A. Black and white
            B. Tortoiseshell, white
               and ginger
            C. Grey, white and
               tabby
Issued: 07/94 - 12/95
Series: Kittens Galore

U.K.:   £15.00
U.S.: $30.00
Can.: $30.00

KITTENS (Two)
Style Four

Model: See Colour
Modeller: Richard Roberts
Height: 4 ¼", 10.8 cm
Colour: B0765 (A1556) Slate
               blue
            B0766 (A1557) Walnut
            B0767 (A1558) Stone
Issued: 06/01 - 12/03
Series: Cubist Cats and Kittens

U.K.:   £15.00
U.S.: $30.00
Can.: $30.00

KITTENS (Two)
Style Five

Model: A1441
Modeller: Unknown
Height: 1 ¾", 4.4 cm
Colour: Brown tabby and
            ginger
Issued: 01/02 - 06/04
Series: Cats and Kittens Galore

U.K.:   £10.00
U.S.: $20.00
Can.: $20.00

KITTENS (Two)
Style Six

Model: A1884
Modeller: Unknown
Height: 3", 7.6 cm
Colour: Tortoiseshell and
           brown
Issued: 01/03 - 06/04
Series: Cats and Kittens Galore

U.K.:   £10.00
U.S.: $20.00
Can.: $20.00

KITTENS (Three)
Style One

Model: KG6A, B, C
Modeller: Anne Wall
Height: 2 ¾", 7.0 cm
Colour: A. Ginger and tabby
           B. Tortoiseshell, ginger
           and grey
           C. Black, white and
           grey
Issued: 07/94 - 12/95
Series: Kittens Galore

U.K.:   £20.00
U.S.: $40.00
Can.: $40.00

KITTENS (Three)
Style Two

Model: See Colour
Modeller: Richard Roberts
Height: 3 ¾", 9.5 cm
Colour: B0693 (A1555) Stone
           B0694 (A1554) Walnut
           B0695 (A1553) Slate
           Blue
Issued: 01/01 - 12/03
Series: Cubist Cats and Kittens

U.K.:   £20.00
U.S.: $40.00
Can.: $40.00

KITTENS (Three)
Style Three

Model: A1442, 43, 44
Modeller: Unknown
Height: 2 ½", 6.4 cm
Colour: A1442 Black, white,
           and brown tabbies
           A1443 Black, white,
           grey and ginger
           A1444 Ginger, brown
           tabby, tortoiseshell
Issued: 01/02 - 06/04
Series: Cats and Kittens Galore

U.K.:   £10.00
U.S.: $20.00
Can.: $20.00

KITTENS (Three)
Style Four

Model: A1885
Modeller: Unknown
Height: 2 ¼", 5.7 cm
Colour: Black and white;
           brown; ginger
Issued: 01/03 - 06/04
Series: Cats and Kittens Galore

U.K.:   £10.00
U.S.: $20.00
Can.: $20.00

KITTENS (Four)

Model: ED2
Modeller: Judy Boyt
Height: 2", 5.0 cm
Colour: Black, white and brown
Issued: 07/82 - 06/85
Series: Early Days

U.K.:   £40.00
U.S.: $80.00
Can.: $80.00

KITTENS IN HOSEPIPE

Model: A5626
Modeller: Anne Wall
Height: 2 ½", 6.4 cm
Colour: Green, gold, ginger,
           black and white
Issued: 01/05 - 06/06
Series: On The Farm

U.K.:   £14.00
U.S.: $27.00
Can.: $27.00

KITTENS IN SHOPPING BAG

Model: 484024
Modeller: Unknown
Height: 3 ¼", 8.3 cm
Colour: Cream, brown and
           green
Issued: 06/98 - 12/00
Series: Kitten Tales

U.K.:   £10.00
U.S.: $20.00
Can.: $20.00

KITTENS IN TOP HAT
Model: 655864
Modeller: Unknown
Height: 3", 7.6 cm
Colour: Black, white, ginger
           and grey
Issued: 06/99 - 12/00
Series: Kitten Tales

U.K.:   £10.00
U.S.: $20.00
Can.: $20.00

**LABRADOR
(Bitch, Light Build)**
Model: MT01A, B, C
Modeller: Margaret Turner
Height: 9 ¼", 23.5 cm
Colour: A. Golden
           B. Black
           C. Chocolate
Issued: A. 01/94 - 12/98
           B. 01/94 - 12/98
           C. 01/94 - 12/96
Series: Dogs by M. Turner

U.K.:   £ 80.00
U.S.: $160.00
Can.: $160.00

**LABRADOR
(Dog, Heavy Build)**
Model: MT02A, B, C
Modeller: Margaret Turner
Height: 9 ¾", 24.7 cm
Colour: A. Golden
           B. Black
           C. Chocolate
Issued: A. 01/94 - 12/98
           B. 01/94 - 12/98
           C. 01/94 - 12/96
Series: Dogs by M. Turner

U.K.:   £ 80.00
U.S.: $160.00
Can.: $160.00

**LABRADOR, Lying
Style One**
Model: DG11
Modeller: Steve McKeown
Height: 4 ¼", 10.8 cm
Colour: A. Yellow
           B. Black
Issued: 01/91 - 08/95
Series: Dogs Galore

U.K.:   £20.00
U.S.: $40.00
Can.: $40.00

**LABRADOR, Lying
Style Two**
Model: B0436A, B
Modeller: Margaret Turner
Height: 3 ½", 8.9 cm
Colour: A. Yellow
           B. Black
Issued: 01/99 - 12/01
Series: Dogs Galore

U.K.:   £20.00
U.S.: $40.00
Can.: $40.00

**LABRADOR, Lying
Style Three**
Model: A2695, 3549
Modeller: Margaret Turner
Height: 10", 25.4 cm
Colour: A2695   Black
           A3549   Yellow
Issued: A2695   06/03-12/04
           A3549   06/03-06/06
Series: Fireside Dogs

U.K.:   £ 70.00
U.S.: $140.00
Can.: $140.00

**LABRADOR, Lying
Style Four**
Model: A3053, 54, 55
Modeller: Margaret Turner
Height: 3 ¼", 8.3 cm
Colour: A3053   Black
           A3054   Yellow
           A3055   Chocolate
Issued: 06/03 - 12/05
Series: Dogs and Pups Galore

U.K.:   £15.00
U.S.: $30.00
Can.: $30.00

**LABRADOR, Seated
Style One**
Model: DL6A, B
Modeller: Ray Ayres
Height: 4 ½", 11.9 cm
Colour: A. Yellow
           B. Black
Issued: 01/83 - 12/93
Series: The World of Dogs

	Yellow	Black
U.K.	£35.	£ 50.
U.S.	$70.	$100.
Can.	$70.	$100.

LABRADOR, Seated
Style Two, First Version

Model: DG32A, B/B0464
Modeller: Margaret Turner
Height: 5 ½", 14.0 cm
Colour: A. Black
           B. Golden
           B0464 - Bronze
Issued: A. 07/95 - 12/01
           B. 07/95 - 12/01
           B0464   06/99-06/00
Series: Dogs Galore/Bronzed

	Black	Gold	Bronze
U.K.:	£25.	£25.	£20.
U.S.:	$50.	$50.	$40.
Can.:	$50.	$50.	$40.

LABRADOR, Seated
Style Two, Second Version

Model: A2083, 84, 85
Modeller: Margaret Turner
Height: 5 ½", 14.0 cm
Colour: A2083   Black
           A2084   Yellow
           A2085   Chocolate
Issued: 06/02 to the present
Series: Dogs and Pups Galore

U.K.:   £21.00
U.S.: $40.00
Can.: $40.00

LABRADOR, Seated
Style Three

Model: A0645/A0649
Modeller: Lesley McKenzie
Height: 15", 38.1 cm
Colour: A0645   Yellow
           A0649   Black
Issued: A0645   01/01-06/05
           A0649   01/01-12/04
Series: Fireside Dogs

U.K.:   £ 75.00
U.S.: $150.00
Can.: $150.00

LABRADOR, Standing
Style One

Model: UK# 065
           USA# 225-129
Modeller: David Geenty
Height: 6 ½", 16.5 cm
Colour: Black
Issued: 07/81 - 12/82

U.K.:   £ 65.00
U.S.: $125.00
Can.: $125.00

LABRADOR, Standing
Style Two

Model: A1156, 57, 58
Modeller: Margaret Turner
Height: 5 ½", 14.0 cm
Colour: A1156   Chocolate
           A1157   Yellow
           A1158   Black
Issued: 06/01 to the present
Series: Dogs and Pups Galore

U.K.:   £23.00
U.S.: $45.00
Can.: $45.00

LABRADOR, Standing
Style Three

Model: A1864, 3092
Modeller: Margaret Turner
Height: 8 ¾", 22.2 cm
Colour: A1864   Black
           A3092   Yellow
Issued: 01/03 - 12/04

U.K.:   £ 50.00
U.S.: $100.00
Can.: $100.00

LABRADOR, Standing
Style Four

Model: A7110, 8144, 8145
Modeller: Unknown
Height: 5 ½", 14.0 cm
Colour: A7110   Black
           A8144   Yellow
           A8145   Chocolate
Issued: 01/07 to the present
Series: Dogs and Pups Galore

U.K.:   £21.00
U.S.: $40.00
Can.: $40.00

LABRADOR, Walking
(Carrying Lead)

Model: B0243A, B
Modeller: Margaret Turner
Height: 6 ¼", 15.9 cm
Colour: A. Yellow
           B. Black
Issued: 01/98 - 12/99
Series: Dogs by Margaret
           Turner

U.K.:   £ 80.00
U.S.: $160.00
Can.: $160.00

LABRADOR AND GUN

Model: 052A, B
Modeller: Anne Wall
Height: 4", 8.9 cm
Colour: A. Black
B. Yellow
Issued: 07/78 - 12/86
Series: The World of Dogs

	Black	Yellow
U.K.	£125.	£100.
U.S.	$250.	$200.
Can.	$250.	$200.

LABRADOR AND JACK RUSSELL

Model: A4673
Modeller: Janet Miller
Height: 8 ½", 21.6 cm
Colour: Light golden yellow, white and tan
Issued: 01/05 - 12/05
Series: Big Dog, Little Dog

U.K.	£25.00
U.S.	$50.00
Can.	$50.00

LABRADOR AND PUP
Style One

Model: DPG01A, B
Modeller: Margaret Turner
Height: 6 ½", 16.5 cm
Colour: A. Golden
B. Black
Issued: 01/96 - 12/98
Series: Dogs Galore

U.K.	£40.00
U.S.	$80.00
Can.	$80.00

LABRADOR AND PUP
Style Two

Model: 135
Modeller: Unknown
Height: 6", 15.0 cm
Colour: A. Black
B. Golden
Issued: Unknown

U.K.:	£40.00
U.S.:	$80.00
Can.:	$80.00

LABRADOR AND PUPS
Style One

Model: UK# 060A, B
USA# 225-121
Modeller: David Geenty
Height: 6", 15.0 cm
Colour: A. Yellow
B. Black
Issued: 01/80 - 12/84

	Yellow	Black
U.K.	£100.	£125.
U.S.	$200.	$250.
Can.	$200.	$250.

LABRADOR AND PUPS
Style Two

Model: 206A, B
Modeller: Anne Butler
Height: 4", 10.1 cm
Colour: A. Yellow
B. Black
Issued: 01/90 - 12/93
Series: 1. The World of Dogs
2. Special Interest

	Yellow	Black
U.K.:	£ 50.	£ 65.
U.S.:	$100.	$125.
Can.:	$100.	$125.

LABRADOR AND PUPS
Style Three

Model: B0350A, B
Modeller: Margaret Turner
Height: 6 ½", 16.5 cm
Colour: A. Yellow bitch
B. Black bitch
Issued: 01/00 in a limited edition of 950
Series: Dogs by Margaret Turner

	Yellow	Black
U.K.:	£100.	£125.
U.S.:	$200.	$250.
Can.:	$200.	$250.

LABRADOR AND THREE PUPS

Model: A3059, 4708
Modeller: Margaret Turner
Height: 4 ½", 11.9 cm
Colour: A3059 Black
A4708 Yellow
Issued: 06/04 - 06/07
Series: Dogs and Pups Galore: Family Groups

U.K.:	£31.00
U.S.:	$60.00
Can.:	$60.00

LABRADOR FAMILY

Model:	B0730A, B, C
Modeller:	Margaret Turner
Height:	8", 20.3 cm
Colour:	B0730A Yellow
	B0730B Black
	B0730C Chocolate
Issued:	06/01 in a limited edition of 950 for a total of all colourways
Series:	Dogs by Margaret Turner
U.K.:	£150.00
U.S.:	$300.00
Can.:	$300.00

LABRADOR FLUSHING OUT PHEASANTS

Model:	A1440, 1671
Modeller:	Margaret Turner
Height:	4", 10.1 cm
Colour:	A1440 Yellow
	A1671 Black
Issued:	01/02 - 12/04
Series:	Action Dogs
U.K.:	£ 75.00
U.S.:	$150.00
Can.:	$150.00

LABRADOR IN LAUNDRY BASKET

Model:	484172/484180
Modeller:	Unknown
Height:	3 ¾", 9.5 cm
Colour:	484172 Yellow
	484180 Black
Issued:	06/98 - 12/00
Series:	Puppy Tales
U.K.:	£12.00
U.S.:	$25.00
Can.:	$25.00

LABRADOR IN PICNIC BASKET

Model:	484156/484164
Modeller:	Unknown
Height:	3", 7.6 cm
Colour:	484156 Yellow
	484164 Black
Issued:	06/98 - 12/00
Series:	Puppy Tales
U.K.:	£12.00
U.S.:	$25.00
Can.:	$25.00

LABRADOR PUP, Lying

Model:	B0437A, B
Modeller:	Margaret Turner
Height:	2 ¼", 5.7 cm
Colour:	A. Yellow
	B. Black
Issued:	01/99 - 12/01
Series:	Pups Galore
U.K.:	£12.00
U.S.:	$25.00
Can.:	$25.00

LABRADOR PUPPIES

Model:	ED1
Modeller:	Judy Boyt
Height:	2", 5.0 cm
Colour:	Golden brown
Issued:	07/82 - 06/85
Series:	Early Days
U.K.:	£40.00
U.S.:	$80.00
Can.:	$80.00

LABRADOR PUPPY, Lying (Stick in Mouth)

Model:	PG02A, B
Modeller:	Margaret Turner
Height:	1 ¾", 4.4 cm
Colour:	A. Golden
	B. Black
Issued:	01/92 - 12/94
Series:	Pups Galore
U.K.:	£12.00
U.S.:	$25.00
Can.:	$25.00

LABRADOR PUPPY, Seated

Model:	PG11A, B/B0454
Modeller:	Margaret Turner
Height:	3 ¼", 8.3 cm
Colour:	A. Golden
	B. Black
	B0454 Bronze
Issued:	PG11A 07/94-12/01
	PG11B 07/94-12/01
	B0454 06/99-06/00
Series:	1. Pups Galore
	2. Bronzed
U.K.:	£12.00
U.S.:	$25.00
Can.:	$25.00

LABRADOR PUPS (Pair)

Model:	B0249A, B/B0463
Modeller:	Margaret Turner
Height:	3 ¼", 8.3 cm
Colour:	A. Yellow
	B. Black
	B0463 Bronze
Issued:	A. 01/98 - 12/01
	B. 01/98 - 12/01
	B0463 06/99-06/00
Series:	1. Pups Galore
	2. Bronzed

	Black	Yellow	Bronze
U.K.:	£25.	£25.	£20.
U.S.:	$50.	$50.	$40.
Can.:	$50.	$50.	$40.

LABRADOR PUPS WITH DECOY DUCK

Model:	123A, B
Modeller:	Anne Butler
Height:	4", 10.1 cm
Colour:	A. Black
	B. Yellow
Issued:	06/91-Dec. 1993
Series:	Agricultural and
	Sporting

	Black	Yellow
U.K.:	£ 50.	£40.
U.S.:	$100.	$80.
Can.:	$100.	$80.

LABRADORS

Model:	Unknown
Modeller:	Victor Hayton
Height:	6", 15.0 cm
Colour:	A. Golden
	B. Black
	C. Bronze
Issued:	01/77 in a limited
	edition of 500

	Gold	Black	Bronze
U.K.:	£175.	£225.	£100.
U.S.:	$350.	$450.	$200.
Can.:	$350.	$450.	$200.

LACKING HORSE POWER

Model:	B0985
Modeller:	Ray Ayres
Size:	4 ¾" x 12¾"
	12.1 x 32.4 cm
Colour:	Green, grey, browns,
	black and white
Issued:	2006 in a limited
	edition of 950
U.K.:	£250.00
U.S.:	$500.00
Can.:	$500.00

LADIES IN WAITING (Two Hens)

Model:	A0163
Modeller:	Anne Wall
Height:	5", 12.7cm
Colour:	Brown, grey and tan
Issued:	01/01 - 12/06
Series:	James Herriot
	Studio Collection
U.K.:	£20.00
U.S.:	$40.00
Can.:	$40.00

LADIES OF THE STREAM (Otter and Young)

Model:	L97
Modeller:	Elizabeth Waugh
Height:	11 ½", 29.2 cm
Colour:	Brown and cream
Issued:	01/90 in a limited
	edition of 950
U.K.:	£450.00
U.S.:	$900.00
Can.:	$900.00

LADY AMHERST'S PHEASANT

Model:	B0328
Modeller:	Richard Roberts
Height:	15 ¼", 38.7 cm
Colour:	White, black, blue,
	yellow and red
Issued:	06/98 in a limited
	edition of 950
Series:	1. Exotic Birds
	2. Birds of the World
U.K.:	£ 550.00
U.S.:	$1,100.00
Can.:	$1,100.00

LAKELAND FELL TERRIER, Seated

Model:	DM5
Modeller:	Ray Ayres
Height:	4 ¾", 12.1 cm
Colour:	Black
Issued:	01/84 - 12/86
Series:	The World of Dogs
U.K.:	£300.00
U.S.:	$600.00
Can.:	$600.00

**LAMB, Lying
Style One**

Model:	FF8A, B, C
Modeller:	Anne Wall
Height:	1 ¾", 4.4 cm
Colour:	A. White; black face
	B. Unknown
	C. Unknown
Issued:	07/90 - 12/95
Series:	First Friends
U.K.:	£12.00
U.S.:	$25.00
Can.:	$25.00

**LAMB, Lying
Style Two**

Model:	B0960, 0960A
Modeller:	Ray Ayres
Height:	6 ¼", 15.9 cm
Colour:	B0960 White
	B0960A Black / white
Issued:	06/05 - 12/06
Series:	Classic Babies
U.K.:	£40.00
U.S.:	$80.00
Can.:	$80.00

LAMB, Standing

Model:	M6
Modeller:	David Geenty
Height:	4", 10.1 cm
Colour:	White
Issued:	07/80 - 12/80
Series:	Beginners, Please
U.K.:	£40.00
U.S.:	$80.00
Can.:	$80.00

**LAMB AND BORDER COLLIE
PUP**

Model:	FE11
Modeller:	Ray Ayres
Height:	3 ½", 8.9 cm
Colour:	Black, white and cream
Issued:	01/86 - 12/97
Series:	First Encounters
U.K.:	£40.00
U.S.:	$80.00
Can.:	$80.00

LAMB AND BUCKET

Model:	A3866
Modeller:	Janet Miller
Height:	1 ¾", 4.4 cm
Colour:	Cream, white, silver
	and brown
Issued:	01/04 - 12/06
Series:	On The Farm
U.K.:	£13.00
U.S.:	$25.00
Can.:	$25.00

LAMB AND BUTTERFLY

Model:	FE14A, B
Modeller:	Ray Ayres
Height:	3 ¾", 9.5 cm
Colour:	A. White lamb
	B. Black-faced lamb
Issued:	01/90 - 12/92
Series:	First Encounters
U.K.:	£ 50.00
U.S.:	$100.00
Can.:	$100.00

LAMB WITH BOOT

Model:	A0170/A0171
Modeller:	Anne Wall
Height:	2", 5.0 cm
Colour:	A0170 White
	A0171 Black-faced
Issued:	06/00 - 12/06
Series:	On The Farm
U.K.:	£12.00
U.S.:	$25.00
Can.:	$25.00

LAMBS AND PUP IN CRATE

Model:	A5624
Modeller:	Kerry Bell
Height:	2 ¼", 5.7 cm
Colour:	B lack, white,
	brown and cream
Issued:	01/05 - 12/06
Series:	On The Farm
U.K.:	£20.00
U.S.:	$40.00
Can.:	$40.00

LAMBS AND SHELTER

Model:	A3704
Modeller:	Kerry Bell
Height:	4 ¼", 10.8 cm
Colour:	White, silver, yellow and green
Issued:	01/04 - 06/06
Series:	James Herriot Studio Collection
U.K.:	£40.00
U.S.:	$80.00
Can.:	$80.00

LAPWING

Model:	RB38
Modeller:	Ray Ayres
Height:	5 ¾", 14.6 cm
Colour:	Grey-brown, white, yellow, red and golden
Issued:	01/93 - 12/95
Series:	RSPB Birds of the Countryside
U.K.:	£300.00
U.S.:	$600.00
Can.:	$600.00

LARGE BLUE
(Butterfly)

Model:	B9	
Modeller:	Ray Ayres	
Height:	3", 7.6 cm	
Colour:	Blue, white, black and green	
Issued:	01/81 - 12/85	
Re-issued:	07/90 - 12/91	
Series:	British Butterflies	

	Original	Re-issued
U.K.:	£ 65.	£40.
U.S.:	$125.	$80.
Can.:	$125.	$80.

Note: Earlier models were issued without antenae. Domes were optional with all butterflies.

LAST BOUT, THE
(Reaper binder)

Model:	B0895
Modeller:	Ray Ayres
Size:	7" x 16 ½" 17.8 x 41.9 cm
Colour:	Browns, white, blue and green
Issued:	06/05 in a limited edition of 600
Series:	Classic Collection
U.K.:	£ 595.00
U.S.:	$1,200.00
Can.:	$1,200.00

LAST LAUGH, THE
(Fergie TE20)

Model:	B0946
Modeller:	Ray Ayres
Length:	15", 38.1 cm
Colour:	Light and dark grey, black, green and sandy brown
Issued:	01/05 in a limited edition of 950
U.K.:	£295.00
U.S.:	$600.00
Can.:	$600.00

Note: Authorised by AGCO Corpoartion.

LAST LOOK, THE
(Dog Fox)

Model:	BFA204
Modeller:	Ray Ayres
Height:	11 ¼", 28.5 cm
Colour:	Reddish-brown
Issued:	01/94 in a limited edition of 1,250
Series:	20th Anniversary
U.K.:	£225.00
U.S.:	$450.00
Can.:	$450.00

LAST TO FINISH
(Pig and Piglets)

Model:	B0011
Modeller:	Kirsty Armstrong
Height:	4 ½", 11.9 cm
Colour:	Pink
Issued:	06/96 - 12/98
Series:	1. All Creatures Great and Small
	2. The James Herriot Collection
U.K.:	£ 65.00
U.S.:	$125.00
Can.:	$125.00

LATE THAW
(Otters)

Model:	MTR07
Modeller:	Ray Ayres
Height:	5 ¾", 14.6 cm
Colour:	Brown and white
Issued:	01/95 in a limited edition of 2,000
Series:	Masters of the River
U.K.:	£100.00
U.S.:	$200.00
Can.:	$200.00

LAYING AWAY
(Hen nesting)

Model:	JH105
Modeller:	Anne Wall
Height:	2", 5.0 cm
Colour:	Golden brown
Issued:	01/96 - 12/00
Series:	1. Every Living Thing
	2. J. Herriot Collection
U.K.:	£20.00
U.S.:	$40.00
Can.:	$40.00

LAYING THE CLAYS
(Farmer laying land drains, Ayrshire cows)

Model:	B0535
Modeller:	Ray Ayres
Size:	5 ½", 14.0 cm
Colour:	Yellow, red, browns and white
Issued:	01/00 in a limited edition of 1,750
Series:	Nature's Kingdom
U.K.:	£400.00
U.S.:	$800.00
Can.:	$800.00

LEADING HAND
(Boy, calf and dog)

Model:	B0297
Modeller:	Anne Wall
Height:	6 ½", 16.5 cm
Colour:	Yellow, blue, black, white and grey
Issued:	06/98 - 12/99
Series:	J. Herriot Collection
U.K.:	£ 75.00
U.S.:	$150.00
Can.:	$150.00

LEARNING TO FLY
(Tawny owl and owlet)

Model:	WB96
Modeller:	Russell Willis
Height:	4", 10.1 cm
Colour:	Golden brown and cream
Issued:	01/95 - 12/97
Series:	1. Owls of the World
	2. Russell Willis Birds
U.K.:	£30.00
U.S.:	$60.00
Can.:	$60.00

LEICESTER FOX

Model:	L58
Modeller:	Ray Ayres
Height:	7", 17.8 cm
Colour:	Reddish-brown
Issued:	01/84 in a limited edition of 500
U.K.:	£375.00
U.S.:	$750.00
Can.:	$750.00

LEONARDO
(Mallard Duck)

Model:	L145
Modeller:	Don Briddell
Height:	9 ½", 24.0 cm
Colour:	Brown, grey, blue and green
Issued:	01/94 in a limited edition of 350
Series:	Masterpiece
U.K.:	£ 500.00
U.S.:	$1,000.00
Can.:	$1,000.00

LEOPARD

Model:	A3065
Modeller:	David Mayer
Height:	6 ½", 16.5 cm
Colour:	Golden brown, cream, black and grey
Issued:	01/05 - 12/06
Series:	Wild World
U.K.:	£ 75.00
U.S.:	$150.00
Can.:	$150.00

LEOPARD AND CUBS

Model:	RW23
Modeller:	Richard Wawrzesta
Height:	3 ¾", 9.5 cm
Colour:	Yellow and black
Issued:	01/92 - 12/95
Series:	Endangered Species (WWF)
U.K.:	£ 65.00
U.S.:	$125.00
Can.:	$125.00

LET SLEEPING DOGS LIE
(Collie and Cats)

Model:	JH36
Modeller:	David Walton
Height:	4 ¾", 12.1 cm
Colour:	Black, white, browns and cream
Issued:	01/90 - 12/97
Series:	1. All Things Wise and Wonderful
	2. The James Herriot Collection
U.K.:	£125.00
U.S.:	$250.00
Can.:	$250.00

LET'S BE FRIENDS
(Border collies and kittens)

Model:	A6864
Modeller:	Unknown
Size:	7" x 7 ¾"
	17.8 x 19.7 cm
Colour:	Black, white, browns and cream
Issued:	06/06 to the present
Series:	James Herriot Studio Collection
U.K.:	£ 55.00
U.S.:	$110.00
Can.:	$110.00

LHASA APSO, Standing

Model:	A3840
Modeller:	Margaret Turner
Height:	3", 7.6 cm
Colour:	White, tan and grey
Issued:	06/04 - 12/06
Series:	Dogs and Pups Galore
U.K.:	£12.00
U.S.:	$24.00
Can.:	$24.00

LIFTING OFF
(Pair of Mallard Ducks)

Model:	B0182
Modeller:	David Walton
Height:	6 ¾", 17.2 cm
Colour:	White, grey, brown and green
Issued:	06/97 in a limited edition of 2,500
Series:	Nature's Kingdom
U.K.:	£125.00
U.S.:	$250.00
Can.:	$250.00

LIFTING THE PINKS
(International B250 tractor)

Model:	B0219
Modeller:	Ray Ayres
Height:	5 ½", 14.0 cm
Colour:	Red, black, blue and white
Issued:	01/98 in a limited edition of 1,750
Series:	All Creatures Great and Small
U.K.:	£ 550.00
U.S.:	$1,100.00
Can.:	$1,100.00

LIKE FATHER LIKE SON

Model:	B0859
Modeller:	Ray Ayres
Height:	6 ¼", 15.9 cm
Colour:	White, orange, black, blue and grey
Issued:	01/04 - 12/04
Series:	Classic Member-only Tractor Figurine
U.K.:	£250.00
U.S.:	$500.00
Can.:	$500.00

LILY AND LION

Model:	FC14
Designer:	Fleur Cowles
Modeller:	Unknown
Height:	Unknown
Colour:	Lemon, pale green, tan and dark brown
Issued:	1987-Dec. 1988
Series:	Fleur's Flowers
U.K.:	£ 80.00
U.S.:	$160.00
Can.:	$160.00

LIMOUSIN BULL
Style One

Model:	L32
Modeller:	Anne Wall
Height:	6", 15.0 cm
Colour:	Brown
Issued:	03/81 in a limited edition of 1,500
Series:	Special Interest
U.K.:	£350.00
U.S.:	$700.00
Can.:	$700.00

LIMOUSIN BULL
Style Two

Model:	B0531
Modeller:	Jack Crewdson
Height:	10", 25.4 cm
Colour:	Reddish-brown and white
Issued:	01/00 in a limited edition of 750
Series:	Agricultural and Sporting
U.K.:	£300.00
U.S.:	$600.00
Can.:	$600.00

LIMOUSIN BULL
Style Three

Model:	A0739
Modeller:	Lesley McKenzie
Height:	5 ¼", 13.3 cm
Colour:	Reddish-brown
Issued:	06/01 - 12/06
Series:	Cattle Breeds
U.K.:	£40.00
U.S.:	$80.00
Can.:	$80.00

LIMOUSIN BULL
Style Five

Model:	B1013
Modeller:	Ray Ayres
Height:	6 ¼", 15.9 cm
Colour:	Reddish-brown and green
Issued:	06/06 in a limited edition of 750
U.K.:	£145.00
U.S.:	$300.00
Can.:	$300.00

LIMOUSIN

		BULL **Style Four**	CALF	COW
Model:		A4578	A4584	A4581
Modeller:	Anne Wall			
Height:		4 ½" 11.9 cm	3 ¼" 8.3 cm	4 ¾" 12.1 cm
Colour:	Reddish-brown			
Issued:	01/04 to the present			
Series:	BFA Pottery Company			
U.K.:		£25.00	£14.95	£25.00
U.S.:		$50.00	$30.00	$50.00
Can.:		$50.00	$30.00	$50.00

LIMOUSIN BULL, Lying

Model:	A5272
Modeller:	Lesley McKenzie
Height:	4 ¼", 10.8 cm
Colour:	Reddish-brown, cream, green and fawn
Issued:	01/05 - 12/06
U.K.:	£ 65.00
U.S.:	$120.00
Can.:	$120.00

LIMOUSIN CALVES

Model:	A5274
Modeller:	Lesley McKenzie
Height:	4 ½", 11.9 cm
Colour:	Reddish-brown, cream green and fawn
Issued:	01/05 to the present
U.K.:	£ 55.00
U.S.:	$110.00
Can.:	$110.00

LIMOUSIN COW AND CALF
Style One

Model:	L157
Modeller:	Anne Wall
Height:	6 ½", 16.5 cm
Colour:	Chestnut
Issued:	06/95 in a limited edition of 1,500
Series:	Agricultural and Sporting
U.K.:	£350.00
U.S.:	$700.00
Can.:	$700.00

LIMOUSIN COW AND CALF
Style Two

Model:	B0657
Modeller:	Jack Crewdson
Height:	9 ¼", 23.5 cm
Colour:	Reddish-brown
Issued:	01/01 in a limited edition of 750
Series:	The County Show
U.K.:	£300.00
U.S.:	$600.00
Can.:	$600.00

LIMOUSIN COW AND CALF
Style Three

Model:	A1250
Modeller:	Lesley McKenzie
Height:	5 ½", 14.0 cm
Colour:	Reddish-brown
Issued:	01/02 - 06/06
Series:	Cattle Breeds
U.K.:	£ 55.00
U.S.:	$110.00
Can.:	$110.00

LIMOUSIN FAMILY

Model:	B0855
Modeller:	Ray Ayres
Size:	6 ½" x 13" 16.5 x 33.0 cm
Colour:	Reddish-brown and green
Issued:	06/04 in a limited edition of 950
U.K.:	£250.00
U.S.:	$500.00
Can.:	$500.00

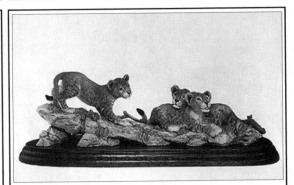

LION
Style One

Model:	B0669, 70, 71	
Modeller:	Richard Roberts	
Height:	4", 10.1 cm	
Colour:	B0669	Slate blue
	B0670	Stone
	B0671	Gold
Issued:	01/01 - 12/01	
Series:	Cubist Africa	
U.K.:	£25.00	
U.S.:	$50.00	
Can.:	$50.00	

LION
Style Two

Model:	A5047
Modeller:	David Mayer
Height:	6", 15.0 cm
Colour:	Golden brown, green and fawn
Issued:	01/05 - 12/06
Series:	Wild World
U.K.:	£ 60.00
U.S.:	$120.00
Can.:	$120.00

LION CUBS

Model:	RW61
Modeller:	Richard Roberts
Height:	4", 10.1 cm
Colour:	Orange, white and grey
Issued:	01/95 - 12/96
Series:	Nursery (WWF)
U.K.:	£ 80.00
U.S.:	$160.00
Can.:	$160.00

LIONESS AND CUB

Model:	WW21
Modeller:	David Walton
Height:	2 ½", 6.4 cm
Colour:	Reddish-brown
Issued:	07/94 - 12/95
Series:	Miniature (WWF)

U.K.:	£20.00
U.S.:	$40.00
Can.:	$40.00

LITTLE EGRET

Model:	B0586
Modeller:	Richard Roberts
Height:	15 ¾", 40.0 cm
Colour:	White, black and green
Issued:	06/00 in a limited edition of 500
Series:	1. Nature's Kingdom 2. Birds of the World

U.K.:	£325.00
U.S.:	$650.00
Can.:	$650.00

LITTLE OWL
Style One

Model:	UK# 036 USA# 225-157
Modeller:	Anne Wall
Height:	6 ½", 16.5 cm
Colour:	Brown and white
Issued:	06/79 - 06/86

U.K.:	£ 65.00
U.S.:	$125.00
Can.:	$125.00

Note: This model was issued as Elf Owl in the USA.

LITTLE OWL
Style Two

Model:	090
Modeller:	Ray Ayres
Height:	6", 15.0 cm
Colour:	Grey-brown and cream
Issued:	01/88 - 12/90
Series:	British Birds

U.K.:	£ 65.00
U.S.:	$125.00
Can.:	$125.00

LITTLE OWL
Style Three

Model:	WB02
Modeller:	Russell Willis
Height:	3 ¾", 9.5 cm
Colour:	Dark brown and white
Issued:	07/92 - 12/94
Series:	1. Owls of the World 2. Russell Willis Birds

U.K.:	£30.00
U.S.:	$60.00
Can.:	$60.00

LITTLE OWL
Style Four

Model:	WB84
Modeller:	Russell Willis
Height:	6 ½", 16.5 cm
Colour:	Dark brown and cream
Issued:	01/94 - 12/95
Series:	1. Owls of the World 2. Russell Willis Birds

U.K.:	£ 65.00
U.S.:	$125.00
Can.:	$125.00

LITTLE OWL
Style Five

Model:	541737
Modeller:	Russell Willis
Height:	6 ¼", 15.9 cm
Colour:	Browns
Issued:	01/99 - 12/00
Series:	Woodland and Garden

U.K.:	£35.00
U.S.:	$70.00
Can.:	$70.00

LITTLE OWL AND OWLET

Model:	RB27
Modeller:	Ray Ayres
Height:	6 ¾", 17.2 cm
Colour:	Brown, grey and beige
Issued:	01/92 - 12/93

U.K.:	£ 75.00
U.S.:	$150.00
Can.:	$150.00

LLEYN EWE AND LAMBS

Model:	B0975
Modeller:	Ray AYres
Size:	5 ¼" x 7 ¾"
	13.3 x 19.7 cm
Colour:	White and green
Issued:	01/06 in a limited edition of 500
U.K.:	£130.00
U.S.:	$250.00
Can.:	$250.00

LOADING UP (MF 35)

Model:	A3448
Modeller:	Ray Ayres
Height:	6", 15.0 cm
Colour:	Red, black, white and light brown
Issued:	01/04 - 06/06
Series:	Tractors
U.K.:	£150.00
U.S.:	$300.00
Can.:	$300.00

LOGGING

Model:	B0700
Modeller:	Ray Ayres
Height:	7" x 18",
	17.8 x 45.7 cm
Colour:	Browns, black, white, blue and yellow
Issued:	06/01 in a limited edition of 1,750
Series:	Classic Collection
U.K.:	£300.00
U.S.:	$600.00
Can.:	$600.00

LONDON OMNIBUS, THE

Model:	B0736
Modeller:	Ray Ayres
Height:	8 ½", 21.5 cm
Colour:	Yellow, red, brown, blue and grey
Issued:	01/02 in a limited edition of 500
Series:	Classic Collection
U.K.:	£ 650.00
U.S.:	$1,300.00
Can.:	$1,300.00

LONG-EARED OWL
Style One

Model:	RB20
Modeller:	Ray Ayres
Height:	11 ½", 29.2 cm
Colour:	Browns
Issued:	01/91 - 12/92
U.K.:	£225.00
U.S.:	$450.00
Can.:	$450.00

LONG-EARED OWL
Style Two

Model:	WB05
Modeller:	Russell Willis
Height:	4", 10.1 cm
Colour:	Browns and cream
Issued:	07/92 - 12/95
Series:	1. Owls of the World
	2. Russell Willis Birds
U.K.:	£25.00
U.S.:	$50.00
Can.:	$50.00

LONG-EARED OWL
Style Three

Model:	541729
Modeller:	Russell Willis
Height:	8 ¼", 21.0 cm
Colour:	Browns
Issued:	01/99 - 12/00
Series:	Woodland and Garden
U.K.:	£40.00
U.S.:	$80.00
Can.:	$80.00

LONG-HAIRED CAT

Model:	CG10A, B, C
Modeller:	Anne Wall
Height:	4 ¼", 10.8 cm
Colour:	A. Tabby and white
	B. Ginger and white
	C. Black and white
Issued:	01/95 - 12/95
Series:	Cats Galore
U.K.:	£25.00
U.S.:	$50.00
Can.:	$50.00

LONG-HAIRED CHIHUAHUA

Model:	DG27
Modeller:	Margaret Turner
Height:	3 ¼", 8.3 cm
Colour:	Golden brown
Issued:	01/94 - 12/95
Series:	Dogs Galore
U.K.:	£20.00
U.S.:	$40.00
Can.:	$40.00

LONG-HAIRED DACHSHUND

Model:	B0316A, B
Modeller:	Margaret Turner
Height:	3 ½", 8.9 cm
Colour:	A. Black and tan
	B. Red
Issued:	06/98 - 06/01
Series:	Dogs Galore
U.K.:	£20.00
U.S.:	$40.00
Can.:	$40.00

LONG-HAIRED KITTEN, Lying

Model:	KG2A, B, C, D, E
Modeller:	Anne Wall
Height:	2", 5.0 cm
Colour:	A. White
	B. Grey and white
	C. Black and white
	D. White and ginger
	E. Tabby
Issued:	07/94 - 12/95
Series:	Kittens Galore
U.K.:	£15.00
U.S.:	$30.00
Can.:	$30.00

LONGHORN COW AND CALF

Model:	B0993
Modeller:	Ray AYres
Size:	6 ½" x 10 ¼"
	16.5 x 26.0 cm
Colour:	Brown, white
	and green
Issued:	04/07 in a limited
	edition of 500
U.K.:	£195.00
U.S.:	$400.00
Can.:	$400.00

LONG-TAILED FIELD MOUSE AND FAMILY

Model:	L13
Modeller:	Anne Wall
Height:	5 ½", 14.0 cm
Colour:	A. Brown and white
	B. Bronze
Issued:	07/78 in a limited
	edition of 850
Series:	Bronze

	Brown	Bronze
U.K.:	£175.	£ 80.
U.S.:	$350.	$160.
Can.:	$350.	$160.

LOOK, LISTEN AND LEARN
(Vixen and cubs)

Model:	L124
Modeller:	Ray Ayres
Height:	7 ¼", 18.4 cm
Colour:	Reddish-brown, brown,
	green and grey
Issued:	01/93 in a limited
	edition of 1,500
Series:	Masterpiece
U.K.:	£200.00
U.S.:	$400.00
Can.:	$400.00

LOOK SEE
(Fox cub and butterfly)

Model:	FT01
Modeller:	David Walton
Height:	2 ¾", 7.0 cm
Colour:	Reddish-brown, white
	and black
Issued:	07/95 - 12/00
Series:	Fox Tales
U.K.:	£25.00
U.S.:	$50.00
Can.:	$50.00

LOOSE RAKING
(Gold Edition)

Model:	B0697
Modeller:	Ray Ayres
Height:	6 ¼", 15.9 cm
Colour:	Blue, browns, white and green
Issued:	06/03 in a limited edition of 350
Series:	Classic Collection
U.K.:	£325.00
U.S.:	$650.00
Can.:	$650.00

(Standard Edition)

Model:	B0697A
Modeller:	Ray Ayres
Height:	6 ¼", 15.9 cm
Colour:	Blue, browns, white and green
Issued:	06/03 in a limited edition of 600
Series:	Classic Collection
U.K.:	£325.00
U.S.:	$650.00
Can.:	$650.00

Note: Numbered 1 to 350.

Note: Numbered 351 to 950.

LORD OF THE GLEN
(Golden eagle)

Model:	L161
Modeller:	Robert Dockwray
Height:	21", 53.3 cm
Colour:	Browns and grey
Issued:	01/96 in a limited edition of 950
Series:	Nature's Kingdom
U.K.:	£325.00
U.S.:	$650.00
Can.:	$650.00

LORD OF THE RIVER
(Otter)

Model:	L85
Modeller:	Elizabeth Waugh
Height:	9", 22.9 cm
Colour:	Brown, white and cream
Issued:	01/88 in a limited edition of 950
U.K.:	£300.00
U.S.:	$600.00
Can.:	$600.00

LOST AND FOUND
(Shepherd, collie and lamb)

Model:	B0300
Modeller:	Ray Ayres
Height:	8 ½", 21.6 cm
Colour:	Browns, green, black and white
Issued:	06/98 - 12/99
Series:	1. Every Living Thing
	2. J. Herriot Collection
U.K.:	£125.00
U.S.:	$250.00
Can.:	$250.00

LOVE YOU TOO!
(Pony and boy)

Model:	A6240
Modeller:	Anne Wall
Height:	4", 10.1 cm
Colour:	Brown, white, red, blue and green
Issued:	01/06 - 12/06
Series:	Hay Days
U.K.:	£25.00
U.S.:	$50.00
Can.:	$50.00

LUNCH AT THE SAVOY
(Cockerel and Two Hens)

Model:	B0441
Modeller:	Anne Wall
Height:	5", 12.7 cm
Colour:	Blue, red, white, brown, yellow and green
Issued:	06/99 - 06/01
Series:	J. Herriot Collection
U.K.:	£ 65.00
U.S.:	$125.00
Can.:	$125.00

LURCHER, Lying
First Variation

Model:	DG35A, B
Modeller:	Margaret Turner
Height:	4 ¼", 10.8 cm
Colour:	A. Grey
	B. Fawn
Issued:	01/96 - 06/01
Series:	Dogs Galore
U.K.:	£25.00
U.S.:	$50.00
Can.:	$50.00

LURCHER, Lying
Second Variation

Model:	A3049, 50
Modeller:	Margaret Turner
Height:	4", 10.1 cm
Colour:	A3049 Grey
	A3050 Fawn
Issued:	06/03 - 12/04
Series:	Dogs and Pups Galore

U.K.:	£20.00
U.S.:	$40.00
Can.:	$40.00

LURCHER, Standing
Style One

Model:	EW1
Modeller:	Elizabeth Waugh
Height:	10 ¾", 27.8 cm
Colour:	A. Browns
	B. Bronze
Issued:	01/86 in a limited edition of 250
Series:	Special Interest

	Browns	Bronze
U.K.:	£350.	£150.
U.S.:	$700.	$300.
Can.:	$700.	$300.

Note: Custom painted.

LURCHER, Standing
Style Two

Model:	A3058, 3788
Modeller:	Margaret Turner
Height:	6 ½", 16.5 cm
Colour:	A3058 Grey
	A3788 Fawn
Issued:	06/03 - 12/05
Series:	Dogs and Pups Galore

U.K.:	£20.00
U.S.:	$40.00
Can.:	$40.00

LURCHER, Standing
Style Three

Model:	B1053, 1053A
Modeller:	Margaret Turner
Height:	10" x 11 ½" 25.4 x 29.2 cm
Colour:	B1053 Grey
	B1053A Fawn
Issued:	06/07 in a limited edition of 500

U.K.:	£199.00
U.S.:	$400.00
Can.:	$400.00

MACAW

Model:	L76
Modeller:	Richard Roberts
Height:	20", 50.8 cm
Colour:	Red, blues and yellow
Issued:	01/87 in a limited edition of 950
Series:	Exotic Birds

U.K.:	£375.00
U.S.:	$750.00
Can.:	$750.00

MAGNOLIA AND LIONESS

Model:	FC15
Designer:	Fleur Cowles
Modeller:	Unknown
Height:	Unknown
Colour:	Lemon, pale green and orange
Issued:	1987 - 12/88
Series:	Fleur's Flowers

U.K.:	£ 75.00
U.S.:	$150.00
Can.:	$150.00

MAKING A SPLASH
(Border collie pups and Indian Runner Ducks)

Model:	A4244
Modeller:	Craig Harding
Height:	3", 7.6 cm
Colour:	Black, white, green, brown and orange
Issued:	06/04 - 12/06
Series:	James Herriot Studio Collection

U.K.:	£30.00
U.S.:	$60.00
Can.:	$60.00

MAKING ADJUSTMENTS
(Farmall McCormick Model M)

Model:	A2142
Modeller:	Ray Ayres
Height:	5 ¼", 13.3 cm
Colour:	Red, black, browns and green
Issued:	06/03 - 06/05
Series:	Tractors

U.K.:	£135.00
U.S.:	$275.00
Can.:	$275.00

MAKING FRIENDS
(Horse and Cat)

Model: A0540
Modeller: Anne Wall
Height: 5 ¼", 13.3 cm
Colour: Browns, orange and tan
Issued: 01/01 - 06/06
Series: Hay Days

U.K.: £25.00
U.S.: $50.00
Can.: $50.00

MALLARD
Style One

Model: RW4
Modeller: Richard Wawrzesta
Height: 3 ½", 8.9 cm
Colour: Brown, yellow and green
Issued: 01/88 - 12/93
Series: 1. WWFN
2. Wildlife Studies (WWF)

U.K.: £40.00
U.S.: $80.00
Can.: $80.00

MALLARD
Style Two

Model: A0477
Modeller: Don Briddell
Height: 10 ¼", 26.0 cm
Colour: Grey, green, blue and brown
Issued: 01/01 - 12/02
Series: Waterfowl of the World by Don Briddell

U.K.: £ 80.00
U.S.: $160.00
Can.: $160.00

MALLARD
Style Three

Model: A6054
Modeller: Unknown
Height: 4 ½", 11.4 cm
Colour: Green, brown, white, grey and orange
Issued: 06/05 to the present

U.K.: £ 9.95
U.S.: $20.00
Can.: $20.00

MALLARD
Style Four

Model: A5268
Modeller: Russell Willis
Height: 4 ½", 11.4 cm
Colour: White, greens, brown, blue and orange
Issued: 01/06 to the present
Series: BFA Pottery Company

U.K.: £16.00
U.S.: $32.00
Can.: $32.00

MALLARD DRAKE

Model: PS13
Modeller: Richard Roberts
Height: 2 ¾", 7.0 cm
Colour: Grey, green and blue
Issued: 01/92 - 12/93
Series: Peter Scott Memorial Appeal (WWF)

U.K.: £ 65.00
U.S.: $125.00
Can.: $125.00

MALLARD DRAKE
(On Plank)

Model: PS04
Modeller: Richard Roberts
Height: 5", 12.7 cm
Colour: Brown, green and yellow
Issued: 12/91 - 12/92
Series: Peter Scott Memorial Appeal (WWF)

U.K.: £100.00
U.S.: $200.00
Can.: $200.00

MALLARD FAMILY

Model: WW17
Modeller: Richard Wawrzesta
Height: 3 ½", 8.9 cm
Colour: Brown, green and yellow
Issued: 01/87 - 12/87
Series: Family Life (WWF)

U.K.: £30.00
U.S.: $60.00
Can.: $60.00

MALLARDS

Model: A1391
Modeller: John Brown
Height: 10 ¾", 27.8 cm
Colour: Grey, white, blue, green, yellow and brown
Issued: 01/02 - 06/04
Series: Game Birds

U.K.: £100.00
U.S.: $200.00
Can.: $200.00

MANDARIN DRAKE

Model: PS15
Modeller: Richard Roberts
Height: 3 ¼", 8.3 cm
Colour: Black, yellow, orange, white, blue and pink
Issued: 01/92 - 12/93
Series: Peter Scott Memorial Appeal (WWF)

U.K.: £ 55.00
U.S.: $110.00
Can.: $110.00

MANDARIN DRAKE
(On Lily Pond)

Model: PS03
Modeller: Richard Roberts
Height: 3 ¾", 9.5 cm
Colour: Black, yellow and orange
Issued: 01/91 - 12/91
Series: Peter Scott Memorial Appeal (WWF)

U.K.: £ 80.00
U.S.: $160.00
Can.: $160.00

MARKET DAY

Model: JH27
Modeller: Elizabeth MacAllister
Height: 8 ½", 21.6 cm
Colour: Grey, brown, white and black
Issued: 01/88 in a limited edition of 950
Series: All Creatures Great and Small

U.K.: £1,750.00
U.S.: $3,500.00
Can.: $3,500.00

MARTHA

Model: A6516, 6643
Modeller: Anne Wall
Height: 4 ¼", 10.8 cm
Colour: A6516 Light Sussex
A6643 Rhode Island Red
Issued: 01/06 to the present
Series: James Herriot Studio Collection

U.K.: £13.00
U.S.: $25.00
Can.: $25.00

MASTER OF THE SKIES
(Golden Eagle)

Model: B0529
Modeller: Richard Roberts
Height: 19", 48.3 cm
Colour: Brown, golden and grey
Issued: 01/00 in a limited edition of 750
Series: 1. Birds of Prey
2. Birds of the World

U.K.: £400.00
U.S.: $800.00
Can.: $800.00

MEDITATION

Model: K229
Designer: Ben Black
Modeller: David Geenty
Height: 5", 12.7 cm
Colour: White and yellow
Issued: 01/88 in a limited edition of 950
Series: Ben Black's Garden of Clowns

U.K.: £225.00
U.S.: $450.00
Can.: $450.00

MERLIN AND CHICKS

Model: RB36
Modeller: Ray Ayres
Height: 6 ¾", 17.2 cm
Colour: Slate blue, green, reddish-brown, grey, and yellow
Issued: 07/92 - 12/94
Series: RSPB Birds of the Countryside

U.K.: £125.00
U.S.: $250.00
Can.: $250.00

MICE

Model:	ED8
Modeller:	Judy Boyt
Height:	2 ¼", 5.7 cm
Colour:	Browns
Issued:	07/83 - 12/84
Series:	Early Days

U.K.:	£40.00
U.S.:	$80.00
Can.:	$80.00

MICE ON CORN COB

Model:	018
Modeller:	Ray Ayres
Height:	5", 12.7 cm
Colour:	Brown, white and yellow
Issued:	01/81 - 12/85
Series:	1. Mammals
	2. Mice by Ray Ayres

U.K.:	£175.00
U.S.:	$350.00
Can.:	$350.00

MIGHT AND MAJESTY
(Snowy Owl and Owlet)

Model:	WB98
Modeller:	Russell Willis
Height:	4 ¼", 10.8 cm
Colour:	Cream
Issued:	01/95 - 12/96
Series:	Russell Willis Birds

U.K.:	£30.00
U.S.:	$60.00
Can.:	$60.00

MIGHTY PREDATORS
(Great Horned Owl and Owlet)

Model:	WB121
Modeller:	Russell Willis
Height:	4 ¼", 10.8 cm
Colour:	Browns and cream
Issued:	01/96 - 12/97
Series:	1. Owls of the World
	2. Russell Willis Birds

U.K.:	£30.00
U.S.:	$60.00
Can.:	$60.00

MILKING AT PETER TRENHOLMS

Model:	JH7
Modeller:	Ray Ayres
Height:	5 ½", 14.0 cm
Colour:	Browns and black
Issued:	01/85 - 12/88
Series:	All Creatures Great and Small

U.K.:	£ 500.00
U.S.:	$1,000.00
Can.:	$1,000.00

MILLIE (EDDIE STOBART)
(Volvo FH12)

Model:	B0544
Modeller:	Mike Harris
Size:	3 ½" x 8" x 6"
	8.9 x 20.3 x 15.0 cm
Colour:	Green, red, yellow and brown
Issued:	10/00 in a limited edition of 500

U.K.:	£250.00
U.S.:	$500.00
Can.:	$500.00

MILKING TIME
(Donkey and cat)

Model:	A3703
Modeller:	Anne Wall
Height:	6 ¼", 15.9 cm
Colour:	Grey, silver, ginger, green, white and blue
Issued:	01/05 - 12/06
Series:	James Herriot Studio Collection

U.K.:	£ 50.00
U.S.:	$100.00
Can.:	$100.00

MINIATURE BLACKBIRD AND NEST

Model:	WB103
Modeller:	Russell Willis
Height:	3", 7.6 cm
Colour:	Black, brown and green
Issued:	01/93 - 12/97
Series:	1. Cidermill
	2. Russell Willis Birds

U.K.:	£30.00
U.S.:	$60.00
Can.:	$60.00

MINIATURE BLUE TIT AND NEST

Model: WB101
Modeller: Russell Willis
Height: 3", 7.6 cm
Colour: Yellow, blue, brown and green
Issued: 01/93 - 12/97
Series: 1. Cidermill
2. Russell Willis Birds

U.K.: £30.00
U.S.: $60.00
Can.: $60.00

Note: See page 35 for Blue Tit with Nest.

MINIATURE BLUE TIT ON NEST

Model: B0234
Modeller: Russell Willis
Height: 3 ¼", 8.3 cm
Colour: Blue, green, tan, yellow and cream
Issued: 07/97 - Unknown
Series: Russell Willis Birds

U.K.: £30.00
U.S.: $60.00
Can.: $60.00

Note: See page 35 for Blue Tit with Nest.

MINIATURE BULLFINCH AND NEST

Model: WB106
Modeller: Russell Willis
Height: 3 ½", 8.9 cm
Colour: Pink, black, blue and white
Issued: 01/94 - 12/95
Series: 1. Cidermill
2. Russell Willis Birds

U.K.: £25.00
U.S.: $50.00
Can.: $50.00

MINIATURE GREAT TIT AND NEST

Model: WB107
Modeller: Russell Willis
Height: 3", 7.6 cm
Colour: Yellow, black, grey and white
Issued: 01/94 - 12/95
Series: 1. Cidermill
2. Russell Willis Birds

U.K.: £25.00
U.S.: $50.00
Can.: $50.00

MINIATURE LONG-TAILED TIT AND NEST

Model: WB104
Modeller: Russell Willis
Height: 3 ½", 8.9 cm
Colour: Cream, black, pink and green
Issued: 01/93 - 12/95
Series: 1. Cidermill
2. Russell Willis Birds

U.K.: £25.00
U.S.: $50.00
Can.: $50.00

MINIATURE NUTHATCH AND NEST

Model: WB108
Modeller: Russell Willis
Height: 2 ¾", 7.0 cm
Colour: Yellow, blue and green
Issued: 01/94 - 12/95
Series: 1. Cidermill
2. Russell Willis Birds

U.K.: £25.00
U.S.: $50.00
Can.: $50.00

**MINIATURE POODLE
(Lamb Cut, Seated)**

Model: DS8A, B
Modeller: Ray Ayres
Height: 3 ¼", 8.3 cm
Colour: A. White
B. Black
Issued: 07/83 - 12/92
Series: 1. The World of Dogs
2. Special Interest

U.K.: £ 50.00
U.S.: $100.00
Can.: $100.00

**MINIATURE POODLE
(Lion Cut)**

Model: UK# DM1
USA# 225-424
Modeller: Ray Ayres
Height: 4 ¼", 10.8 cm
Colour: A. Black
B. White
Issued: 01/83 - 12/84
Series: The World of Dogs

U.K.: £ 65.00
U.S.: $125.00
Can.: $125.00

MINIATURE ROBIN

Model:	B0226
Modeller:	Russell Willis
Height:	3", 7.6 cm
Colour:	Brown, red, grey and white
Issued:	07/97 - Unknown
Series:	Russell Willis Birds
U.K.:	£15.00
U.S.:	$30.00
Can.:	$30.00

MINIATURE ROBIN AND NEST

Model:	WB105
Modeller:	Russell Willis
Height:	3 ½", 8.9 cm
Colour:	Red, brown, copper and purple
Issued:	01/93 - 12/97
Series:	1. Cidermill
	2. Russell Willis Birds
U.K.:	£30.00
U.S.:	$60.00
Can.:	$60.00

MINIATURE SONG THRUSH AND NEST

Model:	WB102
Modeller:	Russell Willis
Height:	3 ½", 8.9 cm
Colour:	Browns, yellow and green
Issued:	01/93 - 12/97
Series:	1. Cidermill
	2. Russell Willis Birds
U.K.:	£30.00
U.S.:	$60.00
Can.:	$60.00

MINIATURE WREN AND NEST

Model:	WB100
Modeller:	Russell Willis
Height:	3 ¼", 8.3 cm
Colour:	Light and dark brown
Issued:	01/93 - 12/97
Series:	1. Cidermill
	2. Russell Willis Birds
U.K.:	£30.00
U.S.:	$60.00
Can.:	$60.00

**MINSTREL
(Clydesdale foal)**

Model:	A6518
Modeller:	Anne Wall
Height:	4", 10.1 cm
Colour:	Brown, white and grey
Issued:	01/06 to the present
Series:	James Herriot Studio Collection
U.K.:	£18.00
U.S.:	$35.00
Can.:	$35.00

**MISBEHAVING
(Spaniel puppy)**

Model:	B0950
Modeller:	Ray Ayres
Height:	4 ½", 11.4 cm
Colour:	Brown, white, green, yellow and orange
Issued:	06/05 - 12/06
Series:	Classic Event Special
U.K.:	£35.00
U.S.:	$70.00
Can.:	$70.00

**MISCHIEF
(Border Collie and groceries)**

Model:	A0905
Modeller:	Kirsty Armstrong
Height:	3", 7.6 cm
Colour:	Black, white, grey, blue, yellow and tan
Issued:	06/01 - 12/03
Series:	Event Special
U.K.:	£20.00
U.S.:	$40.00
Can.:	$40.00

**MISCHIEF
(Piglet and straw hat)**

Model:	JH78A, B
Modeller:	Anne Wall
Height:	2", 5.0 cm
Colour:	A. Pink
	B. Spotted
Issued:	01/93 - 12/94
Series:	Every Living Thing
U.K.:	£20.00
U.S.:	$40.00
Can.:	$40.00

MISSING MUM
(Border Collie pup)

Model: CEV04
Modeller: Ray Ayres
Height: 3", 7.6 cm
Colour: Black, white, blue and red
Issued: 01/96 - 12/98
Series: Event Special

U.K.: £20.00
U.S.: $40.00
Can.: $40.00

Note: One of a set of four.

MIXED BLESSINGS
(Border collies and kittens)

Model: A1860
Modeller: Hans Kendrick
Height: 4 ¼", 10.8 cm
Colour: Black, white, blue, orange and grey
Issued: 01/04 - 12/06
Series: James Herriot Studio Collection

U.K.: £40.00
U.S.: $80.00
Can.: $80.00

MONA
(Female mallard)

Model: L144
Modeller: Don Briddell
Height: 8 ¾", 22.2 cm
Colour: Browns and black
Issued: 01/94 in a limited edition of 350
Series: Masterpiece

U.K.: £ 500.00
U.S.: $1,000.00
Can.: $1,000.00

MONARCH OF GLEN MHOR
(Red Stag and Hinds)

Model: BFA205
Modeller: David Walton
Height: 17", 43.2 cm
Colour: Reddish-brown
Issued: 01/94 in a limited edition of 500
Series: 1. 20th Anniversary
2. Wildlife
3. Nature's Kingdom

U.K.: £ 850.00
U.S.: $1,700.00
Can.: $1,700.00

MONARCH OF THE DAWN
(Barn owl flying)

Model: RB42
Modeller: David Burnham Smith
Height: 9 ¼", 23.5 cm
Colour: Golden, cream and brown
Issued: 07/93 - 12/95

U.K.: £250.00
U.S.: $500.00
Can.: $500.00

MONTY
(Calf)

Model: A6517, 6739
Modeller: Lesley McKenzie
Height: 3 ¼", 8.3 cm
Colour: A6517 Black / white
A6739 Brown / white
Issued: 06/01 to the present
Series: James Herriot Studio Collection

U.K.: £18.00
U.S.: $35.00
Can.: $35.00

MOONLIGHT PORTRAIT
(Barn owls)

Model: B0337
Modeller: John Brown
Height: 6 ¾", 17.2 cm
Colour: Golden, white and brown
Issued: 06/98 - 12/99
Series: Event Special

U.K.: £ 80.00
U.S.: $160.00
Can.: $160.00

MOORLAND ALERT
(Pair of grouse)

Model: B0301
Modeller: John Brown
Height: 6 ¾", 17.2 cm
Colour: Red, brown, mauve and green
Issued: 06/98 in a limited edition of 2,500
Series: Nature's Kingdom

U.K.: £100.00
U.S.: $200.00
Can.: $200.00

176

MOORLAND HUNTERS
(Short-eared owl and owlet)

Model:	WB120
Modeller:	Russell Willis
Height:	4 ¼", 10.8 cm
Colour:	Dark and light brown and cream
Issued:	01/96 - 12/97
Series:	1. Owls of the World 2. Russell Willis Birds
U.K.:	£30.00
U.S.:	$60.00
Can.:	$60.00

MORE UP THAN DOWN
(Swans)

Model:	B0923
Modeller:	Ray Ayres
Size:	7 ½" x 11 ¾" 19.1 x 29.8 cm
Colour:	White, orange, black, grey and green
Issued:	01/05 in a limited edition of 500
Series:	Above and Below
U.K.:	£250.00
U.S.:	$500.00
Can.:	$500.00

MORNING COLLECTION
(Milk Lorry)

Model:	B0956
Modeller:	Ray AYres
Size:	5 ¼" x 12 ¼" 13.3 x 31.1 cm
Colour:	Grey, silver, green and light brown
Issued:	01/06 in a limited edition of 500
U.K.:	£275.00
U.S.:	$550.00
Can.:	$550.00

MORNING EXERCISE AT BALMORAL

Model:	B0814
Modeller:	Craig Harding
Height:	14 ½", 36.8 cm
Colour:	Dark brown, orange, white, light brown, green and cream
Issued:	01/03 in a limited edition of 500
Series:	Classic Collection
U.K.:	£350.00
U.S.:	$700.00
Can.:	$700.00

MORNING FEED
(Calf and bucket)

Model:	JH82A, B
Modeller:	Anne Butler
Height:	3 ¾", 9.5 cm
Colour:	A. Black and white Fresian B. Brown and white
Issued:	A. 01/93 - 12/00 B. 01/93 - 12/97
Series:	1. Every Living Thing 2. J. Herriot Collection
U.K.:	£40.00
U.S.:	$80.00
Can.:	$80.00

MORNING FEED
(Sheep and border collie)

Model:	A4067
Modeller:	Hans Kendrick
Height:	5 ¼", 13.3 cm
Colour:	Grey, silver, cream, brown, green, black and white
Issued:	06/04 - 12/06
Series:	James Herriot Studio Collection
U.K.:	£100.00
U.S.:	$200.00
Can.:	$200.00

MORNING MIST
(Roe deer fawn)

Model:	SRE5
Modeller:	Ray Ayres
Height:	2", 5.0 cm
Colour:	Brown and white
Issued:	06/94 - 05/95
Series:	Membership Gift
U.K.:	£20.00
U.S.:	$40.00
Can.:	$40.00

MOSES (Kitten)
Style One

Model:	JH13
Modeller:	Richard Roberts
Height:	2", 5.0 cm
Colour:	Black
Issued:	01/87 - 12/87
Series:	1. All Creatures Great and Small 2. James Herriot's Favourite Characters
U.K.:	£45.00
U.S.:	$90.00
Can.:	$90.00

MOSES (Kitten)
Style Two

Model: A6614
Modeller: Unknown
Height: 2", 5.0 cm
Colour: Black, fawn and white
Issued: 01/06 to the present
Series: James Herriot
      Studio Collection

U.K.: £ 9.95
U.S.: $20.00
Can.: $20.00

MOSES AND BERTHA
(Cat, Sow and Pigs)

Model: JH3
Modeller: Ray Ayres
Height: 3 ½", 8.9 cm
Colour: Pink and black
Issued: 01/85 - 12/92
Series: All Creatures Great
      and Small

U.K.: £ 75.00
U.S.: $150.00
Can.: $150.00

MOSES AND FRIENDS
(Cat and Piglets)

Model: JH40
Modeller: Anne Butler
Height: 2 ½", 6.4 cm
Colour: Pink and black
Issued: 01/90 - 12/94
Series: All Things Wise and
      Wonderful

U.K.: £40.00
U.S.: $80.00
Can.: $80.00

MOSES WITH PIGLETS

Model: B0180
Modeller: Kirsty Armstrong
Height: 3 ¼", 8.3 cm
Colour: Black and pink
Issued: 06/97 - 05/99
Series: James Herriot's Cat
      Stories

U.K.: £25.00
U.S.: $50.00
Can.: $50.00

MOTHER'S CARE

Model: B0003
Modeller: Richard Roberts
Height: 6 ¼", 15.9 cm
Colour: Grey
Issued: 01/97 in a limited
      edition of 1,250
Series: An African Safari

U.K.: £ 80.00
U.S.: $160.00
Can.: $160.00

MOTHER'S PRIDE

Model: B0806
Modeller: Ray Ayres
Height: 6 ¼", 15.9 cm
Colour: Black, white, grey,
      brown, beige and green
Issued: 06/03 - 05/04
Series: Annual Classic
      Member-only Figurine

U.K.: £150.00
U.S.: $300.00
Can.: $300.00

MOUSE

Model: FF5A, B
Modeller: Ray Ayres
Height: 2 ¼", 5.7 cm
Colour: 1. Brown
      2. White
Issued: 01/89 - 12/93
Series: First Friends

U.K.: £12.00
U.S.: $25.00
Can.: $25.00

MOUSE AND APPLE CORE

Model: MM01
Modeller: Anne Wall
Height: 3 ¼", 8.3 cm
Colour: Brown, white and
      orangey-yellow
Issued: 01/92 - 12/94
Series: Miniature Mice on Fruit

U.K.: £ 65.00
U.S.: $125.00
Can.: $125.00

MOUSE AND BUMBLE BEE

Model: A1495
Modeller: David Mayer
Height: 5 ½", 14.0 cm
Colour: Brown, white, deep
            lilac, green, yellow
            and black
Issued: 01/03 - 06/06
Series: Natural Mice

U.K.:   £25.00
U.S.: $50.00
Can.: $50.00

MOUSE AND BUTTERFLY

Model: A1492
Modeller: David Mayer
Height: 4", 10.1 cm
Colour: Brown, white, cream,
            grey, black, red and
            yellow
Issued: 01/03 - 06/06
Series: Natural Mice

U.K.:   £25.00
U.S.: $50.00
Can.: $50.00

MOUSE AND CHERRIES

Model: MM07
Modeller: Anne Wall
Height: 3 ¼", 8.3 cm
Colour: Brown, white and red
Issued: 01/93 - 12/94
Series: Miniature Mice on Fruit

U.K.:   £ 75.00
U.S.: $150.00
Can.: $150.00

MOUSE AND CHESTNUTS

Model: MM05
Modeller: Anne Wall
Height: 2 ½", 6.4 cm
Colour: Brown, white and
            chestnut
Issued: 01/92 - 12/94
Series: Miniature Mice on Fruit

U.K.:   £ 75.00
U.S.: $150.00
Can.: $150.00

MOUSE AND CORNCOB

Model: MM08
Modeller: Anne Wall
Height: 3", 7.6 cm
Colour: Brown, white and
            yellow
Issued: 01/93 - 12/94
Series: Miniature Mice on Fruit

U.K.:   £ 75.00
U.S.: $150.00
Can.: $150.00

MOUSE AND FROG

Model: A1494
Modeller: David Mayer
Height: 4", 10.1 cm
Colour: Brown, white, cream,
            grey, green, yellow-
            green and black
Issued: 01/03 - 06/06
Series: Natural Mice

U.K.:   £25.00
U.S.: $50.00
Can.: $50.00

MOUSE AND KIWI FRUIT

Model: MM02
Modeller: Anne Wall
Height: 3", 7.6 cm
Colour: Brown, white and green
Issued: 01/92 - 12/94
Series: Miniature Mice on Fruit

U.K.:   £ 75.00
U.S.: $150.00
Can.: $150.00

MOUSE AND NUTS

Model: MM04
Modeller: Anne Wall
Height: 2 ¾", 7.0 cm
Colour: Browns, white and grey
Issued: 01/92 - 12/94
Series: Miniature Mice on Fruit

U.K.:   £ 75.00
U.S.: $150.00
Can.: $150.00

MOUSE AND RASPBERRIES

Model: MM03
Modeller: Anne Wall
Height: 2 ¼", 5.7 cm
Colour: Brown, white and red
Issued: 01/92 - 12/94
Series: Miniature Mice on Fruit

U.K.: £ 75.00
U.S.: $150.00
Can.: $150.00

MOUSE AND SATSUMA

Model: MM06
Modeller: Anne Wall
Height: 2 ½", 6.4 cm
Colour: Brown, white and orange
Issued: 01/92 - 12/94
Series: Miniature Mice on Fruit

U.K.: £ 75.00
U.S.: $150.00
Can.: $150.00

MOUSE ON APPLE

Model: A8003
Modeller: Unknown
Height: 4 ½", 11.4 cm
Colour: Light brown, white, red, green and pink
Issued: 01/07 to the present
Series: Mice on Fruit

U.K.: £13.00
U.S.: $25.00
Can.: $25.00

MOUSE ON APPLE CORE

Model: 017 / 225-072
Modeller: Ray Ayres
Height: 4 ¾", 12.1 cm
Colour: Brown, white and red
Issued: 07/80 - 12/91
Series: 1. Mammals
       2. Mice by Ray Ayres

U.K.: £100.00
U.S.: $200.00
Can.: $200.00

MOUSE ON APPLE CORE
(Bronze)

Model: B0503
Modeller: Ray Ayres
Height: 5", 12.7 cm
Colour: Bronze; gilt
Issued: 01/99 in a limited edition of 500
Series: 1. 25th Anniversary
       2. Bronze

U.K.: £ 60.00
U.S.: $120.00
Can.: $120.00

MOUSE ON BANANA
Style One
(Head down)

Model: UK# 012
       USA# 225-057
Modeller: Anne Wall
Height: 3 ½", 8.9 cm
Colour: Brown, cream and yellow
Issued: 06/79 - 12/82
Series: Mammals

U.K.: £ 75.00
U.S.: $150.00
Can.: $150.00

MOUSE ON BANANA
Style Two
(Head up)

Model: 030
Modeller: Ray Ayres
Height: 5 ½", 14.0 cm
Colour: Brown, white and yellow
Issued: 01/86 - 12/93
Series: Mice by Ray Ayres

U.K.: £175.00
U.S.: $350.00
Can.: $350.00

MOUSE ON BANANA
Style Three

Model: A8004
Modeller: Unkown
Height: 4 ½", 11.4 cm
Colour: Light brown, white, yellow, cream, green and pink
Issued: 01/07 to the present
Series: Mice on Fruit

U.K.: £15.00
U.S.: $30.00
Can.: $30.00

MOUSE ON CANDLESTICK

Model: UK# 024
USA# 225-075
Modeller: Ray Ayres
Height: 4 ¾", 12.1 cm
Colour: Brown and white
Issued: 01/82 - 12/85
Series: 1. Mammals
2. Mice by Ray Ayres

U.K.: £200.00
U.S.: $400.00
Can.: $400.00

Note: This model was also issued without the match.

Photograph not
available
at press time

MOUSE ON CORN COB

Model: 018
Modeller: Ray Ayres
Height: 5", 12.7 cm
Colour: Brown, fawn, white
and yellow
Issued: c.1983 - Unknown
Series: Mice by Ray Ayres

U.K.: £ 85.00
U.S.: $175.00
Can.: $175.00

MOUSE ON GRAPES

Model: 032A, B
Modeller: Ray Ayres
Height: 4 ½", 11.9 cm
Colour: A. Brown mouse, green
grapes
B. Brown mouse, black
grapes
Issued: 01/89 - 12/91
Series: Mice by Ray Ayres

U.K.: £350.00
U.S.: $700.00
Can.: $700.00

MOUSE ON MATCHBOX

Model: 026
Modeller: Ray Ayres
Height: 3 ½", 8.9 cm
Colour: Brown, white and
purple
Issued: 12/83 - 12/84
Series: Mice by Ray Ayres

U.K.: £300.00
U.S.: $600.00
Can.: $600.00

Note: This model is known with
either red or blue tipped
matches.

MOUSE ON ORANGE
Style One

Model: 029
Modeller: Ray Ayres
Height: 4", 10.1 cm
Colour: Brown, white and
orange
Issued: 01/84 - 12/91
Series: Mice by Ray Ayres

U.K.: £125.00
U.S.: $250.00
Can.: $250.00

MOUSE ON ORANGE
Style Two

Model: A8006
Modeller: Unknown
Height: 4 ½", 11.4 cm
Colour: Light brown, white,
orange, grey and pink
Issued: 01/07 to the present
Series: Mice on Fruit

U.K.: £13.00
U.S.: $25.00
Can.: $25.00

MOUSE ON PEACH

Model: 031
Modeller: Ray Ayres
Height: 4 ¼", 10.8 cm
Colour: Brown, white and
peach
Issued: 01/89 - 12/91
Series: Mice by Ray Ayres

U.K.: £250.00
U.S.: $500.00
Can.: $500.00

MOUSE ON PEAR
Style One

Model: 028
Modeller: Ray Ayres
Height: 5", 12.7 cm
Colour: Brown, white and green
Issued: 01/84 - 12/91
Series: Mice by Ray Ayres

U.K.: £150.00
U.S.: $300.00
Can.: $300.00

MOUSE ON PEAR
Style Two

Model:	A8005
Modeller:	Unknown
Height:	4 ¼", 10.8 cm
Colour:	Light brown, white, green, cream and pink
Issued:	01/07 to the present
Series:	Mice on Fruit
U.K.:	£13.00
U.S.:	$25.00
Can.:	$25.00

MOUSE ON PLUM

Model:	A8008
Modeller:	Unknown
Height:	4 ¼", 10.8 cm
Colour:	Light brown, white, black maroon, green and pink
Issued:	01/07 to the present
Series:	Mice on Fruit
U.K.:	£13.00
U.S.:	$25.00
Can.:	$25.00

MOUSE ON STRAWBERRIES
Style One

Model:	033
Modeller:	Ray Ayres
Height:	4 ¼", 10.8 cm
Colour:	Brown, white and red
Issued:	01/90 - 12/93
Series:	Mice by Ray Ayres
U.K.:	£175.00
U.S.:	$350.00
Can.:	$350.00

MOUSE ON STRAWBERRIES
Style Two

Model:	A8007
Modeller:	Unknown
Height:	4", 10.1 cm
Colour:	Light brown, white, red, green, grey and pink
Issued:	01/07 to the present
Series:	Mice on Fruit
U.K.:	£13.00
U.S.:	$25.00
Can.:	$25.00

MOUSE ON TRAP

Model:	025
Modeller:	Ray Ayres
Height:	3", 7.6 cm
Colour:	Brown and white
Issued:	01/82 - 12/82
Series:	1. Mammals
	2. Mice by Ray Ayres
U.K.:	£225.00
U.S.:	$450.00
Can.:	$450.00

MOUSERS

Model:	A8435
Modeller:	Unknown
Height:	6 ¾", 17.2 cm
Colour:	Browns, ginger, white and grey
Issued:	06/07 to the present
Series:	James Herriot Studio Collection
U.K.:	£45.00
U.S.:	$90.00
Can.:	$90.00

MOUSING
(Vixen, two cubs and mice)

Model:	FT06
Modeller:	David Walton
Height:	4 ¼", 10.8 cm
Colour:	Reddish-brown, white and black
Issued:	07/95 in a limited edition of 2,950
Series:	Fox Tales
U.K.	£100.00
U.S.	$200.00
Can.	$200.00

MOVING HOME
(Vixen and cubs)

Model:	L101
Modeller:	David Walton
Height:	9", 22.9 cm
Colour:	Red, white and black
Issued:	Autumn 1990 in a limited edition of 1,500
U.K.:	£125.00
U.S.:	$250.00
Can.:	$250.00

MOVING OFF
(Huntsman and two hounds)

Model:	UK# L36
	USA# 225-153
Modeller:	David Geenty
Height:	10", 25.4 cm
Colour:	Browns, white, black and red
Issued:	01/82 in a limited edition of 300

U.K.:	£ 800.00
U.S.:	$1,600.00
Can.:	$1,600.00

MR. BILLING'S CALF

Model:	JH1
Modeller:	Ray Ayres
Height:	3 ½", 8.9 cm
Colour:	A. Friesian (Black/white)
	B. Hereford (Brown/white)
	C. Shorthorn (Roan/white)
Issued:	A. 01/85 - 12/93
	B-C. Unknown
Series:	All Creatures Great and Small

	Friesian	Hereford	Shorthorn
U.K.:	£ 65.00	£ 75.00	£ 80.00
U.S.:	$125.00	$150.00	$160.00
Can.:	$125.00	$150.00	$160.00

MR. KIRBY'S DOROTHY
(Goat)

Model:	JH2
Modeller:	Ray Ayres
Height:	4", 10.1 cm
Colour:	A. White
	B. Black
Issued:	01/85 - 12/88
Series:	All Creatures Great and Small

	White	Black
U.K.:	£100.	£125.
U.S.:	$200.	$250.
Can.:	$200.	$250.

MR. WORLEY'S QUEENIE
(Sow and piglets)

Model:	JH4
Modeller:	Ray Ayres
Height:	3 ½", 8.9 cm
Colour:	Pink
Issued:	01/85 - 12/91
Series:	All Creatures Great and Small

U.K.:	£100.00
U.S.:	$200.00
Can.:	$200.00

MUD GLORIOUS MUD
(Pigs)

Model:	A0453
Modeller:	Anne Wall
Height:	4 ¼", 10.8 cm
Colour:	Pink, browns and green
Issued:	01/01 - 06/03
Series:	The James Herriot Studio Collection

U.K.:	£40.00
U.S.:	$80.00
Can.:	$80.00

MUD SPA
(Pigs)

Model:	A8436
Modeller:	Unknown
Height:	3 ¼", 8.3 cm
Colour:	Pink, browns and green
Issued:	06/07 to the present
Series:	James Herriot Studio Collection

U.K.:	£40.00
U.S.:	$80.00
Can.:	$80.00

MULE EWE AND LAMBS

Model:	EG03
Modeller:	Mairi Laing Hunt
Height:	6", 15.0 cm
Colour:	Grey, black and white
Issued:	01/89 in a limited edition of 1,500

U.K.:	£ 500.00
U.S.:	$1,000.00
Can.:	$1,000.00

MUMMY'S BOYS
(Sheep and two lambs)
Model: A0454
Modeller: Ray Ayres
Height: 3 ¼", 8.3 cm
Colour: Cream, white and black
Issued: 01/01 - 12/06
Series: The James Herriot
           Studio Collection

U.K.:   £20.00
U.S.: $40.00
Can.: $40.00

MUTE SWANS
Model: A0006
Modeller: Richard Roberts
Height: 5 ½", 14.0 cm
Colour: White, orange, black
           and green
Issued: 01/00 - 12/01
Series: Reflections

U.K.:   £ 50.00
U.S.: $100.00
Can.: $100.00

MY HERO
(Horse and rider)
Model: A0538
Modeller: Anne Wall
Height: 5 ¼", 13.3 cm
Colour: Tan, black and green
Issued: 01/01 - 12/04
Series: Hay Days

U.K.:   £35.00
U.S.: $70.00
Can.: $70.00

NAPOLEON (Wall Mask)
Model: K177
Designer: Ben Black
Modeller: David Geenty
Height: 13", 33.0 cm
Colour: Blue, red, gold and
           white
Issued: 01/88 in a limited
           edition of 2,500
Series: Ben Black's
           Intermission Series

U.K.:   £125.00
U.S.: $250.00
Can.: $250.00

Note: Hat and ruff are fabric material.

NEARLY THERE
(Trout fisherman)
Model: B0254
Modeller: Ray Ayres
Height: 14 ½", 36.8 cm
Colour: Browns and green
Issued: 06/98 in a limited
           edition of 1,750
Series: Agricultural and
           Sporting

U.K.:   £200.00
U.S.: $400.00
Can.: $400.00

NEVER SATISFIED
(Sow and piglets)
Model: B0442A, B
Modeller: Kirsty Armstrong
Height: 4", 10.1 cm
Colour: A. Gloucester Old Spot
           B. Wessex Saddleback
Issued: 01/86 - 06/01
Series: The J. Herriot Collection

U.K.:   £ 80.00
U.S.: $160.00
Can.: $160.00

NEW ARRIVAL AT HARLAND
GRANGE
(Clydesdale mare and foal)
Model: JH11
Modeller: Elizabeth MacAllister
Height: 8 ½", 21.6 cm
Colour: Bay mare, chestnut foal
Issued: 01/86 - 12/88
Series: All Creatures Great
           and Small

U.K.:   £375.00
U.S.: $750.00
Can.: $750.00

NEW DOG, THE
(Two border collies)
Model: A0601
Modeller: Kirsty Armstrong
Height: 4 ¼", 10.8 cm
Colour: Black, white, tan and
           stone
Issued: 01/01 - 12/06
Series: The James Herriot
           Studio Collection

U.K.:   £25.00
U.S.: $50.00
Can.: $50.00

NEW FRIEND
(Clydesdale foal and kitten)

Model:	A6248
Modeller:	Anne Wall
Height:	6", 15.0 cm
Colour:	Brown, white, grey and yellow
Issued:	01/06 to the present
Series:	James Herriot Studio Collection
U.K.:	£ 54.00
U.S.:	$110.00
Can.:	$110.00

NEW SHOES FOR DOLLY
(Blacksmith scene)

Model:	JH29
Modeller:	Elizabeth MacAllister
Height:	10 ½", 26.7 cm
Colour:	Chestnut, browns and white
Issued:	01/89 in a limited edition of 950
Series:	All Creatures Great and Small
U.K.:	£ 800.00
U.S.:	$1,600.00
Can.:	$1,600.00

NEW TECHNOLOGY ARRIVES TODAY
(Fordson tractor)

Model:	JH46
Modeller:	Ray Ayres
Height:	5 ½", 14.0 cm
Colour:	Blue, orange, silver, black and white
Issued:	01/91 in a limited edition of 1,250
Series:	All Creatures Great and Small
U.K.:	£2,250.00
U.S.:	$4,500.00
Can.:	$4,500.00

NEWFOUNDLAND

Model:	EW5
Modeller:	Elizabeth Waugh
Height:	6", 15.0 cm
Colour:	1. Black
	2. Black and white
Issued:	01/87 in a limited edition of 500
Series:	Special Interest

	Black	B&W
U.K.:	£275.	£300.
U.S.:	$550.	$600.
Can.:	$550.	$600.

NEXT GENERATION
(Mare, foal, man and boy)

Model:	B0201
Modeller:	Anne Wall
Height:	6 ½", 16.5 cm
Colour:	Brown, white, red, green and beige
Issued:	06/97 in a limited edition of 1,500
Series:	1. Every Living Thing
	2. J. Herriot Collection
U.K.:	£175.00
U.S.:	$350.00
Can.:	$350.00

NEXT TO GO
(Shepherd and two border collies)

Model:	B0012
Modeller:	Ray Ayres
Height:	8 ¼", 21.0 cm
Colour:	Brown, black, white and grey
Issued:	07/96 - 12/99
Series:	1. All Creatures Great and Small
	2. J. Herriot Collection
U.K.	£125.00
U.S.	$250.00
Can.	$250.00

NIGHT WATCH
(Barn owl)

Model:	B0175
Modeller:	Ray Ayres
Height:	3", 7.6 cm
Colour:	Golden, white and beige
Issued:	06/97 - 05/98
Series:	Membership Gift
U.K.	£25.00
U.S.	$50.00
Can.	$50.00

93RD HIGHLANDER SERGEANT
(CRIMEA)

Model:	MF01
Modeller:	David Burnham Smith
Height:	12 ¼", 31.1 cm
Colour:	Red, white, blue-green and black
Issued:	01/92 in a limited edition of 750
Series:	The Military Collection
U.K.:	£225.00
U.S.:	$450.00
Can.:	$450.00

NIPPED
(Otter)

Model:	A1487
Modeller:	John Brown
Height:	6", 15.0 cm
Colour:	Dark grey, white, orange and green
Issued:	01/03 - 06/05
Series:	Country Characters
U.K.:	£30.00
U.S.:	$60.00
Can.:	$60.00

NO BRAKES
(Pony and Rider)

Model:	A1654
Modeller:	Anne Wall
Height:	5 ¼", 13.3 cm
Colour:	Dark brown, yellow, cream, blue and red
Issued:	01/03 - 12/05
Series:	Hay Days
U.K.:	£30.00
U.S.:	$60.00
Can.:	$60.00

NO FOOT, NO 'OSS
(Blacksmith)

Model:	JH94A, B
Modeller:	Anne Wall
Height:	5 ¾", 14.6 cm
Colour:	A. Bay
	B. Grey
Issued:	01/94 - 12/98
Varieties:	JH94
Series:	All Creatures Great and Small

	Bay	Grey
U.K.	£350	£400.
U.S.	$700.	$800.
Can.	$700.	$800.

NO FOOT, NO 'OSS
(Blacksmith)

Model:	JH94
Modeller:	Anne Wall
Height:	5 ¾", 14.6 cm
Colour:	A. Piebald
	B. Skewbald
Issued:	Unknown
Series:	All Creatures Great and Small
U.K.:	£425.00
U.S.:	$850.00
Can.:	$850.00

Note: Only a very small number were produced.

NO HIDING PLACE
(Jack Russell and Border Terrier)

Model:	209A, B, C
Modeller:	Anne Butler
Height:	4", 10.1 cm
Colour:	A. Brown
	B. Black
	C. Tricolour
Issued:	01/92 - 12/94
Series:	The World of Dogs
U.K.:	£ 65.00
U.S.:	$125.00
Can.:	$125.00

NO SCRUMPING
(Pig and Piglets)

Model:	A1223
Modeller:	Kirsty Armstrong
Height:	4 ¼", 10.8 cm
Colour:	Pink, white, green, red and brown
Issued:	01/02 - 06/05
Series:	James Herriot Studio Collection
U.K.:	£ 55.00
U.S.:	$110.00
Can.:	$110.00

NO WAY THROUGH
(Butcher's delivery boy)

Model:	B0500
Modeller:	Ray Ayres
Size:	6 ¼", 15.9 cm
Colour:	Cream, black, white, blue and grey
Issued:	01/00 in a limited edition of 1,500
Series:	Nature's Kingdom
U.K.	£275.00
U.S.	$550.00
Can.	$550.00

NOISY NEIGHBOURS
(Nuthatches and Woodpeckers)

Model:	B0995
Modeller:	Ray Ayres
Size:	10 ¾" x 8"
	27.8 x 20.3 cm
Colour:	Browns, greens, red, blue and yellow
Issued:	06/06 in a limited edition of 950
U.K.:	£195.00
U.S.:	$400.00
Can.:	$400.00

NORTH COUNTRY CHEVIOT EWE AND LAMB

Model:	A3228
Modeller:	Lesley McKenzie
Height:	5 ¾", 14.6 cm
Colour:	Cream, white and green
Issued:	06/03 - 06/06
Series:	Sheep Breeds
U.K.:	£ 55.00
U.S.:	$110.00
Can.:	$110.00

NORTH COUNTRY CHEVIOT EWE WITH SCOTCH HALFBRED LAMBS

Model:	L147
Modeller	Ray Ayres
Height:	6", 15.0 cm
Colour:	Cream
Issued:	01/94 in a limited edition of 950
U.K.:	£200.00
U.S.:	$400.00
Can.:	$400.00

NORTH COUNTRY CHEVIOT RAM

Model:	A3227
Modeller:	Lesley McKenzie
Height:	5 ¼", 13.3 cm
Colour:	Cream, white and green
Issued:	06/04 - 06/06
U.K.:	£35.00
U.S.:	$70.00
Can.:	$70.00

NOT A MOMENT'S PEACE (Border Collie pups bookends)

Model:	B0093
Modeller:	Kirsty Armstrong
Height:	7 ¾", 19.7 cm
Colour:	Black, white, ginger and green
Issued:	01/97 in a limited edition of 1,500
Series:	1. Every Living Thing 2. The James Herriot Collection
U.K.:	£175.00
U.S.:	$350.00
Can.:	$350.00

NOT FAR TO GO (Border Collie and milestone)

Model:	166/B166
Modeller:	Ray Ayres
Height:	2 ½", 6.4 cm
Colour:	Black and white
Issued:	07/94 - 05/99
Varieties:	Not Long to Go, (170/B170)
Series:	1. All Creatures Great and Small 2. J. Herriot Collection
U.K.:	£20.00
U.S.:	$40.00
Can.:	$40.00

NOT LONG TO GO (Border Collie and clock)

Model:	170/B170
Modeller:	Ray Ayres
Height:	2 ¾", 7.0 cm
Colour:	Black and white
Issued:	01/96 - 12/99
Varieties:	Not Far to Go, (166/B166)
Series:	1. Every Living Thing 2. J. Herriot Collection
U.K.:	£25.00
U.S.:	$50.00
Can.:	$50.00

NUGENT (Piglet) Style One

Model:	JH12
Modeller:	Richard Roberts
Height:	2 ¾", 7.0 cm
Colour:	Pink
Issued:	01/87 - 12/95
Series:	1. All Creatures Great and Small 2. James Herriot's Favourite Characters
U.K.:	£30.00
U.S.:	$60.00
Can.:	$60.00

NUGENT (Piglet) Style Two

Model:	A6514
Modeller:	Anne Wall
Height:	2 ½", 6.4 cm
Colour:	Pink, fawn, white and brown
Issued:	01/06 to the present
Series:	James Herriot Studio Collection
U.K.:	£15.00
U.S.:	$30.00
Can.:	$30.00

NUTHATCH
Style One
Model: 042
Modeller: David Geenty
Height: 7", 17.8 cm
Colour: Blue, yellow, brown
             and green
Issued: 01/81 - 06/86

U.K.:   £ 65.00
U.S.: $125.00
Can.: $125.00

NUTHATCH
Style Two
Model: RB12
Modeller: Ray Ayres
Height: 4 ½", 11.9 cm
Colour: Blue, red, black and
             brown
Issued: 01/90 - 12/93
Series: British Birds

U.K.:   £40.00
U.S.: $80.00
Can.: $80.00

NUTHATCH ON PEBBLE
Model: WB163
Modeller: Russell Willis
Height: 3 ¼", 8.3 cm
Colour: Blue, yellow and brown
Issued: 01/95 - 10/96
Series: 1. Pebble Birds
             2. Russell Willis Birds

U.K.:   £15.00
U.S.: $30.00
Can.: $30.00

NUTHATCH WITH NEST
Model: 652024
Modeller: Russell Willis
Height: 2 ½", 6.4 cm
Colour: Blue, cream and pale
             green
Issued: 06/99 - 12/01
Series: Feathered Friends

U.K.:   £15.00
U.S.: $30.00
Can.: $30.00

OCEAN EXPLORERS
(Humpback whale and young)
Model: L153/L153B
Modeller: Richard Roberts
Height: 10 ¾", 27.8 cm
Colour: L153   Black, white
                       and blue
             L153B   Bronze
Issued: 01/95 in a limited
             edition of 500
Series: WWFN

	B&W	Bronze
U.K.:	£250.	£175.
U.S.:	$500.	$350.
Can.:	$500.	$350.

OCTOPUSSY
(Short-Haired Tabby)
Model: LA12
Designer: Lesley Anne Ivory
Modeller: Anne Butler
Height: 4 ½", 11.9 cm
Colour: Light and dark brown
Issued: 01/92 - 12/93
Varieties: LAM3 (Musical)
Series: Ivory Cats

U.K.:   £40.00
U.S.: $80.00
Can.: $80.00

OCTOPUSSY (Musical)
(Short-Haired Tabby)
Model: LAM3
Designer: Lesley Anne Ivory
Modeller: Anne Butler
Height: 6 ½", 16.5 cm
Colour: Light and dark brown
Issued: 01/92 - 12/93
Varieties: LA12 Octopussy
Series: Ivory Cats (Musical)

U.K.:   £ 50.00
U.S.: $100.00
Can.: $100.00

ODD ONE OUT
(Piglets)
Model: A3398
Modeller: Kerry Bell
Height: 4", 10.1 cm
Colour: White, black, green
             and brown
Issued: 06/03 - 12/05
Series: James Herriot
             Studio Collection

U.K.:   £35.00
U.S.: $70.00
Can.: $70.00

OFF AND PACING
(Horse, Sulky and Rider)

Model:	B0656
Modeller:	Jacqueline Frances Harris-Brown
Height:	10 ½", 26.7 cm
Colour:	Dark brown, black, red, white and blue
Issued:	01/02 in a limited edition of 500
Series:	Classic Collection

U.K.:	£350.00
U.S.:	$700.00
Can.:	$700.00

OFF STAGE

Model:	K40
Designer:	Ben Black
Modeller:	David Geenty
Height:	8 ¾", 22.2 cm
Colour:	White, pink and yellow
Issued:	01/88 in a limited edition of 3,500
Series:	Ben Black's Intermission Series

U.K.	£150.00
U.S.	$300.00
Can.	$300.00

OFF THE FELL
(Farmer, sheep and border collie)

Model:	B1040
Modeller:	Hans Kendrick
Size:	6" x 10 ½" 15.0 x 26.7 cm
Colour:	Cream, browns, grey and black
Issued:	01/07 in a limited edition of 750

U.K.:	£199.00
U.S.:	$400.00
Can.:	$400.00

OFF TO THE FAIR
(Farmer and child on horseback)

Model:	EG06
Modeller:	Anne Wall
Height:	6 ½", 16.5 cm
Colour:	A. Grey B. Bay
Issued:	Spring 1994 in a limited edition of 1,994
Series:	The J. Herriot Collection

U.K.:	£275.00
U.S.:	$550.00
Can.:	$550.00

OFF TO THE FELLS AT SLATERS BRIDGE
(Shepherd, sheep and collie crossing)

Model:	PJ03
Modeller:	Ray Ayres
Height:	5 ½", 14.0 cm
Colour:	Grey and black
Issued:	10/95 in a limited edition of 1,250

U.K.:	£325.00
U.S.:	$650.00
Can.:	$650.00

OFF TO THE SMITHY

Model:	B0955, 0955A
Modeller:	David Mayer
Height:	6" x 6½" 15.2 x 16.5
Colour:	B0955 Grey horse B0955A Bay horse
Issued:	06/05 in a limited edition of 950
Series:	Classic Collection

U.K.:	£175.00
U.S.:	$350.00
Can.:	$350.00

OLD ENGLISH FOXHOUND AND FOX TERRIER

Model:	L91
Modeller:	Mairi Laing Hunt
Height:	6", 15.0 cm
Colour:	White, black and tan
Issued:	01/90 in a limited edition of 750
Series:	Special Interest

U.K.:	£300.00
U.S.:	$600.00
Can.:	$600.00

OLD ENGLISH SHEEPDOG, Lying

Model:	B0606
Modeller:	Margaret Turner
Height:	3", 7.6 cm
Colour:	White, black and grey
Issued:	06/00 - 12/01
Series:	Dogs Galore

U.K.:	£20.00
U.S.:	$40.00
Can.:	$40.00

OLD ENGLISH SHEEPDOG, Seated

Model:	UK# 067
	USA# 225-126
Modeller:	Ray Ayres
Height:	5", 12.7 cm
Colour:	Black and white
Issued:	01/81 - 12/82

U.K.:	£ 75.00
U.S.:	$150.00
Can.:	$150.00

OLD ENGLISH SHEEPDOG AND PEKINESE

Model:	A4674
Designer:	Toni Goffe
Modeller:	Janet Miller
Height:	7 ¼", 18.4 cm
Colour:	Grey, white, fawn, brown and green
Issued:	01/05 - 12/05
Series:	Big Dog, Little Dog

U.K.:	£45.00
U.S.:	$90.00
Can.:	$90.00

OLD MEETS NEW

Model:	B1057
Modeller:	Ray Ayres
Size:	5 ¼" x 14 ¾"
	13.3 x 37.5 cm
Colour:	Orange, grey, browns, green and black
Issued:	04/07 in a limited edition of 950

U.K.:	£295.00
U.S.:	$600.00
Can.:	$600.00

OLLY AND GINNY (Two cats) Style One

Model:	B0179
Modeller:	Kirsty Armstrong
Height:	4 ½", 11.9 cm
Colour:	Black, white and ginger
Issued:	06/97 - 05/99
Series:	James Herriot's Cat Stories

U.K.:	£25.00
U.S.:	$50.00
Can.:	$50.00

Photograph not available at press time

OLLY AND GINNY (Two cats) Style Two

Model:	A6510
Modeller:	Ray Ayres
Height:	3", 7.6 cm
Colour:	Black, white, tan, fawn and green
Issued:	01/06 to the present
Series:	James Herriot Studio Collection

U.K.:	£20.00
U.S.:	$40.00
Can.:	$40.00

ON PARADE

Model:	B0801, B0801A
Modeller:	Anne Wall
Height:	13 ¾", 34,9 cm
Colour:	B0801 Bay
	B0801A Chestnut
Issued:	01/03 in a limited edition of 950
Series:	Classic Collection

U.K.:	£275.00
U.S.:	$550.00
Can.:	$550.00

ON THE CLIFF
(Shag, two Puffins, two Guillemot and Razorbill)

Model:	BS2
Modeller:	Richard Roberts
Height:	6 ½", 16.5 cm
Colour:	Black, white, orange and beige
Issued:	01/87 - 12/88
Series:	Birds of the Seashore

U.K.	£225.00
U.S.	$450.00
Can.	$450.00

ON THE HILL
Shepherd, sheep and border collie)

Model:	B0877
Modeller:	Craig Harding
Size:	6 ¾" x 7 ¼"
	17.2 x 18.4 cm
Colour:	Browns, black, white, grey and green
Issued:	06/04 in a limited edition of 750

U.K.:	£150.00
U.S.:	$300.00
Can.:	$300.00

ON THE LOOK OUT
(Barn Owl)

Model:	B0276
Modeller:	David Walton
Height:	10", 25.4 cm
Colour:	Golden, cream and brown
Issued:	01/98 - 12/98
Series:	Annual Figurine (1998)
U.K.:	£150.00
U.S.:	$300.00
Can.:	$300.00

ON THE RAILS

Model:	B0655
Modeller:	Anne Wall
Height:	7 ¼", 18.4 cm
Colour:	Bay, black and chestnut horses; white jodhpurs; green, white, red, blue and yellow racing colours
Issued:	01/02 in a limited edition of 950
Series:	Classic Collection
U.K.:	£400.00
U.S.:	$800.00
Can.:	$800.00

ONE FOR ME, ONE FOR YOU
(Boy milking goat)

Model:	A1451
Modeller:	Ray Ayres
Height:	6 ½", 16.5 cm
Colour:	Brown, white, blue, yellow, green and black
Issued:	01/03 - 06/05
Series:	Young Farmers
U.K.:	£45.00
U.S.:	$90.00
Can.:	$90.00

ONE MAN AND HIS DOG

Model:	L55
Modeller:	Ray Ayres
Height:	5 ¾", 14.6 cm
Colour:	White, black and brown
Issued:	01/83 in a limited edition of 850
U.K.:	£ 500.00
U.S.:	$1,000.00
Can.:	$1,000.00

OOPS!
(Jack Russell puppy)

Model:	A7047
Modeller:	Barry Snelson
Height:	3 ¼", 8.3 cm
Colour:	Black, white, grey and green
Issued:	06/06 - 06/07
Series:	Puppy Trouble
U.K.:	£16.00
U.S.:	$30.00
Can.:	$30.00

OPPORTUNIST, THE

Model:	B0776
Modeller:	Ray Ayres
Height:	6 ¼", 15.9 cm
Colour:	Dark brown horse; brown, red and yellow wagon; white swans; blue and white clothing
Issued:	01/03 in a limited edition of 1,250
Series:	Classic Collection
U.K.:	£350.00
U.S.:	$700.00
Can.:	$700.00

ORANGE TIPS
(Butterflies)

Model:	B5
Modeller:	Ray Ayres
Height:	3", 7.6 cm
Colour:	Grey, orange, yellow and mauve
Issued:	07/80 - 12/85
Series:	British Butterflies

	Original	Re-issued
U.K.:	£ 50.	£40.
U.S.:	$100.	$80.
Can.:	$100.	$80.

Note: Ealier models issued without antenae. Domes were optional with all butterflies.

OSCAR THE SOCIALITE CAT

Model:	B0186
Modeller:	Kirsty Armstrong
Height:	2 ½", 6.4 cm
Colour:	Black and ginger
Issued:	06/97 - 05/99
Series:	James Herriot's Cat Stories
U.K.:	£20.00
U.S.:	$40.00
Can.:	$40.00

OSPREY
Style One

Model:	RB6
Modeller:	Ray Ayres
Height:	8", 20.3 cm
Colour:	Brown, cream and black
Issued:	07/83 - 12/88
Series:	RSPB Birds
U.K.:	£125.00
U.S.:	$250.00
Can.:	$250.00

OSPREY
Style Two

Model:	L95
Modeller:	David Burnham Smith
Height:	16", 40.6 cm
Colour:	Dark brown, white and blue
Issued:	01/90 in a limited edition of 950
U.K.:	£ 500.00
U.S.:	$1,000.00
Can.:	$1,000.00

OSPREY
Style Three

Model:	B0987
Modeller:	Ray Ayres
Size:	11 ¼" x 8 ¾" 28.5 x 22.2 cm
Colour:	Grey, white, green, pale blue and brown
Issued:	01/06 in a limited edition of 500
U.K.:	£195.00
U.S.:	$400.00
Can.:	$400.00

OSPREYS

Model:	L38
Modeller:	Ray Ayres
Height:	12", 30.5 cm
Colour:	Dark brown, white and green
Issued:	01/82 in a limited edition of 350
U.K.:	£ 500.00
U.S.:	$1,000.00
Can.:	$1,000.00

OTTER
Style One

Model:	UK# 013 USA# 225-055
Modeller:	Anne Wall
Height:	3", 7.6 cm
Colour:	Dark brown, white and yellow
Issued:	06/79 - 12/81
Series:	Mammals
U.K.:	£ 50.00
U.S.:	$100.00
Can.:	$100.00

Note: Named River Otter in USA.

OTTER
Style Two

Model:	M31
Modeller:	Ray Ayres
Height:	4", 10.1 cm
Colour:	Brown and white; bronze base
Issued:	01/84 - 12/87
Series:	Miniatures on Bronze
U.K.:	£100.00
U.S.:	$200.00
Can.:	$200.00

OTTER
Style Three

Model:	WW2
Modeller:	Ray Ayres
Height:	5 ¼", 13.3 cm
Colour:	Browns and white
Issued:	01/86 - 12/92
Series:	1. The Wetlands (WWF) 2. WWFN
U.K.:	£ 50.00
U.S.:	$100.00
Can.:	$100.00

OTTER
Style Four

Model:	RW2
Modeller:	Richard Wawrzesta
Height:	4", 10.1 cm
Colour:	Brown and white
Issued:	01/88 - 12/95
Series:	1. WWFN 2. Wildlife Families (WWF)
U.K.:	£40.00
U.S.:	$80.00
Can.:	$80.00

Note: Also sold with a dome.

OTTER
Style Five

Model:	149
Modeller:	David Walton
Height:	4 ½", 11.9 cm
Colour:	Brown and white
Issued:	01/92 - 12/94

U.K.:	£45.00
U.S.:	$90.00
Can.:	$90.00

OTTER
Style Six

Model:	M22
Modeller:	David Walton
Height:	2 ¾", 7.0 cm
Colour:	Brown and white
Issued:	01/92 - 12/94
Series:	Miniature Wildlife

U.K.:	£30.00
U.S.:	$60.00
Can.:	$60.00

OTTER
Style Seven

Model:	A6725
Modeller:	Unknown
Height:	6", 15.0 cm
Colour:	Dark brown and white
Issued:	06/06 to the present

U.K.:	£18.00
U.S.:	$35.00
Can.:	$35.00

OTTER
(On branch)

Model:	019
Modeller:	Judy Boyt
Height:	5", 12.7 cm
Colour:	Brown and white
Issued:	01/82 - 06/86
Series:	Judy Boyt Woodland

U.K.:	£ 65.00
U.S.:	$125.00
Can.:	$125.00

OTTER AND BROWN TROUT

Model:	WW5
Modeller:	Elizabeth Waugh
Height:	8", 20.3 cm
Colour:	Brown and cream
Issued:	01/90 - 12/92
Series:	1. The Wetlands (WWF)
	2. WWFN

U.K.:	£250.00
U.S.:	$500.00
Can.:	$500.00

OTTER AND FAMILY

Model:	L61
Modeller:	Mairi Laing Hunt
Height:	8 ¼", 21.0 cm
Colour:	Browns, green and lilac
Issued:	01/84 in a limited edition of 850

U.K.:	£ 575.00
U.S.:	$1,150.00
Can.:	$1,150.00

OTTER AND KINGFISHER

Model:	B0208
Modeller:	David Walton
Height:	6 ¼", 15.9 cm
Colour:	Brown, white, blues and orange
Issued:	06/97 - 12/99
Series:	First Encounters

U.K.:	£ 65.00
U.S.:	$125.00
Can.:	$125.00

OTTER AND SALMON

Model:	L54
Modeller:	Elizabeth Waugh
Height:	7 ½", 19.1 cm
Colour:	Brown and stone
Issued:	01/83 in a limited edition of 1,500

U.K.:	£225.00
U.S.:	$450.00
Can.:	$450.00

Note: Also sold with a dome.

OTTER FAMILY

Model: WW14
Modeller: Richard Wawrzesta
Height: 3 ½", 8.9 cm
Colour: Brown
Issued: 01/87 - 12/87
Series: Family Life (WWF)

U.K.: £40.00
U.S.: $80.00
Can.: $80.00

OTTER KIT

Model: B0922
Modeller: Ray Ayres
Size: 6 ½' x 6"
16.5 x 15.0 cm
Colour: Brown and cream
Issued: 06/04 - 12/06
Series: Classic Babies

U.K.: £40.00
U.S.: $80.00
Can.: $80.00

OTTER KIT AND FROG

Model: FE3
Modeller: Ray Ayres
Height: 3 ½", 8.9 cm
Colour: Brown and green
Issued: 01/83 - 12/96
Series: First Encounters

U.K.: £40.00
U.S.: $80.00
Can.: $80.00

OTTER ON A STONE BASE

Model: None
Modeller: Debbie Edelman
Height: 5 ½", 14.0 cm
Colour: A. Grey and white
B. Bronze
Issued: 07/78 in a limited
edition of 350

	Grey	Bronze
U.K.:	£350.	£150.
U.S.:	$700.	$300.
Can.:	$700.	$300.

OTTERS
Style One

Model: SWW1
Modeller: Richard Wawrzesta
Height: 4 ¼", 10.8 cm
Colour: Brown, white and green
Issued: 01/90 - 12/95
Series: Scottish Wildlife
Appeal

U.K.: £45.00
U.S.: $90.00
Can.: $90.00

OTTERS
Style Two

Model: RW30
Modeller: David Walton
Height: 5 ¼", 13.3 cm
Colour: Browns and white
Issued: 07/93 - 12/96
Series: Wildlife Families (WWF)

U.K.: £ 60.00
U.S.: $120.00
Can.: $120.00

OTTERS
(On a stone base)

Model: UK# L26
USA# 225-071
Modeller: David Geenty
Height: 6 ½", 16.5 cm
Colour: Brown, white and green
Issued: 01/80 in a limited
edition of 850

U.K.: £275.00
U.S.: $550.00
Can.: $550.00

Note: Named Otter Family in USA.

OTTERS PLAYING

Model: WW1
Modeller: Elizabeth Waugh
Height: 12 ¼", 31.1 cm
Colour: Brown, green and
cream
Issued: 01/86 in a limited
edition of 950
Series: 1. The Wetlands (WWF)
2. WWFN

U.K.: £475.00
U.S.: $950.00
Can.: $950.00

OUR NELL
(Border Collies)

Model:	B0853
Modeller:	Kerry Bell
Height:	4 ¼", 10.8 cm
Colour:	Black, white, yellow and red
Issued:	01/03 - 12/03
Series:	Classic Event

U.K.:	£ 65.00
U.S.:	$125.00
Can.:	$125.00

OUT FOXED
(Fox and rabbit)

Model:	FT02
Modeller:	David Walton
Height:	3 ¼", 8.3 cm
Colour:	Reddish-brown, white and black
Issued:	07/95 - 12/99
Series:	Fox Tales

U.K.:	£ 65.00
U.S.:	$125.00
Can.:	$125.00

OUT OF HARM'S WAY

Model:	B0537
Modeller:	Anne Wall
Height:	7", 17.8 cm
Colour:	Black, white and brown
Issued:	01/00 - 12/00
Series:	1. Annual Figurine (2000)
	2. Millennium

U.K.:	£ 80.00
U.S.:	$160.00
Can.:	$160.00

OUT WITH THE DOGS

Model:	A2648
Modeller:	Craig Harding
Height:	10 ¾", 27.8 cm
Colour:	Brown, white, grey, green and black
Issued:	01/04 in a limited edition of 1,250

U.K.:	£150.00
U.S.:	$300.00
Can.:	$300.00

OUT WITH THE DOGS (Lamp)

Model:	A2647
Modeller:	Craig Harding
Height:	16 ½", 41.9 cm
Colour:	Brown, white, grey, green and black
Issued:	01/04 - 06/06

U.K.:	£175.00
U.S.:	$350.00
Can.:	$350.00

Note: Available only in U.K.

OWLET
Style One

Model:	RB25
Modeller:	Ray Ayres
Height:	5", 12.7 cm
Colour:	White, beige and brown
Issued:	01/92 - 12/98

U.K.:	£35.00
U.S.:	$70.00
Can.:	$70.00

OWLET
Style Two

Model:	WB26
Modeller:	Russell Willis
Height:	5", 12.7 cm
Colour:	Pale brown and cream
Issued:	01/94 - 12/95
Series:	1. Baby Birds
	2. Russell Willis Birds

U.K.:	£35.00
U.S.:	$70.00
Can.:	$70.00

OWLET AND MOUSE

Model:	FE8
Modeller:	Ray Ayres
Height:	4 ½", 11.9 cm
Colour:	White and brown
Issued:	07/83 - 12/92
Series:	First Encounters

U.K.:	£40.00
U.S.:	$80.00
Can.:	$80.00

OWLETS (Three, Tawny)
Model: 081/B081
Modeller: Ray Ayres
Height: 081   4 ½", 11.9 cm
        B081   5 ¼", 13.3 cm
Colour: Cream and brown
Issued: 01/86 - 12/98
Series: British Birds

U.K.: £ 50.00
U.S.: $100.00
Can.: $100.00

OWLETS (Two, Barn)
Model: RB26
Modeller: Ray Ayres
Height: 4 ¼", 10.8 cm
Colour: Cream, beige and brown
Issued: 01/92 - 12/96

U.K.: £45.00
U.S.: $90.00
Can.: $90.00

PACK LEADER (Wolf)
Model: STW07
Modeller: Richard Roberts
Height: 11 ¼", 28.5 cm
Colour: Blue-grey, white, tan and black
Issued: 07/95 in a limited edition of 1,500
Series: Spirit of the Wolf

U.K.: £225.00
U.S.: $450.00
Can.: $450.00

PAINTED LADY ON ROSE (Butterfly)
Model: A5899
Modeller: Kerry Bell
Height: 4 ¾", 12.1 cm
Colour: Orange, black, green, fawn and white
Issued: 01/06 to the present
Series: Butterflies

U.K.: £20.00
U.S.: $40.00
Can.: $40.00

PAIR OF BLUE TITS
Model: A7388
Modeller: Unknown
Height: 7 ¼", 18.4 cm
Colour: Blue, yellow, white, brown, green and pink
Issued: 06/06 to the present

U.K.: £28.00
U.S.: $55.00
Can.: $55.00

PAIR OF HEDGEHOGS
Model: A7680
Modeller: Unknown
Height: 3 ¼", 8.3 cm
Colour: Brown, green, grey and yellow
Issued: 01/07 to the present
Series: Wildlife

U.K.: £15.00
U.S.: $30.00
Can.: $30.00

PAIR OF KINGFISHERS
Model: A7389
Modeller: Unknown
Height: 5 ¾", 14.6 cm
Colour: Turquoise, orange, brown, yellow, green
Issued: 06/06 to the present

U.K.: £28.00
U.S.: $55.00
Can.: $55.00

PAIR OF KITTENS
Model: A4691, 4694
Modeller: Unknown
Height: 3 ¼", 8.3 cm
Colour: A4691   Rouge
       A4694   Granite
Issued: 06/04 - 06/05
Series: Contemporary Kittens

U.K.: £14.00
U.S.: $28.00
Can.: $28.00

PALS
(Border collie pup and lamb)

Model:	B0007
Modeller:	Anne Wall
Height:	2 ¾", 7.0 cm
Colour:	Black and white collie; white lamb
Issued:	01/96 - 12/00
Series:	1. Every Living Thing
	2. J. Herriot Collection

U.K.:	£25.00
U.S.:	$50.00
Can.:	$50.00

PANDA AND CUB

Model:	WW27
Modeller:	David Walton
Height:	2 ½", 6.4 cm
Colour:	Black and white
Issued:	01/95 - 12/96
Series:	Miniature (WWF)

U.K.:	£15.00
U.S.:	$30.00
Can.:	$30.00

PANDAS

Model:	ED12
Modeller:	Judy Boyt
Height:	2 ½", 6.4 cm
Colour:	Black and white
Issued:	01/84 - 12/84
Series:	Early Days

U.K.:	£40.00
U.S.:	$80.00
Can.:	$80.00

PARTRIDGE
Style One

Model:	Unknown
Modeller:	Anne Wall
Height:	4", 10.1 cm
Colour:	Unknown
Issued:	01/77 - 06/82

U.K.:	£250.00
U.S.:	$500.00
Can.:	$500.00

PARTRIDGE
Style Two

Model:	033
Modeller:	Ray Ayres
Height:	7 ½", 19.1 cm
Colour:	Mauve-brown and green
Issued:	07/78 - 06/83

U.K.:	£175.00
U.S.:	$350.00
Can.:	$350.00

PARTRIDGE
Style Three

Model:	086
Modeller:	James Harvey
Height:	2 ¾", 7.0 cm
Colour:	Grey, brown, beige and chestnut
Issued:	01/86 - 12/87

U.K.:	£ 80.00
U.S.:	$160.00
Can.:	$160.00

PARTRIDGE
Style Four

Model:	A0660
Modeller:	Russell Willis
Height:	9", 22.9 cm
Colour:	Grey, browns and orange
Issued:	01/01 -12/04
Series:	Game Birds

U.K.:	£ 65.00
U.S.:	$125.00
Can.:	$125.00

PARTY'S OVER, THE
(Clown)

Model:	B1043
Modeller:	Richard Roberts
Size:	7 ¾" x 4 ¾"
	19.7 x 12.1 cm
Colour:	White, brown, yellow and red
Issued:	06/06 in a limited edition of 500
Series:	Masquerade Clowns

U.K.:	£100.00
U.S.:	$200.00
Can.:	$200.00

PASCHAL LAMB
Model: L114
Modeller: Richard Roberts
Height: Unknown
Colour: White; blue base
Issued: 01/92 in a limited edition of 950

U.K.: £225.00
U.S.: $450.00
Can.: $450.00

PATCH
(Jack Russell)
Model: JH22
Modeller: Richard Roberts
Height: 3", 7.6 cm
Colour: 1. White and tan
2. Black and white
Issued: 01/88 - 12/93
Series: 1. All Creatures Great and Small
2. James Herriot's Favourite Characters

U.K.: £25.00
U.S.: $50.00
Can.: $50.00

PATIENCE
(Heron)
Model: L123
Modeller: David Walton
Height: 8", 20.3 cm
Colour: White, grey, black and yellow
Issued: 09/92 in a limited edition of 950
Series: Masterpiece

U.K.: £225.00
U.S.: $450.00
Can.: $450.00

PAW PRINTS
(Ginger striped cat)
Model: A6892
Modeller: Andrew Edwards
Height: 4", 10.1 cm
Colour: Orange, blue, red and tan
Issued: 06/06 to the present
Series: Cats Round the World

U.K.: £20.00
U.S.: $40.00
Can.: $40.00

PEACE AND HARMONY
(Two doves)
Model: B0358
Modeller: Ray Ayres
Height: 7", 17.8 cm
Colour: Creamy-pink, green and brown
Issued: 06/99 - 06/00
Series: Annual Society Figurine (1999/2000)

U.K.: £100.00
U.S.: $200.00
Can.: $200.00

PEACOCK
(Butterfly)
Model: B4
Modeller: Ray Ayres
Height: 2", 5.0 cm
Colour: Purple, yellow and green
Issued: 07/80 - 12/85
Series: British Butterflies

U.K.: £ 65.00
U.S.: $125.00
Can.: $125.00

Note: Ealier models issued without antenae. Domes were optional with all butterflies.

PEACOCK ON BLACKBERRIES
(Butterfly)
Model: A5901
Modeller: Kerry Bell
Height: 5", 12.7 cm
Colour: Orange, black, white, green and pink
Issued: 01/06 to the present
Series: Butterflies

U.K.: £20.00
U.S.: $40.00
Can.: $40.00

PEKINESE (Standing)
Model: DG02
Modeller: Steve McKeown
Height: 2 ½", 6.4 cm
Colour: Tan and brown
Issued: 01/91 - 12/93
Series: Dogs Galore

U.K.: £15.00
U.S.: $30.00
Can.: $30.00

PEKINESE AND BAG

Model:	610801
Modeller:	Unknown
Height:	2", 5.0 cm
Colour:	Fawn and brown
Issued:	01/99 - 12/00
Series:	Puppy Tales
U.K.:	£12.00
U.S.:	$25.00
Can.:	$25.00

PEMBROKE CORGI

Model:	DS10
Modeller:	Elizabeth MacAllister
Height:	3", 7.6 cm
Colour:	Golden brown and white
Issued:	01/87 - 12/92
Series:	1. The World of Dogs
	2. Special Interest
U.K.:	£ 65.00
U.S.:	$125.00
Can.:	$125.00

PENGUIN AND CHICK

Model:	WW23
Modeller:	David Walton
Height:	3", 7.6 cm
Colour:	Grey, white, black and yellow
Issued:	07/94 - 12/96
Series:	Miniature (WWF)
U.K.:	£20.00
U.S.:	$40.00
Can.:	$40.00

PERCHERON SUPREME CHAMPION
(Gold Edition)

Model:	L160A, B, C,
Modeller:	Anne Wall
Height:	9 ¾", 24.7 cm
Colour:	A. Dapple grey
	B. Black
	C. Light grey
Issued:	10/95 in a limited edition of 300
Series:	Heavy Horse
U.K.:	£400.00
U.S.:	$800.00
Can.:	$800.00

Note: Issued nos. 1-300.

PERCHERON SUPREME CHAMPION
(Standard Edition)

Model:	L160D
Modeller:	Anne Wall
Height:	9 ¾", 24.7 cm
Colour:	Dapple grey
Issued:	01/96 in a limited edition of 300
Series:	1. Agricultural and Sporting
	2. The County Show
	3. Heavy Horse
U.K.:	£300.00
U.S.:	$600.00
Can.:	$600.00

Note: Issued nos. 301-600.

PEREGRINE FALCON
Style One

Model:	L01
Modeller:	Victor Hayton
Height:	7", 17.8 cm
Colour:	A. Browns, yellow and white
	B. Bronze
Issued:	01/77 in a limited edition of 250

	Brown	Bronze
U.K.:	£ 750.	£ 500.
U.S.:	$1,500.	$1,000.
Can.:	$1,500.	$1,000.

PEREGRINE FALCON
Style Two

Model:	A0657
Modeller:	Russell Willis
Height:	10 ½", 26.7 cm
Colour:	Grey, cream and white
Issued:	01/01 - 06/03
Series:	Birds of Prey
U.K.:	£ 75.00
U.S.:	$150.00
Can.:	$150.00

PEREGRINE FALCON
Style Three

Model:	A1474
Modeller:	Russell Willis
Height:	5 ½", 14.0 cm
Colour:	Grey, white, beige, pink and green
Issued:	01/02 - 06/05
Series:	Birds of Prey
U.K.:	£30.00
U.S.:	$60.00
Can.:	$60.00

PERSIAN CAT
Model: B0399A, B
Modeller: Ann Richmond
Height: 9 ¾", 24.7 cm
Colour: A. Blue
B. Cream
Issued: 01/99 - 12/99

U.K.: £ 80.00
U.S.: $160.00
Can.: $160.00

PERSIAN ON CUSHION
"SOPHISTICAT"
Model: C1
Modeller: Judy Boyt
Height: 1 ½", 3.8 cm
Colour: White and blue
Issued: 01/83 - 12/93
Series: A Cat Around the House

U.K.: £25.00
U.S.: $50.00
Can.: $50.00

Note: Custom painted

PET LAMBS
(Girl with two lambs)
Model: B0010
Modeller: Anne Wall
Height: 5", 12.7 cm
Colour: Pink, blue, white and brown
Issued: 01/97 - 12/98
Series: 1. All Creatures Great and Small
2. The James Herriot Collection

U.K.: £ 65.00
U.S.: $125.00
Can.: $125.00

PHAUN
(Siamese)
Model: LA13
Designer: Lesley Anne Ivory
Modeller: Anne Butler
Height: 4", 10.1 cm
Colour: Creamy-brown and black
Issued: 01/92 - 12/93
Varieties: LAM4 (Musical)
Series: Ivory Cats

U.K.: £35.00
U.S.: $70.00
Can.: $70.00

PHAUN (Musical)
(Siamese)
Model: LAM4
Designer: Lesley Anne Ivory
Modeller: Anne Butler
Height: 6", 15.0 cm
Colour: Creamy-brown and black
Issued: 01/92 - 12/93
Varieties: LA13 Phaun
Series: Ivory Cats (Musical)

U.K.: £40.00
U.S.: $80.00
Can.: $80.00

PHEASANT
Style One
Model: 049
Modeller James Harvey
Height: 5", 12.7 cm
Colour: Reddish-brown, green and red
Issued: 01/85 - 12/90
Series: British Birds

U.K.: £175.00
U.S.: $350.00
Can.: $350.00

PHEASANT
Style Two
Model: A0659
Modeller Russell Willis
Height: 10 ¼", 26.0 cm
Colour: Reddish-brown, brown and grey
Issued: 01/01 - 12/05
Series: 1. Woodland and Garden
2. Game Birds

U.K.: £100.00
U.S.: $200.00
Can.: $200.00

PHEASANT
Style Three

Model:	A6058
Modeller:	Unknown
Height:	5 ¼", 13.3 cm
Colour:	Reddish-brown, green and red
Issued:	06/05 to the present

U.K.:	£10.00
U.S.:	$20.00
Can.:	$20.00

PHEASANT
Style Four

Model:	A6723
Modeller:	Unknown
Height:	4 ½", 11.4 cm
Colour:	Reddish-brown, black and red
Issued:	06/06 to the present

U.K.:	£25.00
U.S.:	$50.00
Can.:	$50.00

PHEASANT (Cock)

Model:	UK# 037
	USA# 225-063
Modeller:	Ray Ayres
Height:	6 ½", 16.5 cm
Colour:	Reddish-brown and green
Issued:	06/79 - 12/84

U.K.:	£175.00
U.S.:	$350.00
Can.:	$350.00

PHEASANT (Walking)

Model:	A1475
Modeller:	Russell Willis
Size:	7 ½" x 11 ¼"
	19.1 x 28.5 cm
Colour	Reddish-brown, red, grey, pink and green
Issued:	06/02 to the present
Series:	Birds by Russell Willis

U.K.:	£ 69.00
U.S.:	$140.00
Can.:	$140.00

PHEASANT HEN AND CHICKS

Model:	041
Modeller:	David Geenty
Height:	5", 12.7 cm
Colour:	Browns, yellow and green
Issued:	01/81 - 12/82

U.K.:	£125.00
U.S.:	$250.00
Can.:	$250.00

PHEASANT RISING

Model:	L46
Modeller:	Frank DiVita
Height:	9", 22.9 cm
Colour:	Browns, green and red
Issued:	01/83 in a limited edition of 950

U.K.:	£325.00
U.S.:	$650.00
Can.:	$650.00

PHEASANTS RISING

Model:	A1392
Modeller:	John Brown
Height:	11 ¾", 29.8 cm
Colour:	Browns, reds, yellows and green
Issued:	01/02 - 12/03
Series:	Game Birds

U.K.:	£100.00
U.S.:	$200.00
Can.:	$200.00

PICK OF THE CROP
(Goat and Kid)

Model:	B0518
Modeller:	Kirsty Armstrong
Height:	8", 20.3 cm
Colour:	White and green
Issued:	01/00 - 06/01
Series:	James Herriot Collection

U.K.:	£ 80.00
U.S.:	$160.00
Can.:	$160.00

PICK OF THE LITTER
(Collie Pups)
Model: JH30
Modeller: Ray Ayres
Height: 4 ¼", 10.8 cm
Colour: Black and white
Issued: 01/89 - 12/92
Series: All Creatures Great
and Small

U.K.: £125.00
U.S.: $250.00
Can.: $250.00

PIED WAGTAIL
Model: RB14
Modeller: Ray Ayres
Height: 4 ¼", 10.8 cm
Colour: Black and white
Issued: 01/90 - 12/92
Series: British Birds

U.K.: £125.00
U.S.: $250.00
Can: $250.00

PIG
Model: A4595
Modeller: Lesley McKenzie
Height: 3 ½", 8.9 cm
Colour: Pale pink
Issued: 06/04 to the present
Series: BFA Pottery Company

U.K.: £25.00
U.S.: $50.00
Can.: $50.00

PIG A
(Lying, Head and Ears Out of Sack)
Model: 130A
Modeller: Anne Butler
Height: 1 ¼", 3.1 cm
Colour: Pink
Issued: 01/91 - 12/95
Series: A Pig in a Poke

U.K.: £12.00
U.S.: $25.00
Can.: $25.00

PIG B
(Seated, Head and Ears Out of Sack)
Model: 130B
Modeller: Anne Butler
Height: 2 ½", 6.4 cm
Colour: Pink
Issued: 01/91 - 12/95
Series: A Pig in a Poke

U.K.: £12.00
U.S.: $25.00
Can.: $25.00

PIG C
(Lying, Bottom Out of Sack)
Model: 130C
Modeller: Anne Butler
Height: 1 ½", 3.8 cm
Colour: Pink
Issued: 01/91 - 12/95
Series: A Pig in a Poke

U.K.: £12.00
U.S.: $25.00
Can.: $25.00

PIG D
(Lying, Sleeping)
Model: 130D
Modeller: Anne Butler
Height: 1 ½", 3.8 cm
Colour: Pink
Issued: 01/91 - 12/95
Series: A Pig in a Poke

U.K.: £12.00
U.S.: $25.00
Can.: $25.00

PIG E
(Peeping Out of Sack, Bottom Up)
Model: 130E
Modeller: Anne Butler
Height: 2 ¼", 5.7 cm
Colour: Pink
Issued: 01/91 - 12/95
Series: A Pig in a Poke

U.K.: £12.00
U.S.: $25.00
Can.: $25.00

PIG F
(Seated, Peeping Out of Sack)

Model:	130F
Modeller:	Anne Butler
Height:	2", 5.0 cm
Colour:	Pink
Issued:	01/91 - 12/95
Series:	A Pig in a Poke

U.K.:	£12.00
U.S.:	$25.00
Can.:	$25.00

PIG G
(Seated, Head Out of Sack)

Model:	130G
Modeller:	Anne Butler
Height:	2 ¾", 7.0 cm
Colour:	Pink
Issued:	01/94 - 12/95
Series:	A Pig in a Poke

U.K.:	£12.00
U.S.:	$25.00
Can.:	$25.00

PIG H
(Standing, Nose in Sack)

Model:	130H
Modeller:	Anne Butler
Height:	2", 5.0 cm
Colour:	Pink
Issued:	01/94 - 12/95
Series:	A Pig in a Poke

U.K.:	£12.00
U.S.:	$25.00
Can.:	$25.00

PIGLET

Model:	FF2A, B, C
Modeller:	Ray Ayres
Height:	1 ¾", 4.4 cm
Colour:	A. Black with pink stripe
	B. Pink
	C. Pink with black spots
Issued:	01/89 - 12/95
Series:	First Friends

U.K.:	£12.00
U.S.:	$25.00
Can.:	$25.00

PIGLET, Seated
Style One

Model:	M2
Modeller:	David Geenty
Height:	3", 7.6 cm
Colour:	Pink
Issued:	07/80 - 12/80
Series:	Beginners, Please

U.K.:	£25.00
U.S.:	$50.00
Can.:	$50.00

PIGLET, Seated
Style Two

Model:	B0961, 0961A
Modeller:	Ray Ayres
Height:	5 ½", 14.0 cm
Colour:	B0961 Pink
	B0961A Pink with black spots
Issued:	06/05 - 12/06
Series:	Classic Babies

U.K.:	£40.00
U.S.:	$80.00
Can.:	$80.00

PIGLET AND HEN

Model:	FE9
Modeller:	Ray Ayres
Height:	2 ½", 6.4 cm
Colour:	Pink, dark grey and white
Issued:	01/84 - 12/86
Series:	First Encounters

U.K.:	£ 50.00
U.S.:	$100.00
Can.:	$100.00

PIGLET SCRUMPING

Model:	A3868
Modeller:	Janet Miller
Height:	2 ¼", 5.7 cm
Colour:	Pale pink, cream, red and green
Issued:	01/04 - 12/06
Series:	On The Farm

U.K.:	£13.00
U.S.:	$26.00
Can.:	$26.00

PIGLET WITH WELLIES

Model: A0172/A0173
Modeller: Anne Wall
Height: 2 ¼", 5.7 cm
Colour: A0172 Pink
A0173 Spotted
Issued: A0172 06/00-12/05
A0173 06/00-06/05
Series: On the Farm

U.K.: £12.00
U.S.: $25.00
Can.: $25.00

PIGLETS

Model: ED7
Modeller: Judy Boyt
Height: 2", 5.0 cm
Colour: Pale pink
Issued: 07/82 - 06/85
Series: Early Days

U.K.: £40.00
U.S.: $80.00
Can.: $80.00

PIGLETS
(Gloucester Old Spot)

Model: L10
Modeller: Victor Hayton
Height: 3", 7.6 cm
Colour: A. Pink and black
B. Bronze
Issued: 01/77 in a limited
edition of 500

	Pink	Bronze
U.K.:	£225.	£100.
U.S.:	$450.	$200.
Can.:	$450.	$200.

PINTAIL

Model: A0478
Modeller: Don Briddell
Height: 10 ¼", 26.0 cm
Colour: Grey, brown, yellow
and stone
Issued: 01/01 - 12/02
Series: Waterfowl of the World
by Don Briddell

U.K.: £100.00
U.S.: $200.00
Can.: $200.00

PINTAIL DRAKE

Model: PS12
Modeller: Richard Roberts
Height: 3 ¼", 8.3 cm
Colour: Black, white and grey
Issued: 01/92 - 12/93
Series: Peter Scott Memorial
Appeal (WWF)

U.K.: £ 65.00
U.S.: $125.00
Can.: $125.00

PIP
(Border Terrier)

Model: A7940
Modeller: Unknown
Height: 3 ¼", 8.3 cm
Colour: Brown, blue and green
Issued: 01/07 to the present
Series: James Herriot
Studio Collection

U.K.: £16.00
U.S.: $32.00
Can.: $32.00

PIPER, THE

Model: B1020, 1020A
Modeller: Paul Back
Height: 10", 25.4 cm
Colour: B1020 Red tartan
B1020A Green tartan
Issued: 2006 in a limited
edition of 600

U.K.: £195.00
U.S.: $400.00
Can.: $400.00

PLAYFUL
(Ginger striped cat)

Model: A6896
Modeller: Andrew Edwards
Height: 4 ¼", 10.8 cm
Colour: Browns, black and red
Issued: 06/06 to the present
Series: Cats Round the House

U.K.: £22.00
U.S.: $45.00
Can.: $45.00

PLOUGHMAN'S LUNCH
(Grey Shire, Farmer and Collie)

Model:	B0090A, B	
Modeller:	Anne Wall	
Height:	5 ½", 14.0 cm	
Colour:	A. Grey	
	B. Bay	
Issued:	01/97 in a limited edition of 1,750	
Series:	The James Herriot Collection	

	Grey	Bay
U.K.:	£300.00	£300.00
U.S.:	$600.00	$600.00
Can.:	$600.00	$600.00

POACHER, THE
(Otter)

Model:	A0003
Modeller:	Ray Ayres
Height:	6 ¼", 15.9 cm
Colour:	Brown, cream, green and grey
Issued:	01/00 - 06/06
Series:	Country Characters

U.K.:	£35.00
U.S.:	$70.00
Can.:	$70.00

POINT OF INTEREST
(Otter and Three Cubs)

Model:	MTR10
Modeller:	Ray Ayres
Height:	8", 20.3 cm
Colour:	Brown, white and green
Issued:	01/96 in a limited edition of 1,750
Series:	Masters of the River

U.K.:	£225.00
U.S.:	$450.00
Can.:	$450.00

POLAR BEAR AND CUB

Model:	RW18
Modeller:	Richard Wawrzesta
Height:	4 ¾", 12.1 cm
Colour:	White
Issued:	01/90 - 12/93
Series:	Endangered Species (WWF)

U.K.:	£ 50.00
U.S.:	$100.00
Can.:	$100.00

POLAR BEAR CUBS

Model:	RW64
Modeller:	Richard Roberts
Height:	6", 15.0 cm
Colour:	Cream, blue-grey and black
Issued:	01/96 - 06/97
Series:	Nursery (WWF)

U.K.:	£ 75.00
U.S.:	$150.00
Can.:	$150.00

POLICE HANDLER AND
GERMAN SHEPHERD DOG

Model:	L122
Modeller:	Anne Butler
Height:	7 ½", 19.1 cm
Colour:	Blue and black
Issued:	08/92 in a limited edition of 950

U.K.:	£425.00
U.S.:	$850.00
Can.:	$850.00

POLO PONY

Model:	B0875, 0875A
Modeller:	Anne Wall
Height:	13 ½" x 11 ½" 34.3 x 29.2 cm
Colour:	B0875 Bay horse B0875A Grey horse
Issued:	06/04 in a limited edition of 500

U.K.:	£250.00
U.S.:	$500.00
Can.:	$500.00

POMERANIAN, Standing Style One
Model: B0607
Modeller: Margaret Turner
Height: 2 ½", 6.4 cm
Colour: Pale golden brown
Issued: 06/00 - 12/01
Series: Dogs Galore

U.K.: £15.00
U.S.: $30.00
Can.: $30.00

POMERANIAN, Standing Style Two
Model: A5182
Modeller: Margaret Turner
Height: 2 ¾", 7.0 cm
Colour: Golden brown
Issued: 01/05 - 06/06
Series: Dogs and Pups Galore

U.K.: £13.00
U.S.: $25.00
Can.: $25.00

POODLE (Lamb Cut)
Model: B0014A, B
Modeller: Margaret Turner
Height: 4 ¼", 10.8 cm
Colour: A. Black
B. White
Issued: 06/96 - 12/97
Series: Dogs Galore

U.K.: £25.00
U.S.: $50.00
Can.: $50.00

POODLE (Lamb Cut, Lying)
Model: B0018A, B
Modeller: Margaret Turner
Height: 2", 5.0 cm
Colour: A. Black
B. White
Issued: 06/96 - 12/97
Series: Pups Galore

U.K.: £12.00
U.S.: $25.00
Can.: $25.00

POODLE (Seated)
Model: DG18A, B
Modeller: Margaret Turner
Height: 3 ¼", 8.3 cm
Colour: A. White
B. Black
Issued: 01/92 - 12/96
Series: Dogs Galore

U.K.: £30.00
U.S.: $60.00
Can.: $60.00

POODLE AND PUP (Pet Trim)
Model: B0106A, B
Modeller: Margaret Turner
Height: 4 ¾", 12.1 cm
Colour: A. Black
B. White
Issued: 06/96 - 12/97
Series: Dogs Galore

U.K.: £40.00
U.S.: $80.00
Can.: $80.00

POODLE AND SOCK
Model: 610836
Modeller: Unknown
Height: 2 ½", 6.4 cm
Colour: Grey and pink
Issued: 01/99 - 12/00
Series: Puppy Tales

U.K.: £12.00
U.S.: $25.00
Can.: $25.00

POODLE (Pet Trim), Seated Style One
Model: B0075A, B
Modeller: Margaret Turner
Height: 4 ¼", 10.8 cm
Colour: A. Black
B. White
Issued: A. 06/96 -12/01
B. 06/96 - 06/01
Series: Dogs Galore

U.K.: £12.00
U.S.: $25.00
Can.: $25.00

POODLE PET TRIM, Seated
Style Two

Model:	A3830, 3879
Modeller:	Margaret Turner
Height:	3 ¼", 8.3 cm
Colour:	A3830 Black
	A3879 White
Issued:	01/04 to the present
Series:	Dogs and Pups Galore
U.K.:	£15.00
U.S.:	$30.00
Can.:	$30.00

POPPY AND LEOPARD

Model:	FC18
Designer:	Fleur Cowles
Modeller:	Unknown
Height:	Unknown
Colour:	Red, black, orange, brown and white
Issued:	1987 - Dec. 1988
Series:	Fleur's Flowers
U.K.:	£ 75.00
U.S.:	$150.00
Can.:	$150.00

POSER, THE
(Cat)

Model:	A7322, 7602
Modeller:	Unknown
Height:	6", 15.0 cm
Colour:	A7322 Grey
	A7602 Siamese
Issued:	06/06 to the present
Series:	Feline Fun
U.K.:	£ 9.95
U.S.:	$20.00
Can.:	$20.00

POT CART

Model:	B1015
Modeller:	Ray Ayres
Size:	6 ½" x 13 ½"
	16.5 x 34.3 cm
Colour:	Grey, browns, tan
	and white
Issued:	01/07 in a limited
	edition of 600
U.K.:	£275.00
U.S.:	$550.00
Can.:	$550.00

POTATO PICKING

Model:	A4062
Modeller:	Paul Back
Height:	6", 15.0 cm
Colour:	Brown, blue and white
Issued:	06/04 - 06/05
Series:	Young Farmers
U.K.:	£40.00
U.S.:	$80.00
Can.:	$80.00

PREENER, THE
(Cat)

Model:	A7598, 7604
Modeller:	Unknown
Height:	4 ¼", 10.8 cm
Colour:	A7598 Grey
	A7604 Siamese
Issued:	06/06 to the present
Series:	Feline Fun
U.K.:	£ 9.95
U.S.:	$20.00
Can.:	$20.00

PRETTY BOY
(Clown)

Model:	B1042
Modeller:	Richard Roberts
Size:	10 ¼" x 5 ¼"
	26.0 x 13.3 cm
Colour:	White, blue, green
	black and red
Issued:	06/06 in a limited
	edition of 500
Series:	Masquerade Clowns
U.K.:	£100.00
U.S.:	$200.00
Can.:	$200.00

**PRICKLY MOMENTS
(Calves)**

Model:	A1859, 2638
Modeller:	Hans Kendrick
Height:	3 ¾", 9.5 cm
Colour:	A1859 Black/white (Ayrshire)
	A2638 Brown/white (Friesian)
Issued:	01/03 - 12/04
Series:	James Herriot Studio Collection
U.K.:	£45.00
U.S.:	$90.00
Can.:	$90.00

**PRINCE OF THE LOCH
(Osprey)**

Model:	B0651
Modeller	Richard Roberts
Height:	21", 53.5 cm
Colour:	Browns, grey, cream and stone
Issued:	01/01 in a limited edition of 750
Series:	Birds of the World
U.K.:	£ 550.00
U.S.:	$1,100.00
Can.:	$1,100.00

**PRIZE BLOOMS
(Goat and Roses)**

Model:	A0458
Modeller	Kirsty Armstrong
Height:	6", 15.0 cm
Colour:	Brown, cream, green and red
Issued:	01/01 - 06/03
Series:	James Herriot Studio Collection
U.K.:	£35.00
U.S.:	$70.00
Can.:	$70.00

**PRODIGAL'S RETURN
(Border Collie, sheep and lambs)**

Model:	A1224
Modeller:	Kirsty Armstrong
Height:	3 ¾", 9.5 cm
Colour:	Black, white, brown, tan and green
Issued:	01/02 - 12/06
Series:	James Herriot Studio Collection
U.K.:	£ 50.00
U.S.:	$100.00
Can.:	$100.00

**PRUDENCE
(Pig)**

Model:	A6862
Modeller:	Kerry Bell
Height:	3 ¼", 8.5 cm
Colour:	Pink, grey and brown
Issued:	06/06 to the present
Series:	James Herriot Studio Collection
U.K.:	£22.00
U.S.:	$45.00
Can.:	$45.00

PUFFIN

Model:	M29
Modeller:	David Walton
Height:	3 ¾", 9.5 cm
Colour:	Black, white and orange
Issued:	01/93 - 12/95
Series:	Miniature Wildlife
U.K.:	£30.00
U.S.:	$60.00
Can.:	$60.00

PUFFINS

Model:	B0991
Modeller:	Ray AYres
Size:	7 ¼" x 6 ¼" 18.4 x 15.9 cm
Colour:	Black, white, orange, grey, green and pink
Issued:	01/06 in a limited edition of 500
U.K.:	£150.00
U.S.:	$300.00
Can.:	$300.00

PUG, Begging

Model:	B0603
Modeller:	Margaret Turner
Height:	4 ¼", 10.8 cm
Colour:	Fawn and black
Issued:	06/00 - 12/01
Series:	Dogs Galore
U.K.:	£20.00
U.S.:	$40.00
Can.:	$40.00

PUG, Standing
Style One

Model: 063
Modeller: David Geenty
Height: 5", 12.7 cm
Colour: Tan and black
Issued: 07/81 - 12/81

U.K.: £125.00
U.S.: $250.00
Can.: $250.00

PUG, Standing
Style Two

Model: A5183
Modeller: Margaret Turner
Height: 3¼", 8.3 cm
Colour: Cream, brown, black
Issued: 01/05 to the present
Series: Dogs and Pups Galore

U.K.: £18.00
U.S.: $35.00
Can.: $35.00

PULL (Clay Pigeon Shooter)

Model: 116
Modeller: Ray Ayres
Height: 8", 20.3 cm
Colour: Blue, green and brown
Issued: 01/89 - 12/92
Series: 1. Agricultural and
          Sporting
        2. Special Interest

U.K.: £150.00
U.S.: $300.00
Can.: $300.00

PULLING A FAST ONE
(Gander and Two Jack Russell
Terriers)

Model: B0338
Modeller: Kirsty Armstrong
Height: 5 ¾", 14.6 cm
Colour: White, brown and black
Issued: 01/99 - 06/00
Series: The James Herriot
          Collection

U.K.: £ 80.00
U.S.: $160.00
Can.: $160.00

PUP AND SLIPPER

Model: FE6
Modeller: Ray Ayres
Height: 3", 7.6 cm
Colour: Golden and maroon
Issued: 01/83 - 12/84
Series: First Encounters

U.K.: £ 65.00
U.S.: $125.00
Can.: $125.00

PUPPY
Style One

Model: M1
Modeller: David Geenty
Height: 4", 10.1 cm
Colour: Browns and white
Issued: 07/80 - 12/82
Series: Beginners, Please

U.K.: £30.00
U.S.: $60.00
Can.: $60.00

PUPPY
Style Two

Model: FF4A, B, C
Modeller: Ray Ayres
Height: 2", 5.0 cm
Colour: A. Black, white and
          pink
        B. Golden and green
        C. Tan, white and blue
Issued: 01/89 - 12/95
Series: First Friends

U.K.: £12.00
U.S.: $25.00
Can.: $25.00

PUPPY AND ROBIN

Model: FE16/ FE16A, B
Modeller: Ray Ayres
Height: 3 ¾", 9.5 cm
Colour: FE16   Black, brown,
                  white
        FE16A Brown / white
        FE16B Black / white
Issued: FE16- 06/91 - 12/95
        A-B.01/96 - 12/97
Series: First Encounters

U.K.   £40.00
U.S. $80.00
Can. $80.00

PUPPY LOVE
(Border Collies)

Model:	A1861
Modeller:	Anne Wall
Height:	3 ¾", 9.5 cm
Colour:	Black, white, green and brown
Issued:	01/03 to the present
Series:	James Herriot Studio Collection
U.K.:	£30.00
U.S.:	$60.00
Can.:	$60.00

PUPPY ON A STRING

Model:	A7049, 7462, 3
Modeller:	Barry Snelson
Height:	2 ¼", 5.7 cm
Colour:	A7049 Black
	A7462 Yellow
	A7463 Chocolate
Issued:	06/06 - 06/07
Series:	Puppy Trouble
U.K.:	£16.00
U.S.:	$30.00
Can.:	$30.00

PUPPY TRAINING

Model:	A4063
Modeller:	Paul Back
Height:	6 ½", 16.5 cm
Colour:	Blue, black, white, light brown and green
Issued:	06/04 - 06/06
Series:	Young Farmers
U.K.:	£40.00
U.S.:	$80.00
Can.:	$80.00

PUTTING OUT THE MILK
(Landrover)

Model:	JH66
Modeller:	Ray Ayres
Height:	7", 17.8 cm
Colour:	Green, brown and silver
Issued:	01/92 in a limited edition of 1,500
Series:	All Things Wise and Wonderful
U.K.:	£ 500.00
U.S.:	$1,000.00
Can.:	$1,000.00

PUTTING THE WORLD TO RIGHTS
(Farmer, bull and dog)

Model:	B0890
Modeller:	Ray Ayres
Size:	8 ¼" x 10 ¼" 21.0 x 26.0 cm
Colour:	Golden brown, grey, brown, white, green and pale blue
Issued:	01/05 in a limited editio of 500
U.K.:	£200.00
U.S.:	$400.00
Can.:	$400.00

QUARTER HORSE MARE AND FOAL

Model:	A0185
Modeller:	Anne Wall
Height:	5 ¼", 13.3 cm
Colour:	Dark brown, light brown and green
Issued:	06/00 - 12/02
Series:	Mares and Foals
U.K.:	£ 50.00
U.S.:	$100.00
Can.:	$100.00

QUARTER HORSE STALLION

Model:	A1462
Modeller:	Anne Wall
Height:	6 ¾", 17.2 cm
Colour:	Dark brown
Issued:	01/03 - 12/04
Series:	Horse Breeds
U.K.:	£40.00
U.S.:	$80.00
Can.:	$80.00

QUEEN'S HAFLINGER AT BALMORAL, THE

Model:	Unknown
Modeller:	Anne Wall
Height:	7 ½", 19.1 cm
Colour:	Palomino horse; grey base
Issued:	1978 in a limited edition of 200
U.K.:	£ 675.00
U.S.:	$1,350.00
Can.:	$1,350.00

**QUENCHING THEIR THIRST
(Cows, Calf and Ducks)**

Model:	B0342
Modeller:	Kirsty Armstrong
Height:	5 ¼", 13.3 cm
Colour:	Black, brown, white and green
Issued:	01/99 in a limited edition of 1,500
Series:	The James Herriot Collection
U.K.:	£175.00
U.S.:	$350.00
Can.:	$350.00

RABBIT

Model:	JB4
Modeller:	Judy Boyt
Height:	4 ½", 11.9 cm
Colour:	Brown
Issued:	07/83 - 12/85
Series:	Judy Boyt Woodland
U.K.:	£ 60.00
U.S.:	$120.00
Can.:	$120.00

**RABBIT
(Adult with four young)**

Model:	RW6
Modeller:	Richard Wawrzesta
Height:	4", 10.1 cm
Colour:	Tan, white and green
Issued:	01/88 - 12/93
Series:	1. WWFN
	2. Wildlife Families (WWF)
U.K.:	£40.00
U.S.:	$80.00
Can.:	$80.00

RABBIT (Scratching Ear)

Model:	020
Modeller:	Judy Boyt
Height:	4 ¾", 12.1 cm
Colour:	Browns and white
Issued:	01/82 - 12/82
Series:	Woodland
U.K.:	£ 70.00
U.S.:	$140.00
Can.:	$140.00

RABBIT (With Carrot)

Model:	FF6A, B
Modeller:	Ray Ayres
Height:	2 ½", 6.4 cm
Colour:	A. Brown
	B. White
Issued:	01/89 - 12/93
Series:	First Friends
U.K.:	£12.00
U.S.:	$25.00
Can.:	$25.00

RABBIT AND YOUNG

Model:	A7681
Modeller:	Unknown
Height:	2 ½", 6.4 cm
Colour:	Light brown, white, green and yellow
Issued:	01/07 to the present
Series:	Wildlife
U.K.:	£15.00
U.S.:	$30.00
Can.:	$30.00

RABBIT CROUCHING

Model:	UK# 001/001B
	USA# 225-008
Modeller:	Ray Ayres
Height:	4", 10.1 cm
Colour:	A. Brown
	B. Bronze
Issued:	07/78 - 12/81

	Brown	Bronze
U.K.:	£ 80.	£40.
U.S:	$160.	$80.
Can.:	$160.	$80.

Note: This model was available in 1982 in the USA.

**RABBIT FAMILY
Style One**

Model:	WW10
Modeller:	Richard Wawrzesta
Height:	3 ½", 8.9 cm
Colour:	Browns, cream and green
Issued:	01/87 - 12/87
Series:	Family Life (WWF)
U.K.:	£40.00
U.S.:	$80.00
Can.:	$80.00

RABBIT FAMILY
Style Two

Model:	B0223
Modeller:	Kirsty Armstrong
Height:	5", 12.7 cm
Colour:	Brown, cream and green
Issued:	01/98 - 12/99
Series:	Wildlife Families

U.K.:	£ 65.00
U.S.:	$125.00
Can.:	$125.00

RABBIT SCRATCHING

Model:	001A
Modeller:	Victor Hayton
Height:	4", 10.1 cm
Colour:	A. Brown
	B. Bronze
Issued:	01/77 - 01/82
Series:	Mammals

	Brown	Bronze
U.K.:	£125.	£ 65.
U.S.:	$250.	$125.
Can.:	$250.	$125.

RABBIT SITTING
Style One

Model:	015
Modeller:	Ray Ayres
Height:	5", 12.7 cm
Colour:	Brown and white
Issued:	01/80 - 12/81
Series:	Mammals

U.K.:	£100.00
U.S.:	$200.00
Can.:	$200.00

RABBIT SITTING
Style Two

Model:	FF17
Modeller:	Anne Wall
Height:	2", 5.0 cm
Colour:	Light brown and white
Issued:	01/93 - 12/95
Series:	First Friends

U.K.:	£12.00
U.S.:	$25.00
Can.:	$25.00

RABBIT STANDING

Model:	L08
Modeller:	Victor Hayton
Height:	7 ½", 19.1 cm
Colour:	A. Brown and cream
	B. Bronze
Issued:	01/77 in a limited edition of 500

	Brown	Bronze
U.K.:	£375.	£ 75.
U.S.:	$750.	$150.
Can.:	$750.	$150.

RABBITS
Style One

Model:	ED6
Modeller:	Judy Boyt
Height:	2", 5.0 cm
Colour:	Brown and cream
Issued:	07/82 - 12/84
Series:	Early Days

U.K.:	£40.00
U.S.:	$80.00
Can.:	$80.00

RABBITS
Style Two

Model:	ML02
Modeller:	Mairi Laing Hunt
Height:	5 ½", 14.0 cm
Colour:	Brown and green
Issued:	01/88 - 12/90
Series:	Woodland

U.K.:	£ 50.00
U.S.:	$100.00
Can.:	$100.00

RABBITS
Style Three

Model:	145
Modeller:	David Walton
Height:	3 ¾", 9.5 cm
Colour:	Grey-brown
Issued:	01/91 - 12/92

U.K.:	£40.00
U.S.:	$80.00
Can.:	$80.00

RABBITS (Adult and Three Young)

Model:	RW32
Modeller:	David Walton
Height:	4 ½", 11.9 cm
Colour:	Browns and white
Issued:	07/93 - 12/95
Series:	Wildlife Families (WWF)

U.K.:	£40.00
U.S.:	$80.00
Can.:	$80.00

RACING PIGEON
Style One

Model:	048
Modeller:	Anne Wall
Height:	6 ½", 16.5 cm
Colour:	Dark grey and white
Issued:	01/82 - 12/91
Series:	Special Interest

U.K.:	£150.00
U.S.:	$300.00
Can.:	$300.00

Note: Custom painted.

RACING PIGEON
Style Two

Model:	A1862
Modeller:	Hans Kendrich
Height:	8 ¼", 21.0 cm
Colour:	Silver-grey, brown, green, red and beige
Issued:	01/03 - 06/05
Series:	Sporting Bird

U.K.:	£ 50.00
U.S.:	$100.00
Can.:	$100.00

RAG, BONE, ANY OLD IRON?

Model:	B0989
Modeller:	Ray Ayres
Size:	6 ½" x 14 ½" 16.5 x 36.8 cm
Colour:	Brown, black, white, grey and fawn
Issued:	01/06 in a limited edition of 500

U.K.:	£295.00
U.S.:	$600.00
Can.:	$600.00

RAINBOW TROUT

Model:	141
Modeller:	David Walton
Height:	5 ½", 14.0 cm
Colour:	Grey, white and pink
Issued:	01/91 - 12/93

U.K.:	£125.00
U.S.:	$250.00
Can.:	$250.00

RAJAH

Model:	FC10
Designer:	Fleur Cowles
Modeller:	Richard Roberts
Height:	6", 15.0 cm
Colour:	1. Blue 2. Natural 3. White
Issued:	1987 in a limited edition of 300
Series:	The Imagined World of Fleur Cowles

U.K.:	£325.00
U.S.:	$650.00
Can.:	$650.00

RAMBLER, THE
(Badger)

Model:	A0002
Modeller:	Ray Ayres
Height:	7 ½", 19.1 cm
Colour:	Grey, black, white, fawn and green
Issued:	01/00 - 06/04
Series:	Country Characters

U.K.:	£35.00
U.S.:	$70.00
Can.:	$70.00

REACHING FOR THE HIGH BIRD
First Version - Labradors

Model:	108A, B, C
Modeller:	Ray Ayres
Height:	10 ¼", 26.0 cm
Colour:	A. Yellow B. Black C. Black and yellow
Issued:	01/84 - 12/92
Series:	1. Agricultural and Sporting 2. Special Interest

U.K.:	£175.00
U.S.:	$350.00
Can.:	$350.00

REACHING FOR THE HIGH BIRD
Second Version - Spaniels

Model:	109A, B, C
Modeller:	Ray Ayres
Height:	10 ¼", 26.0 cm
Colour:	A. Liver and white
	B. Black and white
	C. Liver/white, black/white
Issued:	01/84 - 12/92
Series:	1. Agricultural Sporting
	2. Special Interest.

U.K.:	£175.00
U.S.:	$350.00
Can.:	$350.00

READY AND WAITING
(Border Collie)

Model:	A6129
Modeller:	Hans Kendrick
Height:	7 ¾", 19.7 cm
Colour:	Black, white, grey and green
Issued:	01/06 to the present
Series:	Border Collie Collection

U.K.	£ 65.00
U.S.	$125.00
Can.:	$125.00

READY AND WAITING (Lamp)
(Border Collie)

Model:	A8104
Modeller:	Hans Kendrick
Height:	18", 45.7 cm
Colour:	Black, white, grey and green
Issued:	01/07 to the present
Series:	Border Collie Collection

U.K.:	£195.00
U.S.:	$400.00
Can.:	$400.00

Note: Avaiable in U.K. only.

REARING BLACK STALLION/THE BLACK STALLION RETURNS

Model:	K236
Modeller:	Fred Stone
Height:	10 ¼", 26.0 cm
Colour:	A. Black
	B. Bronze
Issued:	01/90 Ltd Ed. of 3,500

	Black	Bronze
U.K.:	£125.	£ 80.
U.S.:	$250.	$160.
Can.:	$250.	$160.

Note: ©United Artists Corporation. Exclusive for American Artists. Available in the US UK.

RED ADMIRAL
(Butterfly)

Model:	B2
Modeller:	Anne Wall
Height:	3", 7.6 cm
Colour:	Red, black and beige
Issued:	07/80 - 12/85
Re-issued:	07/90 - 12/91
Series:	British Butterflies

	Original	Re-issued
U.K.:	£ 65.	£40.
U.S:	$125.	$80.
Can.:	$125.	$80.

Note: Earlier models were issued without antenae. Domes were optional with all butterflies.

RED ADMIRAL AND CLEMATIS
(Butterfly)

Model:	A5900
Modeller:	Kerry Bell
Height:	5", 12.7 cm
Colour:	Black, orange, white, fawn, green and pink
Issued:	01/06 to the present
Series:	Butterflies

U.K.:	£20.00
U.S.:	$40.00
Can.:	$40.00

RED GROUSE
Style One

Model:	087
Modeller:	James Harvey
Height:	6", 15.0 cm
Colour:	Red, dark brown and white
Issued:	01/86 - 12/87

U.K.:	£100.00
U.S.:	$200.00
Can.:	$200.00

RED GROUSE
Style Two

Model:	A1279
Modeller:	John Brown
Height:	10", 25.4 cm
Colour:	Browns, grey, red, yellow, pink and green
Issued:	01/02 - 12/03
Series:	Game Birds

U.K.:	£ 60.00
U.S.:	$120.00
Can.:	$120.00

RED GROUSE WITH YOUNG

Model:	None
Modeller:	Victor Hayton
Height:	8 ½", 21.6 cm
Colour:	A. Brown
	B. Bronze
Issued:	01/77 in a limited
	edition of 350

	Brown	Bronze
U.K.:	£300.	£100.
U.S.:	$600.	$200.
Can.:	$600.	$200.

RED HIND AND FAWN

Model:	152/B152
Modeller:	David Walton
Height:	5 ½", 14.0 cm
Colour:	Reddish-brown, white
	and green
Issued:	01/93 - 12/98

U.K.:	£125.00
U.S.:	$250.00
Can.:	$250.00

RED HIND, FOLLOWER AND CALF

Model:	A1486
Modeller:	John Brown
Height:	7", 17.8 cm
Colour	Reddish-brown, white,
	purple and green
Issued:	06/02 - 06/05
Series:	British Mammals

U.K.:	£ 75.00
U.S.:	$150.00
Can.:	$150.00

RED KITE

Model:	B0794
Modeller:	Richard Roberts
Height:	15 ¼", 38.7 cm
Colour:	Dark brown, black,
	grey, brown and yellow
Issued:	01/03 in a limited
	edition of 600
Series:	Classic Collection

U.K.:	£350.00
U.S.:	$700.00
Can.:	$700.00

RED SQUIRREL
Style One

Model:	JB3
Modeller:	Judy Boyt
Height:	5 ½", 14.0 cm
Colour:	Reddish-brown
Issued:	07/83 - 12/85
Series:	Judy Boyt Woodland

U.K.:	£ 80.00
U.S.:	$160.00
Can.:	$160.00

RED SQUIRREL
Style Two

Model:	M27
Modeller:	David Walton
Height:	3 ¾", 9.5 cm
Colour:	Reddish-brown and
	white
Issued:	01/93 - 12/95
Series:	Miniature Wildlife

U.K.:	£45.00
U.S.:	$90.00
Can.:	$90.00

RED SQUIRREL
Style Three

Model:	A7684
Modeller:	Unknown
Height:	3 ¼", 8.3 cm
Colour:	Reddish-brown, white
	and green
Issued:	01/07 to the present
Series:	Wildlife

U.K.:	£13.00
U.S.:	$25.00
Can.:	$25.00

RED SQUIRREL
(On Trunk with Acorn)

Model:	009/009B
Modeller:	Mairi Laing Hunt
Height:	6", 15.0 cm
Colour:	Reddish-brown
Issued:	07/78 - 06/83
Series:	Mammals

U.K.:	£ 80.00
U.S.:	$160.00
Can.:	$160.00

RED SQUIRREL
(Standing, Tail Down)

Model:	009A
Modeller:	Mairi Laing Hunt
Height:	3", 7.6 cm
Colour:	Reddish-brown and white
Issued:	07/78 - 06/83
Series:	Mammals
U.K.:	£ 80.00
U.S.:	$160.00
Can.:	$160.00

RED SQUIRREL AND
GOLDCRESTS

Model:	B0862
Modeller:	Ray Ayres
Height:	11 ¾", 29.8 cm
Colour:	Reddish-brown, brown, white, green and orange
Issued:	01/04 in a limited edition of 950
Series:	1. Classic Collection 2. Thirtieth Anniversary
U.K.:	£250.00
U.S.:	$500.00
Can.:	$500.00

Note: 30th Anniversary piece.

RED SQUIRRELS

Model:	L02
Modeller:	Victor Hayton
Height:	12", 30.5 cm
Colour:	A. Reddish-brown B. Bronze
Issued:	01/77 in a limited edition of 100

	Red-brown	Bronze
U.K.:	£ 600.	£175.
U.S.:	$1,200.	$350.
Can.:	$1,200.	$350.

RED STAG
Style One

Model:	UK# L20 USA# 225-061
Modeller:	Ray Ayres
Height:	8 ½", 21.6 cm
Colour:	Reddish-brown and black
Issued:	01/80 in a limited edition of 750
U.K.:	£375.00
U.S.:	$750.00
Can.:	$750.00

Note: This model was named American Elk in the USA.

RED STAG
Style Two

Model:	151/B151
Modeller:	David Walton
Height:	8", 20.3 cm
Colour:	Reddish-brown
Issued:	01/92 - 12/98
U.K.:	£150.00
U.S.:	$300.00
Can.:	$300.00

RED STAG
Style Three

Model:	A1485
Modeller:	John Brown
Height:	7 ¼", 18.4 cm
Colour	Reddish-brown, purple, grey and brown
Issued:	06/02 to the present
Series:	British Mammals
U.K.:	£ 65.00
U.S.:	$125.00
Can.:	$125.00

RED STAG
Style Four

Model:	A5270
Modeller:	Richard Roberts
Height:	8 ¾", 22.2 cm
Colour:	Brown, cream and black
Issued:	01/05 to the present
Series:	BFA Pottery Company
U.K.:	£39.00
U.S.:	$80.00
Can.:	$80.00

RED STAG
Style Five

Model:	A7686
Modeller:	Unknown
Height:	6", 15.2 cm
Colour:	Browns, grey and blue
Issued:	01/07 to the present
Series:	Wildlife
U.K.:	£20.00
U.S.:	$40.00
Can.:	$40.00

RED STAG, Lying

Model:	B0437
Modeller:	Jack Crewdson
Height:	14 ¼", 36.2 cm
Colour:	Reddish-brown
Issued:	06/99 in a limited edition of 250
U.K.:	£300.00
U.S.:	$600.00
Can.:	$600.00

RED-BREASTED GOOSE

Model:	A2097
Modeller:	Jack Crewdson
Height:	12", 30.5 cm
Colour:	Black, white, grey, reddish-brown, green
Issued:	06/02 in a limited edition of 500
Series:	Studio Limited Editions
U.K.:	£125.00
U.S.:	$250.00
Can.:	$250.00

REFLECTION
(Otters)

Model:	MTR02
Modeller:	Ray Ayres
Height:	3", 7.6 cm
Colour:	Brown and white
Issued:	01/95 - 12/00
Series:	Masters of the River
U.K.:	£25.00
U.S.:	$50.00
Can.:	$50.00

REGAL SPLENDOUR
(Peacock)

Model:	B0364
Modeller:	Richard Roberts
Height:	30", 76.2 cm
Colour:	Blues, green and gold
Issued:	01/99 in a limited edition of 500
Series:	Millennium
U.K.:	£1,250.00
U.S.:	$2,500.00
Can.:	$2,500.00

RELUCTANT PUPIL, THE
(Otters)

Model:	MTR08
Modeller:	Ray Ayres
Height:	14", 35.5 cm
Colour:	Browns and white
Issued:	01/95 in a limited edition of 1,500
Series:	Masters of the River
U.K.:	£425.00
U.S.:	$850.00
Can.:	$850.00

REPRISE

Model:	K43
Designer:	Ben Black
Modeller:	David Geenty
Height:	6 ¾", 17.2 cm
Colour:	White, pink and brown
Issued:	01/88 in a limited edition of 2,500
Series:	Ben Black's Intermission Series
U.K.:	£150.00
U.S.:	$300.00
Can.:	$300.00

RESUMING THE JOURNEY

Model:	147
Modeller:	David Maass
Height:	7 ¼", 18.4 cm
Colour:	Grey, black and blue
Issued:	06/91 - 12/93
U.K.:	£125.00
U.S.:	$250.00
Can.:	$250.00

REVERSIBLE PLOUGHING
(Nuffield 4/65 Diesel Tractor)

Model:	B0978
Modeller:	Ray Ayres
Size:	6 ¼" x 15 ¼" 15.9 x 38.7 cm
Colour:	Orange, black, green, browns and silver
Issued:	01/06 in a limited edition of 1,500
Series:	Tractors
U.K.:	£395.00
U.S.:	$800.00
Can.:	$800.00

RHINO AND BABY

Model: RW21
Modeller: Richard Wawrzesta
Height: 4 ½", 11.9 cm
Colour: Grey and beige
Issued: 01/91 - 12/93
Series: Endangered Species (WWF)

U.K.: £ 50.00
U.S.: $100.00
Can.: $100.00

RHINO AND CALF

Model: WW31
Modeller: David Walton
Height: 2 ¼", 5.7 cm
Colour: Grey
Issued: 01/95 - 12/96
Series: Miniature (WWF)

U.K.: £20.00
U.S.: $40.00
Can.: $40.00

RHODESIAN RIDGEBACK, Standing Style One

Model: L27
Modeller: David Geenty
Height: 8 ½", 21.6 cm
Colour: Reddish-brown
Issued: 01/80 in a limited edition of 500

U.K.: £275.00
U.S.: $550.00
Can.: $550.00

RHODESIAN RIDGEBACK, Standing Style Two

Model: A7743
Modeller: Unknown
Height: 6", 15.2 cm
Colour: Brown
Issued: 01/07 to the present
Series: Dogs and Pups Galore

U.K.: £23.00
U.S.: $45.00
Can.: $45.00

RIDGING UP (Fordson Dexta)

Model: A2141
Modeller: Ray Ayres
Height: 4 ¼", 10.8 cm
Colour: Blue, red, brown, grey, beige and white
Issued: 06/02 - 12/05
Series: Tractors

U.K.: £100.00
U.S.: $200.00
Can.: $200.00

Note: Available in UK / Ireland only.

RIDING OUT

Model: L81
Modeller: David Geenty
Height: 11", 27.9 cm
Colour: Brown, green and grey
Issued: 01/88 in a limited edition of 750

U.K. £400.00
U.S. $800.00
Can. $800.00

RIGHT OF WAY (Blackie ewes and border collie)

Model: A6026
Modeller: Unknown
Height: 5 ½", 14.0 cm
Colour: Cream, red, blue, grey and green
Issued: 06/05 to the present
Series: James Herriot Studio Collection

U.K.: £108.00
U.S.: $200.00
Can.: $200.00

RIGHT PLACE WRONG TIME
(Swaledale Tup, Ewes and
Border Collie)

Model:	JH104
Modeller:	Ray Ayres
Height:	7 ¼", 18.4 cm
Colour:	Cream, grey, brown, black and white
Issued:	10/95 in a limited edition of 1,750
Series:	1. Every Living Thing 2. The James Herriot Collection
U.K.:	£225.00
U.S.:	$450.00
Can.:	$450.00

RIPPING TIMES
(German shepherd puppy)

Model:	A7045
Modeller:	Barry Snelson
Height:	3 ¼", 8.3 cm
Colour:	Black, brown and white
Issued:	06/06 - 06/07
Series:	Puppy Trouble
U.K.:	£16.00
U.S.:	$30.00
Can.:	$30.00

RISING MALLARD

Model:	L68, 200-148
Modeller:	Frank Falco
Height:	9 ¼", 23.5 cm
Colour:	Sandy brown, black, white, blue, yellow, green and grey
Issued:	c.1986 in a limited edition of 950
Series:	Birds by Frank Falco
U.K.:	£225.00
U.S.:	$450.00
Can.:	$450.00

RISING PHEASANT

Model:	UK - L46 USA - 200-146
Modeller:	Frank Falco
Height:	9", 22.9 cm
Colour:	Orange, red, brown, white, green and grey
Issued:	c.1986 in a limited edition of 950
Series:	Birds by Frank Falco
U.K.:	£300.00
U.S.:	$600.00
Can.:	$600.00

RIVER HIDEAWAY
(Otters)

Model:	A0401
Modeller:	John Brown
Height:	5 ¾", 14.6 cm
Colour:	Browns, cream and stone
Issued:	01/01 - 06/05
Series:	1. Country Characters 2. Secret Places
U.K.:	£40.00
U.S.:	$80.00
Can.:	$80.00

RIVER MAJESTY
(Otters)

Model:	MTR06
Modeller:	Ray Ayres
Height:	7 ¼", 18.4 cm
Colour:	Brown and white
Issued:	01/95 in a limited edition of 3,000
Series:	Masters of the River
U.K.:	£150.00
U.S.:	$300.00
Can.:	$300.00

RIVER SENTINEL
(Otter)

Model:	B0362
Modeller:	Ray Ayres
Height:	12 ½" x 14", 31.7 x 35.5 cm
Colour:	Brown and white
Issued:	01/99 in a limited edition of 1,250
Series:	Millennium
U.K.:	£325.00
U.S.:	$650.00
Can.:	$650.00

RIVER VIEW
(Otters)

Model:	B0195
Modeller:	Richard Roberts
Height:	8 ¾", 22.2 cm
Colour:	Brown, white and green
Issued:	06/97 in a limited edition of 3,000
Series:	Nature's Kingdom
U.K.:	£125.00
U.S.:	$250.00
Can.:	$250.00

RIVER WATCH
(Otter)

Model:	SRE3
Modeller:	Ray Ayres
Height:	3", 7.6 cm
Colour:	Brown
Issued:	06/92 - 05/93
Series:	Membership Gift
U.K.:	£40.00
U.S.:	$80.00
Can.:	$80.00

RIVERDANCE
(Otters)

Model:	A1018
Modeller:	John Brown
Height:	5 ¼", 13.3 cm
Colour:	Black, white, cream, pink, brown, green yellow and blue
Issued:	01/02 - 06/04
Series:	Country Characters
U.K.:	£40.00
U.S.:	$80.00
Can.:	$80.00

RIVERSIDE JEWEL
(Kingfisher)

Model:	B0103
Modeller:	Ray Ayres
Height:	3 ½", 8.9 cm
Colour:	Blue, white, brown, reddish-yellow, green and yellow
Issued:	06/03 - 05/04
Series:	BFA Symbol of Membership 2003/04
U.K.:	£20.00
U.S.:	$40.00
Can.:	$40.00

ROBIN
Style One

Model:	046
Modeller:	Ray Ayres
Height:	4 ½", 11.9 cm
Colour:	Red, brown and white
Issued:	01/81 - 12/92
Series:	British Birds
U.K.:	£ 55.00
U.S.:	$110.00
Can.:	$110.00

ROBIN
Style Two

Model:	M12
Modeller:	David Fryer
Height:	3", 7.6 cm
Colour:	Red, white and brown; bronze base
Issued:	July 1983-Dec. 1987
Series:	Miniatures on Bronze
U.K.:	£ 65.00
U.S.:	$125.00
Can.:	$125.00

ROBIN
Style Three

Model:	RB11
Modeller:	Ray Ayres
Height:	5 ½", 14.0 cm
Colour:	Brown, red and cream
Issued:	01/90 - 12/92
Series:	British Birds
U.K.:	£ 55.00
U.S.:	$110.00
Can.:	$110.00

ROBIN
Style Four

Model:	M23
Modeller:	David Walton
Height:	3 ½", 8.9 cm
Colour:	Red, brown and grey
Issued:	01/92 - 12/95
Series:	Miniature Wildlife
U.K.:	£30.00
U.S.:	$60.00
Can.:	$60.00

ROBIN
Style Five

Model:	GP01
Modeller:	David Walton
Height:	Unknown
Colour:	Brown, red, white, light tan and black
Issued:	10/92 - 10/93
U.K.:	£35.00
U.S.:	$70.00
Can.:	$70.00

ROBIN
Style Six

Model:	B0021
Modeller:	Russell Willis
Height:	4 ¼", 10.8 cm
Colour:	Red, brown and grey
Issued:	06/96 - 12/97
Series:	Russell Willis Birds

U.K.:	£40.00
U.S.:	$80.00
Can.:	$80.00

ROBIN
Style Seven

Model:	484237
Modeller:	Russell Willis
Height:	2 ¾", 7.0 cm
Colour:	Brown, white and orange
Issued:	06/98 - 12/02
Series:	Miniature Figurines

U.K.:	£10.00
U.S.:	$20.00
Can.:	$20.00

ROBIN
Style Eight

Model:	A0408
Modeller:	Russell Willis
Height:	3 ¼", 8.3 cm
Colour:	Brown, orange, cream, white, red and green
Issued:	01/01 - 12/06
Series:	1. Feathered Friends
	2. Birds by Russell Willis

U.K.:	£12.00
U.S.:	$25.00
Can.:	$25.00

ROBIN
Style Nine

Model:	A1471
Modeller:	Russell Willis
Height:	4 ¼", 10.8 cm
Colour:	Brown, white, pink, orangey-red, and green
Issued:	01/02 - 12/03
Series:	Birds by Russell Willis

U.K.:	£20.00
U.S.:	$40.00
Can.:	$40.00

ROBIN
Style Ten

Model:	A2318
Modeller:	Russell Willis
Height:	3 ¾", 9.5 cm
Size:	Small
Colour:	Light brown, white, orangey-red, yellow and green
Issued:	01/03 - 06/06
Series:	Garden Guests

U.K.:	£15.00
U.S.:	$30.00
Can.:	$30.00

ROBIN
Style Eleven

Model:	A2322
Modeller:	Russell Willis
Height:	2 ¾", 7.0 cm
Size:	Medium
Colour:	Brown, white, green, reddish-yellow and light brown
Issued:	01/03 - 06/06
Series:	Garden Guests

U.K.:	£20.00
U.S.:	$40.00
Can.:	$40.00

ROBIN
Style Twelve

Model:	A3458
Modeller:	Russell Willis
Height:	5 ½", 14.0 cm
Colour:	Brown, white, orange and green
Issued:	01/04 - 06/06
Series:	Birds by Russell Willis

U.K.:	£30.00
U.S.:	$60.00
Can.:	$60.00

ROBIN
Style Thirteen

Model:	A4607
Modeller:	Russell Willis
Height:	4 ¼", 10.8 cm
Colour:	Brown, white, orange and green
Issued:	01/04 - 12/06
Series:	BFA Pottery Company

U.K.:	£15.00
U.S.:	$30.00
Can.:	$30.00

ROBIN
Style Fourteen
Model:	A6055
Modeller:	Unknown
Height:	4 ¾", 12.1 cm
Colour:	Red, brown, green and white
Issued:	06/05 to the present
U.K.:	£ 9.95
U.S.:	$20.00
Can.:	$20.00

ROBIN AND CHARM BRACELET
Model:	484407
Modeller:	Russell Willis
Height:	4", 10.1 cm
Colour:	Brown, red, white, grey and green
Issued:	06/98 - 12/99
Series:	Finders Keepers
U.K.:	£25.00
U.S.:	$50.00
Can.:	$50.00

ROBIN AND CHICK
Model:	WB80
Modeller:	Russell Willis
Height:	5 ½", 14.0 cm
Colour:	Brown, red and white
Issued:	01/93 - 12/94
Series:	Russell Willis Birds
U.K.:	£40.00
U.S.:	$80.00
Can.:	$80.00

ROBIN AND CHICKS
Style One
Model:	B0345
Modeller:	John Brown
Height:	10 ¼", 26.0 cm
Colour:	Browns, red, yellow and green
Issued:	01/99 in a limited edition of 1,250
Series:	Border Classic Birds
U.K.:	£125.00
U.S.:	$250.00
Can.:	$250.00

ROBIN AND CHICKS
Style Two
Model:	A7390
Modeller:	Unknown
Height:	4 ½", 11.4 cm
Colour:	Browns, red, black, green and mauve
Issued:	06/06 to the present
U.K.:	£28.00
U.S.:	$55.00
Can.:	$55.00

ROBIN AND HONEYSUCKLE
Model:	A0910
Modeller:	David Mayer
Height:	7 ¾", 19.7 cm
Colour:	Light brown, white, orangey-red, pink and green
Issued:	06/02 - 06/04
Series:	Garden Guests
U.K.:	£40.00
U.S.:	$80.00
Can.:	$80.00

ROBIN AND ONIONS
Model:	RB7
Modeller:	Ray Ayres
Height:	3 ½", 8.9 cm
Colour:	Red, brown and yellow
Issued:	01/84 - 12/85
Series:	RSPB Birds
U.K.:	£45.00
U.S.:	$90.00
Can.:	$90.00

ROBIN AND SNOWDROP
Model:	RB8
Modeller:	Ray Ayres
Height:	4 ¾", 12.1 cm
Colour:	Red, brown and grey
Issued:	01/86 - 12/92
Series:	1. RSPB Birds
	2. British Birds
U.K.:	£ 55.00
U.S.:	$110.00
Can.:	$110.00

ROBIN AND TROWEL

Model: B0229
Modeller: Russell Willis
Height: 6 ¼", 15.9 cm
Colour: Brown, red, green and purple
Issued: 07/97 - Unknown
Series: Russell Willis Collection

U.K.: £ 50.00
U.S.: $100.00
Can.: $100.00

ROBIN AND YOUNG

Model: 484423
Modeller: Russell Willis
Height: 4", 10.1 cm
Colour: Brown, red, cream and green
Issued: 06/98 - 12/99
Series: Families

U.K.: £25.00
U.S.: $50.00
Can.: $50.00

ROBIN FLYING

Model: WB11
Modeller: Russell Willis
Height: 6 ¾", 17.2 cm
Colour: Brown, red and white
Issued: 07/92 - 12/93
Series: Russell Willis Birds

U.K.: £ 50.00
U.S.: $100.00
Can.: $100.00

ROBIN ON CLAY PIPE

Model: WB54
Modeller: Russell Willis
Height: 3 ½", 8.9 cm
Colour: Brown, red, white and cream
Issued: 12/94 - 12/95
Series: 1. Birds In Your Garden
2. Russell Willis Birds

U.K.: £30.00
U.S.: $60.00
Can.: $60.00

ROBIN ON GARDEN STRING

Model: F3
Modeller: David Burnham Smith
Height: 5 ¾", 14.6 cm
Colour: Red, white, brown and grey
Issued: 01/89 - 12/91
Series: Finesse Birds

U.K.: £ 65.00
U.S.: $125.00
Can.: $125.00

ROBIN ON HORSESHOE
Style One

Model: WB150
Modeller: Russell Willis
Height: 4 ¼", 10.8 cm
Colour: Red, brown and blue-grey
Issued: 01/95 - c.1997
Series: 1. Birds In Your Garden
2. Russell Willis Birds

U.K.: £40.00
U.S.: $80.00
Can.: $80.00

ROBIN ON HORSESHOE
Style Two

Model: 484318
Modeller: Russell Willis
Height: 4", 10.1 cm
Colour: Brown, red, white, grey and green
Issued: 06/98 - 12/05
Series: Birds And ...

U.K.: £25.00
U.S.: $50.00
Can.: $50.00

ROBIN ON PEBBLE

Model: WB161
Modeller: Russell Willis
Height: 3 ¾", 9.5 cm
Colour: Red, brown and blue-grey
Issued: 01/95 - 12/97
Series: 1. Pebble Birds
2. Russell Willis Birds

U.K.: £15.00
U.S.: $30.00
Can.: $30.00

ROBIN ON TAP
Model: A0650
Modeller: Russell Willis
Height: 4", 10.1 cm
Colour: Brown, red, cream,
           silver and green
Issued: 01/01 - 12/03
Series: Birds And ...

U.K.:   £20.00
U.S.: $40.00
Can.: $40.00

ROBIN ON TEACUP
Model: WB40
Modeller: Russell Willis
Height: 5 ¼", 13.3 cm
Colour: Red, brown, white
           and green
Issued: 07/92 - 12/97
Series: 1. Birds In Your Garden
           2. Russell Willis Birds

U.K.:   £ 50.00
U.S.: $100.00
Can.: $100.00

ROBIN ON TROWEL
Model: 541559
Modeller: Russell Willis
Height: 3 ¼", 8.3 cm
Colour: Brown, red, grey
           and green
Issued: 06/99 - 12/06
Series: 1. Birds And ...
           2. Birds by Russell
              Willis

U.K.:   £12.00
U.S.: $25.00
Can.: $25.00

ROBIN WITH CHICKS IN BOOT
Model: RB45
Modeller: Ray Ayres
Height: 4 ¾", 12.1 cm
Colour: Red, brown and grey
Issued: 01/95 - 12/00
Series: 1. Garden Birds
           2. Border Classic Birds

U.K.:   £ 75.00
U.S.: $150.00
Can.: $150.00

ROBIN WITH DAISIES
Model: RB43
Modeller: Ray Ayres
Height: 3 ½", 8.9 cm
Colour: Red, brown and grey
Issued: 01/95 - 05/99
Series: 1. Garden Birds
           2. Border Classic Birds

U.K.:   £25.00
U.S.: $50.00
Can.: $50.00

ROBIN WITH DOG ROSES
Model: WB30
Modeller: Russell Willis
Height: 5", 12.7 cm
Colour: Brown, red, pink
           and green
Issued: 07/92 - 12/93
Series: 1. Birds In Your Garden
           2. Russell Willis Birds

U.K.:   £40.00
U.S.: $80.00
Can.: $80.00

ROBIN WITH NEST
Style One
Model: RB44
Modeller: Ray Ayres
Height: 4", 10.1 cm
Colour: Red, brown and grey
Issued: 01/95 - 05/99
Series: 1. Garden Birds
           2. Border Classic Birds

U.K.:   £40.00
U.S.: $80.00
Can.: $80.00

ROBIN WITH NEST
Style Two
Model: 541648
Modeller: Russell Willis
Height: 3", 7.6 cm
Colour: Brown, orange, copper,
           blue and pink
Issued: 01/99 - 06/04
Series: 1. Feathered Friends
           2. Birds by Russell
              Willis

U.K.:   £12.00
U.S.: $25.00
Can.: $25.00

ROBIN WITH POCKET WATCH

Model:	B0123
Modeller:	Russell Willis
Height:	4 ¼", 10.8 cm
Colour:	Red, brown and gold
Issued:	01/97 - 12/97
Series:	Finders Keepers
U.K.:	£45.00
U.S.:	$90.00
Can.:	$90.00

ROBINS AND ROSES (Pair)

Model:	A1024
Modeller:	David Mayer
Height:	9", 22.9 cm
Colour:	Red, brown, white and dark green
Issued:	06/02 - 06/05
Series:	Garden Guests
U.K.:	£40.00
U.S.:	$80.00
Can.:	$80.00

ROBINS NESTING

Model:	EG2
Modeller:	Richard Roberts
Height:	6 ¾", 17.2 cm
Colour:	Browns and red
Issued:	01/89 in a limited edition of 950
U.K.:	£250.00
U.S.:	$500.00
Can.:	$500.00

ROBINS WITH TREE MALLOW / LAVATERA

Model:	A3451
Modeller:	Russell Willis
Height:	9", 22.9 cm
Colour:	Red, white, brown, green, lilac and mauve
Issued:	01/04 - 12/05
Series:	Birds by Russell Willis
U.K.:	£ 60.00
U.S.:	$120.00
Can.:	$120.00

ROCKY DEN
(Fox and Cubs)

Model:	A0400
Modeller:	John Brown
Height:	6 ¾", 17.2 cm
Colour:	Reddish-brown, white and grey
Issued:	01/01 - 06/03
Series:	1. Country Characters
	2. Secret Places
U.K.:	£40.00
U.S.:	$80.00
Can.:	$80.00

ROE BUCK

Model:	007
Modeller:	Anne Wall
Height:	5 ½", 14.0 cm
Colour:	Reddish-brown
Issued:	07/78 - 12/81
Series:	Mammals
U.K.:	£175.00
U.S.:	$350.00
Can.:	$350.00

ROE BUCK (Leg Up)

Model:	L66
Modeller:	James Harvey
Height:	8 ½", 21.6 cm
Colour:	Reddish-brown
Issued:	01/85 in a limited edition of 850
Series:	Special Interest
U.K.:	£175.00
U.S.:	$350.00
Can.:	$350.00

ROE BUCK (Lying)

Model:	B0330
Modeller:	Jack Crewdson
Height:	6 ½", 16.5 cm
Colour:	Dark and reddish-brown
Issued:	06/98 - 12/99
U.K.:	£ 80.00
U.S.:	$160.00
Can.:	$160.00

BFA STUDIO - Butterflies

Painted Lady on Rose (A5899)

Red Admiral and Clematis (A5900)

Peacock on Blackberries (A5901)

Small White on Hydrangea (A5902)

Common Blue on Apple Blossom
(A5903)

Small Tortoiseshell and Coneflower
(A5904)

BFA STUDIO - Horses

Exmoor Stallion (A4058)

Highland Stallion (A4069)

Highland Mare and Foal (A2691)

Shetland Mare and Foal (A2690)

Dales Pony Mare and Foal (A5054)

Exmoor Pony Mare and Foal (A3257)

BFA STUDIO - Hay Days

Making Friends (A0540)

I'm Hungry (A0537)

I'm So Stubborn (A1242)

First Prize (A3781)

Shetland Grand National (A3695)

First Time Out (A4699)

BFA STUDIO - Dogs

German Short-haired Pointer (A7114)

Schnauzer, Standing (A2317)

Weimaraner, Style Two (A3839)

Boxer, Standing, Style Three (A3836)

Rhodesian Ridgeback, Standing, Style Two (A7743)

Cocker Spaniel, Standing, Style Two (A4447)

BFA STUDIO - Young Farmers

Dog Bath (A5029)

Feeding Piglets (A5030)

Puppy Training (A4063)

Potato Picking (A4062)

Wash and Brush Up (A1450)

One For Me, One For You (A1451)

BFA STUDIO - James Herriot Studio Collection

Baby Sitter (A8437)

New Friend (A6248)

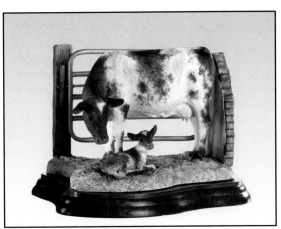

Clover's New Calf (A6519)

Upsetting the Apple Cart (A7935)

Breaking the Ice (A2682)

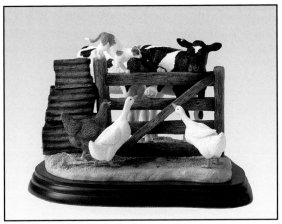

Farm Meeting (A8434)

BFA STUDIO - Wildlife

River Hideaway (A0401)

Forest Family (A0403)

Unwelcome Guest (A1873)

Discovery (A1283)

Leopard (A3065)

Lion, Style Two (A5047)

BFA STUDIO - Birds

Robin and Honeysuckle (A0910)

Robins and Roses [Pair] (A1024)

Kingfisher, Style Sixteen (A3459)

Thrush (A0651)

Blue Tit, Style Eight (A1473)

Tawny Owl, Style Eleven (A4054)

ROE DEER FAWN (Lying)
Style One

Model:	L09
Modeller:	Victor Hayton
Height:	3", 7.6 cm
Colour:	A. Brown and white
	B. Bronze
Issued:	01/77 in a limited
	edition of 500

	Brown	Bronze
U.K.:	£325.	£ 80.
U.S.:	$650.	$160.
Can.:	$650.	$160.

ROE DEER FAWN (Lying)
Style Two

Model:	022
Modeller:	Judy Boyt
Height:	3 ¾", 9.5 cm
Colour:	Brown and white
Issued:	01/82 - 12/84
Series:	Woodland

U.K.:	£ 50.00
U.S.:	$100.00
Can.:	$100.00

ROE DOE

Model:	008
Modeller:	Anne Wall
Height:	5", 12.7 cm
Colour:	Reddish-brown
Issued:	07/78 - 12/81
Series:	Mammals

U.K.:	£175.00
U.S.:	$350.00
Can.:	$350.00

ROOM FOR TWO
(Labrador puppy and lamb)

Model:	A3873
Modeller:	Hans Kendrick
Height:	3 ¼", 8.3 cm
Colour:	Tan, yellow, white,
	cream and pink
Issued:	06/04 - 12/06
Series:	On The Farm

U.K.:	£15.00
U.S.:	$30.00
Can.:	$30.00

ROSE AND TIGER

Model:	FC16
Designer:	Fleur Cowles
Modeller:	Unknown
Height:	Unknown
Colour:	Pink, orange, brown
	and white
Issued:	1987 - 12/88
Series:	Fleur's Flowers

U.K.:	£ 75.00
U.S.:	$150.00
Can.:	$150.00

ROTTWEILER, Seated
Style One, First Variation

Model:	B0314/B0473	
Modeller:	Margaret Turner	
Height:	6," 15.0 cm	
Colour:	B0314	Black and tan
	B0473	Bronze
Issued:	B0314	06/98-12/01
	B0473	06/99-06/00
Series:	B0314	Dogs Galore
	B0473	Bronzed

	Black/tan	Bronze
U.K.:	£30.	£25.
U.S.:	$60.	$50.
Can.:	$60.	$50.

ROTTWEILER, Seated
Style One, Second Variation

Model:	A2077
Modeller:	Margaret Turner
Height:	5 ¾", 14.6 cm
Colour:	Black and tan
Issued:	06/02 to the present
Series:	Dogs and Pups Galore

U.K.:	£21.00
U.S.:	$40.00
Can.:	$40.00

ROTTWEILER, Seated
Style Two

Model:	A1254
Modeller:	Margaret Turner
Height:	17", 43.2 cm
Colour:	Black and tan
Issued:	06/02 - 12/04
Series:	Fireside Dogs

U.K.:	£ 90.00
U.S.:	$175.00
Can.:	$175.00

ROTTWEILER, Standing
Style One
Model: 073
Modeller: Elizabeth Waugh
Height: 8", 20.3 cm
Colour: Black and tan
Issued: 01/85 - 12/92
Series: 1. The World of Dogs
           2. Special Interest

U.K.:   £175.00
U.S.: $350.00
Can.: $350.00

ROTTWEILER, Standing
Style Two
Model: A1258
Modeller: Margaret Turner
Height: 6", 15.0 cm
Colour: Black and tan
Issued: 01/02 - 06/06
Series: Dogs and Pups Galore

U.K.:   £20.00
U.S.: $40.00
Can.: $40.00

ROTTWEILER, Standing
Style Three
Model: A2699
Modeller: Margaret Turner
Height: 9 ½", 24.0 cm
Colour: Black and tan
Issued: 06/03 - 12/05
Series: Dogs and Pups Galore

U.K.:   £ 75.00
U.S.: $150.00
Can.: $150.00

ROTTWEILER IN HAT
Model: 484113
Modeller: Unknown
Height: 2 ¼", 5.7 cm
Colour: Black, tan and pale blue
Issued: 06/98 - 12/00
Series: Puppy Tales

U.K.:   £12.00
U.S.: $25.00
Can.: $25.00

ROUGH COLLIE
Model: UK# 069
           USA# 225-131
Modeller: Anne Wall
Height: 5 ½", 14.0 cm
Colour: Browns and white
Issued: 01/82 - 12/84

U.K.:   £150.00
U.S.: $300.00
Can.: $300.00

ROUGH COLLIE (Lying)
First Variation
Model: DG37/B0475
Modeller: Margaret Turner
Height: 3 ¾", 9.5 cm
Colour: DG37   Brown / white
           B0475   Bronze
Issued: DG37   01/96-12/01
           B0475   06/99-06/00
Series: DG37   Dogs Galore
           B0475   Bronzed

U.K.:   £30.00
U.S.: $60.00
Can.: $60.00

ROUGH COLLIE (Lying)
Second Variation
Model: A3048
Modeller: Margaret Turner
Height: 3 ½", 8.9 cm
Colour: Golden brown and
           white
Issued: 06/03 - 06/06
Series: Dogs and Pups Galore

U.K.:   £20.00
U.S.: $40.00
Can.: $40.00

ROWING UP
(Gold Edition)

Model:	B0598 A
Modeller:	Ray Ayres
Height:	5 ¼", 13.3 cm
Colour:	Brown, red and pale yellowish-green
Issued:	06/01 in a limited edition of 350
Series:	Classic Collection
U.K.:	£300.00
U.S.:	$600.00
Can.:	$600.00

Note: Gold version has name plate on the base. Issued nos. 1 - 350.

(Standard Edition)

Model:	B0598 A
Modeller:	Ray Ayres
Height:	5 ¼", 13.3 cm
Colour:	Brown, red and pale yellowish-green
Issued:	06/01 in a limited edition of 350
Series:	Classic Collection
U.K.:	£300.00
U.S.:	$600.00
Can.:	$600.00

Note: Issued nos. 351 - 700.

RUN, RABBIT, RUN
(Terriers and rabbits)

Model:	JH42
Modeller:	Anne Butler
Height:	4", 10.1 cm
Colour:	Yellow, brown, white and black
Issued:	07/90 - 12/92
Series:	All Things Wise and Wonderful
U.K.:	£ 80.00
U.S.:	$160.00
Can.:	$160.00

RUNNER, THE (Hare)

Model:	A0004
Modeller:	Ray Ayres
Height:	7", 17.8 cm
Colour:	Brown, green, white and yellow
Issued:	01/00 - 12/01
Series:	Country Characters
U.K.:	£40.00
U.S.:	$80.00
Can.:	$80.00

RUNNING FOX

Model:	M30
Modeller:	Ray Ayres
Height:	2 ½", 6.4 cm
Colour:	Red, white and black; bronze base
Issued:	01/84 - 12/86
Series:	Miniatures on Bronze
U.K.:	£ 75.00
U.S.:	$150.00
Can.:	$150.00

SAFE DELIVERY
(Shepherd with ewe lambing)

Model:	JH96
Modeller:	Ray Ayres
Height:	6 ½", 16.5 cm
Colour:	Grey, black, blue and green
Issued:	07/94 in a limited edition of 1,500
Series:	Every Living Thing
U.K.:	£175.00
U.S.:	$350.00
Can.:	$350.00

SAFE HAVEN
(Otters)

Model:	MTR04
Modeller:	Ray Ayres
Height:	3 ¾", 9.5 cm
Colour:	Brown and white
Issued:	01/95 - 12/00
Series:	Masters of the River
U.K.:	£40.00
U.S.:	$80.00
Can.:	$80.00

SAFE LANDING
(Steeplechaser)

Model:	L155
Modeller:	Anne Wall
Height:	8", 20.3 cm
Colour:	Brown, blue and white
Issued:	07/95 in a limited edition of 1,850
Series:	Agricultural and Sporting
U.K.:	£300.00
U.S.:	$600.00
Can.:	$600.00

SAFE OUTLOOK
(Fox on rocky outcrop)
Model: B0091
Modeller: David Walton
Height: 7", 17.8 cm
Colour: Reddish-brown, white, grey and green
Issued: 01/97 - 06/00
Series: Fox Tales

U.K.: £ 75.00
U.S.: $150.00
Can.: $150.00

SALMON
Model: 140
Modeller: David Walton
Height: 8 ¼", 21.0 cm
Colour: Blue and white
Issued: 01/91 - 12/93

U.K.: £175.00
U.S.: $350.00
Can.: $350.00

SALMON
(Atlantic Hen)
Model: 080
Modeller: Janet Nightingale
Height: 5 ½", 14.0 cm
Colour: Silver-grey, cream and turquoise
Issued: Pre-1981

U.K.: £150.00
U.S.: $300.00
Can.: $300.00

SAM (Beagle Pup)
Style One
Model: JH21
Modeller: Richard Roberts
Height: 2 ½", 6.4 cm
Colour: Black, brown and white
Issued: 01/88 - 12/93
Series: 1. All Creatures Great and Small
2. James Herriot's Favourite Characters

U.K.: £30.00
U.S.: $60.00
Can.: $60.00

SAM (Beagle Pup)
Style Two
Model: A6506
Modeller: Kerry Bell
Height: 3 ¼", 8.3 cm
Colour: Black, tan and white
Issued: 01/06 to the present
Series: James Herriot Studio Collection

U.K.: £15.00
U.S.: $30.00
Can.: $30.00

SAVANNAH SPRING
(Group of Impala)
Model: L138
Modeller: Richard Roberts
Height: 10", 25.4 cm
Colour: Reddish-brown
Issued: 01/94 in a limited edition of 850
Series: WWFN

U.K.: £375.00
U.S.: $750.00
Can.: $750.00

SCABIOSA AND OCELOT
Model: FC13
Designer: Fleur Cowles
Modeller: Unknown
Height: Unknown
Colour: Lilac, pale green, orange and black
Issued: 1987-Dec. 1988
Series: Fleur's Flowers

U.K.: £ 75.00
U.S.: $150.00
Can.: $150.00

SCENTING THE AIR
(Otters)
Model: MTR03
Modeller: Ray Ayres
Height: 6 ¼", 15.9 cm
Colour: Brown and white
Issued: 01/95 - 12/00
Series: Masters of the River

U.K.: £ 50.00
U.S.: $100.00
Can.: $100.00

SCHNAUZER (Seated)
Style One

Model: DG07A, B
Modeller: Steve McKeown
Height: 5", 12.7 cm
Colour: A. Black and white
B. Black and silver
Issued: 01/91 - 12/96
Series: Dogs Galore

U.K.: £25.00
U.S.: $50.00
Can.: $50.00

SCHNAUZER (Seated)
Style Two

Model: A3846
Modeller: Adrian Hughes
Height: 13 ½", 34.3 cm
Colour: Grey, white and
sandy brown
Issued: 06/04 - 06/05
Series: Fireside Dogs

U.K.: £ 75.00
U.S.: $150.00
Can.: $150.00

SCHNAUZER (Standing)

Model: A2317
Modeller: Margaret Turner
Height: 3 ¾", 9.5 cm
Colour: Dark grey, white,
light brown
Issued: 01/03 to the present
Series: Dogs and Pups Galore

U.K.: £17.50
U.S.: $35.00
Can.: $35.00

SCOTTIE (Seated)
Style One

Model: DG03
Modeller: Steve McKeown
Height: 4 ¾", 12.1 cm
Colour: Black
Issued: 01/91 - 12/95
Series: Dogs Galore

U.K.: £25.00
U.S.: $50.00
Can.: $50.00

SCOTTIE (Seated)
Style Two

Model: B0605
Modeller: Margaret Turner
Height: 3 ¼", 8.3 cm
Colour: Black
Issued: 06/00 - 12/01
Series: Dogs Galore

U.K.: £15.00
U.S.: $30.00
Can.: $30.00

SCOTTIE (Seated)
Style Three

Model: A3056
Modeller: Margaret Turner
Height: 3 ¾", 9.5 cm
Colour: Black
Issued: 06/03 to the present
Series: Dogs and Pups Galore

U.K.: £ 9.95
U.S.: $20.00
Can.: $20.00

SCOTTIE (Standing)

Model: DS9
Modeller: Elizabeth MacAllister
Height: 3", 7.6 cm
Colour: Black
Issued: 01/86 - 12/92
Series: 1. The World of Dogs
2. Special Interest

U.K.: £40.00
U.S.: $80.00
Can.: $80.00

SCOTTISH DEERHOUND

Model: EW3
Modeller: Elizabeth Waugh
Height: 5", 12.7 cm
Colour: Grey
Issued: 01/86 - 12/92
Series: 1. The World of Dogs
2. Special Interest

U.K.: £150.00
U.S.: $300.00
Can.: $300.00

SCOTTISH WILDCAT

Model:	005
Modeller:	Mairi Laing Hunt
Height:	4", 10.1 cm
Colour:	Browns and yellow
Issued:	07/78 - 12/82
Series:	Mammals
U.K.:	£150.00
U.S.:	$300.00
Can.:	$300.00

SCRAMBLE

Model:	B0879
Modeller:	Ray Ayres
Height:	4 ¼", 10.8 cm
Colour:	Brown, green, yellow, black, navy and red
Issued:	06/03 in a limited edition of 750
Series:	Science Collection
U.K.:	£200.00
U.S.:	$400.00
Can.:	$400.00

SCRATCHER, THE
(Dog)

Model:	A7609, 7615
Modeller:	Unknown
Height:	6", 15.0 cm
Colour:	A7609 Black / tan
	A7615 Tan / white
Issued:	06/06 to the present
Series:	Canine Capers
U.K.:	£18.00
U.S.:	$35.00
Can.:	$35.00

SCROUNGER, THE
(Fox)

Model:	A0001
Modeller:	Ray Ayres
Height:	9", 22.9 cm
Colour:	Red, brown, white, fawn and green
Issued:	01/00 - 06/04
Series:	Country Characters
U.K.:	£40.00
U.S.:	$80.00
Can.:	$80.00

SEAL AND CRAB

Model:	FE7
Modeller:	Ray Ayres
Height:	3", 7.6 cm
Colour:	Brown and green
Issued:	07/83 - 12/85
Series:	First Encounters
U.K.:	£ 65.00
U.S.:	$125.00
Can.:	$125.00

SEAL PUPS
Style One

Model:	ED3
Modeller:	Judy Boyt
Height:	2", 5.0 cm
Colour:	Cream
Issued:	07/82 - 12/84
Series:	Early Days
U.K.:	£40.00
U.S.:	$80.00
Can.:	$80.00

SEAL PUPS
Style Two

Model:	RW63
Modeller:	Richard Roberts
Height:	4 ¼", 10.8 cm
Colour:	Cream, blue-grey and black
Issued:	01/96 - 06/97
Series:	Nursery (WWF)
U.K.:	£ 65.00
U.S.:	$125.00
Can.:	$125.00

SECOND BREWED
(Robins and chicks)

Model:	B0880
Modeller:	Ray Ayres
Size:	7 ¾" x 8 ¾" 19.7 x 22.2 cm
Colour:	Red, brown, black and green
Issued:	06/04 - 05/05
Series:	16th BFA Society Member-only figurine
U.K.:	£150.00
U.S.:	$300.00
Can.:	$300.00

SEEKING ATTENTION
(Border Collies)

Model:	A7937
Modeller:	Unknown
Height:	6 ½", 16.5 cm
Colour:	Black, white, red and green
Issued:	01/07 to the present
Series:	Border Collie Collection
U.K.:	£ 65.00
U.S.:	$130.00
Can.:	$130.00

SELF SUFFICIENCY
(Cockerel, hen and chicks)

Model:	JH39
Modeller:	David Walton
Height:	6", 15.0 cm
Colour:	Black, white, red, and yellow
Issued:	01/90 - 12/91
Series:	All Things Wise and Wonderful
U.K.:	£ 65.00
U.S.:	$125.00
Can.:	$125.00

SEPTEMBER FRUITS
(Dormice)

Model:	B1017
Modeller:	Ray Ayres
Size:	8' x 6 ¾" 20.3 x 17.2 cm
Colour:	Golden brown, red, browns and green
Issued:	06/07 - 05/08
Series:	Annual Classic Society Member-only Figurine
U.K.:	£175.00
U.S.:	$350.00
Can.:	$350.00

SETTLE DOWN
(Two Geese)

Model:	A2680
Modeller:	Unknown
Height:	5", 12.7 cm
Colour:	White, yellow, blue, pink and green
Issued:	06/03 - 06/06
Series:	James Herriot Studio Collection
U.K.:	£35.00
U.S.:	$70.00
Can.:	$70.00

SETTLED IN
(Border collie)

Model:	B0290
Modeller:	Ray Ayres
Height:	2 ½", 6.4 cm
Colour:	Black, white, blue and red
Issued:	01/98 - 12/98
Series:	Event Special
U.K.:	£20.00
U.S.:	$40.00
Can.:	$40.00

Note: One of a set of four.

SEVEN-TIMES-THREE
(Kittens)

Model:	B0194
Modeller:	Kirsty Armstrong
Height:	3 ½", 8.9 cm
Colour:	Grey, white, ginger and black
Issued:	06/97 - 12/99
Series:	James Herriot's Cat Stories
U.K.:	£30.00
U.S.:	$60.00
Can.:	$60.00

SHARED RESOURCES
(Calves, ducks and sheep)

Model:	A0455
Modeller:	Kirsty Armstrong
Height:	4 ¼", 10.8 cm
Colour:	Black, white, orange and brown
Issued:	01/01 - 12/05
Series:	James Herriot Studio Collection
U.K.:	£40.00
U.S.:	$80.00
Can.:	$80.00

SHARING THE BOUNTY
(Blue tit and mouse)

Model:	B1002
Modeller:	Ray Ayres
Size:	4 ʏ" x 5 ½" 11.9 x 14.0 cm
Colour:	Blue, green, lemon, white and browns
Issued:	01/06 - 12/06
Series:	Classic Event Special
U.K.:	£ 75.00
U.S.:	$150.00
Can.:	$150.00

SHARING THE SPOILS
(Two cats and jug of milk)

Model:	B0009
Modeller:	Kirsty Armstrong
Height:	3", 7.6 cm
Colour:	Black, ginger and white
Issued:	06/96 - 06/99
Series:	1. Every Living Thing
	2. J. Herriot Collection
U.K.:	£30.00
U.S.:	$60.00
Can.:	$60.00

SHEDDING
(Shepherd, collie and sheep)

Model:	L113
Modeller:	Ray Ayres
Height:	5 ½", 14.0 cm
Colour:	Cream, black, brown and green
Issued:	07/92 in a limited edition of 1,250
U.K.:	£325.00
U.S.:	$650.00
Can.:	$650.00

SHEDDING LAMBS

Model:	B0769
Modeller:	Ray Ayres
Height:	5 ½", 14.0 cm
Colour:	Brown, grey, black, white and green
Issued:	06/02 in a limited edition of 1,250
Series:	James Herriot Classic Collection
U.K.:	£250.00
U.S.:	$500.00
Can.:	$500.00

SHEEPDOG IN FLOWER POT

Model:	484121
Modeller:	Unknown
Height:	3", 7.6 cm
Colour:	White, grey, brick red and green
Issued:	06/98 - 12/00
Series:	Puppy Tales
U.K.:	£15.00
U.S.:	$30.00
Can.:	$30.00

SHELF CAT

Model:	A4680, 4686
Modeller:	Unknown
Height:	6 ½", 16.5 cm
Colour:	A4680 Rouge
	A4686 Granite
Issued:	01/04 - 06/05
Series:	Contemporary Cats
U.K.:	£35.00
U.S.:	$70.00
Can.:	$70.00

SHELTIE (Seated)

Model:	DG19/B0483
Modeller:	Margaret Turner
Height:	4 ½", 11.9 cm
Colour:	DG19 Tan and white
	B0483 Bronze
Issued:	DG19 01/93-12/01
	B0483 06/99-06/00
Series:	1. Dogs Galore
	2. Bronzed
U.K.:	£20.00
U.S.:	$40.00
Can.:	$40.00

SHETLAND (Pony)

Model:	A5245, 7469
Modeller:	Unknown
Height:	3 ¾", 9.5 cm
Colour:	A5245 Bay
	A7469 Skewbald
Issued:	06/06 to the present
U.K.:	£16.00
U.S.:	$30.00
Can.:	$30.00

SHETLAND GRAND NATIONAL

Model:	A3695
Modeller:	Anne Wall
Height:	5 ¾", 14.6 cm
Colour:	Chestnut, brown, white, green, pink, blue and yellow
Issued:	01/04 - 06/06
Series:	Hay Days
U.K.:	£ 55.00
U.S.:	$100.00
Can.:	$100.00

SHETLAND MARE AND FOAL

Model: A2690
Modeller: Anne Wall
Height: 4 ½", 11.9 cm
Colour: Dark brown, light
brown, white and green
Issued: 06/03 to the present
Series: Horse Breeds

U.K.: £35.00
U.S.: $70.00
Can.: $70.00

SHETLAND PONY (Leg Up)

Model: NP1
Modeller: Judy Boyt
Height: 4", 10.1 cm
Colour: A. Dark brown
B. Skewbald
C. Piebald
Issued: 01/82 - 12/84
Series: Native Ponies of Britain

U.K.: £300.00
U.S.: $600.00
Can.: $600.00

SHETLAND PONY (On base)

Model: 164
Modeller: Anne Wall
Height: 3 ¼", 8.3 cm
Colour: Dark bay
Issued: 07/93 - 12/95
Series: Agricultural and
Sporting

U.K.: £ 50.00
U.S.: $100.00
Can.: $100.00

SHETLAND SHEEP FAMILY GROUP

Model: B0597A, B, C
Modeller: Ray Ayres
Height: 6 ¾", 17.2 cm
Colour: A. White
B. Moorit
C. Catmogit
Issued: 01/01 in a limited
edition of 1,250
Series: The County Show

U.K.: £100.00
U.S.: $200.00
Can.: $200.00

SHETLAND SHEEPDOG, Seated

Model: A3833
Modeller: Margaret Turner
Height: 4 ½", 11.4 cm
Colour: Light golden brown
and white
Issued: 01/04 to the present
Series: Dogs and Pups Galore

U.K.: £17.00
U.S.: $35.00
Can.: $35.00

SHETLAND SHEEPDOG (Sheltie)

Model: DM4
Modeller: Ray Ayres
Height: 3 ¾", 9.5 cm
Colour: Golden brown and
white
Issued: 07/83 - 12/92
Series: 1. The World of Dogs
2. Special Interest

U.K.: £100.00
U.S.: $200.00
Can.: $200.00

SHETLAND STALLION

Model: A4057
Modeller: Anne Wall
Height: 5", 12.7 cm
Colour: Brown, black
and green
Issued: 06/04 - 06/06
Series: Horse Breeds

U.K.: £20.00
U.S.: $40.00
Can.: $40.00

SHIH-TZU (Standing)
Style One

Model: DG21
Modeller: Margaret Turner
Height: 2 ¾", 7.0 cm
Colour: Black and white
Issued: 01/93 - 12/96
Series: Dogs Galore

U.K.: £30.00
U.S.: $60.00
Can.: $60.00

SHIH-TZU (Standing)
Style Two

Model:	A4963
Modeller:	Margaret Turner
Height:	2 ½", 6.4 cm
Colour:	Black, tan, and white
Issued:	06/04 to the present
Series:	Dogs and Pups Galore

U.K.:	£13.00
U.S.:	$26.00
Can.:	$26.00

SHIH-TZU ON HAT

Model:	656747
Modeller:	Unknown
Height:	2 ¾", 7.0 cm
Colour:	Grey, cream, fawn and green
Issued:	06/99 - 12/00
Series:	Puppy Tales

U.K.:	£12.00
U.S.:	$25.00
Can.:	$25.00

SHIRE GELDING

Model:	126A, B
Modeller:	Anne Wall
Height:	4 ¾", 12.1 cm
Colour:	A. Bay
	B. Grey
Issued:	07/92 - 12/94
Series:	Agricultural and Sporting

U.K.:	£ 75.00
U.S.:	$150.00
Can.:	$150.00

SHIRE MARE AND FOAL

Model:	A0188
Modeller:	Anne Wall
Height:	5 ¾", 14.6 cm
Colour:	Brown, white and green
Issued:	06/00 - 12/03
Series:	Horse Breeds

U.K.:	£ 60.00
U.S.:	$120.00
Can.:	$120.00

SHIRE STALLION
Style One

Model:	A1460
Modeller:	Anne Wall
Height:	7 ¾", 19.7 cm
Colour:	Dark brown, white and green
Issued:	06/02 - 12/04
Series:	Horse Breeds

U.K.:	£45.00
U.S.:	$90.00
Can.:	$90.00

SHIRE STALLION
Style Two

Model:	A4593
Modeller:	Anne Wall
Height:	7", 17.8 cm
Colour:	Iron grey and white
Issued:	06/04 to the present
Series:	BFA Pottery Company

U.K.:	£35.00
U.S.:	$70.00
Can.:	$70.00

SHORELINE SURVEILLANCE
(Otters)

Model:	A1488
Modeller:	John Brown
Height:	6 ¼", 15.9 cm
Colour:	Dark grey, white, yellow and green
Issued:	01/03 - 12/05
Series:	Country Characters

U.K.:	£40.00
U.S.:	$80.00
Can.:	$80.00

SHORT-EARED OWL

Model:	083
Modeller:	Ray Ayres
Height:	9 ¼", 23.5 cm
Colour:	Brown and cream
Issued:	01/86 - 12/90
Series:	British Birds

U.K.:	£125.00
U.S.:	$250.00
Can.:	$250.00

SHORT-EARED OWL AND EGGS

Model:	RB29
Modeller:	Ray Ayres
Height:	5 ¾", 14.6 cm
Colour:	Brown, golden and white
Issued:	01/92 - 12/93

U.K.:	£ 80.00
U.S.:	$160.00
Can.:	$160.00

SHORTHORN COW

Model:	161
Modeller:	Ray Ayres
Height:	4 ¼", 10.8 cm
Colour:	Reddish-brown and white
Issued:	07/02 - 12/95
Series:	Agricultural and Sporting

U.K.:	£400.00
U.S.:	$800.00
Can.:	$800.00

SHOWDAY AT DARROWBY

Model:	EG1
Modeller:	Elizabeth MacAllister
Height:	7 ¾", 19.7 cm
Colour:	A. Bay
	B. Light grey
Issued:	A. 09/87 - 12/92
	B. 1992-1992
Series:	All Creatures Great and Small

	Bay	Grey
U.K.:	£225.	£375.
U.S.:	$450.	$750.
Can.:	$450.	$750.

SHOW-JUMPING
(Horse and rider)

Model:	B0366
Modeller:	Rob Donaldson
Height:	9 ¼", 23.5 cm
Colour:	Light dapple grey, red, white and black
Issued:	01/99 in a limited edition of 850
Series:	1. Agricultural and Sporting
	2. Three-Day Eventing

U.K.:	£250.00
U.S.:	$500.00
Can.:	$500.00

Photograph not
available
at press time

SIAMESE CAT, Seated

Model:	B0396A, B
Modeller:	Ann Richmond
Height:	9 ¼", 23.5 cm
Colour:	A. Seal Point
	B. Lilac Point
Issued:	01/99 - 12/99

U.K.:	£ 80.00
U.S.:	$160.00
Can.:	$160.00

SIAMESE CAT, Standing

Model:	CL1
Modeller:	Judy Boyt
Height:	6", 15.0 cm
Colour:	Cream and black
Issued:	01/84 - 12/86
Series:	A Cat Around the House

U.K.:	£40.00
U.S.:	$80.00
Can.:	$80.00

SIAMESE CAT "ARISTOCAT"

Model:	C4
Modeller:	Judy Boyt
Height:	4 ¼", 10.8 cm
Colour:	Cream, black and red
Issued:	01/83 - 12/92
Series:	A Cat Around the House

U.K.:	£40.00
U.S.:	$80.00
Can.:	$80.00

SIBERIAN TIGER

Model:	B0988
Modeller:	David Mayer
Size:	9 ¼" x 14 ¼"
	23.5 x 36.2 cm
Colour:	Tan, black, white and green
Issued:	01/06 in a limited edition of 395

U.K.:	£250.00
U.S.:	$500.00
Can.:	$500.00

SIBLING PLAY
(Three wolf cubs)

Model: STW02
Modeller: Richard Roberts
Height: 6", 15.0 cm
Colour: Blue-grey, white,
            tan and black
Issued: 07/95 - 12/97
Series: Spirit of the Wolf

U.K.:   £ 55.00
U.S.: $110.00
Can.: $110.00

SILENT SANCTUARY
(Barn owls)

Model: SOC1
Modeller: Ray Ayres
Height: 7 ¾", 19.7 cm
Colour: Pale golden brown
Issued: 06/89 - 05/90
Series: Annual Society Figurine

U.K.:   £225.00
U.S.: $450.00
Can.: $450.00

SILENT WINGS
(Barn Owl)

Model: B0746
Modeller: Richard Roberts
Height: 22", 56.0 cm
Colour: White, golden-brown
            barn owl; dark browns,
            greens, pink and white
Issued: 01/02 in a limited
            edition of 600
Series: Classic Collection

U.K.:   £ 500.00
U.S.: $1,000.00
Can.: $1,000.00

SIMMENTAL BULL
Style One

Model: UK# L18
            USA# 225-165
Modeller: Anne Wall
Height: 6 ¾", 17.2 cm
Colour: Tan and white
Issued: 01/79 in a limited
            edition of 850
Series: Special Interest

U.K.:   £1,000.00
U.S.: $2,000.00
Can.: $2,000.00

SIMMENTAL BULL
Style Two

Model: L102
Modeller: Ray Ayres
Height: 5", 12.7 cm
Colour: Tan and white
Issued: 01/91 in a limited
            edition of 1,500
Series: 1. Agricultural and
               Sporting
            2. Special Interest

U.K.:   £250.00
U.S.: $500.00
Can.: $500.00

SIMMENTAL BULL
Style Three

Model: A0741
Modeller: Lesley McKenzie
Height: 5 ¾", 14.6 cm
Colour: Brown and white
Issued: 06/01 - 12/05
Series: Cattle Breeds

U.K.:   £45.00
U.S.: $90.00
Can.: $90.00

SIMMENTAL	BULL Style Four	CALF Style Two	COW
Model:	A5235	A5238	A5278
Modeller:	Kirsty Armstrong		
Height:	4 ¾" 12.1 cm	3" 7.6 cm	4 ¼" 10.8 cm
Colour:	Golden brown and white		
Issued:	01/05 to the present		
Series:	BFA Pottery Company		
U.K.:	£25.00	£14.95	£25.00
U.S.:	$50.00	$30.00	$50.00
Can.:	$50.00	$30.00	$50.00

SIMMENTAL CALF
Style One

Model: 103
Modeller: Ray Ayres
Height: 4 ½", 11.9 cm
Colour: Tan and white
Issued: 01/81 - 12/82
Series: Farm Series

U.K.:   £225.00
U.S.: $450.00
Can.: $450.00

SIMMENTAL CALVES (Pair)
Style One

Model: 168/B168
Modeller: David Walton
Height: 4 ½", 11.9 cm
Colour: Orange and white
Issued: 07/95 - 06/00
Series: Agricultural and
            Sporting

U.K.:   £ 65.00
U.S.: $125.00
Can.: $125.00

SIMMENTAL CALVES (Pair)
Style Two

Model: A1468
Modeller: Anne Wall
Height: 4 ¼", 10.8 cm
Colour: Reddish-brown and
            white
Issued: 06/02 - 12/03
Series: Cattle Breeds

U.K.:   £40.00
U.S.: $80.00
Can.: $80.00

SIMMENTAL COW AND CALF
Style One

Model: UK# L21
            USA# 225-166
Modeller: Anne Wall
Height: 6 ¼", 15.9 cm
Colour: Tan and white
Issued: 01/80 in a limited
            edition of 850
Series: Special Interest

U.K.:   £ 625.00
U.S.: $1,250.00
Can.: $1,250.00

SIMMENTAL COW AND CALF
Style Two

Model: L103
Modeller: Ray Ayres
Height: 4 ¼", 10.8 cm
Colour: Tan and white
Issued: 01/91 in a limited
            edition of 1,500
Series: 1. Agricultural and
               Sporting
            2. Special Interest

U.K.:   £275.00
U.S.: $550.00
Can.: $550.00

SIMMENTAL COW AND CALF
Style Three

Model: A1253
Modeller: Lesley McKenzie
Height: 5 ½", 14.0 cm
Colour: Dark brown/white cow;
            light brown/white calf
Issued: 01/02 - 06/04
Series: Cattle Breeds

U.K.:   £45.00
U.S.: $90.00
Can.: $90.00

SIMMENTAL FAMILY

Model: L72
Modeller: Elizabeth MacAllister
Height: 6", 15.0 cm
Colour: Tan and white
Issued: 01/86 in a limited
            edition of 850
Series: Special Interest

U.K.:   £350.00
U.S.: $700.00
Can.: $700.00

SIMMENTAL FAMILY GROUP

Model: B0401
Modeller: Kirsty Armstrong
Height: 7", 17.8 cm
Colour: Chestnut and white
Issued: 01/00 in a limited
            edition of 1,250
Series: 1. Agricultural and
               Sporting
            2. The County Show

U.K.:   £225.00
U.S.: $450.00
Can.: $450.00

SINGLE TAWNY OWLET

Model:	A5203
Modeller:	Russell Willis
Height:	6", 15.0 cm
Colour:	Cream, brown, green and pink
Issued:	01/05 -06/06
Series:	Birds by Russell Willis
U.K.:	£30.00
U.S.:	$60.00
Can.:	$60.00

SITTING BARN OWL

Model:	A7392
Modeller:	Unknown
Height:	7 ¼", 18.4 cm
Colour:	Golden brown and white
Issued:	06/06 to the present
U.K.:	£28.00
U.S.:	$55.00
Can.:	$55.00

SITTING SAFE
(Fox)

Model:	A2027
Modeller:	Ray Ayres
Height:	7 ½", 19.1 cm
Colour:	Dark golden brown
Issued:	06/02 - 06/03
Series:	Studio Member-only Figurine
U.K.:	£30.00
U.S.:	$60.00
Can.:	$60.00

SITTING TIGHT
(Fox and pheasant)

Model:	FT04
Modeller:	David Walton
Height:	5 ¾", 14.6 cm
Colour:	Reddish-brown, white and black
Issued:	07/95 - 12/99
Series:	Fox Tales
U.K.:	£ 75.00
U.S.:	$150.00
Can.:	$150.00

SIZE 9

Model:	A8386
Modeller:	Barry Snelson
Height:	3 ¼", 8.3 cm
Colour:	Black, white, browns and green
Issued:	06/07 to the present
Series:	Puppy Trouble
U.K.:	£14.00
U.S.:	$28.00
Can.:	$28.00

SKELDALE HOUSE

Model:	JH54
Modeller:	Richard Young
Height:	5", 12.7 cm
Colour:	Reddish-brown and green
Issued:	01/89 - 09/90
Series:	James Herriot's Yorkshire
U.K.:	£ 75.00
U.S.:	$150.00
Can.:	$150.00

SKIER

Model:	BB04
Modeller:	John Warren
Height:	5 ½", 14.0 cm
Colour:	Bronze
Issued:	01/88 - 12/89
Series:	Studio Bronze
U.K.:	£ 65.00
U.S.:	$125.00
Can.:	$125.00

SMALL TORTOISESHELL
(Butterfly)

Model:	B8
Modeller:	Ray Ayres
Height:	1 ½", 3.8 cm
Colour:	Copper, yellow, red and pink
Issued:	01/81 - 12/85
Series:	British Butterflies
U.K.:	£ 65.00
U.S.:	$125.00
Can.:	$125.00

Note: Earlier models were issued without antenae. Domes were available for all Butterflies.

SMALL TORTOISESHELL AND CONEFLOWER
(Butterfly)

Model:	A5904
Modeller:	Kerry Bell
Height:	4 ¾", 12.1 cm
Colour:	Orange, blue and green
Issued:	01/06 to the present
Series:	Butterflies

U.K.:	£20.00
U.S.:	$40.00
Can.:	$40.00

SMALL WHITE ON HYDRANGEA
(Butterfly)

Model:	A5902
Modeller:	Kerry Bell
Height:	5 ¼", 13.3 cm
Colour:	White, black, green and lilac
Issued:	01/06 to the present
Series:	Butterflies

U.K.:	£20.00
U.S.:	$40.00
Can.:	$40.00

SNIFFER
(Cat sitting)

Model:	K216
Designer:	Zoë Stokes
Modeller:	Mairi Laing Hunt
Height:	4 ½", 11.9 cm
Colour:	Browns, yellow, pink and green
Issued:	01/89 in a limited edition of 12,500
Series:	Zoë's Cats

U.K.:	£40.00
U.S.:	$80.00
Can.:	$80.00

SNIFFER, THE
(Dog sniffing)

Model:	A7331, 7613
Modeller:	Unknown
Height:	5 ¼", 13.3 cm
Colour:	A7331 Black / tan
	A7613 Tan / white
Issued:	06/06 to the present
Series:	Canine Capers

U.K.:	£20.00
U.S.:	$40.00
Can.:	$40.00

SNOOZER, THE
(Dog sleeping)

Model:	A7608, 7614
Modeller:	Unknown
Height:	2", 5.0 cm
Colour:	A7608 Black / tan
	A7614 Tan / white
Issued:	06/06 to the present
Series:	Canine Capers

U.K.:	£14.00
U.S.:	$28.00
Can.:	$28.00

SNOW SLIDE
(Otters)

Model:	B0097
Modeller:	Ray Ayres
Height:	6", 15.0 cm
Colour:	Brown and white
Issued:	01/97 in a limited edition of 2,500
Series:	Masters of the River

U.K.:	£175.00
U.S.:	$350.00
Can.:	$350.00

SNOWY OWL
Style One

Model:	084
Modeller:	Ray Ayres
Height:	6", 15.0 cm
Colour:	White and brown
Issued:	01/86 - 12/88

U.K.:	£ 75.00
U.S.:	$150.00
Can.:	$150.00

SNOWY OWL
Style Two

Model:	WB04
Modeller:	Russell Willis
Height:	3 ¾", 9.5 cm
Colour:	White with black markings
Issued:	07/92 - 12/95
Series:	1. Owls of the World
	2. Russell Willis Birds

U.K.:	£25.00
U.S.:	$50.00
Can.:	$50.00

SNOWY OWL
Style Three

Model:	WB90
Modeller:	Russell Willis
Height:	6 ½", 16.5 cm
Colour:	White
Issued:	01/93 - 12/95
Series:	1. Owls of the World
	2. Russell Willis Birds

U.K.:	£45.00
U.S.:	$90.00
Can.:	$90.00

SNOWY OWL
Style Four

Model:	WB09
Modeller:	Russell Willis
Height:	5 ½", 14.0 cm
Colour:	Cream and brown
Issued:	01/95 - 12/96
Series:	1. Owls of the World
	2. Russell Willis Birds

U.K.:	£45.00
U.S.:	$90.00
Can.:	$90.00

SNOWY OWL
Style Five

Model:	A4056
Modeller:	Russell Willis
Height:	11 ¼", 28.5 cm
Colour:	White, grey, brown,
	green and yellow
Issued:	06/04 - 12/05
Series:	Birds by Russell Willis

U.K.:	£ 75.00
U.S.:	$150.00
Can.:	$150.00

SNOWY TRAIL
(Fox in Snow)

Model:	FT03
Modeller:	David Walton
Height:	6", 15.0 cm
Colour:	Reddish-brown,
	white and grey
Issued:	07/95 - 12/96
Series:	Fox Tales

U.K.:	£ 55.00
U.S.:	$110.00
Can.:	$110.00

SO CLOSE YET...!
(Fox and phesant)

Model:	B1065
Modeller:	Ray Ayres
Size:	7 ¼" x 12"
	18.4 x 30.5 cm
Colour:	Reddish-brown
	and green
Issued:	01/07 in a limited
	edition of 750

U.K.:	£250.00
U.S.:	$500.00
Can.:	$500.00

SO VAIN
(Clown)

Model:	B1044
Modeller:	Richard Roberts
Height:	10½", 26.7 cm
Colour:	White, red, black
	and gold
Issued:	06/06 in a limited
	edition of 500
Series:	Masquerade Clowns

U.K.:	£100.00
U.S.:	$200.00
Can.:	$200.00

SOFT LANDING
(Horse and Rider)

Model:	A1655
Modeller:	Anne Wall
Height:	3 ½", 8.9 cm
Colour:	Dark brown, white, red,
	cream, blue and black
Issued:	01/03 - 12/05
Series:	Hay Days

U.K.:	£30.00
U.S.:	$60.00
Can.:	$60.00

SONG THRUSH
Style One

Model:	093
Modeller:	David Burnham Smith
Height:	4 ½", 11.9 cm
Colour:	Brown, cream and
	green
Issued:	01/89 - 12/91
Series:	British Birds

U.K.:	£ 50.00
U.S.:	$100.00
Can.:	$100.00

SONG THRUSH
Style Two

Model:	RB31
Modeller:	David Walton
Height:	4 ¾", 12.1 cm
Colour:	Dark brown and cream
Issued:	01/92 - 12/93
U.K.:	£ 50.00
U.S.:	$100.00
Can.:	$100.00

SOUNDS OF NIGHT
(Long-eared owl and owlet)

Model:	WB97
Modeller:	Russell Willis
Height:	4 ¾", 12.1 cm
Colour:	Browns and cream
Issued:	01/95 - 12/96
Series:	1. Owls of the World
	2. Russell Willis Birds
U.K.:	£40.00
U.S.:	$80.00
Can.:	$80.00

SOW
(Large White)

Model:	107
Modeller:	Ray Ayres
Height:	3 ½", 8.9 cm
Colour:	Pink
Issued:	01/82 - 12/84
Series:	1. Agricultural and
	Sporting
	2. Farm Series
U.K.:	£350.00
U.S.:	$700.00
Can.:	$700.00

SPADE WORK
Jack Russell and smooth-haired terrier)

Model:	B1034
Modeller:	Anne Wall
Size:	7 ¼" x 7 ½"
	18.4 x 19.1 cm
Colour:	White, black, browns
	green and grey
Issued:	01/07 in a limited
	edition of 500
U.K.:	£125.00
U.S.:	$250.00
Can.:	$250.00

SPANIEL IN DOG BOWL

Model:	484083
Modeller:	Unknown
Height:	2 ½", 6.4 cm
Colour:	White and golden
Issued:	06/98 - 12/00
Series:	Puppy Tales
U.K.:	£12.00
U.S.:	$25.00
Can.:	$25.00

SPILT MILK
(Collie and pups)

Model:	JH99
Modeller:	Ray Ayres
Height:	5 ½", 14.0 cm
Colour:	Black, white and beige
Issued:	01/95 - 12/00
Series:	1. All Creatures Great
	and Small
	2. The James Herriot
	Collection
U.K.:	£115.00
U.S.:	$230.00
Can.:	$230.00

SPLIT DECISION
(Border collies)

Model:	A4072
Modeller:	Hans Kendrick
Height:	5 ¼", 13.3 cm
Colour:	Black, white, grey,
	brown and green
Issued:	06/04 to the present
Series:	James Herriot
	Studio Collection
U.K.:	£ 55.00
U.S.:	$110.00
Can.:	$110.00

SPRING ARRIVALS
(Shetland and Cob Foals)

Model:	B0008
Modeller:	Anne Wall
Height:	2 ¾", 7.0 cm
Colour:	Chestnut and black
Issued:	06/96 - 12/98
Series:	1. Every Living Thing
	2. J. Herriot Collection
U.K.:	£30.00
U.S.:	$60.00
Can.:	$60.00

SPRING CHORES
(Shepherdess, Lamb and Collie)

Model:	JH69A, B
Modeller:	Anne Butler
Height:	5 ½", 14.0 cm
Colour:	A. Blonde shepherdess
	B. Brunette shepherdess
Issued:	01/93 - 12/94
Series:	All Things Wise and Wnderful
U.K.:	£150.00
U.S.:	$300.00
Can.:	$300.00

SPRING COVER
(Lamb Creep and Texel Lambs)

Model:	B0298
Modeller:	Ray Ayres
Height:	3 ¾", 9.5 cm
Colour:	Cream, white and brown
Issued:	06/98 in a limited edition of 1,500
Series:	1. Every Living Thing
	2. J. Herriot Collection
U.K.:	£ 75.00
U.S.:	$150.00
Can.:	$150.00

SPRING LAMBING
(Swaledale Lamb and Ewes)

Model:	JH6
Modeller:	Ray Ayres
Height:	4 ½", 11.9 cm
Colour:	Cream, black and brown
Issued:	01/85 - 12/92
Series:	All Creatures Great and Small
U.K.:	£150.00
U.S.:	$300.00
Can.:	$300.00

SPRING LAMBS

Model:	A8052
Modeller:	Unknown
Height:	3", 7.6 cm
Colour:	Creamy white, green and brown
Issued:	01/07 to the present
Series:	James Herriot Studio Collection
U.K.:	£16.00
U.S.:	$32.00
Can.:	$32.00

SPRING OUTING
(Dormice)

Model:	BCM06
Modeller:	Anne Wall
Height:	3", 7.6 cm
Colour:	Golden, white and pink
Issued:	01/92 - 12/93
Series:	The Country Mouse
U.K.:	£ 65.00
U.S.:	$125.00
Can.:	$125.00

SPRING PASTURES
(Clydesdale mare and foal)

Model:	JH32
Modeller:	Ray Ayres
Height:	6 ½", 16.5 cm
Colour:	Bay mare, chestnut foal
Issued:	01/90 - 12/92
Series:	All Creatures Great and Small
U.K.:	£225.00
U.S.:	$450.00
Can.:	$450.00

SPRING ROMANCE
(Otters)

Model:	MTR05
Modeller:	Ray Ayres
Height:	6", 15.0 cm
Colour:	Brown and white
Issued:	01/95 in a limited edition of 2,500
Series:	Masters of the River
U.K.:	£ 50.00
U.S.:	$100.00
Can.:	$100.00

SPRING SHOW
(Fox and three young)

Model:	B0796
Modeller:	Ray Ayres
Height:	8 ¾", 22.2 cm
Colour	Reddish-brown, white, green, yellow and brown
Issued:	01/03 in a limited edition of 1,750
Series:	Classic Collection
U.K.:	£200.00
U.S.:	$400.00
Can.:	$400.00

SPRINGER SPANIEL, Seated Style One

Model: 204A, B
Modeller: Ray Ayres
Height: 4", 10.1 cm
Colour: A. Liver and white
B. Black and white
Issued: 01/89 - 12/92
Series: 1. The World of Dogs
2. Special Interest

U.K.: £ 55.00
U.S.: $110.00
Can.: $110.00

SPRINGER SPANIEL, Seated Style Two

Model: DG10A, B
Modeller: Steve McKeown
Height: 5 ½", 14.0 cm
Colour: A. Liver and white
B. Black and white
Issued: 01/91 - 08/95
Series: Dogs Galore

U.K.: £20.00
U.S.: $40.00
Can.: $40.00

SPRINGER SPANIEL AND PUP

Model: 207A, B
Modeller: Anne Butler
Height: 4 ½", 11.9 cm
Colour: A. Liver and white
B. Black and white
Issued: 01/92 - 12/94
Series: The World of Dogs

U.K.: £ 65.00
U.S.: $125.00
Can.: $125.00

SPRINGER SPANIEL AND PUPS

Model: 205A, B
Modeller: Ray Ayres
Height: 5 ½", 14.0 cm
Colour: A. Liver and white
B. Black and white
Issued: 01/89 - 12/92
Series: 1. The World of Dogs
2. Special Interest

U.K.: £125.00
U.S.: $250.00
Can.: $250.00

SPRINGER SPANIEL AND RABBIT

Model: A1298, 1628
Modeller: Margaret Turner
Height: 8", 20.3 cm
Colour: A1298 Black / white
A1628 Liver / white
Issued: 06/02 - 12/04
Series: Action Dogs

U.K.: £ 75.00
U.S.: $150.00
Can.: $150.00

SPRINGER SPANIEL PUPS (Three)

Model: A3844, 4448
Modeller: Adrian Hughes
Height: 2 ½", 6.4 cm
Colour: A3844 Liver / white
A4448 Black / white
Issued: 0604 - 06/06
Series: Dogs and Pups Galore

U.K.: £18.00
U.S.: $35.00
Can.: $35.00

SPRINGTIME (Lamb)

Model: JH76A, B
Modeller: Anne Butler
Height: 2 ½", 6.4 cm
Colour: A. Black-faced lamb
B. White-faced lamb
Issued: 01/93 - 12/95
Series: Every Living Thing

U.K.: £30.00
U.S.: $60.00
Can.: $60.00

SQUIRREL

Model: ML06
Modeller: Mairi Laing Hunt
Height: 6", 15.0 cm
Colour: Reddish-brown and white
Issued: 01/88 - 12/90
Series: Woodland

U.K.: £ 50.00
U.S.: $100.00
Can.: $100.00

SQUIRREL FAMILY
Style One
Model: WW15
Modeller: Richard Wawrzesta
Height: 3 ½", 8.9 cm
Colour: Reddish-brown
Issued: 01/87 - 12/87
Series: Family Life (WWF)

U.K.:   £40.00
U.S.: $80.00
Can.: $80.00

SQUIRREL FAMILY
Style Two
Model: RW8
Modeller: Richard Wawrzesta
Height: 4", 10.1 cm
Colour: Reddish-brown
Issued: 01/88 - 12/89
Series: 1. WWFN
           2. Wildlife Families
              (WWF)

U.K.:   £ 50.00
U.S.: $100.00
Can.: $100.00

SQUIRREL FAMILY
Style Three
Model: B0224
Modeller: Kirsty Armstrong
Height: 5 ½", 14.0 cm
Colour: Reddish-brown,
           yellow and green
Issued: 01/98 - 12/99
Series: Wildlife Families

U.K.:   £ 60.00
U.S.: $120.00
Can.: $120.00

ST. BERNARD
Model: L65
Modeller: Elizabeth Waugh
Height: 9 ½", 24.0 cm
Colour: Chestnut, white
           and black
Issued: 01/85 in a limited
           edition of 500
Series: Special Interest

U.K.:   £250.00
U.S.: $500.00
Can.: $500.00

Note: Custom painted.

ST. MARY MAGDALENE'S
CHURCH
Model: JH51
Modeller: Richard Young
Height: 5 ½", 14.0 cm
Colour: Grey and green
Issued: Jan. 1989-Sep. 1990
Series: James Herriot's
           Yorkshire

U.K.:   £ 75.00
U.S.: $150.00
Can.: $150.00

STAFFORDSHIRE BULL
TERRIER, Lying
Model: DG09A, B
Modeller: Steve McKeown
Height: 2 ¼", 5.7 cm
Colour: A. Dark brindle
           B. Red
Issued: 01/91 - 12/96
Series: Dogs Galore

U.K.:   £20.00
U.S.: $40.00
Can.: $40.00

STAFFORDSHIRE BULL
TERRIER, Seated
First Variation
Model: B0191/B0471
Modeller: Margaret Turner
Height: 4 ¼", 10.8 cm
Colour: B0191   Black, rust
                   and white
           B0471   Bronze
Issued: B0191   06/97-12/01
           B0471   06/99-06/00
Series: 1. Dogs Galore
           2. Bronzed

U.K.:   £20.00
U.S.: $40.00
Can.: $40.00

STAFFORDSHIRE BULL
TERRIER, Seated
Second Variation
Model: A2074
Modeller: Margaret Turner
Height: 4 ¼", 10.8 cm
Colour: Chocolate brown and
           white
Issued: 06/02 to the present
Series: Dogs and Pups Galore

U.K.:   £19.00
U.S.: $40.00
Can.: $40.00

STAFFORDSHIRE BULL TERRIER, Standing
Style One

Model:	DM6
Modeller:	Ray Ayres
Height:	3 ¾", 9.5 cm
Colour:	Black and rust - brindle
Issued:	01/86 - 12/92
Series:	1. The World of Dogs
	2. Special Interest
U.K.:	£125.00
U.S.:	$250.00
Can.:	$250.00

STAFFORDSHIRE BULL TERRIER, Standing
Style Two

Model:	A1260
Modeller:	Margaret Turner
Height:	4 ¼", 10.8 cm
Colour:	Dark brown and white
Issued:	01/02 to the present
Series:	Dogs and Pups Galore
U.K.:	£21.00
U.S.:	$40.00
Can.:	$40.00

STAFFORDSHIRE BULL TERRIER, Standing
Style Three

Model:	A3231
Modeller:	Margaret Turner
Height:	13", 33.0 cm
Colour:	Brindle
Issued:	06/03 - 12/06
Series:	Fireside Dogs
U.K.:	£ 75.00
U.S.:	$150.00
Can.:	$150.00

STAND OFF
(Border Collie and Sheep)

Model:	B0701
Modeller:	Ray Ayres
Height:	6 ¼", 15.9 cm
Colour:	Black, white, cream and grey
Issued:	06/01 in a limited edition of 1,750
Series:	James Herriot Classic Collection
U.K.:	£200.00
U.S.:	$400.00
Can.:	$400.00

STANDING FOX

Model:	A7679
Modeller:	Unknown
Height:	4 ¼", 10.8 cm
Colour:	Reddish brown, grey, green and pink
Issued:	01/07 to the present
Series:	Wildlife
U.K.:	£18.00
U.S.:	$35.00
Can.:	$35.00

STARRY EYED
(Two Fox Cubs)

Model:	B0542
Modeller:	Ray Ayres
Height:	2 ½", 6.4 cm
Colour:	Reddish-brown and white
Issued:	2000 - 2001
Series:	Membership Gift
U.K.:	£20.00
U.S.:	$40.00
Can.:	$40.00

STARTS FIRST TIME
(Fowler Diesel Crawler Mark VF)

Model:	B0702
Modeller:	Ray Ayres
Height:	5 ¾", 14.6 cm
Colour:	Green, steel grey, tan, black, white, brown, green and yellow
Issued:	01/02 - 12/02
Series:	BFA Society Member-only Figurine 2001/2002
U.K.:	£250.00
U.S.:	$500.00
Can.:	$500.00

STAYING COOL
(Duck and Ducklings)

Model:	B0440
Modeller:	Kirsty Armstrong
Height:	5", 12.7 cm
Colour:	White, yellow and grey
Issued:	06/99 - 06/01
Series:	J. Herriot Collection
U.K.:	£ 75.00
U.S.:	$150.00
Can.:	$150.00

STEADY LAD, STEADY
(Shepherd, Sheep and Collie)

Model:	JH90
Modeller:	Ray Ayres
Height:	6 ¼", 15.9 cm
Colour:	Green, brown, cream, black and white
Issued:	08/93 in a limited edition of 1,500
Series:	Every Living Thing
U.K.:	£250.00
U.S.:	$500.00
Can.:	$500.00

STEAM PLOUGH, THE
'20 Acres A Day'

Model:	B0744
Modeller:	Ray Ayres
Size:	21" x 13 ½", 8", 53.3 x 34.3 x 20.3 cm
Colour:	Black, red, brown, blue, beige and grey
Issued:	2003 in a limited edition of 500
Series:	Classic Collection
U.K.:	£ 750.00
U.S.:	$1,500.00
Can.:	$1,500.00

STEPPING OUT
(Pheasants)

Model:	B1019
Modeller:	Ray Ayres
Size:	8 ¾" x 9 ¾" 22.2 x 24.7 cm
Colour:	Reddish-brown, black. browns, red and green
Issued:	06/06 - 05/07
Series:	BFA Classic Member-only Figurine
U.K.:	£195.00
U.S.:	$400.00
Can.:	$400.00

STEPPING STONES
(Pony and child)

Model:	A3696
Modeller:	Anne Wall
Height:	5 ½", 14.0 cm
Colour:	White, red, brown, black and green
Issued:	01/04 - 06/06
Series:	Hay Days
U.K.:	£37.00
U.S.:	$70.00
Can.:	$70.00

STOAT

Model:	B0981
Modeller:	Ray Ayres
Size:	7 ¼" x 6 ¼" 18.4 cm x 15.9 cm
Colour:	Brown, cream, green, grey, pink, yellow and white
Issued:	01/06 - 12/06
Series:	Classic Event Special
U.K.:	£150.00
U.S.:	$300.00
Can.:	$300.00

STOAT AND VOLE

Model:	L19
Modeller:	Anne Wall
Height:	7", 17.8 cm
Colour:	Browns and red
Issued:	06/79 in a limited edition of 300
U.K.:	£450.00
U.S.:	$900.00
Can.:	$900.00

STOOP, THE
(Peregrine falcon)

Model:	B0331
Modeller:	Ray Ayres
Height:	7", 17.8 cm
Colour:	Grey, white, black and yellow
Issued:	06/98 - 05/99
Series:	Annual Society Figurine (1998/99 10th Anniv.)
U.K.:	£ 75.00
U.S.:	$150.00
Can.:	$150.00

STOUT HEARTS
(Ploughing scene)

Model:	JH34
Modeller:	Ray Ayres
Height:	7 ½", 19.1 cm
Colour:	Grey, bay, blue and green
Issued:	01/90 - 12/95
Series:	All Things Wise and Wonderful
U.K.:	£ 600.00
U.S.:	$1,200.00
Can.:	$1,200.00

STRAWBERRY PATCH
(Two ducks)

Model:	A0451
Modeller:	Anne Wall
Height:	3 ½", 8.9 cm
Colour:	White, orange, red, green and brown
Issued:	01/01 - 12/02
Series:	The James Herriot Studio Collection
U.K.:	£20.00
U.S.:	$40.00
Can.:	$40.00

STREAM SENTINEL
(Kingfisher)

Model:	SRE2
Modeller:	Ray Ayres
Height:	3 ¼", 8.3 cm
Colour:	Turquoise, fawn and orange
Issued:	06/91 - 05/92
Series:	Membership Gift
U.K.:	£ 80.00
U.S.:	$160.00
Can.:	$160.00

STRETCHER, THE
(Cat stretching)

Model:	A7601, 7607	
Modeller:	Unknown	
Height:	5 ½", 14.0 cm	
Colour:	A7601	Siamese
	A7607	Ginger
Issued:	06/06 to the present	
Series:	Feline Fun	
U.K.:	£ 9.95	
U.S.:	$20.00	
Can.:	$20.00	

STRIKING A DEAL AT APPLEBY FAIR

Model:	B0664
Modeller:	Ray Ayres
Size:	11" x 28" x 10"
	28.0 x 70.0 x 25.0 cm
Colour:	Red, yellow, black, white, browns, grey and green
Issued:	2001 in a limited edition of 600
Series:	Classic Collection – Appleby Fair
U.K.:	£1,250.00
U.S.:	$2,500.00
Can.:	$2,500.00

STUBBLE SURPRISE
(Two Partridges)

Model:	B0302
Modeller:	John Brown
Height:	6 ¾", 17.2 cm
Colour:	Browns, grey, green and yellow
Issued:	06/98 in a limited edition of 2,500
Series:	Nature's Kingdom
U.K.:	£100.00
U.S.:	$200.00
Can.:	$200.00

SUFFOLK

	EWE	LAMB	RAM Style Three
Model:	A4613	A4590	A4587
Modeller:	R. Ayres	L. Mackenzie	R. Ayres
Height:	4 ¼"	3"	4 ¼"
	10.8 cm	7.6 cm	10.8 cm
Colour:	Cream, white and black		
Issued:	01/04 to the present		
Series:	BFA Pottery Company		
U.K.:	£18.00	£ 9.95	£18.00
U.S.:	$35.00	$20.00	$35.00
Can.:	$35.00	$20.00	$35.00

SUFFOLK EWE AND LAMB

Model: 119
Modeller: Ray Ayres
Height: 4 ¼", 10.8 cm
Colour: White, black and grey
Issued: 01/91 - 12/94
Series: Agricultural and Sporting

U.K.: £225.00
U.S.: $450.00
Can.: $450.00

SUFFOLK EWE AND LAMBS
Style One

Model: L87
Modeller: Ray Ayres
Height: 4 ½", 11.9 cm
Colour: White and black
Issued: 01/88 in a limited edition of 1,250
Series: Special Interest

U.K.: £475.00
U.S.: $950.00
Can.: $950.00

SUFFOLK EWE AND LAMBS
Style Two

Model: A1245
Modeller: Lesley McKenzie
Height: 5", 12.7 cm
Colour: Cream and black
Issued: 01/02 - 12/04
Series: Sheep Breeds

U.K.: £45.00
U.S.: $90.00
Can.: $90.00

SUFFOLK EWE AND LAMBS
Style Three

Model: B0778
Modeller: Jack Crewdson
Height: 7", 17.8 cm
Colour: Black and white; green base
Issued: 01/03 in a limited edition of 1,250
Series: Classic Collection

U.K.: £175.00
U.S.: $350.00
Can.: $350.00

SUFFOLK EWES AND COLLIES

Model: 101
Modeller: Ray Ayres
Height: 4 ¼", 10.8 cm
Colour: Cream, black and white
Issued: 01/81 - 06/86
Series: 1. Agricultural and Sporting
2. Farm Series

U.K.: £300.00
U.S.: $600.00
Can.: $600.00

SUFFOLK FAMILY GROUP
(Ram with Gimmer and Ewe Lambs)

Model: B0197
Modeller: Ray Ayres
Height: 5 ½", 14.0 cm
Colour: Cream and black
Issued: 06/97 in a limited edition of 1,250
Series: Agricultural and Sporting

U.K.: £150.00
U.S.: $300.00
Can.: $300.00

SUFFOLK PUNCH STALLION,
Standing

Model: L70
Modeller: Anne Wall
Height: 7 ½", 19.1 cm
Colour: Chestnut
Issued: 01/85 in a limited edition of 350

U.K.: £450.00
U.S.: $900.00
Can.: $900.00

Note: Initially issued for Suffolk Punch Horse Society.

SUFFOLK PUNCH STALLION, Walking
(Gold Edition)

Model:	B0042
Modeller:	Anne Wall
Height:	9 ½", 24.0 cm
Colour:	Chestnut
Issued:	09/96 in a limited edition of 350
Series:	Heavy Horse

U.K.:	£350.00
U.S.:	$700.00
Can.:	$700.00

Note: Issued nos. 1-350.

(Standard Edition)

	B0042A
	Anne Wall
	9 ½", 24.0 cm
	Chestnut
	01/97 in a limited edition of 600
	Agricultural and Sporting

U.K.:	£250.00
U.S.:	$500.00
Can.:	$500.00

Note: Issued nos. 351-950.

SUFFOLK RAM
Style One

Model:	L40
Modeller:	Ray Ayres
Height:	5", 12.7 cm
Colour:	Cream, black and green
Issued:	07/82 in a limited edition of 1,250

U.K.:	£ 750.00
U.S.:	$1,500.00
Can.:	$1,500.00

SUFFOLK RAM
Style Two

Model:	A0735
Modeller:	Lesley McKenzie
Height:	5 ¼", 13.3 cm
Colour:	Cream and black
Issued:	06/01 - 06/06
Series:	Sheep Breeds

U.K.:	£35.00
U.S.:	$70.00
Can.:	$70.00

SUFFOLK TUP
Style One

Model:	B0196
Modeller:	Ray Ayres
Height:	5 ¼", 13.3 cm
Colour:	Cream and black
Issued:	06/97 - 12/99
Series:	Agricultural and Sporting

U.K.:	£ 80.00
U.S.:	$160.00
Can.:	$160.00

SUFFOLK TUP
Style Two

Model:	B0777
Modeller:	Jack Crewdson
Height:	8", 20.3 cm
Colour:	Cream and black; green base
Issued:	06/03 in a limited edition of 1,250
Series:	Classic Collection

U.K.:	£100.00
U.S.:	$200.00
Can.:	$200.00

SUMMER DAYS
(Shire mare and foal)

Model:	JH33
Modeller:	Ray Ayres
Height:	6", 15.0 cm
Colour:	Bay and grey
Issued:	01/90 - 12/91
Varieties:	JH33A Gently Grazing
Series:	All Creatures Great and Small

U.K.:	£250.00
U.S.:	$500.00
Can.:	$500.00

SUMMER FUN
(Two fox cubs and butterfly)

Model:	SOC4
Modeller:	Ray Ayres
Height:	6 ½", 16.5 cm
Colour:	Reddish-brown, pink and green
Issued:	06/92 - 05/93
Series:	Annual Society Figurine (1992/93)

U.K.:	£175.00
U.S.:	$350.00
Can.:	$350.00

SUMMER SHADE
(Three sheep)

Model:	B0340
Modeller:	Ray Ayres
Height:	5 ¼", 13.3 cm
Colour:	Cream, black, green and brown
Issued:	01/99 in a limited edition of 1,500
Series:	James Herriot Collection
U.K.:	£100.00
U.S.:	$200.00
Can.:	$200.00

SUMMER SPLENDOUR
(Pheasant)

Model:	B1076
Modeller:	Ray Ayres
Size:	14 ¾" x 10 ½" 37.5 x 26.7 cm
Colour:	Reddish-brown, green and brown
Issued:	06/07 in a limited edition of 350
U.K.:	£ 495.00
U.S.:	$1,000.00
Can.:	$1,000.00

SUNDAY MORNING
(Cat and kittens)

Model:	JH80A, B
Modeller:	Anne Butler
Height:	3 ¾", 9.5 cm
Colour:	A. Black and white B. Ginger
Issued:	01/93 - 12/96
Series:	1. Every Living Thing 2. The James Herriot Collection
U.K.:	£40.00
U.S.:	$80.00
Can.:	$80.00

SUNNY AFTERNOON

Model:	A1872
Modeller:	Richard Roberts
Height:	7 ¼", 18.4 cm
Colour:	White, blue, light brown, green, yellow, orange and grey
Issued:	01/03 in a limited edition of 1,250
Series:	Studio Limited Editions
U.K.:	£125.00
U.S.:	$250.00
Can.:	$250.00

SUNSHINE
(Two Cats)

Model:	K257
Designer:	Zoë Stokes
Modeller:	Mairi Laing Hunt
Height:	3 ½", 8.9 cm
Colour:	Grey and cream
Issued:	01/89 - 12/92
Series:	Zoë's Cats
U.K.:	£ 65.00
U.S.:	$125.00
Can.:	$125.00

SUNWORSHIPPERS, THE
(Two Lambs)

Model:	JH102A, B, C, D
Modeller:	Anne Wall
Height:	2", 5.0 cm
Colour:	A. Black-faced B. White-faced C. Herdwick D. Suffolk
Issued:	01/95 - 12/97
Series:	1. Every Living Thing 2. J. Herriot Collection
U.K.:	£25.00
U.S.:	$50.00
Can.:	$50.00

SUPPLEMENTARY FEEDING
(Tip Cart)

Model:	JH57
Modeller:	Anne Butler
Height:	7", 17.8 cm
Colour:	Brown, cream and green
Issued:	01/91 in a limited edition of 1,750
Series:	All Things Wise and Wonderful
U.K.:	£ 550.00
U.S.:	$1,100.00
Can.:	$1,100.00

SURPISE!
(Rabbits)

Model: A1280
Modeller: John Brown
Height: 4 ¼", 10.8 cm
Colour: Light brown, brown, white, green, yellow, pink and black
Issued: 01/02 - 12/03
Series: Country Characters

U.K.: £30.00
U.S.: $60.00
Can.: $60.00

SURROGATE MOTHER
(Hen and Border Collie Pups)

Model: B0489A, B
Modeller: Anne Wall
Height: 3 ¾", 9.5 cm
Colour: A. Rhode Island Red hen
B. Light Sussex hen
Issued: 06/99 - 06/00
Series: James Herriot Collection

U.K.: £40.00
U.S.: $80.00
Can.: $80.00

SWALEDALE		EWE	LAMB	RAM Style Two
Model:		A4614	A4591	A4588
Modeller:	Ray Ayres			
Height:		3 ¾" 9.5 cm	2 ¾" 7.0 cm	4" 10.1 cm
Colour:	Cream, white and black			
Issued:	01/04 to the present			
Series:	BFA Pottery Company			
U.K.:		£18.00	£ 9.95	£18.00
U.S.:		$35.00	$20.00	$35.00
Can.:		$35.00	$20.00	$35.00

SWALEDALE EWE AND LAMB
Style One

Model: B0307
Modeller: Ray Ayres
Height: 6", 15.0 cm
Colour: Tan, black and green
Issued: 06/98 in a limited edition of 1,250
Series: Agricultural and Sporting

U.K.: £100.00
U.S.: $200.00
Can.: $200.00

SWALEDALE EWE AND LAMB
Style Two

Model: A1248
Modeller: Lesley McKenzie
Height: 5", 12.7 cm
Colour: Cream/white/black
Issued: 01/03 - 06/06
Series: Sheep Breeds

U.K.: £ 50.00
U.S.: $100.00
Can.: $100.00

SWALEDALE RAM
Style One

Model: A1243
Modeller: Lesley McKenzie
Height: 5", 12.7 cm
Colour: Cream/white/black
Issued: 01/03 - 06/06
Series: Sheep Breeds

U.K.: £35.00
U.S.: $70.00
Can.: $70.00

SWALEDALE TUP
(The Monarch of the Dales)

Model: L148
Modeller: Ray Ayres
Height: 4", 10.1 cm
Colour: Beige, black and white
Issued: 07/94 in a limited edition of 950

U.K.: £225.00
U.S.: $450.00
Can.: $450.00

SWALLOW
Style One

Model:	M16
Modeller:	David Fryer
Height:	3", 7.6 cm
Colour:	Black, yellow and red; bronze base
Issued:	07/83 - 06/86
Series:	Miniatures on Bronze

U.K.:	£ 65.00
U.S.:	$125.00
Can.:	$125.00

SWALLOW
Style Two

Model:	A3457
Modeller:	Russell Willis
Height:	6", 15.0 cm
Colour:	Blue, white, red, green and brown
Issued:	01/04 - 06/06
Series:	Birds by Russell Willis

U.K.:	£30.00
U.S.:	$60.00
Can.:	$60.00

SWALLOWTAIL
(Butterfly)

Model:	B6
Modeller:	Ray Ayres
Height:	4 ½", 11.9 cm
Colour:	Black, yellow and brown
Issued:	07/80 - 12/82
Series:	British Butterflies

U.K.:	£ 65.00
U.S.:	$125.00
Can.:	$125.00

Note: Earlier models were issued without antenae. Domes were optional with all butterflies.

SWAN AND CYGNETS
Style One

Model:	WW4
Modeller:	Ray Ayres
Height:	4 ¼", 10.8 cm
Colour:	White, black and orange
Issued:	01/86 - 12/92
Series:	1. The Wetlands (WWF)
	2. WWFN

U.K.:	£ 80.00
U.S.:	$160.00
Can.:	$160.00

SWAN AND CYGNETS
(Mute Swan)
Style Two

Model:	PS10
Modeller:	Richard Roberts
Height:	4", 10.1 cm
Colour:	White, yellow, orange and grey
Issued:	01/92 - 12/94
Series:	Peter Scott Memorial Appeal (WWF)

U.K.:	£ 65.00
U.S.:	$125.00
Can.:	$125.00

SWEEP (Collie)

Model:	JH58
Modeller:	Anne Butler
Height:	3 ¼", 8.3 cm
Colour:	Black and white
Issued:	01/91 - 12/97
Series:	1. All Things Wise and Wonderful
	2. J. Herriot Collection

U.K.:	£ 65.00
U.S.:	$125.00
Can.:	$125.00

SWEET DREAMS

Model:	A1202
Modeller:	Unknown
Height:	1 ¼", 3.1 cm
Colour:	Black and white dog; ginger tabby kitten; red and black cushion; grey and pink mouse
Issued:	06/01
Series:	Gift with Purchase

U.K.:	£15.00
U.S.:	$30.00
Can.:	$30.00

SWIMMING CLASS
(Otters and Seal)

Model:	A1281
Modeller:	John Brown
Height:	3 ½", 8.9 cm
Colour:	Dark brown, white, yellow and green
Issued:	01/02 - 12/03
Series:	Country Characters

U.K.:	£30.00
U.S.:	$60.00
Can.:	$60.00

SWIMMING OTTER AND FISH

Model:	A7683
Modeller:	Unknown
Height:	5 ¼", 13.3 cm
Colour:	Dark brown, cream, green and grey
Issued:	01/07 to the present
Series:	Wildlife

U.K.:	£18.00
U.S.:	$35.00
Can.:	$35.00

SWIMMING OTTER (Lamp)

Model:	A5026
Modeller:	Adrian Hughes
Height:	18 ¼", 47.0 cm
Colour:	Brown, cream, grey and green
Issued:	01/05 - 06/07
Series:	Wildlife

U.K.:	£175.00
U.S.:	$350.00
Can.:	$350.00

SYMBOL OF LOYALTY
(Peregrine Falcon)

Model:	B0854
Modeller:	Ray Ayres
Height:	3 ½", 8.9 cm
Colour:	Silvery-blue, white, grey and green
Issued:	06/03 to the present
Series:	15th Membership Anniversary

U.K.:	£20.00
U.S.:	$40.00
Can.:	$40.00

TAKING FLIGHT
(Brace of pheasants)

Model:	B0183
Modeller:	David Walton
Height:	8", 20.3 cm
Colour:	Browns, greens and yellow
Issued:	06/97 in a limited edition of 2,500
Series:	Nature's Kingdom

U.K.:	£125.00
U.S.:	$250.00
Can.:	$250.00

TAKING NO NOTICE
(Border collie and cat)

Model:	A0194
Modeller:	Unknown
Height:	4 ¾", 12.1 cm
Colour:	Black, white, orange, brown, red and green
Issued:	01/01 - 12/05
Series:	James Herriot Studio Collection

U.K.:	£20.00
U.S.:	$40.00
Can.:	$40.00

TAKING THE PLUNGE
(Otters)

Model:	L143
Modeller:	Ray Ayres
Height:	30 ¼", 76.8 cm
Colour:	Browns, green and yellow
Issued:	01/94 in a limited edition of 350
Series:	1. Masterpiece 2. 20th Anniversary

U.K.:	£1,500.00
U.S.:	$3,000.00
Can.:	$3,000.00

TARZAN
(Cat Swinging)

Model:	K235
Designer:	Zoë Stokes
Modeller:	Mairi Laing Hunt
Height:	5 ½", 14.0 cm
Colour:	Ginger, white, purple, blue and brown
Issued:	01/89 in a limited edition of 12,500
Series:	Zoë's Cats

U.K.:	£ 50.00
U.S.:	$100.00
Can.:	$100.00

TATTIE SPAYING
(David Brown Tractor)

Model:	A5894
Modeller:	Ray Ayres
Height:	5 ¼", 14.0 cm
Colour:	Red, black, green and sandy brown
Issued:	06/05 to the present
Series:	Tractors

U.K.:	£110.00
U.S.:	$220.00
Can.:	$220.00

TAWNY OWL
Style One

Model:	031
Modeller:	Victor Hayton
Height:	10", 25.4 cm
Size:	Large
Colour:	Browns
Issued:	01/77 - 12/79

U.K.:	£375.00
U.S.:	$750.00
Can.:	$750.00

TAWNY OWL
Style Two

Model:	030
Modeller:	Victor Hayton
Height:	7 ½", 19.1 cm
Size:	Small
Colour:	Browns and cream
Issued:	01/77 - 12/79

U.K.:	£225.00
U.S.:	$450.00
Can.:	$450.00

TAWNY OWL
Style Three

Model:	082
Modeller:	Ray Ayres
Height:	11", 27.9 cm
Colour:	Grey-brown and cream
Issued:	01/86 - 12/90
Series:	British Birds

U.K.:	£150.00
U.S.:	$300.00
Can.:	$300.00

TAWNY OWL
Style Four

Model:	WB01
Modeller:	Russell Willis
Height:	3 ¾", 9.5 cm
Colour:	Browns and cream
Issued:	07/92 - 12/96
Series:	1. Owls of the World
	2. Russell Willis Birds

U.K.:	£20.00
U.S.:	$40.00
Can.:	$40.00

TAWNY OWL
Style Five

Model:	WB70
Modeller:	Russell Willis
Height:	9 ½", 24.0 cm
Colour:	Brown, copper and cream
Issued:	01/93 in a limited edition of 1,850
Series:	Russell Willis Birds

U.K.:	£125.00
U.S.:	$250.00
Can.:	$250.00

TAWNY OWL
Style Six

Model:	WB91
Modeller:	Russell Willis
Height:	6 ½", 16.5 cm
Colour:	Copper, cream and red
Issued:	01/93 - 12/96
Series:	1. Owls of the World
	2. Russell Willis Birds

U.K.:	£ 75.00
U.S.:	$150.00
Can.:	$150.00

TAWNY OWL
Style Seven

Model:	WB08
Modeller:	Russell Willis
Height:	6", 15.0 cm
Colour:	Browns, cream and golden
Issued:	01/95 - 12/97
Series:	1. Owls of the World
	2. Birds by Russell Willis

U.K.:	£45.00
U.S.:	$90.00
Can.:	$90.00

TAWNY OWL
Style Eight

Model:	B0233
Modeller:	Russell Willis
Height:	4", 10.1 cm
Colour:	Browns and cream
Issued:	07/97 - Unknown
Series:	Russell Willis Collection

U.K.:	£25.00
U.S.:	$50.00
Can.:	$50.00

TAWNY OWL
Style Nine

Model:	484245
Modeller:	Russell Willis
Height:	3", 7.6 cm
Colour:	Brown, fawn and pale green
Issued:	06/98 - 12/02
Series:	1. Miniature Figurines 2. Birds by Russell Willis

U.K.:	£10.00
U.S.:	$20.00
Can.:	$20.00

TAWNY OWL
Style Ten

Model:	A4868
Modeller:	Russell Willis
Height:	4 ½", 11.4 cm
Colour:	Brown, fawn and green
Issued:	01/04 - 12/06
Series:	BFA Pottery Company

U.K.:	£15.00
U.S.:	$30.00
Can.:	$30.00

TAWNY OWL
Style Eleven

Model:	A4054
Modeller:	Russell Willis
Height:	8 ¾", 22.2 cm
Colour:	Tan, grey, green, brown, and pale blue
Issued:	06/04 - 12/05
Series:	Birds by Russell Willis

U.K.:	£ 75.00
U.S.:	$150.00
Can.:	$150.00

TAWNY OWL
(With two owlets)

Model:	A2483
Modeller:	Russell Willis
Height:	8", 20.3 cm
Colour:	Browns, cream, pink, yellow and green
Issued:	01/03 - 12/04
Series:	Birds by Russell Willis

U.K.:	£ 65.00
U.S.:	$125.00
Can.:	$125.00

TAWNY OWL (With Wildroses)

Model:	A1476
Modeller:	Russell Willis
Height:	6", 15.0 cm
Colour:	Browns, white, pink and green
Issued:	06/02 - 12/04
Series:	Birds by Russell Willis

U.K.:	£30.00
U.S.:	$60.00
Can.:	$60.00

TAWNY OWL AND CHICK

Model:	652008
Modeller:	Russell Willis
Height:	5 ¼", 13.3 cm
Colour:	Browns, pink and green
Issued:	06/99 - 06/00
Series:	Families

U.K.:	£30.00
U.S.:	$60.00
Can.:	$60.00

TAWNY OWL AND FUNGI

Model:	484431
Modeller:	Russell Willis
Height:	7 ¼", 18.4 cm
Colour:	Browns, fawn, cream, grey and green
Issued:	06/98 - 12/99
Series:	Woodland and Garden

U.K.:	£40.00
U.S.:	$80.00
Can.:	$80.00

TAWNY OWL AND OWLETS
Style One

Model:	UK# 039 USA# 225-069
Modeller:	Janet Nightingale
Height:	7", 17.8 cm
Colour:	Browns
Issued:	01/80 - 06/83

U.K.:	£100.00
U.S.:	$200.00
Can.:	$200.00

TAWNY OWL AND OWLETS
Style Two
Model: RB28
Modeller: Ray Ayres
Height: 6 ¾", 17.2 cm
Colour: Chestnut, grey
            and white
Issued: 01/92 - 12/93

U.K.:   £ 80.00
U.S.: $160.00
Can.: $160.00

TAWNY OWL AND YOUNG
Model: RB16
Modeller: Ray Ayres
Height: 10", 25.4 cm
Colour: Brown, grey and cream
Issued: 01/90 - 12/92
Series: British Birds

U.K.:   £175.00
U.S.: $350.00
Can.: $350.00

TAWNY OWL ON AXE
Model: F2
Modeller: David Burnham Smith
Height: 4 ½", 11.9 cm
Colour: Chestnut, white and
            grey
Issued: 01/89 - 12/91
Series: Finesse Birds

U.K.:   £ 65.00
U.S.: $125.00
Can.: $125.00

TAWNY OWL ON MILESTONE
Model: 088
Modeller: Ray Ayres
Height: 6 ¾", 17.2 cm
Colour: Brown and cream
Issued: 01/88 - 12/92
Series: British Birds

U.K.:   £ 65.00
U.S.: $125.00
Can.: $125.00

TAWNY OWL ON SINK
Model: 484350
Modeller: Russell Willis
Height: 4 ½", 11.9 cm
Colour: Browns, grey and
            green
Issued: 06/98 - 06/00
Series: 1. Birds And ...
            2. Birds by Russell
               Willis

U.K.:   £20.00
U.S.: $40.00
Can.: $40.00

TAWNY OWL ON WHEEL
Model: B0228
Modeller: Russell Willis
Height: 5 ¼", 13.3 cm
Colour: Browns and cream
Issued: 07/97 - Unknown
Series: Russell Willis Collection

U.K.:   £40.00
U.S.: $80.00
Can.: $80.00

TAWNY OWL WITH NEST
Model: 541699
Modeller: Russell Willis
Height: 3 ¼", 8.3 cm
Colour: Browns, cream and
            green
Issued: 01/99 - 12/03
Series: 1. Feathered Friends
            2. Birds by Russell
               Willis

U.K.:   £12.00
U.S.: $25.00
Can.: $25.00

TAWNY OWLETS (Pair)
Model: B0236
Modeller: Russell Willis
Height: 4", 10.1 cm
Colour: Browns and cream
Issued: 07/97 - Unknown
Series: Russell Willis Collection

U.K.:   £25.00
U.S.: $50.00
Can.: $50.00

TEA BREAK
(JCB)

Model:	B0274
Modeller:	Ray Ayres
Height:	7 ½", 19.1 cm
Colour:	Yellow, brown and black
Issued:	06/97 in a limited edition of 950
Series:	Tractors
U.K.:	£ 575.00
U.S.:	$1,150.00
Can.:	$1,150.00

TEA TIME
(Cat)

Model:	A6893
Modeller:	Andrew Edwards
Height:	3 ½", 8.9 cm
Colour:	Black, white, orange, blue and cream
Issued:	06/06 to the present
Series:	Cats Round the House
U.K.:	£20.00
U.S.:	$40.00
Can.:	$40.00

TEAM WORK

Model:	B0729
Modeller:	Ray Ayres
Height:	7 ¼", 18.4 cm
Colour:	Black, yellow, brown, green and white
Issued:	01/02 in a limited edition of 500
Series:	Classic Collection
U.K.:	£475.00
U.S.:	$950.00
Can.:	$950.00

TEMPORARY HOME
(Collie pups in barrel)

Model:	JH97
Modeller:	David Walton
Height:	4 ¼", 10.8 cm
Colour:	Black, white and brown
Issued:	07/94 in a limited edition of 1,500
Series:	Every Living Thing
U.K.:	£100.00
U.S.:	$200.00
Can.:	$200.00

TEMPTED
(Cat)

Model:	A6894
Modeller:	Andrew Edwards
Height:	6", 15.0 cm
Colour:	Ginger, brown, blue and pink
Issued:	06/06 to the present
Series:	Cats Round the House
U.K.:	£22.00
U.S.:	$45.00
Can.:	$45.00

10 O'CLOCK BREAK
(Bookends)

Model:	L158
Modeller:	Adrian Hughes
Height:	6 ¼", 15.9 cm
Colour:	Brown, white, black and grey
Issued:	10/95 in a limited edition of 1,500
Series:	James Herriot Collection
U.K.:	£150.00
U.S.:	$300.00
Can.:	$300.00

TENDER MOMENTS
(Elephant Family)

Model:	B0002
Modeller:	Richard Roberts
Height:	7 ¼", 18.4 cm
Colour:	Grey and green
Issued:	01/97 in a limited edition of 850
Series:	An African Safari
U.K.:	£225.00
U.S.:	$450.00
Can.:	$450.00

TENNIS PLAYER

Model:	BB02
Modeller:	John Warren
Height:	4 ½", 11.9 cm
Colour:	Bronze
Issued:	01/88 - 12/89
Series:	Studio Bronze
U.K.:	£ 65.00
U.S.:	$125.00
Can.:	$125.00

TERRIER

Model:	UK# 054
	USA# 225-123
Modeller:	Anne Wall
Height:	3 ½", 8.9 cm
Colour:	White and brown
Issued:	06/79 - 12/86
Series:	The World of Dogs
U.K.:	£ 75.00
U.S.:	$150.00
Can.:	$150.00

TERRIER AND RABBIT

Model:	068
Modeller:	Anne Wall
Height:	3 ½", 8.9 cm
Colour:	White, browns and white
Issued:	01/82 - 06/86
U.K.:	£100.00
U.S.:	$200.00
Can.:	$200.00

TERRIER PUP

Model:	FF9A, B
Modeller:	Anne Wall
Height:	2 ¼", 5.7 cm
Colour:	A. Brown
	B. Unknown
Issued:	01/92 - 12/95
Series:	First Friends
U.K.:	£12.00
U.S.:	$25.00
Can.:	$25.00

TERRIER PUP AND MOUSE

Model:	FE13A, B
Modeller:	Ray Ayres
Height:	3 ¾", 9.5 cm
Colour:	A. Brown and white
	B. Black and white
Issued:	01/90 - 12/92
Series:	First Encounters
U.K.:	£ 65.00
U.S.:	$125.00
Can.:	$125.00

TERRIER PUPS

Model:	ED9
Modeller:	Judy Boyt
Height:	2", 5.0 cm
Colour:	Brown, black and white
Issued:	07/83 - 12/85
Series:	Early Days
U.K.:	£40.00
U.S.:	$80.00
Can.:	$80.00

TERRIER RACE

Model:	B0242
Modeller:	Margaret Turner
Height:	5 ½", 14.0 cm
Colour:	Golden brown, white and tan
Issued:	01/98 - 12/99
Series:	Dogs by Margaret Turner
U.K.:	£125.00
U.S.:	$250.00
Can.:	$250.00

TERRIERS RATTING

Model:	B0884
Modeller:	Anne Wall
Size:	6" x 10"
	15.0 x 25.4 cm
Colour:	Black, browns, white and grey
Issued:	01/05 in a limited edition of 500
U.K.:	£175.00
U.S.:	$350.00
Can.:	$350.00

TÊTE-À-TÊTE
(Woman Milking)
Model:	B0515
Modeller:	Kirsty Armstrong
Height:	6 ½", 16.5 cm
Colour:	Black, white, brown and blue
Issued:	01/00 - 12/01
Series:	James Herriot Collection
U.K.:	£150.00
U.S.:	$300.00
Can.:	$300.00

TEXEL

	EWE	LAMB	RAM Style Four
Model:	A5231	A5232	A5230
Modeller:	R. Ayres	L. Mackenzie	R. Ayres
Height:	3 ½"	2 ½"	3 ¼"
	8.9 cm	6.4 cm	8.3 cm
Colour:	Cream and white		
Issued:	06/04 to the present		
Series:	BFA Pottery Company		
U.K.:	£18.00	£ 9.95	£18.00
U.S.:	$35.00	$20.00	$35.00
Can.:	$35.00	$20.00	$35.00

TEXEL EWE AND LAMB
Model:	120/B120
Modeller:	Ray Ayres
Height:	4 ¼", 10.8 cm
Colour:	White
Issued:	01/91 - 12/99
Series:	Agricultural and Sporting
U.K.:	£ 65.00
U.S.:	$125.00
Can.:	$125.00

TEXEL EWE AND LAMBS
Style One
Model:	L37
Modeller:	Ray Ayres
Height:	5", 12.7 cm
Colour:	Cream and green
Issued:	01/82 in a limited edition of 850
U.K.:	£ 550.00
U.S.:	$1,100.00
Can.:	$1,100.00

TEXEL EWE AND LAMBS
Style Two
Model:	B0658
Modeller:	Jack Crewdson
Height:	6 ¾", 17.2 cm
Colour:	Cream, white and green
Issued:	01/01 in a limited edition of 1,500
Series:	The County Show
U.K.:	£175.00
U.S.:	$350.00
Can.:	$350.00

TEXEL EWE AND LAMBS
Style Three
Model:	A1246
Modeller:	Lesley McKenzie
Height:	4 ¼", 10.8 cm
Colour:	Cream/white/black
Issued:	01/02 - 12/05
Series:	Sheep Breeds
U.K.:	£ 50.00
U.S.:	$100.00
Can.:	$100.00

TEXEL EWE AND LAMBS
Style Four
Model:	B1054
Modeller:	Ray Ayres
Size:	5 ½" x 9 ¼" 14.0 x 23.5 cm
Colour:	Cream, white and green
Issued:	04/07 in a limited edition of 500
U.K.:	£150.00
U.S.:	$300.00
Can.:	$300.00

TEXEL RAM
Style One

Model:	L108
Modeller:	Ray Ayres
Height:	5 ¼", 13.3 cm
Colour:	Off-white
Issued:	07/92 in a limited edition of 850
U.K.:	£450.00
U.S.:	$900.00
Can.:	$900.00

TEXEL RAM
Style Two

Model:	B0530
Modeller:	Jack Crewdson
Height:	8", 20.3 cm
Colour:	Cream, white and black
Issued:	01/00 in a limited edition of 1,500
Series:	1. Agricultural and Sporting
	2. The County Show
U.K.:	£110.00
U.S.:	$225.00
Can.:	$225.00

TEXEL RAM
Style Three

Model:	A0736
Modeller:	Lesley McKenzie
Height:	5", 12.7 cm
Colour:	Cream/white/black
Issued:	06/01 - 06/06
Series:	Sheep Breeds
U.K.:	£35.00
U.S.:	$70.00
Can.:	$70.00

THINKER, THE
(Dog)

Model:	A7186. 7611
Modeller:	Unknown
Height:	6 ¾", 17.2 cm
Colour:	A7186 Black / tan
	A7611 Tan / white
Issued:	06/06 to the present
Series:	Canine Capers
U.K.:	£18.00
U.S.:	$35.00
Can.:	$35.00

THIRSTY WORK
(Geese and water pump)

Model:	JH45
Modeller:	David Walton
Height:	6 ½", 16.5 cm
Colour:	White, brown and green
Issued:	01/91 - 12/95
Series:	All Creatures Great and Small
U.K.:	£ 65.00
U.S.:	$125.00
Can.:	$125.00

THIRSTY WORK
(Man and boy)

Model:	B0740
Modeller:	Craig Harding
Height:	8", 20.3 cm
Colour:	White, blue, brown, yellow, grey and green
Issued:	01/02 in a limited edition of 1,250
Series:	Classic Collection
U.K.:	£200.00
U.S.:	$400.00
Can.:	$400.00

THOROUGHBRED FOAL
Style One

Model:	070
Modeller:	Anne Wall
Height:	6", 15.0 cm
Colour:	Bay
Issued:	01/77 - 12/81
Series:	Horses
U.K.:	£325.00
U.S.:	$650.00
Can.:	$650.00

THOROUGHBRED FOAL
Style Two

Model:	014
Modeller:	Anne Wall
Height:	6", 15.0 cm
Colour:	Chestnut
Issued:	06/79 - 06/80
Series:	Mammals
U.K.:	£350.00
U.S.:	$700.00
Can.:	$700.00

THOROUGHBRED FOAL
Style Three
Model: A6543
Modeller: Unknown
Height: 4 ½", 11.4 cm
Colour: Light brown
Issued: 06/06 to the present
Series: BFA Pottery Company

U.K.: £14.95
U.S.: $30.00
Can.: $30.00

THOROUGHBRED (Foal)
Style Four
Model: A6727
Modeller: Unknown
Height: 6 ¼", 15.9 cm
Colour: Brown
Issued: 06/06 to the present
Series: BFA Pottery Company

U.K.: £30.00
U.S.: $60.00
Can.: $60.00

THOROUGHBRED MARE AND
FOAL, Cantering
Model: 122
Modeller: Anne Wall
Height: 6 ½", 16.5 cm
Colour: Chestnut and brown
Issued: 01/91 - 12/93
Series: Agricultural and
Sporting

U.K.: £150.00
U.S.: $300.00
Can.: $300.00

Note: Model found in various
colourways.

THOROUGHBRED MARE AND
FOAL, Standing
Style One
Model: L45
Modeller: David Geenty
Height: 8", 20.3 cm
Colour: Brown and chestnut
Issued: 01/83 in a limited
edition of 750
Series: Special Interest

U.K.: £350.00
U.S.: $700.00
Can.: $700.00

Note: This illustration is a portrait
piece.

THOROUGHBRED MARE AND
FOAL, Standing
Style Two
Model: A0147
Modeller: Anne Wall
Height: 5 ¼", 13.3 cm
Colour: Dark and light brown,
green
Issued: 06/00 - 12/03
Series: Horse Breeds

U.K.: £ 60.00
U.S.: $120.00
Can.: $120.00

THOROUGHBRED MARE AND
FOAL, Walking
Model: B0357A, B
Modeller: Anne Wall
Height: 11 ½", 29.2 cm
Colour: A. Dark and light bay
B. Grey and chestnut
Issued: 01/99 in a limited
edition of 1,500
Series: 1. Agricultural and
Sporting
2. The County Show

	Bay	Grey
U.K.:	£300.	£300.
U.S.:	$600.	$600.
Can.:	$600.	$600.

THOROUGHBRED STALLION,
Cantering
Model: 121
Modeller: Anne Wall
Height: 6 ½", 16.5 cm
Colour: Dark brown
Issued: 01/91 - 12/93
Series: Agricultural and
Sporting

U.K. £150.00
U.S. $300.00
Can. $300.00

THOROUGHBRED STALLION,
Standing
Style One
Model: L44
Modeller: David Geenty
Height: 8 ½", 21.6 cm
Colour: Dark brown
Issued: 01/83 in a limited
edition of 750
Series: Special Interest

U.K.: £300.00
U.S.: $600.00
Can.: $600.00

**THOROUGHBRED STALLION,
Standing
Style Two**

Model:	B0241A, B	
Modeller:	Anne Wall	
Height:	12 ½", 31.7 cm	
Colour:	A. Dark bay	
	B. Grey	
Issued:	1998 in a limited edition of 1,500	
Series:	Agricultural and Sporting	

	Dark Bay	**Grey**
U.K.:	£250.	£250.
U.S.:	$500.	$500.
Can.:	$550.	$500.

**THOROUGHBRED STALLION,
Standing
Style Three**

Model:	A0730
Modeller:	Anne Wall
Height:	6 ¾", 17.2 cm
Colour:	Dark brown
Issued:	06/01 - 12/03
Series:	Horse Breeds

U.K.:	£45.00
U.S.:	$90.00
Can.:	$90.00

**THE 3a
(Field Marshal Series 3)**

Model:	B0918
Modeller:	Ray Ayres
Size:	6 ¼" x 17 ¼", 15.9 x 43.8 cm
Colour:	Orange, blue, browns, grey and green
Issued:	01/05 in a limited edition of 1,500
Series:	Tractors

U.K.:	£400.00
U.S.:	$800.00
Can.:	$800.00

THREE BORDER COLLIE PUPS

Model:	A1445
Modeller:	Margaret Turner
Height:	2 ¼", 5.7 cm
Colour:	Black and white
Issued:	01/02 to the present
Series:	Dogs and Pups Galore

U.K.:	£13.00
U.S.:	$25.00
Can.:	$25.00

THREE BOXER PUPS

Model:	A2316
Modeller:	Margaret Turner
Height:	2 ½", 6.4 cm
Colour:	Golden brown, white, black and blue
Issued:	01/02 to the present
Series:	Dogs and Pups Galore

U.K.:	£15.00
U.S.:	$30.00
Can.:	$30.00

**THREE CAVALIER KING
CHARLES PUPS**

Model:	A1448
Modeller:	Margaret Turner
Height:	2 ½", 6.4 cm
Colour:	Tricolour
Issued:	01/02 - 06/06
Series:	Dogs and Pups Galore

U.K.:	£12.00
U.S.:	$25.00
Can.:	$25.00

THREE DOBERMAN PUPS

Model:	A2315
Modeller:	Margaret Turner
Height:	3", 7.6 cm
Colour:	Black and tan
Issued:	01/03 - 12/04
Series:	Dogs and Pups Galore

U.K.:	£15.00
U.S.:	$30.00
Can.:	$30.00

THREE GOLDEN RETRIEVER PUPS

Model:	A2314
Modeller:	Margaret Turner
Height:	2 ½", 6.4 cm
Colour:	Golden white
Issued:	01/03 to the present
Series:	Dogs and Pups Galore
U.K.:	£17.50
U.S.:	$35.00
Can.:	$35.00

THREE JACK RUSSELL PUPS

Model:	A1447
Modeller:	Margaret Turner
Height:	2", 5.0 cm
Colour:	Tricolour
Issued:	01/02 to the present
Series:	Dogs and Pups Galore
U.K.:	£13.00
U.S.:	$25.00
Can.:	$25.00

THREE KITTENS "CAT-KINS"

Model:	C3
Modeller:	Judy Boyt
Height:	2 ½", 6.4 cm
Colour:	White and red
Issued:	01/83 - 12/91
Series:	A Cat Around the House
U.K.:	£25.00
U.S.:	$50.00
Can.:	$50.00

THREE LABRADOR PUPS

Model:	A1446, 1645
Modeller:	Margaret Turner
Height:	2 ½", 6.4 cm
Colour:	A1446 Black
	A1645 Yellow
Issued:	01/02 - 12/06
Series:	Dogs and Pups Galore
U.K.:	£13.00
U.S.:	$25.00
Can.:	$25.00

THREE MUSKATEERS
Lakeland Fell, Border, and Wire-haired Terriers)

Model:	B0990
Modeller:	Anne Wall
Size:	4 ¾" x 8"
	12.1 x 20.3 cm
Colour:	Browns, white and green
Issued:	01/06 in a limited edition of 500
U.K.:	£150.00
U.S.:	$300.00
Can.:	$300.00

THREE OWLETS

Model:	A7391
Modeller:	Unknown
Height:	4 ½", 11.4 cm
Colour:	White, grey, browns grey and cream
Issued:	01/07 to the present
U.K.:	£25.00
U.S.:	$50.00
Can.:	$50.00

THREE ROTTWEILER PUPS

Model:	A2313
Modeller:	Margaret Turner
Height:	2 ½", 6.4 cm
Colour:	Black and tan
Issued:	01/03 - 12/05
Series:	Dogs and Pups Galore
U.K.:	£12.00
U.S.:	$25.00
Can.:	$25.00

THREE YOUNG CALVES

Model:	B0519
Modeller:	Kirsty Armstrong
Height:	5", 12.7 cm
Colour:	Black, white and brown
Issued:	01/00 - 06/01
Series:	1. Agricultural and Sporting
	2. The County Show
U.K.:	£ 80.00
U.S.:	$160.00
Can.:	$160.00

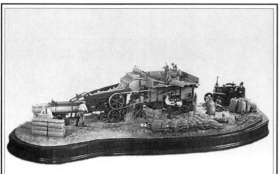

THRESHING MILL, THE

Model:	B0361
Modeller:	Ray Ayres
Height:	8" x 30", 20.3 x 76.2 cm
Colour:	Red, salmon, golden and black
Issued:	01/99 in a limited edition of 600
Series:	Millennium

U.K.	£2,250.00
U.S.	$4,500.00
Can.	$4,500.00

THROUGH THE HOOP
(Border collie)

Model:	B0953
Modeller:	Margaret Turner
Size:	7 ¼" x 8 ½" 18.4 x 21.6 cm
Colour:	Black, white, red and green
Issued:	06/05 in a limited edition of 500

U.K.:	£150.00
U.S.:	$300.00
Can.:	$300.00

THRUSH

Model:	A0651
Modeller:	Russell Willis
Height:	3", 7.6 cm
Colour:	Brown, tan, white and green
Issued:	01/01 - 06/05
Series:	Feathered Friends

U.K.	£20.00
U.S.	$40.00
Can.	$40.00

THRUSH AND BUTTERCUPS

Model:	WB37
Modeller:	Russell Willis
Height:	5 ¾", 14.6 cm
Colour:	Browns, yellow and green
Issued:	01/94 - 12/95
Series:	1. Birds In Your Garden 2. Birds by Russell Willis

U.K.	£40.00
U.S.	$80.00
Can.	$80.00

THRUSH ON THIMBLE

Model:	WB53
Modeller:	Russell Willis
Height:	3 ½", 8.9 cm
Colour:	Browns, cream and silver
Issued:	01/94 - 12/95
Series:	1. Birds In Your Garden 2. Birds by Russell Willis

U.K.:	£30.00
U.S.:	$60.00
Can.:	$60.00

THRUSH WITH NEST

Model:	541680
Modeller:	Russell Willis
Height:	3", 7.6 cm
Colour:	Brown, cream, lemon and green
Issued:	01/99 - 12/01
Series:	1. Feathered Friends 2. Birds by Russell Willis

U.K.:	£15.00
U.S.:	$30.00
Can.:	$30.00

TIGER

Model:	A5048
Modeller:	David Mayer
Height:	7", 17.8 cm
Colour:	Golden brown, black, cream, green and fawn
Issued:	01/05 - 12/06
Series:	Wild World

U.K.:	£ 75.00
U.S.:	$150.00
Can.:	$150.00

TIGER AND CUB

Model: WW29
Modeller: David Walton
Height: 2 ¾", 7.0 cm
Colour: Orange, black and white
Issued: 01/95 - 12/95
Series: Miniature (WWF)

U.K.: £20.00
U.S.: $40.00
Can.: $40.00

TIGER CUBS

Model: RW62
Modeller: Richard Roberts
Height: 3 ¾", 9.5 cm
Colour: Orange, white and dark brown
Issued: 01/95 - 06/97
Series: Nursery (WWF)

U.K.: £ 75.00
U.S.: $150.00
Can.: $150.00

TIGER FLOWER

Model: FC1
Designer: Fleur Cowles
Modeller: Richard Roberts
Height: 5", 12.7 cm
Colour: A. Blue
B. Natural
C. White
Issued: 1987 in a limited edition of 500
Series: The Imagined World of Fleur Cowles

	Blue	Natural	White
U.K.:	£300.	£350.	£250.
U.S.:	$600.	$700.	$500.
Can.:	$600.	$700.	$500.

TIME FOR REFLECTION

Model: JH19
Modeller: Ray Ayres
Height: 7 ¾", 19.7 cm
Colour: Browns, black and white
Issued: 01/87 - 12/96
Series: 1. All Creatures Great and Small
2. The James Herriot Collection

U.K.: £150.00
U.S.: $300.00
Can.: $300.00

TIMES OF PLENTY
(Wood Mouse and blackberries)

Model: BCM02
Modeller: Ray Ayres
Height: 3 ¾", 9.5cm
Colour: Browns, black and green
Issued: 01/91 - 12/95
Series: 1. The Country Mouse
2. Wildlife

U.K.: £ 80.00
U.S.: $160.00
Can.: $160.00

TIPPING TURNIPS

Model: B1037
Modeller: Ray Ayres
Height: 6" x 19", 15.0 x 48.0 cm
Colour: Browns, charcoal and red
Issued: 01/07 in a limited edition of 950
Series: Tractors

U.K.: £450.00
U.S.: $900.00
Can.: $900.00

Note: Authorised by AGCO Corporation.

TLC
(Boy with three lambs)

Model: A1453
Modeller: Adrian Hughes
Height: 7 ½", 19.1 cm
Colour: Black, white, pink and green
Issued: 06/02 - 12/04
Series: Young Farmers

U.K.: £35.00
U.S.: $70.00
Can.: $70.00

266

TO THE TUP SALE
(Morris 1000 Pick-Up)

Model:	JH72
Modeller:	David Walton
Height:	4 ¼", 10.8 cm
Colour:	Green, cream and browns
Issued:	01/93 in a limited edition of 1,850
Series:	All Things Wise and Wonderful
U.K.:	£250.00
U.S.:	$500.00
Can.:	$500.00

TOBY
(Cocker Spaniel Pup)
Style One

Model:	JH26
Modeller:	Richard Roberts
Height:	3 ½", 8.9 cm
Colour:	Golden and brown
Issued:	01/88 - 12/93
Series:	1. All Creatures Great and Small
	2. James Herriot's Favourite Characters
U.K.:	£25.00
U.S.:	$50.00
Can.:	$50.00

TOBY
(Cocker Spaniel Pup)
Style Two

Model:	A6508
Modeller:	Kerry Bell
Height:	3", 7.6 cm
Colour:	Light brown, green and white
Issued:	01/06 to the present
Series:	James Herriot Studio Collection
U.K.:	£15.00
U.S.:	$30.00
Can.:	$30.00

TODAY'S CATCH
(Kingfishers)

Model:	B1016
Modeller:	Ray Ayres
Size:	9 ¾" x 10"
	24.7 x 25.4 cm
Colour:	Turquoise, orange, white, browns, green and pink
Issued:	01/07 in a limited edition of 500
U.K.:	£199.00
U.S.:	$400.00
Can.:	$400.00

TOGETHER AGAIN
(Two Otters)

Model:	SOC3
Modeller:	Ray Ayres
Height:	6 ¼", 15.9 cm
Colour:	Brown and grey
Issued:	06/91 - 05/92
Series:	Annual Society Figurine
U.K.:	£ 80.00
U.S.:	$160.00
Can.:	$160.00

TOGETHERNESS
(Little Owl and Owlet)

Model:	WB99
Modeller:	Russell Willis
Height:	4 ¼", 10.8 cm
Colour:	Dark and light brown
Issued:	01/96 - 12/97
Series:	Russell Willis Birds
U.K.:	£35.00
U.S.:	$70.00
Can.:	$70.00

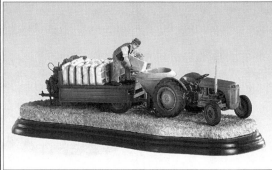

TOP DRESSING

Model:	A6349
Modeller:	Unknown
Size:	4 ¾" x 13 ¾", 11.8 x 35.0 cm
Colour:	Browns, greys, greens, orange and white
Issued:	06/06 to the present
Series:	Tractors
U.K.:	£159.00
U.S.:	$300.00
Can.:	$300.00

Note: Authorised by AGCO Corporation.

TOP OF THE MORNING
(Three Blue Tits and milk bottle)

Model: B0538
Modeller: John Brown
Height: 3", 7.6 cm
Colour: Yellow, blue and white
Issued: 01/00 - 12/00
Series: Event Special

U.K.: £ 65.00
U.S.: $125.00
Can.: $125.00

TORTOISE

Model: FF14
Modeller: Anne Wall
Height: 1 ½", 3.8 cm
Colour: Brown, yellow and green
Issued: 01/93 - 12/95
Series: First Friends

U.K.: £12.00
U.S.: $25.00
Can.: $25.00

TORTOISE AND LEVERET

Model: FE12
Modeller: Ray Ayres
Height: 2 ¾", 7.0 cm
Colour: Browns and green
Issued: 01/87 - 12/88
Series: First Encounters

U.K.: £ 65.00
U.S.: $125.00
Can.: $125.00

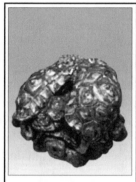

TORTOISES

Model: ED5
Modeller: Judy Boyt
Height: 2 ¼", 5.7 cm
Colour: Brown and yellow
Issued: 07/82 - 12/82
Series: Early Days

U.K.: £40.00
U.S.: $80.00
Can.: $80.00

TOUCAN

Model: L77
Modeller: Richard Roberts
Height: 14", 35.5 cm
Colour: Black, white and yellow
Issued: 01/87 in a limited edition of 950
Series: Exotic Birds

U.K.: £225.00
U.S.: $450.00
Can.: $450.00

TRANQUILITY (Bust)
(Thoroughbred Mare and Foal)

Model: K214
Modeller: Fred Stone
Height: 7 ¼", 18.4 cm
Colour: Bay mare, chestnut foal
Issued: 01/90 in a limited edition of 2,500

U.K.: £125.00
U.S.: $250.00
Can.: $250.00

TRAVELLING HOME FROM APPLEBY FAIR

Model: B0775
Modeller: Ray Ayres
Size: 22" x 12" x 7", 55.9 x 30.5 x 17.8 cm
Colour: Red, yellow, turquoise, black, white, reddish-brown, brown, beige and green
Issued: 2004 in a limited edition of 600
Series: Classic Collection – Appleby Fair

U.K.: £ 750.00
U.S.: $1,500.00
Can.: $1,500.00

TRICKY WOO
(Pekinese)

Model: JH16
Modeller: Richard Roberts
Height: 2 ½", 6.4 cm
Colour: Golden, black, green
          and pink
Issued: 01/87 - 12/91
Series: 1. All Creatures Great
             and Small
          2. James Herriot's
             Favourite Characters

U.K.:   £25.00
U.S.: $50.00
Can.: $50.00

TRIPLE TAWNY OWLETS

Model: A5207
Modeller: Russell Willis
Height: 9 ¼", 23.5 cm
Colour: Cream, brown,
          green and grey
Issued: 01/05 - 06/06
Series: Birds by Russell Willis

U.K.:   £ 60.00
U.S.: $120.00
Can.: $120.00

TROOPING THE COLOUR

Model: B0968
Modeller: Ray Ayres
Size: 6 ¼" x 17 ½"
          15.9 x 44.5 cm
Colour: White, grey, red, gold,
          green and black
Issued: 01/06 in a limited
          edition of 395

U.K.:   £350.00
U.S.: $700.00
Can.: $700.00

TROTTER, THE

Model: B0836
Modeller: Jacqueline Francis
          Harris-Brown
Height: 10 ½", 26.7 cm
Colour: Dark brown, black, red,
          white, blue and green
Issued: 06/03 in a limited
          edition of 500
Series: Classic Collection

U.K.:   £300.00
U.S.: $600.00
Can.: $600.00

TROUBLE
(Puppy and kittens)

Model: A5907
Modeller: Unknown
Height: 3", 7.6 cm
Colour: White, ginger, brown
          and black
Issued: 06/05 to the present
Series: James Herriot
          Studio Collection

U.K.:   £26.00
U.S.: $50.00
Can.: $50.00

TROUBLE AHEAD
(Collie pup and biscuits)

Model: JH74
Modeller: Anne Wall
Height: 3 ½", 8.9 cm
Colour: Black, white and brown
Issued: 01/93 - 12/98
Series: 1. Every Living Thing
          2. James Herriot
             Collection

U.K.:   £40.00
U.S.: $80.00
Can.: $80.00

TROUBLE IN STORE
(Jack Russell and pups)

Model: 201
Modeller: Mairi Laing Hunt
Height: 4 ½", 11.9 cm
Colour: White and brown
Issued: 01/88 - 12/89
Series: The World of Dogs

U.K.:   £125.00
U.S.: $250.00
Can.: $250.00

TUG OF LOVE
(Spaniel puppies)

Model: A8384, 8385
Modeller: Barry Snelson
Height: 3", 7.6 cm
Colour: A8384 Black / white
          A8385 Liver / white
Issued: 06/07 to the present
Series: Puppy Trouble

U.K.:   £15.00
U.S.: $30.00
Can.: $30.00

TUG O'WAR
(Collie Pups)

Model:	JH61
Modeller:	David Walton
Height:	4 ½", 11.9 cm
Colour:	Black, white, brown and beige
Issued:	01/91 - 12/97
Series:	1. All Things Wise and Wonderful
	2. J. Herriot Collection

U.K.	£ 60.00
U.S.	$120.00
Can.	$120.00

TULIPS
(Cat)

Model:	A6891
Modeller:	Andrew Edwards
Height:	5", 12.7 cm
Colour:	Grey, orange, red, green and black
Issued:	06/06 to the present
Series:	Cats Round the House
U.K.:	£22.00
U.S.:	$45.00
Can.:	$45.00

TURKEY

Model:	162A, B, C
Modeller:	David Walton
Height:	3 ¾", 9.5 cm
Colour:	A. Bronze
	B. Black and white
	C. White
Issued:	07/92 - 12/93
Series:	Agricultural and Sporting

	Bronze	B&W	White
U.K.:	£40.	£100.	£40.
U.S.:	$80.	$200.	$80.
Can.:	$80.	$200.	$80.

TURKEYS

Model:	A0452
Modeller:	Anne Wall
Height:	3 ¾", 9.5 cm
Colour:	Bronze and white
Issued:	01/01 - 06/03
Series:	James Herriot Studio Collection
U.K.:	£20.00
U.S.:	$40.00
Can.:	$40.00

TURNING WITH CARE
(Nuffield tractor)

Model:	B0094
Modeller:	Ray Ayres
Height:	5 ½", 14.0 cm
Colour:	Red, black, blue and white
Issued:	01/97 in a limited edition of 1,750
Series:	1. All Creatures Great and Small
	2. James Herriot Collection

U.K.:	£ 650.00
U.S.:	$1,300.00
Can.:	$1,300.00

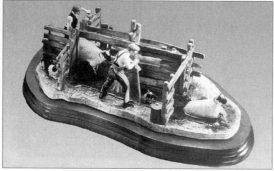

TWICE UNDER
(Sheep dipping)

Model:	B0217
Modeller:	Ray Ayres
Height:	5 ½", 14.0 cm
Colour:	Browns, blue, black, white and green
Issued:	01/98 in a limited edition of 1,750
Series:	1. Every Living Thing
	2. The James Herriot Collection

U.K.:	£250.00
U.S.:	$500.00
Can.:	$500.00

TWO AGAINST ONE
(Border collie and lambs)

Model:	A4243
Modeller:	Craig Harding
Height:	3", 7.6 cm
Colour:	Black, white, tan, cream and green
Issued:	06/04 to the present
Series:	James Herriot Studio Collection
U.K.:	£28.00
U.S.:	$55.00
Can.:	$55.00

TWO FOR TEA
(Kitten and rabbit in teapot)

Model:	A3872
Modeller:	Kerry Bell
Height:	3 ¼", 8.3 cm
Colour:	White, red, green, blue, pale ginger, and grey
Issued:	06/04 - 12/06
Series:	On The Farm

U.K.:	£15.00
U.S.:	$30.00
Can.:	$30.00

TWO FOR THE PRICE OF ONE
(Piglets)

Model:	A7939
Modeller:	Unknown
Height:	3 ¼", 8.3 cm
Colour:	Pink, yellow and light brown
Issued:	01/07 to the present
Series:	James Herriot Studio Collection

U.K.:	£12.00
U.S.:	$25.00
Can.:	$25.00

TWO'S COMPANY
(Three terriers)

Model:	L56
Modeller:	Ray Ayres
Height:	4 ¾", 12.1 cm
Colour:	Brown, black and cream
Issued:	01/84 in a limited edition of 850
Series:	Special Interest

U.K.:	£300.00
U.S.:	$600.00
Can.:	$600.00

UNDER HER WING
(Hen and kittens)

Model:	A4064
Modeller:	Kerry Bell
Height:	3 ¾", 9.5 cm
Colour:	White, ginger, black, brown, grey, green
Issued:	06/04 - 06/06
Series:	James Herriot Studio Collection

U.K.:	£35.00
U.S.:	$70.00
Can.:	$70.00

UNDER MOTHER'S WING
(Barn owl and owlet)

Model:	WB95
Modeller:	Russell Willis
Height:	4", 10.1 cm
Colour:	Golden and cream
Issued:	01/95 - 12/97
Series:	1. Owls of the World
	2. Russell Willis Birds

U.K.:	£30.00
U.S.:	$60.00
Can.:	$60.00

UNDER THE HAMMER

Model:	B0666A, B, C, D
Modeller:	Kirsty Armstrong
Height:	6", 15.0 cm
Colour:	A. Limousin Cross
	B. Charolais Cross
	C. Belgian Blue Cross
	D. Simmental Cross
Issued:	A. 01/01 in a limited edition of 665 (nos. 11-675)
	B. 01/01 in a limited edition of 325 (nos. 676-1,000)
	C. 01/01 in a limited edition of 475 (nos. 1001-1,475)
	D. 01/01 in a limited edition of 275 (nos. 1,476-1,750)

U.K.:	£300.00
U.S.:	$600.00
Can.:	$600.00

Note: Initially released in Autumn 2000 for Harrison and Hetherington Ltd., 500 of these models feature their logo.

UNDERCOVER
(Hedgehog Family)

Model:	A0402
Modeller:	John Brown
Height:	6", 15.0 cm
Colour:	Grey, green, tan and stone
Issued:	01/01 - 12/02
Series:	1. Secret Places
	2. Country Characters

U.K.:	£40.00
U.S.:	$80.00
Can.:	$80.00

UNDERSTUDY, THE
(Border Collie Bitch and Pup)

Model:	L150
Modeller:	Margaret Turner
Height:	8 ¼", 21.0 cm
Colour:	Black and white
Issued:	01/95 in a limited edition of 1,500
Series:	Dogs by Margaret Turner
U.K.:	£125.00
U.S.:	$250.00
Can.:	$250.00

UNWELCOME GUEST
(Deer)

Model:	A1873
Modeller:	John Brown
Height:	6 ½", 16.5 cm
Colour:	Browns, grey, green and red
Issued:	06/03 - 06/06
Series:	Country Characters
U.K.:	£45.00
U.S.:	$90.00
Can.:	$90.00

UPSETTING THE APPLE CART
(Pig)

Model:	A7935
Modeller:	Unknown
Height:	5", 12.7 cm
Colour:	Black, pink, brown, green and red
Issued:	01/07 to the present
Series:	James Herriot Studio Collection
U.K.:	£39.00
U.S.:	$80.00
Can.:	$80.00

URBAN BADGERS
(Pair of badgers and pillar box)

Model:	L151
Modeller:	David Walton
Height:	7 ½", 19.1 cm
Colour:	Grey, white, black and red
Issued:	01/95 in a limited edition of 1,500
U.K.:	£200.00
U.S.:	$400.00
Can.:	$400.00

URBAN FOX

Model:	B1067
Modeller:	Ray Ayres
Size:	5 ¾" x 7" 14.6 x 17.8 cm
Colour:	Reddish-brown, bronze and beige
Issued:	01/07 in a limited edition of 250
Series:	Event Special
U.K.:	£125.00
U.S.:	$250.00
Can.:	$250.00

URBAN FOXES

Model:	L134
Modeller:	David Walton
Height:	5", 12.7 cm
Colour:	Reddish-brown, white and grey
Issued:	03/93 in a limited edition of 1,250
U.K.:	£225.00
U.S.:	$450.00
Can.:	$450.00

URBAN SQUIRRELS

Model:	B0043
Modeller:	David Walton
Height:	5 ½", 14.0 cm
Colour:	Reddish-brown and white
Issued:	09/96 in a limited edition of 1,500
U.K.:	£ 50.00
U.S.:	$100.00
Can.:	$100.00

VANNA, THE
(Horse)

Model:	B0952, 0952A
Modeller:	Anne Wall
Height:	11" x 11 ½" 27.9 x 29.2 cm
Colour:	B0952 Piebald B0952A Skewbald
Issued:	06/05 in a limited edition of 750
Series:	Classic Collection
U.K.:	£175.00
U.S.:	$350.00
Can.:	$350.00

VANTAGE POINT
(Fox)

Model: SRE1
Modeller: Ray Ayres
Height: 2 ¾", 7.0 cm
Colour: Red, white and brown
Issued: 06/90 - 05/91
Series: Membership Gift

U.K.:   £150.00
U.S.: $300.00
Can.: $300.00

VICTORY AT THE HIGHLAND
Clydesdale Stallion (Gold Ed.)

Model: L149A, B, C
Modeller: Anne Wall
Height: 10 ¼", 26.0 cm
Colour: A. Bay
            B. Strawberry roan
            C. Blue roan
Issued: 07/94 in a limited
            edition of 350
Varieties: Standard Edition, L149D
Series: Heavy Horse

U.K.:   £450.00
U.S.: $900.00
Can.: $900.00

Note: Issued nos. 1-350.

VICTORY AT THE HIGHLAND
Clydesdale Stallion (Std.
Edition)

Model: L149D
Modeller: Anne Wall
Height: 10 ¼", 26.0 cm
Colour: Bay, white and blue
Issued: 07/94 in a limited
            edition of 600
Varieties: Gold Edition
            (L149A, B, C)
Series: Heavy Horse

U.K.:   £300.00
U.S.: $600.00
Can.: $600.00

Note: Issued nos. 351-950.

VIEWING THE PRACTICE

Model: JH8
Modeller: Ray Ayres
Height: 5", 12.7 cm
Colour: Blue, brown and white
Issued: 01/85 - 12/86
Series: All Creatures Great
            and Small

U.K.:   £ 650.00
U.S.: $1,300.00
Can.: $1,300.00

VISITOR, THE
(Hedgehog with Brush)

Model: A0130
Modeller: Ray Ayres
Height: 5 ½", 14.0 cm
Colour: Brown and grey
Issued: 06/00 - 12/02
Series: Country Characters

U.K.:   £25.00
U.S.: $50.00
Can.: $50.00

VIXEN, Walking

Model: 006
Modeller: Mairi Laing Hunt
Height: 3 ½", 8.9 cm
Colour: Reddish-brown
Issued: 07/78 - 12/81
Series: Mammals

U.K.:   £100.00
U.S.: $200.00
Can.: $200.00

WAGTAIL

Model: A0008
Modeller: Richard Roberts
Height: 5 ½", 14.0 cm
Colour: Grey, yellow, black
            and fawn
Issued: 01/00 - 06/03
Series   Reflections

U.K.:   £25.00
U.S.: $50.00
Can.: $50.00

WAIT FOR ME
(Border collie and five pups)

Model: SOC6
Modeller: Ray Ayres
Height: 5", 12.7 cm
Colour: Black and white
Issued: 01/94 - 12/94
Series   1. Annual Figurine
               (1994)
            2. 20th Anniversary
               Society

U.K.:   £150.00
U.S.: $300.00
Can.: $300.00

WAITING
(Siamese Cat)

Model: K256
Designer: Zoë Stokes
Modeller: Mairi Laing Hunt
Height: 5 ½", 14.0 cm
Colour: Brown and cream
Issued: 01/89 - 12/93
Series: Zoë's Cats

U.K.: £ 50.00
U.S.: $100.00
Can.: $100.00

WAITING GAME, THE
(Heron)

Model: B0907
Modeller: Ray Ayres
Size: 11 ½", 10 ¼"
29.2 x 26.0 cm
Colour: Grey, white, green
yellow and tan
Issued: 06/04 in a limited
edition of 950
Series: Above and Below

U.K.: £175.00
U.S.: $350.00
Can.: $350.00

WAKE UP CALL (Clock)
(Border Collie, Cat and Barrel)

Model: B0095
Modeller: Anne Wall
Height: 4", 10.1 cm
Colour: Brown, black, white
and ginger
Issued: 01/97 - 12/99
Series: 1. All Creatures Great
and Small
2. James Herriot
Collection

U.K.: £40.00
U.S.: $80.00
Can.: $80.00

WALKIES
(Border collie)

Model: B0860
Modeller: Kirsty Armstrong
Height: 2 ¼", 5.7 cm
Colour: Black and white
Issued: 06/04 - 05/05
Series: Membership Gift

U.K.: £15.00
U.S.: $30.00
Can.: $30.00

WARBLER

Model: M10
Modeller: David Fryer
Height: 3", 7.6 cm
Colour: Yellow; bronze base
Issued: 07/83 - 12/84
Series: Miniatures on Bronze

U.K.: £ 80.00
U.S.: $160.00
Can.: $160.00

WARM FRIENDS
(Border collie)

Model: 1. B1032 - Standard
2. B1032A - Bespoke
Modeller: Ray Ayres
Height: 4 ½" x 7 ¼"
11.4 x 18.4 cm
Colour: 1. Black/white dog
2. Dog to be coloured
to buyer's request
Issued: 01/07 - 12/07
Series: Member-only Figurine

U.K.: £150.00
U.S.: $300.00
Can.: $300.00

WARM WORK ON A COLD
DAY

Model: B1028
Modeller: Hans Kendrick
Height: 6 ¾" x 16 ¼"
17.2 x 41.2 cm
Colour: Browns, white, grey,
black and green
Issued: 06/07 in a limited
edition of 500

U.K.: £295.00
U.S.: $600.00
Can.: $600.00

WASH AND BRUSH UP
(Border Collies)

Model: A6128
Modeller: Hans Kendrick
Height: 4", 10.1 cm
Colour: Black, white, brown,
pink, blue and fawn
Issued: 01/06 to the present
Series: Border Collie Collection

U.K.: £38.00
U.S.: $80.00
Can.: $80.00

**WASH AND BRUSH UP
(Boy and Calf)**

Model:	A1450
Modeller:	Craig Harding
Height:	7 ¾", 19.7 cm
Colour:	Brown, red, blue, green and grey
Issued:	01/03 - 06/05
Series:	Young Farmers

U.K.:	£45.00
U.S.:	$90.00
Can.:	$90.00

WASH DAY

Model:	A0193
Modeller:	Anne Wall
Height:	2 ¾", 7.0 cm
Colour:	Black, white, yellow and tan
Issued:	01/01 - 12/05
Series:	The James Herriot Studio Collection

U.K.:	£20.00
U.S.:	$40.00
Can.:	$40.00

**WATCHING AND WAITING
(Pair owlets)**

Model:	PR01
Modeller:	Ray Ayres
Height:	2 ½", 6.4 cm
Colour:	Pale golden brown
Issued:	07/93 - 12/94
Series:	Special Offer

U.K.:	£20.00
U.S.:	$40.00
Can.:	$40.00

Note: Available with purchase of £65.00 or over from the BFA Collection.

**WATCHING AND WAITING
(Fox)**

Model:	A1489
Modeller:	John Brown
Height:	7", 17.8 cm
Colour:	Golden brown, white, grey and green
Issued:	01/03 - 06/06
Series:	Country Characters

U.K.:	£30.00
U.S.:	$60.00
Can.:	$60.00

**WATER BABIES
(Otters)**

Model:	B0103
Modeller:	Ray Ayres
Height:	2 ½", 6.4 cm
Colour:	Dark brown and white
Issued:	06/01 - 05/02
Series:	Society Symbol of Membership 2001-2002

U.K.:	£20.00
U.S.:	$40.00
Can.:	$40.00

**WATERLOO CHASE
(Greyhounds and hare)**

Model:	B1009
Modeller:	Hans Kendrick
Size:	5 ¾" x 17 ¼" 14.6 x 43.8 cm
Colour:	Tan, brown, white green and red
Issued:	2006 in a limited edition of 350

U.K.:	£250.00
U.S.:	$500.00
Can.:	$500.00

WEASEL AND WREN

Model:	None
Modeller:	Victor Hayton
Height:	12", 30.5 cm
Colour:	Brown, white and yellow
Issued:	01/77 in a limited edition of 125

U.K.:	£ 650.00
U.S.:	$1,300.00
Can.:	$1,300.00

**WEIGHING UP THE PROBLEM
(Bull)**

Model:	B1014
Modeller:	Ray Ayres
Size:	6 ¼" x 10" 15.9 x 25.4 cm
Colour:	Cream, brown, grey, blue and green
Issued:	06/06 in a limited edition of 500

U.K.:	£225.00
U.S.:	$450.00
Can.:	$450.00

**WEIMARANER, Standing
Style One**

Model:	B0732
Modeller:	Margaret Turner
Height:	6 ½", 16.5 cm
Colour:	Tan, brown, grey and green
Issued:	06/01 - 12/02
Series:	Dogs by Margaret Turner
U.K.:	£ 75.00
U.S.:	$150.00
Can.:	$150.00

**WEIMARANER, Standing
Style Two**

Model:	A3839
Modeller:	Margaret Turner
Height:	6 ¼", 15.9 cm
Colour:	Pale brown
Issued:	06/04 to the present
Series:	Dogs and Pups Galore
U.K.:	£23.00
U.S.:	$45.00
Can.:	$45.00

**WELL GROOMED
(Boy and Pony)**

Model:	A1241
Modeller:	Anne Wall
Height:	4 ¼", 10.8 cm
Colour:	Dark brown, green, white and beige
Issued:	01/02 - 12/04
Series:	Hay Days
U.K.:	£25.00
U.S.:	$50.00
Can.:	$50.00

**WELL WARMED
(Cat and two Calves)**

Model:	A1454
Modeller:	Hans Kendrick
Height:	7", 17.8 cm
Colour:	Black, grey, green and white
Issued:	06/02 - 12/04
Series:	The James Herriot Studio Collection
U.K.:	£40.00
U.S.:	$80.00
Can.:	$80.00

WELSH BLACK BULL

Model:	B0999
Modeller:	David Mayer
Size:	6 ¼" x 8" 15.9 x 20.3 cm
Colour:	Black and green
Issued:	2006 in a limited edition of 500
U.K.:	£150.00
U.S.:	$300.00
Can.:	$300.00

**WELSH BLACK COW AND
CALF**

Model:	B0998
Modeller:	David Mayer
Size:	6" x 9 ¼" 15.0 x 23.5 cm
Colour:	Black and green
Issued:	2006 in a limited edition of 500
U.K.:	£165.00
U.S.:	$325.00
Can.:	$325.00

**WELSH COB
Style One**

Model:	L11A, B
Modeller:	Anne Wall
Height:	7 ½", 19.1 cm
Colour:	A. Dark brown B. Bronze
Issued:	07/78 in a limited edition of 350

	Brown	Bronze
U.K.:	£ 600.	£150.
U.S.:	$1,200.	$300.
Can.:	$1.200.	$300.

**WELSH COB
Style Two**

Model:	NP6
Modeller:	Judy Boyt
Height:	6 ½", 16.5 cm
Colour:	Brown with black shading
Issued:	01/82 - 12/84
Series:	Native Ponies of Britain
U.K.:	£475.00
U.S.:	$950.00
Can.:	$950.00

WELSH COB
Style Three

Model:	129A, B, C
Modeller:	Anne Wall
Height:	3 ¼", 8.3 cm
Colour:	A. Dark bay
	B. Grey
	C. Palomino
Issued:	07/92 - 12/94
Series:	Agricultural and
	Sporting
U.K.:	£ 50.00
U.S.:	$100.00
Can.:	$100.00

WELSH COB
Style Four

Model:	B1035, 1035A
Modeller:	David Mayer
Height:	13" x 17 ¾"
	33.0 x 45.1 cm
Colour:	B1035 Bay
	B1035A Black
Issued:	06/07 in a limited
	edition of 150
U.K.:	£ 650.00
U.S.:	$1,300.00
Can.:	$1,300.00

WELSH COB MARE AND FOAL
Style One

Model:	A0728
Modeller:	Anne Wall
Height:	5 ¼", 13.3 cm
Colour:	Dark and light brown
Issued:	06/01 - 06/04
Series:	Horse Breeds
U.K.:	£ 50.00
U.S.:	$100.00
Can.:	$100.00

WELSH COB MARE AND FOAL
Style Two

Model:	B0906, 0906A
Modeller:	Anne Wall
Height:	8 ½" x 10 ½"
	21.6 x 26.7 cm
Colour:	B0906 Bay
	B0906A Black
Issued:	01/05 in a limited
	edition of 950
U.K.:	£250.00
U.S.:	$500.00
Can.:	$500.00

WELSH COB STALLION

Model:	B0240A, B
Modeller:	Anne Wall
Height:	9", 22.9 cm
Colour:	A. Black
	B. Bay
Issued:	01/98 in a limited
	edition of 1,250
Series:	Agricultural and
	Sporting
U.K.:	£250.00
U.S.:	$500.00
Can.:	$500.00

Note: Also available: portrait model
(skewbald, chestnut and
piebald known).

WELSH MOUNTAIN PONY
Style One

Model:	NP5
Modeller:	Judy Boyt
Height:	5 ½", 14.0 cm
Colour:	Grey
Issued:	01/82 - 12/84
Series:	Native Ponies of Britain
U.K.:	£225.00
U.S.:	$450.00
Can.:	$450.00

WELSH MOUNTAIN PONY
Style Two

Model:	127A, B, C
Modeller:	Anne Wall
Height:	3 ¾", 9.5 cm
Colour:	A. Bay
	B. Grey
	C. Palomino
Issued:	07/92 - 12/94
Series:	Agricultural and
	Sporting
U.K.:	£ 50.00
U.S.:	$100.00
Can.:	$100.00

WELSH MOUNTAIN PONY
Style Three

Model:	B0534A, B
Modeller:	Anne Wall
Height:	7 ½", 19.1 cm
Colour:	A. Grey B. Bay
Issued:	01/00 in a limited
	edition of 1,250
Series:	Agricultural and
	Sporting
U.K.:	£100.00
U.S.:	$200.00
Can.:	$200.00

Note: Several portrait models exist.

WELSH MOUNTAIN PONY STALLION

Model:	A1461, 2007
Modeller"	Anne Wall
Height:	6 ¼", 15.9 cm
Colour:	A1461 Grey
	A2007 Bay
Issued:	06/02 - 12/04
Series:	Horse Breeds
U.K.:	£35.00
U.S.:	$70.00
Can.:	$70.00

WELSH MOUNTAIN RAM

Model:	A1886
Modeller:	Lesley McKenzie
Height:	5 ¾", 14.6 cm
Colour:	White and very light brown
Issued:	06/02 - 12/04
Series:	Sheep Breeds
U.K.:	£35.00
U.S.:	$70.00
Can.:	$70.00

WEST HIGHLAND TERRIER, Lying

Model:	A3052
Modeller:	Margaret Turner
Height:	2 ½", 6.4 cm
Colour:	White
Issued:	06/03 to the present
Series:	Dogs and Pups Galore
U.K.:	£ 8.95
U.S.:	$18.00
Can.:	$18.00

WEST HIGHLAND TERRIER, Seated
Style One

Model:	DG01
Modeller:	Steve McKeown
Height:	4 ½", 11.9 cm
Colour:	White
Issued:	01/91 - 12/96
Series:	Dogs Galore
U.K.:	£15.00
U.S.:	$30.00
Can.:	$30.00

WEST HIGHLAND TERRIER, Seated
Style Two

Model:	MT10
Modeller:	Margaret Turner
Height:	6 ¼", 15.9 cm
Colour:	White
Issued:	01/96 - 06/01
Series:	Dogs by Margaret Turner
U.K.:	£35.00
U.S.:	$70.00
Can.:	$70.00

WEST HIGHLAND TERRIER, Seated
Style Three

Model:	A6549
Modeller:	Unknown
Height:	4 ¼", 10.8 cm
Colour:	White
Issued:	06/06 - 12-06
Series:	BFA Pottery Company
U.K.:	£12.00
U.S.:	$25.00
Can.:	$25.00

WEST HIGHLAND TERRIER, Standing

Model:	A7124
Modeller:	Unknown
Height:	2 ¾", 7.0 cm
Colour:	White
Issued:	06/07 to the present
Series:	Dogs and Pups Galore
U.K.:	£14.00
U.S.:	$28.00
Can.:	$28.00

WEST HIGHLAND TERRIER FAMILY GROUP

Model:	A5888
Modeller:	Margaret Turner
Height:	4 ¼", 10.8 cm
Colour:	White
Issued:	01/06 to the present
Series:	Dogs and Pups Galore
U.K.:	£20.00
U.S.:	$40.00
Can.:	$40.00

WEST HIGHLAND WHITE TERRIER, Begging

Model: B0497
Modeller: Margaret Turner
Height: 4", 10.1 cm
Colour: White
Issued: 06/99 - 12/01
Series: Dogs Galore

U.K.: £15.00
U.S.: $30.00
Can.: $30.00

WEST HIGHLAND WHITE TERRIER, Lying

Model: B0118/B0474
Modeller: Margaret Turner
Height: 2 ¾", 7.0 cm
Colour: B0118 White
B0474 Bronze
Issued: B0118 01/97-05/99
B0474 06/99-06/00
Series: 1. Dogs Galore
2. Bronzed

	White	Bronze
U.K.:	£15.	£12.
U.S.:	$30.	$25.
Can.:	$30.	$25.

WEST HIGHLAND WHITE TERRIER, Standing

Model: DS1
Modeller: Ray Ayres
Height: 3 ½", 8.9 cm
Colour: White
Issued: 01/83 - 12/94
Series: The World of Dogs

U.K.: £35.00
U.S.: $70.00
Can.: $70.00

WESTIE, Begging

Model: A2076
Modeller: Margaret Turner
Height: 3 ¾", 9.5 cm
Colour: White/pale yellow
Issued: 06/02 to the present
Series: Dogs and Pups Galore

U.K.: £ 9.95
U.S.: $20.00
Can.: $20.00

WESTIE, Seated

Model: A0646
Modeller: Lesley McKenzie
Height: 12 ¼", 31.1 cm
Colour: White
Issued: 01/01 to the present
Series: Fireside Dogs

U.K.: £ 75.00
U.S.: $150.00
Can.: $150.00

WESTIE, Standing Style One

Model: A1393
Modeller: Margaret Turner
Height: 3 ½", 8.9 cm
Colour: White
Issued: 01/02 to the present
Series: Dogs and Pups Galore

U.K.: £14.00
U.S.: $28.00
Can.: $28.00

WESTIE, Standing Style Two

Model: A2698
Modeller: Margaret Turner
Height: 12 ¾", 32.4 cm
Colour: White
Issued: 06/03 - 06/05
Series: Fireside Dogs

U.K.: £ 75.00
U.S.: $150.00
Can.: $150.00

WESTIE BITCH AND THREE PUPS
First Variation

Model: B0548
Modeller: Margaret Turner
Height: 3 ¼", 8.3 cm
Colour: White
Issued: 01/00 - 12/01
Series: Dogs Galore

U.K.: £25.00
U.S.: $50.00
Can.: $50.00

WESTIE BITCH WITH PUPS
Second Variation
Model:	A1387
Modeller:	Margaret Turner
Height:	3 ¼", 8.3 cm
Colour:	White
Issued:	01/02 - 12/04
Series:	Dogs and Pups Galore
U.K.:	£20.00
U.S.:	$40.00
Can.:	$40.00

WESTIE IN BAG
Model:	484067
Modeller:	Unknown
Height:	3 ¼", 8.3 cm
Colour:	White, blue and brown
Issued:	06/98 - 12/00
Series:	Puppy Tales
U.K.:	£12.00
U.S.:	$25.00
Can.:	$25.00

WESTIE PUP, Lying
Style One
Model:	PG01
Modeller:	Margaret Turner
Height:	2", 5.0 cm
Colour:	White
Issued:	01/92 - 08/95
Series:	Pups Galore
U.K.:	£15.00
U.S.:	$30.00
Can.:	$30.00

WESTIE PUP, Lying
Style Two
Model:	B0492
Modeller:	Margaret Turner
Height:	2 ¼", 5.7 cm
Colour:	White
Issued:	06/99 - 12/01
Series:	Pups Galore
U.K.:	£10.00
U.S.:	$20.00
Can.:	$20.00

WESTIE PUPPY, Seated
Model:	PG13/B0456	
Modeller:	Margaret Turner	
Height:	2 ¾", 7.0 cm	
Colour:	PG13	White
	B0456	Bronze
Issued:	PG13	01/95-05/99
	B0456	06/99-06/00
Series:	1. Pups Galore	
	2. Bronzed	

	White	Bronze
U.K.:	£12.	£10.
U.S.:	$25.	$20.
Can.:	$25.	$20.

WESTIE PUPS
(Three)
Model:	B0549
Modeller:	Margaret Turner
Height:	3", 7.6 cm
Colour:	White
Issued:	01/00 - 12/01
Series:	Pups Galore
U.K.:	£20.00
U.S.:	$40.00
Can.:	$40.00

WESTIES (Two Adults)
First Variation
Model:	B0547
Modeller:	Margaret Turner
Height:	3 ¼", 8.3 cm
Colour:	White
Issued:	01/00 - 12/01
Series:	Dogs Galore
U.K.:	£20.00
U.S.:	$40.00
Can.:	$40.00

WESTIES (Two Adults)
Second Variation
Model:	A1386
Modeller:	Margaret Turner
Height:	3 ¼", 8.3 cm
Colour:	White
Issued:	01/02 to the present
Series:	Dogs and Pups Galore
U.K.:	£17.00
U.S.:	$35.00
Can.:	$35.00

WESTIES PAIR

Model:	DS13
Modeller:	Ray Ayres
Height:	4 ¼", 10.8 cm
Colour:	White
Issued:	01/89 - 12/94
Series:	The World of Dogs
U.K.:	£40.00
U.S.:	$80.00
Can.:	$80.00

"WHAT AM I BID?.."

Model:	B0865, 0902, 0903, 0904		
Modeller:	Ray Ayres		
Height:	6 ¼ x 12 ¾",15.9 x 32.4 cm		
Colour:	B0865	Swaledale	01/04 Ltd. ed. 350
	B0902	Texel	06/04 Ltd. ed. 350
	B0903	Blackface	01/05 Ltd. ed. 350
	B0904	Suffolk	06/05 Ltd. ed. 350
Issued:	See above		
Series:	Classic Collection		
U.K.:	£275.00		
U.S.:	$550.00		
Can.:	$550.00		

Note: The figures and colouring of the clothes vary between models.

WHAT NOW?
(Swalesdale Sheep and Collie)

Model:	L120
Modeller:	Ray Ayres
Height:	4", 10.1 cm
Colour:	Black, white and beige
Issued:	09/92 in a limited edition of 1,250
U.K.:	£225.00
U.S.:	$450.00
Can.:	$450.00

WHEEL TO WHEEL

Model:	B0957
Modeller:	Paul Back
Height:	6" x 12"
	15.0 x 30.5 cm
Colour:	Blue, white, grey, black, yellow and gold
Issued:	01/06 in a limited edition of 500
U.K.:	£195.00
U.S.:	$400.00
Can.:	$400.00

WHERE THERE'S MUCK THERE'S MONEY

Model:	B0857
Modeller:	Ray Ayres
Height:	7 ¼", 18.5 cm
Colour:	Red, black, brown, tan, grey and white
Issued:	01/04 in a limited edition of 1,500
Series:	Classic Collection
U.K.:	£425.00
U.S.:	$850.00
Can.:	$850.00

Note: MF135 authorised by AGCO Corporation.

WHERE'S HE GONE?
(Border collies)

Model:	B1078
Modeller:	Anne Wall
Height:	7" x 9 ½"
	17.8 x 24.0 cm
Colour:	Dark green, grey, black, white, brown
Issued:	06/07 in a limited edition of 750
U.K.:	£190.00
U.S.:	$400.00
Can.:	$400.00

WHIPPET, Seated
Style One

Model:	B0120/B0476	
Modeller:	Margaret Turner	
Height:	4 ½", 11.9 cm	
Colour:	B0120	Tan and white
	B0476	Bronze
Issued:	B0120	01/97-12/01
	B0476	06/99-06/00
Series:	1. Dogs Galore	
	2. Bronzed	

	Tan/white	Bronze
U.K.:	£20.	£15.
U.S.:	$40.	$30.
Can.:	$40.	$30.

WHIPPET, Seated
Style Two

Model:	A2086, 2639	
Modeller:	Margaret Turner	
Height:	4 ½", 11.9 cm	
Colour:	A2086	Brindle
	A2639	Light sandy
Issued:	A2086	01/03 to the present
	A2639	01/03-06/06
Series:	Dogs and Pups Galore	
U.K.:	£15.00	
U.S.:	$30.00	
Can.:	$30.00	

WHIPPET, Standing
Style One

Model:	080
Modeller:	Elizabeth Waugh
Height:	6", 15.0 cm
Colour:	White and light brown
Issued:	01/87 - 12/92
Series:	1. The World of Dogs
	2. Special Interest
U.K.:	£250.00
U.S.:	$500.00
Can.:	$500.00

Note: Can also be found in different colourways.

WHIPPET, Standing
Style Two

Model:	A1399
Modeller:	Margaret Turner
Height:	3 ¾", 9.5 cm
Colour:	Light sandy and white
Issued:	01/02 to the present
Series:	Dogs and Pups Galore
U.K.:	£15.00
U.S.:	$30.00
Can.:	$30.00

WHO'S MILK IS IT?
(Calves and kitten)

Model:	JH83A, B
Modeller:	David Walton
Height:	2 ¾", 7.0 cm
Colour:	A. Brown and white
	B. Black and white
Issued:	07/93 - 12/96
Series:	1. Every Living Thing
	2. The James Herriot Collection
U.K.:	£ 50.00
U.S.:	$100.00
Can.:	$100.00

WHOOPER SWAN

Model:	PS07
Modeller:	Richard Roberts
Height:	10 ¾", 27.8 cm
Colour:	White, yellow and black
Issued:	06/91 - 12/93
Series:	Peter Scott Memorial Appeal (WWF)
U.K.:	£125.00
U.S.:	$250.00
Can.:	$250.00

WIGEON

Model:	A0479
Modeller:	Don Briddell
Height:	8 ¼", 21.0 cm
Colour:	Grey, brown, yellow and stone
Issued:	01/01 - 12/02
Series:	Waterfowl of the World by Don Briddell
U.K.:	£ 75.00
U.S.:	$150.00
Can.:	$150.00

WILLING TO SHARE
(Border collies and ginger striped cat)

Model:	A6130
Modeller:	Hanas Kendrick
Height:	6 ½", 16.5 cm
Colour:	Black, white, ginger, green and grey
Issued:	01/06 to the present
Series:	Border Collie Collection

U.K.:	£ 60.00
U.S.:	$120.00
Can.:	$120.00

WILLOW TITS

Model:	L24
Modeller:	Anne Wall
Height:	7", 17.8 cm
Colour:	Browns, white and pink
Issued:	01/80 in a limited edition of 850

U.K.:	£150.00
U.S.:	$300.00
Can.:	$300.00

WINNING SMILE
(Boy and Suffolk ram)

Model:	B0341
Modeller:	Anne Wall
Height:	6 ½", 16.5 cm
Colour:	Cream, black, white and blue
Issued:	01/99 - 12/00
Series:	The James Herriot Collection

U.K.:	£ 75.00
U.S.:	$150.00
Can.:	$150.00

WINTER AT SEA
(Male/Female Elder Ducks, Two Long-Tailed Ducks, Storm Petrel and Iving Goldeneye Duck)

Model:	BS1
Modeller:	Richard Roberts
Height:	4 ½", 11.9 cm
Colour:	Black, brown, white and grey
Issued:	01/87 - 12/88
Series:	Birds of the Seashore

U.K.:	£125.00
U.S.:	$250.00
Can.:	$250.00

WINTER FEEDING

Model:	JH10
Modeller:	Judy Boyt
Height:	5", 12.7 cm
Colour:	Dark brown, cream and black
Issued:	01/85 in a limited edition of 1,250
Series:	All Creatures Great and Small

U.K.:	£ 600.00
U.S.:	$1,200.00
Can.:	$1,200.00

WINTER FRIEND
(Robin)

Model:	B0148
Modeller:	Ray Ayres
Height:	6", 15.0 cm
Colour:	Brown, orange, white, green and red
Issued:	01/97 - 12/98
Series:	Event Special

U.K.:	£ 50.00
U.S.:	$100.00
Can.:	$100.00

WINTER RATIONS
First Version
(Three Quarter Limousin Cross Steers)

Model:	B0581
Modeller:	Kirsty Armstrong
Height:	4 ¾", 12.1 cm
Colour:	Black, brown, green and yellow
Issued:	06/00 - 12/04
Series:	James Herriot Classic Collection

U.K.:	£200.00
U.S.:	$400.00
Can.:	$400.00

WINTER RATIONS
Second Version
(Belgian Blue Cross, Charolais Cross and Simmental Cross)

Model:	B0803A, B, C
Modeller:	Kirsty Armstrong
Height:	A. 4 ¾", 12.1 cm
	B. 5 ¼", 13.3 cm
	C. 5 ¼", 13.3 cm
Colour:	A. Belgian Blue Cross: Blue-grey
	B. Charolais Cross: Cream
	C. Simmental Cross: Golden brown
Issued:	01/03 - 12/04
Series:	Classic Collection
U.K.:	£200.00
U.S.:	$400.00
Can.:	$400.00

WINTER RESCUE
(Shepherd carrying ewe)

Model:	JH41
Modeller:	Anne Butler
Height:	8", 20.3 cm
Colour:	Cream, black, white, brown and green
Issued:	01/90 - 12/94
Series:	All Creatures Great and Small
U.K.:	£175.00
U.S.:	$350.00
Can.:	$350.00

WINTER SHELTER
(Three sheep)

Model:	B0203
Modeller:	Ray Ayres
Height:	4 ¾", 12.1 cm
Colour:	Cream, black, white, and grey
Issued:	01/98 in a limited edition of 1,500
Series:	1. Every Living Thing
	2. The James Herriot Collection
U.K.:	£ 80.00
U.S.:	$160.00
Can.:	$160.00

WINTER WATCH
(Canada goose)

Model:	L131
Modeller:	Frank DiVita
Height:	11 ½", 29.2 cm
Colour:	Black, brown and grey
Issued:	01/93 in a limited edition of 750
Series:	Masterpiece
U.K.:	£300.00
U.S.:	$600.00
Can.:	$600.00

WIRE-HAIRED FOX TERRIER

Model:	DS11
Modeller:	Elizabeth MacAllister
Height:	4", 10.1 cm
Colour:	White, black and tan
Issued:	01/87 - 12/92
Series:	1. The World of Dogs
	2. Special Interest
U.K.:	£ 80.00
U.S.:	$160.00
Can.:	$160.00

WOLF AND CUB

Model:	WW26
Modeller:	David Walton
Height:	2 ¾", 7.0 cm
Colour:	Grey, white and black
Issued:	01/95 - 12/96
Series:	Miniature (WWF)
U.K.:	£20.00
U.S.:	$40.00
Can.:	$40.00

WON'T START
(Tractor, farmer and collie)

Model:	B0299
Modeller:	Ray Ayres
Height:	4 ¾", 12.1 cm
Colour:	Blue, green, black, white and blue
Issued:	01/99 - 12/00
Series:	Every Living Thing
U.K.:	£250.00
U.S.:	$500.00
Can.:	$500.00

WOODCOCK

Model:	085
Modeller:	James Harvey
Height:	6 ¼", 15.9 cm
Colour:	Beige, brown, black and white
Issued:	01/86 - 12/88
U.K.:	£100.00
U.S.:	$200.00
Can.:	$200.00

WOODLAND FEAST
(Wood mice)

Model:	B0192
Modeller:	Anne Wall
Height:	5 ½", 14.0 cm
Colour:	Brown, yellow and green
Issued:	06/97 - 12/98
Series:	The Country Mouse
U.K.:	£ 65.00
U.S.:	$125.00
Can.:	$125.00

WOODLAND MAJESTY
(Cock pheasant)

Model:	BFA96
Modeller:	David Walton
Height:	10 ½", 26.7 cm
Colour:	Browns, red and green
Issued:	01/96 - 12/96
Series:	Annual Figurine (1996)
U.K.:	£250.00
U.S.:	$500.00
Can.:	$500.00

WOODLAND RAMBLE
(Badger)

Model:	B0979
Modeller:	Ray Ayres
Height:	2 ½", 6.4 cm
Colour:	Grey, black, white, fawn, green and blue
Issued:	06/05 - 05/06
Series:	Symbol of Membership
U.K.:	£20.00
U.S.:	$40.00
Can.:	$40.00

WORKING SPANIEL

Model:	B0244A, B
Modeller:	Margaret Turner
Height:	6 ¼", 15.9 cm
Colour:	A. Liver and white
	B. Black and white
Issued:	01/98 - 12/99
Series:	Dogs by Margaret Turner
U.K.:	£ 80.00
U.S.:	$160.00
Can.:	$160.00

WREN
Style One

Model:	M15
Modeller:	David Fryer
Height:	2", 5.0 cm
Colour:	Brown with dark brown highlights; bronze base
Issued:	07/83 - 12/87
Series:	Miniatures on Bronze
U.K.:	£ 65.00
U.S.:	$125.00
Can.:	$125.00

WREN
Style Two

Model:	RB5
Modeller:	Ray Ayres
Height:	4", 10.1 cm
Colour:	Brown, green and white
Issued:	07/83 - 12/92
Series:	1. RSPB Birds
	2. British Birds
U.K.:	£40.00
U.S.:	$80.00
Can.:	$80.00

WREN
Style Three

Model:	B0023
Modeller:	Russell Willis
Height:	5", 12.7 cm
Colour:	Browns and cream
Issued:	06/96 - 12/97
Series:	Birds by Russell Willis
U.K.:	£40.00
U.S.:	$80.00
Can.:	$80.00

WREN
Style Four

Model:	484288
Modeller:	Russell Willis
Height:	2 ¾", 7.0 cm
Colour:	Brown, fawn, green, yellow and black
Issued:	06/98 - 12/06
Series:	Birds by Russell Willis

U.K.:	£10.00
U.S.:	$20.00
Can.:	$20.00

WREN
Style Five

Model:	A0406
Modeller:	Russell Willis
Height:	3 ¾", 9.5 cm
Colour:	Brown, cream, green and red
Issued:	01/01 - 12/05
Series:	Birds by Russell Willis

U.K.:	£12.00
U.S.:	$25.00
Can.:	$25.00

WREN
Style Six

Model:	A1472
Modeller:	Russell Willis
Height:	4 ¼", 10.8 cm
Colour:	Light brown , white, pink and green
Issued:	06/02 - 12/03
Series:	Birds by Russell Willis

U.K.:	£20.00
U.S.:	$40.00
Can.:	$40.00

WREN
Style Seven

Model:	A2320
Modeller:	Russell Willis
Height:	3 ¼", 8.3 cm
Size:	Small
Colour:	Light brown Wren; yellow flowers; green leaves
Issued:	01/03 - 06/06
Series:	Garden Guests

U.K.:	£15.00
U.S.:	$30.00
Can.:	$30.00

WREN
Style Eight

Model:	A4608
Modeller:	Russell Willis
Height:	4 ½", 11.4 cm
Colour:	Brown, fawn, cream and green
Issued:	01/04 - 12/06
Series:	BFA Pottery Company

U.K.:	£15.00
U.S.:	$30.00
Can.:	$30.00

WREN
Style Nine

Model:	A6053
Modeller:	Unknown
Height:	4 ¾", 12.1 cm
Colour:	Brown, cream and green
Issued:	06/05 to the present

U.K.:	£ 9.95
U.S.:	$20.00
Can.:	$20.00

WREN AND APPLE BLOSSOM

Model:	A0908
Modeller:	Unknown
Height:	5 ¼", 13.3 cm
Colour:	Light brown, white, pink and green
Issued:	06/02 - 12/03
Series:	Garden Guests

U.K.:	£25.00
U.S.:	$50.00
Can.:	$50.00

WREN AND BRAMBLES
Style One

Model:	RB50
Modeller:	Ray Ayres
Height:	5", 12.7 cm
Colour:	Browns, greens and deep purples
Issued:	01/96 - 12/97

U.K.:	£ 50.00
U.S.:	$100.00
Can.:	$100.00

WREN AND BRAMBLES
Style Two
Model: 484369
Modeller: Russell Willis
Height: 4 ¼", 10.8 cm
Colour: Brown, fawn and green
Issued: 06/98 - 12/01
Series: Birds And ...

U.K.:   £20.00
U.S.: $40.00
Can.: $40.00

WREN AND CHICKS
Style One
Model: UK# 035
             USA# 225-004
Modeller: Anne Wall
Height: 4", 10.1 cm
Colour: Browns and yellow
Issued: 07/78 - 06/83

U.K.:   £ 75.00
U.S.: $150.00
Can.: $150.00

WREN AND CHICKS
Style Two
Model: 541702
Modeller: Russell Willis
Height: 4 ½", 11.9 cm
Colour: Brown, cream, green
             and blue
Issued: 01/99 - 06/00
Series: Families

U.K.:   £30.00
U.S.: $60.00
Can.: $60.00

WREN AND CHICKS
Style Three
Model: B0346
Modeller: John Brown
Height: 7 ¼", 18.4 cm
Colour: Browns, green and
             white
Issued: 01/99 in a limited
             edition of 1,250
Series: Border Classic Birds

U.K.:   £100.00
U.S.: $200.00
Can.: $200.00

WREN AND CHICKS (Two)
Model: WB81
Modeller: Russell Willis
Height: 4 ½", 11.9 cm
Colour: Browns
Issued: 01/93 - 12/94
Series: Birds by Russell Willis

U.K.:   £ 50.00
U.S.: $100.00
Can.: $100.00

WREN AND DAISIES
Model: WB33
Modeller: Russell Willis
Height: 4 ½", 11.9 cm
Colour: Dark and light brown,
             purple, yellow and
             green
Issued: 01/93 - 12/94
Series: 1. Birds In Your Garden
             2. Birds by Russell
                Willis

U.K.:   £40.00
U.S.: $80.00
Can.: $80.00

WREN AND DIAMOND RING
Model: 484393
Modeller: Russell Willis
Height: 4 ¼", 10.8 cm
Colour: Brown, cream, grey
             and green
Issued: 06/98 - 05/00
Series: Finders Keepers

U.K.:   £25.00
U.S.: $50.00
Can.: $50.00

WREN AND FARTHING
Model: A0652
Modeller: Russell Willis
Height: 4", 10.1 cm
Colour: Brown, cream, tan,
             green and stone
Issued: 01/01 - 12/01
Series: 1. Birds And ...
             2. Birds by Russell
                Willis

U.K.:   £20.00
U.S.: $40.00
Can.: $40.00

WREN AND NEST WITH BINDWEED

Model:	RB51
Modeller:	Ray Ayres
Height:	4 ½", 11.9 cm
Colour:	Browns, greens and lemon
Issued:	01/96 - 12/97
U.K.:	£ 55.00
U.S.:	$110.00
Can.:	$110.00

WREN AND SILVER THIMBLE

Model:	A0654
Modeller:	Russell Willis
Height:	4 ¼", 10.8 cm
Colour:	Brown, cream, green and silver
Issued:	01/01 - 12/01
Series:	1. Birds And ...
	2. Birds by Russell Willis
U.K.:	£25.00
U.S.:	$50.00
Can.:	$50.00

WREN AND WILD ROSE

Model:	RB49
Modeller:	Ray Ayres
Height:	4 ½", 11.9 cm
Colour:	Browns, pink and red
Issued:	01/96 - 12/98
U.K.:	£40.00
U.S.:	$80.00
Can.:	$80.00

WREN FAMILY

Model:	B0899
Modeller:	David Mayer
Height:	13 ¼", 33.6 cm
Colour:	Brown, beige, pink and green
Issued:	01/04 in a limited edition of 500
Series:	Classic Collection
U.K.:	£200.00
U.S.:	$400.00
Can.:	$400.00

WREN FLYING

Model:	WB13
Modeller:	Russell Willis
Height:	5 ¼", 13.3 cm
Colour:	Dark and light brown, white and red
Issued:	07/92 - 12/93
Series:	Birds by Russell Willis
U.K.:	£ 50.00
U.S.:	$100.00
Can.:	$100.00

WREN ON GATE HASP

Model:	541605
Modeller:	Russell Willis
Height:	3 ½", 8.9 cm
Colour:	Brown, cream, pink, green and grey
Issued:	06/99 - 12/00
Series:	1. Birds And ...
	2. Birds by Russell Willis
U.K.:	£20.00
U.S.:	$40.00
Can.:	$40.00

WREN ON IVY

Model:	F4
Modeller:	David Burnham Smith
Height:	3 ½", 8.9 cm
Colour:	Brown, white, black and green
Issued:	01/89 - 12/91
Series:	Finesse Birds
U.K.:	£ 65.00
U.S.:	$125.00
Can.:	$125.00

WREN ON KEYS

Model:	WB151
Modeller:	Russell Willis
Height:	5", 12.7 cm
Colour:	Browns, silver and grey
Issued:	01/95 - 12/97
Series:	1. Birds In Your Garden
	2. Birds by Russell Willis
U.K.:	£40.00
U.S.:	$80.00
Can.:	$80.00

WREN ON PEAS

Model: WB36
Modeller: Russell Willis
Height: 5 ½", 14.0 cm
Colour: Brown, cream, lilac
and green
Issued: 01/94 - 12/95
Series: 1. Birds In Your Garden
2. Birds by Russell
Willis

U.K.: £40.00
U.S.: $80.00
Can.: $80.00

WREN ON PEBBLE

Model: WB162
Modeller: Russell Willis
Height: 3 ½", 8.9 cm
Colour: Light and dark brown
and grey
Issued: 01/95 - 12/97
Series: 1. Pebble Birds
2. Birds by Russell
Willis

U.K.: £25.00
U.S.: $50.00
Can.: $50.00

WREN ON PORCELAIN BOTTLE

Model: WB52
Modeller: Russell Willis
Height: 3 ½", 8.9 cm
Colour: Browns and cream
Issued: 01/94 - 12/95
Series: 1. Birds In Your Garden
2. Birds by Russell
Willis

U.K.: £30.00
U.S.: $60.00
Can.: $60.00

WREN ON POST

Model: RB9
Modeller: Ray Ayres
Height: 6", 15.0 cm
Colour: Brown and cream
Issued: 01/90 - 12/92
Series: British Birds

U.K.: £ 50.00
U.S.: $100.00
Can.: $100.00

**WREN WITH CHAIN AND
LOCKET**

Model: B0124
Modeller: Russell Willis
Height: 5 ¼", 13.3 cm
Colour: Browns, cream
and silver
Issued: 01/97 - 12/97
Series: Finders Keepers

U.K.: £ 50.00
U.S.: $100.00
Can.: $100.00

WREN WITH NEST EGGS

Model: 541656
Modeller: Russell Willis
Height: 3", 7.6 cm
Colour: Brown, cream, purple,
yellow and green
Issued: 01/99 - 12/04
Series: 1. Feathered Friends
2. Birds by Russell
Willis

U.K.: £12.00
U.S.: $25.00
Can.: $25.00

WRENS AND ROSES

Model: A2485
Modeller: Russell Willis
Height: 8 ¾", 22.2 cm
Colour: Brown, white
and green
Issued: 01/04 - 06/06
Series: Birds by Russell Willis

U.K.: £ 60.00
U.S.: $120.00
Can.: $120.00

WRENS AND TULIPS, (A Pair)

Model: A1022
Modeller: David Mayer
Height: 9 ¼", 23.5 cm
Colour: Light brown, yellow
and green
Issued: 06/02 - 12/03
Series: Garden Guests

U.K.: £25.00
U.S.: $50.00
Can.: $50.00

WRONG SIDE OF THE FENCE
(Ewe and lambs)

Model:	JH100
Modeller:	Anne Wall
Height:	5", 12.7 cm
Colour:	Cream, black, brown and green
Issued:	01/95 in a limited edition of 1,500
Series:	All Creatures Great and Small
U.K.:	£150.00
U.S.:	$300.00
Can.:	$300.00

YELLOW WAGTAIL

Model:	A7115
Modeller:	Unknown
Height:	4 ½", 11.4 cm
Colour:	Yellow, green, grey and black
Issued:	06/06 to the present
U.K.:	£ 9.95
U.S.:	$20.00
Can.:	$20.00

YELLOW-NECKED
WOODMOUSE

Model:	None
Modeller:	Victor Hayton
Height:	5 ½", 14.0 cm
Colour:	Browns and cream
Issued:	01/77 in a limited edition of 500
U.K.:	£300.00
U.S.:	$600.00
Can.:	$600.00

YORKIE IN SHOPPING BAG

Model:	484148
Modeller:	Unknown
Height:	3 ¼", 8.3 cm
Colour:	Cream and black
Issued:	06/98 - 12/00
Series:	Puppy Tales
U.K.:	£12.00
U.S.:	$25.00
Can.:	$25.00

YORKSHIRE TERRIER (Lying)
Style One

Model:	DS6
Modeller:	Ray Ayres
Height:	2 ½", 6.4 cm
Colour:	Black and golden brown
Issued:	07/83 - 12/94
Series:	The World of Dogs
U.K.:	£40.00
U.S.:	$80.00
Can.:	$80.00

YORKSHIRE TERRIER (Lying)
Style Two, First Variation

Model:	B0604
Modeller:	Margaret Turner
Height:	2 ½", 6.4 cm
Colour:	Black, tan and red
Issued:	06/00 -12/01
Series:	Dogs Galore
U.K.:	£12.00
U.S.:	$25.00
Can.:	$25.00

YORKSHIRE TERRIER (Lying)
Style Two, Second Variation

Model:	A3043
Modeller:	Margaret Turner
Height:	2 ½", 6.4 cm
Colour:	Black and brown
Issued:	06/03 to the present
Series:	Dogs and Pups Galore
U.K.:	£ 9.95
U.S.:	$20.00
Can.:	$20.00

YORKSHIRE TERRIER, Seated

Model:	DG17
Modeller:	Margaret Turner
Height:	3 ¼", 8.3 cm
Colour:	Black and tan
Issued:	01/92 - 12/98
Series:	Dogs Galore
U.K.:	£25.00
U.S.:	$50.00
Can.:	$50.00

YORKSHIRE TERRIER (Show)

Model:	DS2
Modeller:	Ray Ayres
Height:	3 ½", 8.9 cm
Colour:	Golden and dark brown
Issued:	01/83 - 12/84
Series:	The World of Dogs
U.K.:	£100.00
U.S.:	$200.00
Can.:	$200.00

YORKSHIRE TERRIER, Standing

Model:	A3847
Modeller:	Adrian Hughes
Height:	10 ¾", 27.8 cm
Colour:	Black and tan
Issued:	06/04 - 06/06
Series:	Fireside Dogs
U.K.:	£ 50.00
U.S.:	$100.00
Can.:	$100.00

YORKSHIRE TERRIER PUP, Seated

Model:	PG07
Modeller:	Margaret Turner
Height:	2 ½", 6.4 cm
Colour:	Black and tan
Issued:	01/94 - 12/01
Series:	Pups Galore
U.K.:	£15.00
U.S.:	$30.00
Can.:	$30.00

YOU CAN LEAD A HORSE TO WATER (Heavy horses)

Model:	BFA202
Modeller:	Anne Wall
Height:	6 ½", 16.5 cm
Colour:	Grey, bay, green, brown, yellow and blue
Issued:	01/94 in a limited edition of 1,500
Series:	1. Every Living Thing
	2. Heavy Horse
	3. 20th Anniversary
U.K.:	£350.00
U.S.:	$700.00
Can.:	$700.00

YOUNG FRIENDS (Boy with two Border Collie Pups)

Model:	A1452
Modeller:	Adrian Hughes
Height:	5 ¼", 13.3 cm
Colour:	Black and white pups; red, blue, grey and light brown
Issued:	06/02 - 12/04
Series:	Young Farmers
U.K.:	£35.00
U.S.:	$70.00
Can.:	$70.00

YOUNG GIRAFFE

Model:	RW27
Modeller:	Richard Wawrzesta
Height:	8 ½", 21.6 cm
Colour:	Brown and cream
Issued:	01/94 - 12/95
Series:	Endangered Species (WWF)
U.K.:	£ 50.00
U.S.:	$100.00
Can.:	$100.00

YOURS OR MINE? (Hen and duck)

Model:	JH68
Modeller:	Anne Wall
Height:	2 ¾", 7.0 cm
Colour:	White, reddish-brown and yellow
Issued:	01/92 - 12/95
Series:	All Creatures Great and Small
U.K.:	£40.00
U.S.:	$80.00
Can.:	$80.00

CHAPTER TWO

AMERICAN COLLECTION

A SHOE TO FILL
(Foal lying next to horseshoe)
Model: 225-229/095
Modeller: Lowell Davis
Height: 2 ¼"5.7 cm
Colour: 1. Grey
            2. Palomino
Issued: 07/81 - 1986 (USA)
            1981 - 1982 (UK)
Series: American Farm

U.K.:   £30.00
U.S.: $60.00
Can.: $60.00

A WOLF IN SHEEP'S
CLOTHING
Model: 225-518
Modeller: Lowell Davis
Height: Unknown
Colour: Brown, white, tan,
            black and green
Issued: 01/92 Unknown (USA)
            12/92 Unknown (UK)
Series: World of Little Critters

U.K.:   £ 50.00
U.S.: $100.00
Can.: $100.00

AND DOWN THE HATCH
(Cat and goldfish bowl)
Model: 94105
Modeller: Lowell Davis
Height: 3 ½", 8.9 cm
Colour: Grey, white, brown,
            pink, green and purple
Issued: 1994 - 1994
Series: American Farm

U.K.:   £45.00
U.S.: $90.00
Can.: $90.00

ANGLERS
(Brown bears by the river)
Model: 210-406
Modeller: Boyd Perry
Height: 1 ¾", 4.4 cm
Colour: Dark brown, light
            brown, green and
            blue-grey
Issued: c.1986 - Unknown
Series: Wind River Collection

U.K.:   £35.00
U.S.: $70.00
Can.: $70.00

ANNIE
Model: 210-524
Modeller: Boyd Perry
Height: 2 ¾", 7.0 cm
Colour: Tan, blue, brown,
            red and black
Issued: c.1986 - Unknown
Series: Little Heavyweights

U.K.:   £20.00
U.S.: $40.00
Can.: $40.00

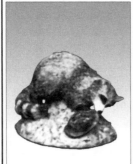

ANYBODY HOME?
(Racoon and tortoise)
Model: 225-239
Modeller: Lowell Davis
Height: 2", 5.0 cm
Colour: Black, grey, white
            and green
Issued: 1984 - 1987
Series: Farm Collection

U.K.:   £30.00
U.S.: $60.00
Can.: $60.00

ARNIE
Model: 210-523
Modeller: Boyd Perry
Height: 2 ¾", 7.0 cm
Colour: Light blue, brown, red,
            white, beige and green
Issued: c.1986 - Unknown
Series: Little Heavyweights

U.K.:   £20.00
U.S.: $40.00
Can.: $40.00

ATTIC ANTICS
(Pair of Siamese cats and
chest)
Model: 96905
Modeller: Lowell Davis
Height: 4", 10.1 cm
Colour: Black, light brown,
            white, blue and grey
Issued: 1994 - 1995
Series: Farm Collection

U.K.:   £ 50.00
U.S.: $100.00
Can.: $100.00

BAA BAA/LITTLE BLACK LAMB
(Chick on lamb's back)

Model:	225-297/LD5
Modeller:	Lowell Davis
Height:	2 ½", 6.4 cm
Colour:	Black, yellow and green
Issued:	1990 - 1995
Series:	Farm Collection
U.K.:	£20.00
U.S.:	$40.00
Can.:	$40.00

BABY BLOSSOM
(Jersey cow lying with cow bell)

Model:	225-227/097
Modeller:	Lowell Davis
Height:	2 ¼", 5.7 cm
Colour:	Reddish-brown, grey, black, white and green
Issued:	1981 - 1984 (USA) 07/82 - 12/82 (UK)
Series:	American Farm
U.K.:	£30.00
U.S.:	$60.00
Can.:	$60.00

BABY BOBS
(Quail chicks)

Model:	225-222
Modeller:	Lowell Davis
Height:	2 ½", 6.4 cm
Colour:	Light brown, yellow, dark grey and green
Issued:	1982 - 1984
Series:	Farm Collection
U.K.:	£45.00
U.S.:	$90.00
Can.:	$90.00

BARN, THE

Model:	225-352
Modeller:	Lowell Davis
Height:	3", 7.6 cm
Colour:	Tan, red, grey, green and browns
Issued:	1985 - 1987
Series:	FoxFire Farm Buildings
U.K.:	£ 65.00
U.S.:	$130.00
Can.:	$130.00

BARN CATS
(Cats with milk pail)

Model:	225-257/LD35
Modeller:	Lowell Davis
Height:	2 ¾", 7.0 cm
Colour:	Black, white, grey and fawn
Issued:	1985 - 1992 (USA) 01/91 - Unknown (UK)
Series:	Farm Collection
U.K.:	£35.00
U.S.:	$70.00
Can.:	$70.00

BARN OWL

Model:	200-149
Modeller:	Frank Falco
Height:	7", 17.8 cm
Colour:	Dark yellow, white, black, grey and beige
Issued:	c.1986 in a limited edition of 950
Series:	Birds by Frank Falco
U.K.:	£200.00
U.S.:	$400.00
Can.:	$400.00

BE MY VALENTINE
(Cats and heart-shaped cake)

Model:	27561
Modeller:	Lowell Davis
Height:	2 ½", 6.4 cm
Colour:	White, orange, pink and grey
Issued:	1993 - 1995
Series:	1. Cats in Season 2. Farm Collection
U.K.:	£20.00
U.S.:	$40.00
Can.:	$40.00

BIG HORN SHEEP

Model:	200-404
Modeller:	Daniel Parker
Height:	7 ½", 19.1 cm
Colour:	Browns, white, grey and cream
Issued:	c.1986 in a limited edition of 1,450
Series:	North American Animals by Daniel Parker
U.K.:	£125.00
U.S.:	$250.00
Can.:	$250.00

**BIT OFF MORE THAN HE
COULD CHEW
(Cat with head in tin)**

Model: 225-279/LD2
Modeller: Lowell Davis
Height: 2", 5.0 cm
Colour: Ginger cat
Issued: 1986 - c.1995
Series: Farm Collection

U.K.: £20.00
U.S.: $40.00
Can.: $40.00

**BLACKIE
(Bear)**

Model: 210-551
Modeller: Boyd Perry
Height: 1 ¾", 4.4 cm
Colour: Black, tan, brown
and green
Issued: Unknown
Series: Little Rascals

U.K.: £20.00
U.S.: $40.00
Can.: $40.00

**BLOSSOM
(Cow)**

Model: 1. 225-032
2. 96844
Modeller: Lowell Davis
Height: 1. 6", 15.0 cm
2. 3 ¾", 9.5 cm
Colour: Reddish-brown
Issued: 1. 1979 - 1983
2. 1993 - 1994
Series: 1. Farm Collection
2. 15th Anniv. of issue

	225-302	96844
U.K.:	£125.	£45.
U.S.:	$250.	$90.
Can.:	$250.	$90.

BLOSSOM AND CALF

Model: 225-326
Modeller: Lowell Davis
Height: 5", 12.7 cm
Colour: Light brown, black,
yellow and grey
Issued: 1982 in a limited
edition of 1,000
Series: Farm Collection

U.K.: £175.00
U.S.: $350.00
Can.: $350.00

**BLOSSOM'S BEST
(Blossom the cow being
milked)**

Model: Unknown
Modeller: Lowell Davis
Height: 5 ¾", 14.6 cm
Colour: Light brown, black,
blue, white, orange
and yellow
Issued: 1995 in a limited
edition of 750
Series: Farm Collection

U.K.: £175.00
U.S.: $350.00
Can.: $350.00

**BOTTOMS UP
(Cats in dustbin)**

Model: 225-270/LD27
Modeller: Lowell Davis
Height: 4 ¾", 12.1 cm
Colour: Grey, black, white,
ginger, green, blue
and pink
Issued: 1987 - 1993
Series: Farm Collection

U.K.: £35.00
U.S.: $70.00
Can.: $70.00

**BOY'S NIGHT OUT
(Running dogs)**

Model: 225-339
Modeller: Lowell Davis
Height: 3 ¾", 9.5 cm
Colour: Brown, black, white,
tan and green
Issued: 1989 in a limited
edition of 1,500
Series: Farm Collection

U.K.: £ 70.00
U.S.: $140.00
Can.: $140.00

**BRAND NEW DAY
(Chick)**

Model: 225-226
Modeller: Lowell Davis
Height: 1", 2.5 cm
Colour: Golden yellow, black
and white
Issued: 1982 - 1984
Series: Farm Collection

U.K.: £20.00
U.S.: $40.00
Can.: $40.00

BRER BEAR

Model: 225-251
Modeller: Lowell Davis
Height: 6", 15.0 cm
Colour: Brown, blue, red, yellow and black
Issued: 1981 - 1984
Series: Uncle Remus

U.K.: £ 85.00
U.S.: $175.00
Can.: $175.00

BRER COYOTE

Model: 225-255
Modeller: Lowell Davis
Height: 4 ¼", 10.8 cm
Colour: Brown, blue, yellow and black
Issued: 1981 - 1984
Series: Uncle Remus

U.K.: £ 85.00
U.S.: $175.00
Can.: $175.00

BRER FOX

Model: 225-250
Modeller: Lowell Davis
Height: 4 ¼", 10.8 cm
Colour: Red-brown, blue, white, red and yellow
Issued: 1981 - 1984
Series: Uncle Remus

U.K.: £ 85.00
U.S.: $175.00
Can.: $175.00

BRER RABBIT

Model: 225-252
Modeller: Lowell Davis
Height: 4 ¼", 10.8 cm
Colour: Brown, red, blue, green and yellow
Issued: 1981 - 1984
Series: Uncle Remus

U.K.: £ 85.00
U.S.: $175.00
Can.: $175.00

BRER WEASLE

Model: 225-254
Modeller: Lowell Davis
Height: 4", 10.1 cm
Colour: Brown, green, red, grey and yellow
Issued: 1981 - 1984
Series: Uncle Remus

U.K.: £ 85.00
U.S.: $175.00
Can.: $175.00

BRER WOLF

Model: 225-253
Modeller: Lowell Davis
Height: 3 ¾", 9.5 cm
Colour: Grey, blue, red, yellow and brown
Issued: 1981 - 1984
Series: Uncle Remus

U.K.: £ 85.00
U.S.: $175.00
Can.: $175.00

BROKEN DREAMS
(Birds of Prey/Broken Plough)

Model: 1. 225-035
2. 96847
Modeller: Lowell Davis
Height: 1. 5", 12.7 cm
2. 3 ¼", 8.3 cm
Colour: Browns, white, green and black
Issued: 1. 1979 - 1983
2. 1993 - 1994
Series: 1. Farm Collection
2. 15th Anniv. of issue

	225-035	96847
U.K.:	£ 60.	£30.
U.S.:	$120.	$60.
Can.:	$120.	$60.

BROTHERS
(Ducklings)

Model: 225-286/LD14
Modeller: Lowell Davis
Height: 3 ½", 8.9 cm
Colour: Yellow, pink, blue-grey and beige
Issued: 1988 - 1990
Series: Farm Collection

U.K.: £20.00
U.S.: $40.00
Can.: $40.00

BURNING RUBBER
(Polar bear and two cubs)

Model:	210-417
Modeller:	Boyd Perry
Height:	1 ½", 3.8 cm
Colour:	White, grey and light brown
Issued:	c.1986 - Unknown
Series:	Wind River Collection
U.K.:	£40.00
U.S.:	$80.00
Can.:	$80.00

BUSTIN' WITH PRIDE
(Ducks and ducklings)

Model:	225-203
Modeller:	Lowell Davis
Height:	2 ½", 6.4 cm
Colour:	Yellow, white and green
Issued:	1981 in a limited edition of 2,500
Series:	American Farm
U.K.:	£ 85.00
U.S.:	$175.00
Can.:	$175.00

CAMPERS
(Bear)

Model:	210-411
Modeller:	Boyd Perry
Height:	2 ½", 6.4 cm
Colour:	Dark brown, sandy brown, blue, terracotta, black and grey
Issued:	Unknown
Series:	Wind River Collection
U.K.:	£30.00
U.S.:	$60.00
Can.:	$60.00

CANADA GOOSE

Model:	1. 200-147
	2. L47
Modeller:	Frank Falco
Height:	10", 25.4 cm
Colour:	Dark grey, white, black and brown
Issued:	01/83 in a limited edition of 950
Series:	Birds by Frank Falco
U.K.:	£225.00
U.S.:	$450.00
Can.:	$450.00

Note: Has been seen without the metal reeds.

CAT AND JENNY WREN
(Cat lying in hay, bird looking on)

Model:	223-633
Modeller:	Lowell Davis
Height:	3", 7.6 cm
Colour:	Browns, orange, white, yellow and black
Issued:	1992 in a limited edition of 5,000
Series:	Friends of Mine
U.K.:	£35.00
U.S.:	$70.00
Can.:	$70.00

CAT AND JENNY WREN LYING
IN HAY

Model:	223-634
Modeller:	Lowell Davis
Height:	1 ½", 3.8 cm
Colour:	Browns, white and black
Issued:	1992 - 1995
Series:	1. Dated Ornament
	2. Friends of Mine
	3. Miniature Figurine
U.K.:	£20.00
U.S.:	$40.00
Can.:	$40.00

CATNAPPING TOO?
(Cat asleep on chair)

Model:	225-247/LD29
Modeller:	Lowell Davis
Height:	4 ¾", 12.1 cm
Colour:	Black, white, beige, brown and red
Issued:	1984 - c.1995
Series:	Farm Collection
U.K.:	£30.00
U.S.:	$60.00
Can.:	$60.00

CHAPSTICK

Model:	210-503
Modeller:	Boyd Perry
Height:	2 ¾", 7.0 cm
Colour:	Blue, red, white and black
Issued:	c.1986 - Unknown
Series:	Little Heavyweight
U.K.:	£20.00
U.S.:	$40.00
Can.:	$40.00

CHARIVARI
(Cockerel pushing hen in wheelbarrow)

Model: 225-707
Modeller: Lowell Davis
Height: 3 ¼", 8.3 cm
Colour: Unknown
Issued: 1992 in a limited
                  edition of 950
Series: The World of Little
                  Critters

U.K.:   £40.00
U.S.: $80.00
Can.: $80.00

CHEERLEADER

Model: 210-517
Modeller: Boyd Perry
Height: 2 ¾", 7.0 cm
Colour: Red, white and
                  brown
Issued: c.1986 - Unknown
Series: Little Heavyweights

U.K.:   £20.00
U.S.: $40.00
Can.: $40.00

CHICKADEE

Model: 200-151
Modeller: Frank Falco
Height: 5 ½", 14.0 cm
Colour: White, grey, black,
                  light brown and green
Issued: c.1986 in a limited
                  edition of 950
Series: Birds by Frank Falco

U.K.:   £150.00
U.S.: $300.00
Can.: $300.00

CHICKEN HOUSE

Model: 225-358
Modeller: Lowell Davis
Height: 1", 2.5 cm
Colour: Terracotta, white, grey,
                  green, blue and yellow
Issued: 1985 - 1987
Series: FoxFire Farm Buildings

U.K.:   £20.00
U.S.: $40.00
Can.: $40.00

CHICKEN THIEF
(Lowell Davis in bath, chicken running away)

Model: 225-338
Modeller: Lowell Davis
Height: 5 ¼", 13.3 cm
Colour: White, red, blue,
                  fleshtones and browns
Issued: 1987 in a limited
                  edition of 950
Series: Farm Collection

U.K.:   £ 75.00
U.S.: $150.00
Can.: $150.00

CHIPPER
(Chipmunk)

Model: 210-555
Modeller: Boyd Perry
Height: 2", 5.0 cm
Colour: Red-brown, black,
                  white, tan and green
Issued: Unknown
Series: Little Rascals

U.K.:   £20.00
U.S.: $40.00
Can.: $40.00

CHRISTOPHER CRITTER
(Wolf holding sword and hat)

Model: 225-514
Modeller: Lowell Davis
Height: 5 ½", 14.0 cm
Colour: Brown, white, purple,
                  grey, black and green
Issued: 1992 in a limited
                  edition of 1,192
Series: The World of Little
                  Critters

U.K.:   £30.00
U.S.: $60.00
Can.: $60.00

Note: Issued to commemorate the
                500th anniversary of the
                discovery of America.

CITY SLICKERS
(Three seated Dogs, Cockeral on kennel)

Model: 225-329
Modeller: Lowell Davis
Height: 5", 12.7 cm
Colour: Black, tan, brown,
                  orange, white and
                  green
Issued: 1983 in a limited
                  edition of 1,500
Series: Farm Collection

U.K.:   £ 65.00
U.S.: $125.00
Can.: $125.00

COCK OF THE WALK
(Turkey, wheelbarrow and
pumpkins)

Model:	25347
Modeller:	Lowell Davis
Height:	5", 12.7 cm
Colour:	Browns, orange, black, red and green
Issued:	1991 in a limited edition of 2,500
Series:	American Farm
U.K.:	£100.00
U.S.:	$200.00
Can.:	$200.00

COMFY?
(Hound and frog)

Model:	225-273
Modeller:	Lowell Davis
Height:	2 ½", 6.4 cm
Colour:	Black, white, tan, green and grey
Issued:	1986 - 1993
Series:	Farm Collection
U.K.:	£35.00
U.S.:	$70.00
Can.:	$70.00

COMPANY'S COMING
(Cat and pie)

Model:	225-205
Modeller:	Lowell Davis
Height:	3 ¼", 8.3 cm
Colour:	Black, white, brown and grey
Issued:	1982 in a limited edition of 4,000
Series:	Farm Collection
U.K.:	£ 50.00
U.S.:	$100.00
Can.:	$100.00

COON CAPERS
(Racoon)

Model:	225-291
Modeller:	Lowell Davis
Height:	2 ¼", 6.4 cm
Colour:	Grey, silver-grey, brown, black, white and green
Issued:	1989 - 1995
Series:	Farm Collection
U.K.:	£35.00
U.S.:	$70.00
Can.:	$70.00

CORN CRIB AND SHEEP PEN

Model:	225-354
Modeller:	Lowell Davis
Height:	1 ½", 3.8 cm
Colour:	Reddish-brown, red, yellow, green and blue-grey
Issued:	1985 - 1987
Series:	FoxFire Farm Buildings
U.K.:	£40.00
U.S.:	$80.00
Can.:	$80.00

CORN CRIB MOUSE
(Mouse on corn cob)

Model:	225-295/LD4
Modeller:	Lowell Davis
Height:	1 ¾", 4.4 cm
Colour:	Grey, white, brown, yellow, red and green
Issued:	1990 - 1993
Series:	Farm Collection
U.K.:	£20.00
U.S.:	$40.00
Can.:	$40.00

COUNTER SIGN
"The American West"

Model:	100-910
Modeller:	Don Polland
Height:	4 ½", 11.9 cm
Colour:	Tan, white, red, grey, black and yellow
Issued:	1984 - Unknown (UK)
Series:	The American West
U.K.:	£45.00
U.S.:	$90.00
Can.:	$90.00

COUNTER SIGN
"The Wind River Collection by
Boyd Perry"

Model:	210-413
Modeller:	Boyd Perry
Height:	3 ¼", 8.3 cm
Colour:	Tan, orange, brown, blue, green and white
Issued:	c.1986 - Unknown
Series:	Wind River Collection
U.K.:	£40.00
U.S.:	$80.00
Can.:	$80.00

COUNTER SIGN
"FoxFire Farm by Lowell Davis"

Model:	888-907
Modeller:	Lowell Davis
Height:	4", 10.1 cm
Colour:	Cream, black, yellow, white, grey and red
Issued:	1985 - Unknown
Series:	Farm Collection
U.K.:	£ 50.00
U.S.:	$100.00
Can.:	$100.00

COUNTER SIGN
"Little Heavyweights by Boyd Perry"

Model:	210-514
Modeller:	Boyd Perry
Height:	2 ¾", 6.4 cm
Colour:	Cream, terracotta, brown and grey
Issued:	c.1986 - Unknown
Series:	Little Heavyweights
U.K.:	£25.00
U.S.:	$50.00
Can.:	$50.00

COUNTER SIGN
"Little Rascals by Boyd Perry"

Model:	210-562
Modeller:	Boyd Perry
Height:	3 ¾", 9.5 cm
Colour:	Terracotta, cream, red, browns and white
Issued:	c.1986 - Unknown
Series:	Little Rascals
U.K.:	£30.00
U.S.:	$60.00
Can.:	$60.00

COUNTER SIGN
"Uncle Remus Characters by Lowell Davis"

Model:	888904
Modeller:	Lowell Davis
Height:	Unknown
Colour:	Beige, red, blue, green and brown
Issued:	1981 - 1984
Series:	Uncle Remus
U.K.:	£30.00
U.S.:	$60.00
Can.:	$60.00

COUNTING THE DAYS
(Rabbit looking at carrot label)

Model:	225-233
Modeller:	Lowell Davis
Height:	1 ½", 3.8 cm
Colour:	Reddish-brown, brown, white, cream and green
Issued:	1983 - 1992
Series:	Farm Collection
U.K.:	£40.00
U.S.:	$80.00
Can.:	$80.00

COUNTRY BOY
(Dog and milk churn)

Model:	225-213
Modeller:	Lowell Davis
Height:	2 ¼", 5.7 cm
Colour:	Brown, silver, yellow and green
Issued:	1981 - 1984
Series:	Farm Collection
U.K.:	£30.00
U.S.:	$60.00
Can.:	$60.00

COUNTRY CHRISTMAS 1983
(Dog and mailbox in snow)

Model:	223-550
Modeller:	Lowell Davis
Height:	4 ¼", 10.8 cm
Colour:	White, red-brown, brown, red and green
Issued:	1983 in a limited edition of 2,500
Series:	Annual Figurine
U.K.:	£ 50.00
U.S.:	$100.00
Can.:	$100.00

COUNTRY CHRISTMAS 1983
(Mailbox with snow)

Model:	223-500
Modeller:	Lowell Davis
Height:	3 ¼", 8.3 cm
Colour:	White, brown, red and orange
Issued:	1983 - 1983
Series:	Annual Ornament
U.K.:	£20.00
U.S.:	$40.00
Can.:	$40.00

**COUNTRY CHRISTMAS 1984
(Kittens with presents)**

Model: 223-551
Modeller: Lowell Davis
Height: 3 ¾", 9.5 cm
Colour: Ginger kittens; black shoe; blue, red and yellow presents
Issued: 1984 in a limited edition of 2,500
Series: Annual Figurine

U.K.: £45.00
U.S.: $90.00
Can.: $90.00

**COUNTRY CHRISTMAS 1984
(Kitten in boot)**

Model: 223-501
Modeller: Lowell Davis
Height: 2 ½", 6.4 cm
Colour: Ginger tabby; black boot
Issued: 1984 - 1984
Series: Annual Ornament

U.K.: £12.00
U.S.: $25.00
Can.: $25.00

**COUNTRY CHRISTMAS 1985
(Christmas at FoxFire Farm)**

Model: 223-552
Modeller: Lowell Davis
Height: 2", 5.0 cm
Colour: White and brown
Issued: 1985 in a limited edition of 2,500
Series: Annual Figurine

U.K.: £40.00
U.S.: $80.00
Can.: $80.00

**COUNTRY CHRISTMAS 1985
(Piglet sat in cradle)**

Model: 223-502
Modeller: Lowell Davis
Height: 2 ¾", 7.0 cm
Colour: Pink, white and red
Issued: 1985 - 1985
Series: Annual Ornament

U.K.: £20.00
U.S.: $40.00
Can.: $40.00

**COUNTRY CHRISTMAS 1986
CHRISTMAS AT RED OAK
(Cars outside snow covered church)**

Model: 223-553
Modeller: Lowell Davis
Height: 4 ¾", 12.1 cm
Colour: White, blue, grey, red and black
Issued: 1986 in a limited edition of 2,500
Series: Annual Figurine

U.K.: £40.00
U.S.: $80.00
Can.: $80.00

**COUNTRY CHRISTMAS 1986
CHRISTMAS AT RED OAK
(Snow covered church)**

Model: 223-503
Modeller: Lowell Davis
Height: 2 ¼", 5.7 cm
Colour: White, blue-grey, green and yellow
Issued: 1986 - 1986
Series: Annual Ornament

U.K.: £25.00
U.S.: $50.00
Can.: $50.00

**COUNTRY CHRISTMAS 1987
(Blossom's gift)**

Model: 223-554
Modeller: Lowell Davis
Height: 3 ¼", 9.5 cm
Colour: White, tan, black, blue and red
Issued: 1988 in a limited edition of 2,500
Series: Annual Figurine

U.K.: £ 75.00
U.S.: $150.00
Can.: $150.00

**COUNTRY CHRISTMAS 1987
(Cow's head in holly wreath)**

Model: 223-504
Modeller: Lowell Davis
Height: 2 ½", 6.4 cm
Colour: Red, green, brown and white
Issued: 1987 - 1987
Series: Annual Ornament

U.K.: £10.00
U.S.: $20.00
Can.: $20.00

COUNTRY CHRISTMAS 1988
(Cutting the family Christmas tree)

Model: 223-555
Modeller: Lowell Davis
Height: 4 ½", 11.9 cm
Colour: White, green, blue, red, grey and brown
Issued: 1988 in a limited edition of 2,500
Series: Annual Figurine

U.K.:   £ 65.00
U.S.: $125.00
Can.: $125.00

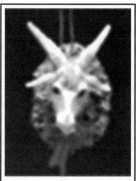

COUNTRY CHRISTMAS 1988
(Goat's head in holly wreath)

Model: 223-505
Modeller: Lowell Davis
Height: 3", 7.6 cm
Colour: Green, white and red
Issued: 1988 - 1988
Series: Annual Ornament

U.K.:   £10.00
U.S.: $20.00
Can.: $20.00

COUNTRY CHRISTMAS 1989
(Peter and the wren)

Model: 223-556/LD32
Modeller: Lowell Davis
Height: 6", 15.0 cm
Colour: Browns, white and green
Issued: 1989 in a limited edition of 2,500
Series: Annual Figurine

U.K.:   £40.00
U.S.: $80.00
Can.: $80.00

COUNTRY CHRISTMAS 1989
(Wren on holly leaf)

Model: 223-506
Modeller: Lowell Davis
Height: 2", 5.0 cm
Colour: Reddish-brown, brown, white, black, red and green
Issued: 1989 - 1989
Series: Annual Ornament

U.K.:   £10.00
U.S.: $20.00
Can.: $20.00

COUNTRY CHRISTMAS 1990
(Wintering deer)

Model: 223-557
Modeller: Lowell Davis
Height: 4 ½", 11.9 cm
Colour: Red-brown, yellow, white and cream
Issued: 1990 in a limited edition of 2,500
Series: Annual Figurine

U.K.:   £ 55.00
U.S.: $110.00
Can.: $110.00

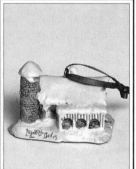

COUNTRY CHRISTMAS 1990
(Farm building in snow)

Model: 223-507
Modeller: Lowell Davis
Height: 1 ½", 3.8 cm
Colour: White, light brown and yellow
Issued: 1990 - 1990
Series: Annual Ornament

U.K.:   £25.00
U.S.: $50.00
Can.: $50.00

COUNTRY CLUB
(Beavers)

Model: 210-414
Modeller: Boyd Perry
Height: 2", 5.0 cm
Colour: Red-brown, brown, beige, green and blue-grey
Issued: c.1986 - Unknown
Series: Wind River Collection

U.K.:   £35.00
U.S.: $70.00
Can.: $70.00

COUNTRY COUSINS
(Cat and skunk)

Model: 225-266
Modeller: Lowell Davis
Height: 3 ½", 8.9 cm
Colour: Black, white, brown, green and blue
Issued: 1985 - 1993
Series: Farm Collection

U.K.:   £25.00
U.S.: $50.00
Can.: $50.00

COUNTRY CROOK
(Crows)

Model: 225-280
Modeller: Lowell Davis
Height: 1 ¾", 4.4 cm
Colour: Browns, black, pink and yellow
Issued: 1982 - 1984
Series: Farm Collection

U.K.: £100.00
U.S.: $200.00
Can.: $200.00

COUNTRY CROONER
(Cat on post)

Model: 225-256/LD9
Modeller: Lowell Davis
Height: 3 ¼", 8.3 cm
Colour: White, ginger, black and brown
Issued: 1985 - c.1995
Series: Farm Collection

U.K.: £20.00
U.S.: $40.00
Can.: $40.00

COUNTRY KITTY
(Skunk and hen house)

Model: 225-246
Modeller: Lowell Davis
Height: 2 ¾", 7.0 cm
Colour: Black, white, browns and green
Issued: 1984 - 1987
Series: Farm Collection

U.K.: £40.00
U.S.: $80.00
Can.: $80.00

COUNTRY ROAD
(Dog, mailbox, milk churn)

Model: 1. 225-030
2. 96842
Modeller: Lowell Davis
Height: 1. 5", 12.7 cm
2. 3", 7.6 cm
Colour: Browns, white, and green
Issued: 1. 1979 - 1983
2. 1993 - 1994
Series: Farm Collection

	225-030	96842
U.K.:	£ 65.	£30.
U.S.:	$125.	$60.
Can.:	$125.	$60.

COURTIN'
(Birds)

Model: 225-220
Modeller: Lowell Davis
Height: 4 ¾", 12.1 cm
Colour: Browns, blue, white and yellow
Issued: 1984 - 1986
Series: Farm Collection

U.K.: £35.00
U.S.: $70.00
Can.: $70.00

CREEK BANK BANDIT
(Raccoon)

Model: 225-038
Modeller: Lowell Davis
Height: 3 ½", 8.9 cm
Colour: Browns, black, white and green
Issued: 1980 - 1985
Series: Farm Collection

U.K.: £35.00
U.S.: $70.00
Can.: $70.00

CRITICS, THE
(Lowell Davis painting, watched by animals)

Model: 223-600
Modeller: Lowell Davis
Height: 6 ¼", 15.9 cm
Colour: Blues, white, pink, browns, yellow, red, black and green
Issued: 1983 in a limited edition of 1,200
Series: Farm Collection

U.K.: £ 500.00
U.S.: $1,000.00
Can.: $1,000.00

CUSSIN' UP A STORM
(Squirrel and bird feeder)

Model: Unknown
Modeller: Lowell Davis
Height: 5 ¼", 13.3 cm
Colour: Red-brown, tan, blue, white, black and green
Issued: 1995 - 1995
Series: Farm Collection

U.K.: £35.00
U.S.: $70.00
Can.: $70.00

DEN MOTHER
(Two foxes)

Model: 210-409
Modeller: Boyd Perry
Height: 2 ¼", 5.7 cm
Colour: Red-browns, green, white and black
Issued: c.1986 - Unknown
Series: Wind River Collection

U.K.: £35.00
U.S.: $70.00
Can.: $70.00

DON'T OPEN 'TIL CHRISTMAS
(Cat and present)

Model: 27562
Modeller: Lowell Davis
Height: 2 ¼", 5.7 cm
Colour: Black, white, green, yellow and pink
Issued: 1993 - 1995
Series: 1. Farm Collection
2. Cats in Season

U.K.: £20.00
U.S.: $40.00
Can.: $40.00

DON'T PLAY WITH FIRE
(Mouse, matches and candlestick)

Model: 25319
Modeller: Lowell Davis
Height: 3 ½", 8.9 cm
Colour: Gold, white, brown, red and black
Issued: 1992 - 1995
Series: American Farm

U.K.: £ 75.00
U.S.: $150.00
Can.: $150.00

DON'T PLAY WITH YOUR FOOD
(Two chicks pulling a worm)

Model: 225-258
Modeller: Lowell Davis
Height: 2", 5.0 cm
Colour: Yellow, red, blue-grey and beige
Issued: 1985 - 1992
Series: Farm Collection

U.K.: £25.00
U.S.: $50.00
Can.: $50.00

"DOUBLE TROUBLE"
(Ewe and lambs)

Model: 225-211/092
Modeller: Lowell Davis
Height: 2 ½", 6.4 cm
Colour: Black, white and green
Issued: 1981 - 1984 (USA)
07/82 - 12/82 (UK)
Series: American Farm

U.K.: £30.00
U.S.: $60.00
Can.: $60.00

Photograph not
available
at press time

DOUBLE YOLKER
(Mother hen pushing baby buggy)

Model: 225-516
Modeller: Lowell Davis
Height: 2 ¾", 7.0 cm
Colour: Unknown
Issued: 01/92 - 12/93
Series: The World of Little Critters

U.K.: £35.00
U.S.: $70.00
Can.: $70.00

DOWN FROM THE HIGH COUNTRY

Model: 100-117/AA0102
Modeller: Don Polland
Height: 5 ½", 14.0 cm
Colour: Grey, brown, sandy yellow, red, black and green
Issued: 1984 in a limited edition of 2,250 (UK)
Series: The American West

U.K.: £225.00
U.S.: $450.00
Can.: $450.00

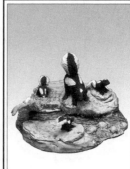

DOWN WIND
(Skunks)

Model: 210-402
Modeller: Boyd Perry
Height: 2 ¼", 5.7 cm
Colour: Black, white, light terracotta, green and yellow
Issued: c.1986 - Unknown
Series: Wind River Collection

U.K.: £35.00
U.S.: $70.00
Can.: $70.00

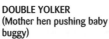

DRY AS A BONE
(Dog next to water pump)

Model:	225-216
Modeller:	Lowell Davis
Height:	3 ¼", 8.3 cm
Colour:	Brown, black, tan, silver and grey
Issued:	1981 - 1984
Series:	Farm Collection
U.K.:	£30.00
U.S.:	$60.00
Can.:	$60.00

DRY HOLE
(Bird and water pump)

Model:	25374
Modeller:	Lowell Davis
Height:	2 ½", 6.4 cm
Colour:	Brown, white, red, green and grey
Issued:	1993 - 1995
Series:	American Farm
U.K.:	£20.00
U.S.:	$40.00
Can.:	$40.00

DUKE'S MIXTURE
(Cockerel, hen and chicks)

Model:	225-202
Modeller:	Lowell Davis
Height:	4", 10.0 cm
Colour:	Gold, yellow, browns, red and white
Issued:	1981 in a limited edition of 2,500
Series:	American Farm
U.K.:	£ 75.00
U.S.:	$150.00
Can.:	$150.00

EAGLE

Model:	200-154
Modeller:	Frank Falco
Height:	12", 30.5 cm
Colour:	Dark brown, black, white, yellow and blue-green
Issued:	c.1986 in a limited edition of 950
Series:	Birds by Frank Falco
U.K.:	£325.00
U.S.:	$650.00
Can.:	$650.00

EAGLE DANCER / INDIAN DANCER

Model:	100-113/AA0113
Modeller:	Don Polland
Height:	6 ½", 16.5 cm
Colour:	White, blue, red, black, yellow and fleshtones
Issued:	1984 in a limited edition of 2,500 (UK)
Series:	The American West
U.K.:	£200.00
U.S.:	$400.00
Can.:	$400.00

EASY PICKIN'S

Model:	225-269
Modeller:	Lowell Davis
Height:	2", 5.0 cm
Colour:	Light brown, red, green, beige, grey and black
Issued:	1987 - 1990
Series:	Farm Collection
U.K.:	£20.00
U.S.:	$40.00
Can.:	$40.00

ELK

Model:	200-401
Modeller:	Daniel Parker
Height:	8", 20.3 cm
Colour:	Tan, black and grey
Issued:	c.1986 in a limited edition of 1,450
Series:	North American Animals by Daniel Parker
U.K.:	£150.00
U.S.:	$300.00
Can.:	$300.00

FAIR WEATHER FRIENDS
(Three ducklings)

Model:	225-236
Modeller:	Lowell Davis
Height:	1 ¼", 3.1 cm
Colour:	Yellow, brown and white
Issued:	1983 - 1987
Series:	Farm Collection
U.K.:	£20.00
U.S.:	$40.00
Can.:	$40.00

FALSE ALARM
(Cockerel on post)

Model:	225-237
Modeller:	Lowell Davis
Height:	3 ½", 8.9 cm
Colour:	White, green, black and red
Issued:	1983 – 1985
Series:	Farm Collection

U.K.:	£40.00
U.S.:	$80.00
Can.:	$80.00

FAMILY OUTING
(Geese and goslings)

Model:	225-289/LD10
Modeller:	Lowell Davis
Height:	2 ½", 6.4 cm
Colour:	White, yellow, orange, beige and green
Issued:	1989 - 1995
Series:	Farm Collection

U.K.:	£20.00
U.S.:	$40.00
Can.:	$40.00

FAVOURITE SPORT
(Terrier chasing piglets)

Model:	25381
Modeller:	Lowell Davis
Height:	3 ¾", 9.5 cm
Colour:	White, tan, pink, black, green and grey
Issued:	1993 in a limited edition of 1,250
Series:	American Farm

U.K.:	£ 70.00
U.S.:	$140.00
Can.:	$140.00

FEELIN' HIS OATS
(Foal jumping a fence with running dog)

Model:	225-275
Modeller:	Lowell Davis
Height:	4", 10.1 cm
Colour:	Reddish-brown, beige, green and brown
Issued:	1985 in a limited edition of 1,500
Series:	Farm Collection

U.K.:	£ 75.00
U.S.:	$150.00
Can.:	$150.00

FINDERS KEEPERS
(Cat with mouse trap)

Model:	225-299/LD32
Modeller:	Lowell Davis
Height:	1 ½", 3.8 cm
Colour:	Orange, black, white and green
Issued:	1990 - 1991 (UK)
Series:	Farm Collection

U.K.:	£20.00
U.S.:	$40.00
Can.:	$40.00

FIRST OUTING
(Racoon family)

Model:	25390
Modeller:	Lowell Davis
Height:	2", 5.0 cm
Colour:	Brown, black, white, tan, blue-grey and green
Issued:	1994 - 1995
Series:	Farm Collection

U.K.:	£30.00
U.S.:	$60.00
Can.:	$60.00

FLATFOOT

Model:	210-502
Modeller:	Boyd Perry
Height:	2 ¾", 7.0 cm
Colour:	Blue, black and silver
Issued:	c.1986 - Unknown
Series:	Little Heavyweights

U.K.:	£20.00
U.S.:	$40.00
Can.:	$40.00

FLEAS
(Dog scratching)

Model:	225-272
Modeller:	Lowell Davis
Height:	1 ½", 3.8 cm
Colour:	Red-brown, sandy brown, green and black
Issued:	1988 - 1993
Series:	Farm Collection

U.K.:	£15.00
U.S.:	$30.00
Can.:	$30.00

FLEW THE COOP
(Cat and overturned bird cage)

Model:	225-207
Modeller:	Lowell Davis
Height:	3 ½", 8.9 cm
Colour:	Orange, white, gold and browns
Issued:	c.1985 in a limited edition of 4,000
Series:	Farm Collection
U.K.:	£40.00
U.S.:	$80.00
Can.:	$80.00

FLIP
(Mouse)

Model:	210-556
Modeller:	Boyd Perry
Height:	2", 5.0 cm
Colour:	Reddish-brown, white and green
Issued:	Unknown
Series:	Little Rascals
U.K.:	£20.00
U.S.:	$40.00
Can.:	$40.00

FORBIDDEN FRUIT
(Rabbit and trap)

Model:	225-022
Modeller:	Lowell Davis
Height:	2", 5.0 cm
Colour:	Browns, green and white
Issued:	1980 - 1985
Series:	Farm Collection
U.K.:	£30.00
U.S.:	$60.00
Can.:	$60.00

FOREPLAY
(Cockerel and hen)

Model:	225-300/LD16
Modeller:	Lowell Davis
Height:	2", 5.0 cm
Colour:	Terracotta, white, blue, green, brown, yellow and red
Issued:	1990 - 1993
Series:	Farm Collection
U.K.:	£25.00
U.S.:	$50.00
Can.:	$50.00

FOWL PLAY
(Chick and worm)

Model:	1. 225-033
	2. 96845
Modeller:	Lowell Davis
Height:	1. 3", 7.6 cm
	2. 1¾", 4.4 cm
Colour:	Yellow, brown, green and orange
Issued:	1. 1979 - 1983
	2. 1993 - 1994
Series:	Farm Collection

	225-033	96845
U.K.:	£35.	£25.
U.S.:	$70.	$50.
Can.:	$70.	$50.

FRANKIE

Moel:	210-509
Modeller:	Boyd Perry
Height:	3", 7.6 cm
Colour:	White, cream, yellow, red, blue and black
Issued:	c.1986 - Unknown
Series:	Little Heavyweights
U.K.:	£20.00
U.S.:	$40.00
Can.:	$40.00

FREE LUNCH
(Squirrel on Bucket)

Model:	25321
Modeller:	Lowell Davis
Height:	3 ¼", 8.3 cm
Colour:	Browns, white, green and red
Issued:	1992 - 1995
Series:	American Farm
U.K.:	£35.00
U.S.:	$70.00
Can.:	$70.00

FREE THROW

Model:	210-521
Modeller:	Boyd Perry
Height:	2 ¾", 7.0 cm
Colour:	Yellow-green, brown, black and red
Issued:	c.1986 - Unknown
Series:	Little Heavyweights
U.K.:	£20.00
U.S.:	$40.00
Can.:	$40.00

FREELOADERS, THE
(Flash the Bloodhound Puppy
and two Guinea Fowl)

Model: 95042
Modeller: Lowell Davis
Height: 3 ¾", 9.5 cm
Colour: White, dark brown,
           red, orange, yellow
           and green
Issued: 1993 - 1995
Series: American Farm

U.K.:   £ 60.00
U.S.: $120.00
Can.: $120.00

FRESH SQUEEZED*

Model: 225-609
Modeller: Lowell Davis
Height: 3 ½", 8.9 cm
Colour: Light brown, green,
           yellow, blue and red
Issued: 1992 in a limited
           edition numbered
           1 to 350
Series: Route 66

U.K.:   £100.00
U.S.: $200.00
Can.: $200.00

Note: * Issued with a piece of
         Route 66 in a Lucite block.

FRESH SQUEEZED

Model: 225-608
Modeller: Lowell Davis
Height: 3 ½", 8.9 cm
Colour: Light brown, green,
           yellow, blue and red
Issued: 1992 in a limited
           edition numbered
           351 to 2500
Series: Route 66

U.K.:   £100.00
U.S.: $200.00
Can.: $200.00

FROM A FRIEND TO A FRIEND
(Lowell and dog in
horse-drawn carriage)

Model: 223-602
Modeller: Lowell Davis
Height: 7", 17.8 cm
Colour: Black, beige, blue,
           white, green, tan
           brown and red
Issued: 1989 in a limited
           edition of 1,200
Series: Farm Collection

U.K.:   £450.00
U.S.: $900.00
Can.: $900.00

FUR'S GONNA FLY
(Cockerel chasing cat)

Model: 225-335
Modeller: Lowell Davis
Height: 2 ½", 6.4 cm
Colour: Black, tan, white, pink,
           red and grey
Issued: 1985 in a limited
           edition of 1,500
Series: Farm Collection

U.K.:   £ 50.00
U.S.: $100.00
Can.: $100.00

G.I.

Moedl: 210-504
Modeller: Boyd Perry
Height: 2 ¾" 7.0 cm
Colour: Brown army fatigues,
           black and white
Issued: c.1986 - Unknown
Series: Little Heavyweights

U.K.:   £20.00
U.S.: $40.00
Can.: $40.00

GARDEN AND WOOD SHED

Model: 225-359
Modeller: Lowell Davis
Height: 1 ½", 3.8 cm
Colour: Yellow, terracotta,
           green, grey and blue
Issued: 1985 - 1987
Series: FoxFire Farm Buildings

U.K.:   £30.00
U.S.: $60.00
Can.: $60.00

GET WELL
(Cat and first aid box)

Model: 96707
Modeller: Lowell Davis
Height: 2", 5.0 cm
Colour: Ginger tabby; red,
           black and browns
Issued: 1994 - 1995
Series: 1. Cats in Season
           2. Farm Collection

U.K.:   £20.00
U.S.: $40.00
Can.: $40.00

GITTIN' A NIBBLE
(Tortoise and fishing rod)

Model:	225-294
Modeller:	Lowell Davis
Height:	2 ¼", 5.7 cm
Colour:	Light brown, green, black and grey
Issued:	1989 - 1993
Series:	Farm Collection
U.K.:	£25.00
U.S.:	$50.00
Can.:	$50.00

GLUTTON FOR PUNISHMENT
(Goat with bra)

Model:	225-268/LD35
Modeller:	Lowell Davis
Height:	5", 12.7 cm
Colour:	Dark brown, brown, white, blue-grey, pink and green
Issued:	1987 - 1991 (UK)
U.K.:	£ 75.00
U.S.:	$150.00
Can.:	$150.00

GOAT YARD AND STUDIO

Model:	225-353
Modeller:	Lowell Davis
Height:	1 ½", 3.8 cm
Colour:	Light brown, red, grey, green, white, brown and yellow
Issued:	1985 - 1987
Series:	FoxFire Farm Buildings
U.K.:	£40.00
U.S.:	$80.00
Can.:	$80.00

GOING TO GRANDMA'S

Model:	225-619
Modeller:	Lowell Davis
Height:	2 ½", 6.4 cm
Colour:	Blue, orange, white, pink and brown
Issued:	1992 - 1995
Series:	Route 66
U.K.:	£30.00
U.S.:	$60.00
Can.:	$60.00

GOLDIE AND HER PEEPS
(Hen and chicks)

Model:	225-283/LD3
Modeller:	Lowell Davis
Height:	1 ¾", 4.4 cm
Colour:	Yellow, golden-brown, brown, blue-grey and red
Issued:	1988 - 1995
Series:	Farm Collection
U.K.:	£20.00
U.S.:	$40.00
Can.:	$40.00

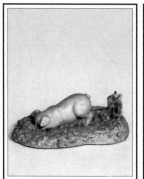

GONNA PAY FOR HIS SINS
(Pig in garden)

Model:	225-243/LD11
Modeller:	Lowell Davis
Height:	1 ¼", 3.1 cm
Colour:	Cream, beige, mauve and green
Issued:	1983 - c.1995
Series:	Farm Collection
U.K.:	£20.00
U.S.:	$40.00
Can.:	$40.00

GOOD CLEAN FUN
(Ducks in washing tub)

Model:	225-020/LD23
Modeller:	Lowell Davis
Height:	3 ¾", 9.5 cm
Colour:	Browns, grey, white and yellow
Issued:	1980 - 1989
Series:	Farm Collection
U.K.:	£25.00
U.S.:	$50.00
Can.:	$50.00

GOSSIPS
(Group of hens)

Model:	225-248
Modeller:	Lowell Davis
Height:	3 ½", 8.9 cm
Colour:	White, brown, silver, tan and green
Issued:	1984 - 1987
Series:	Farm Collection
U.K.:	£ 50.00
U.S.:	$100.00
Can.:	$100.00

GRASS IS ALWAYS GREENER, THE (Jersey cow)

Model: 25367
Modeller: Lowell Davis
Height: 7", 17.8 cm
Colour: Tan, black, green, white and grey
Issued: 1992 - 1993
Series: Farm Collection

U.K.: £ 65.00
U.S.: $125.00
Can.: $125.00

GREAT AMERICAN CHICKEN RACE
(Cockerel pulling hen and eggs in a wheeled whicker basket)

Model: 225-500
Modeller: Lowell Davis
Height: 4", 10.1 cm
Colour: Tan, white, red, black, blue and browns
Issued: 12/91 in a limited edition of 2,500
Series: The World of Little Critters

U.K.: £ 60.00
U.S.: $120.00
Can.: $120.00

HANKY PANKY
(Cats in basket)

Model: 225-298/LD21a/166
Modeller: Lowell Davis
Height: 2 ¾", 7.0 cm
Colour: Brown, ginger, black, pink, red, blue and white
Issued: 1990 - 1993
Series: Farm Collection

U.K.: £20.00
U.S.: $40.00
Can.: $40.00

HAPPY ANNIVERSARY
(Cats in picnic basket)

Model: Unknown
Modeller: Lowell Davis
Height: 3 ¾", 9.5 cm
Colour: Grey, ginger, white, fawn, red and green
Issued: 1995 - 1995
Series: 1. Cats in Season
       2. Farm Collection

U.K.: £25.00
U.S.: $50.00
Can.: $50.00

HAPPY BIRTHDAY MY SWEET
(Cat and birthday cake)

Model: 27560
Modeller: Lowell Davis
Height: 2 ¼", 5.7 cm
Colour: Grey tabby; pink and yellow
Issued: 1993 - 1995
Series: 1. Cats in Season
       2. Farm Collection

U.K.: £20.00
U.S.: $40.00
Can.: $40.00

HAPPY HOUR
(Coon hound feeding puppies)

Model: 225-287
Modeller: Lowell Davis
Height: 2 ½", 6.4 cm
Colour: Black, tan, white and brown
Issued: 1988 - 1992
Series: Farm Collection

U.K.: £25.00
U.S.: $50.00
Can.: $50.00

HAPPY HUNTING GROUND
(Owl on gravestone)

Model: 225-330
Modeller: Lowell Davis
Height: 5 ¼", 13.3 cm
Colour: Browns, yellow, grey and green
Issued: 1983 in a limited edition of 1,750
Series: Farm Collection

U.K.: £ 50.00
U.S.: $100.00
Can.: $100.00

HEADED HOME
(Running dog)

Model: 225-240
Modeller: Lowell Davis
Height: 1 ¼", 3.1 cm
Colour: Black, tan, grey and beige
Issued: 1984 - 1991
Series: Farm Collection

U.K.: £20.00
U.S.: $40.00
Can.: $40.00

HEADED SOUTH
(Bird on spade)

Model:	25327
Modeller:	Lowell Davis
Height:	2 ½", 6.4 cm
Colour:	Browns, white, green, yellow and black
Issued:	1992 - 1993
Series:	American Farm
U.K.:	£15.00
U.S.:	$30.00
Can.:	$30.00

HELPIN' HIMSELF
(Coon hound "Ole blue" and
bag of food)

Model:	96821
Modeller:	Lowell Davis
Height:	2", 5.0 cm
Colour:	Grey, black, tan, red, white and browns
Issued:	1994 - 1995
Series:	Farm Collection
U.K.:	£25.00
U.S.:	$50.00
Can.:	$50.00

HEN HOUSE

Model:	225-356
Modeller:	Lowell Davis
Height:	1 ½", 3.84 cm
Colour:	Light brown, blue, yellow, grey, orange and green
Issued:	1985 - 1987
Series:	FoxFire Farm Buildings
U.K.:	£25.00
U.S.:	$50.00
Can.:	$50.00

HI GIRLS! THE NAME'S BIG
JACK
(Cockerel and hens)

Model:	225-328
Modeller:	Lowell Davis
Height:	4 ½", 11.9 cm
Colour:	Yellow, red, white and green
Issued:	1983 in a limited edition of 2,500
Series:	Farm Collection
U.K.:	£ 80.00
U.S.:	$160.00
Can.:	$160.00

"HIGHTAILIN' IT"
(Goose and pup)

Model:	225-214/090
Modeller:	Lowell Davis
Height:	2 ½", 6.4 cm
Colour:	Reddish-brown dog; cream-yellow goose, green base
Issued:	1981 - 1984 (USA) 07/82 - 12/82 (UK)
Series:	American Farm
U.K.:	£40.00
U.S.:	$80.00
Can.:	$80.00

HIS EYES ARE BIGGER THAN
HIS STOMACH
(Hens, Cockerel and hen house

Model:	225-332
Modeller:	Lowell Davis
Height:	7 ½", 19.1 cm
Colour:	Browns, yellow, red and white
Issued:	1983 in a limited edition of 2,500
Series:	Farm Collection
U.K.:	£125.00
U.S.:	$250.00
Can.:	$250.00

HIS MASTER'S DOG
(Dog lying on clothes)

Model:	225-244
Modeller:	Lowell Davis
Height:	1 ¼", 3.1 cm
Colour:	1. Black and white dog 2. Brown dog
Issued:	1984 - 1988
Series:	Farm Collection

	B&W	Brown
U.K.:	£25.	£25.
U.S.:	$50.	$50.
Can.:	$50.	$50.

Photograph not
available
at press time

HITTIN' THE SACK
(Fox in night clothes)

Model:	225-510
Modeller:	Lowell Davis
Height:	2 ¼", 5.7 cm
Colour:	Unknown
Issued:	1991 - 1993
Series:	The World of Little Critters
U.K.:	£25.00
U.S.:	$50.00
Can.:	$50.00

HITTIN' THE TRAIL
(Cats and kittens in barn corner)

Model:	96908
Modeller:	Lowell Davis
Height:	4 ¼", 10.8 cm
Colour:	Orange, browns, black, silver, red-brown, grey and white
Issued:	1994 - 1995

U.K.:	£ 80.00
U.S.:	$160.00
Can.:	$160.00

HOG HEAVEN
(Pigs, piglets and cockerel)

Model:	225-336 (LD37)
Modeller:	Lowell Davis
Height:	3", 7.6 cm
Colour:	Pink, black, red, orange and brown
Issued:	1985 in a limited edition of 1,500
Series:	Farm Collection

U.K.:	£ 65.00
U.S.:	$125.00
Can.:	$125.00

HOG HOUSE

Model:	225-355
Modeller:	Lowell Davis
Height:	1", 2.5 cm
Colour:	LIght brown, green, yellow and pink
Issued:	1985 - 1987
Series:	FoxFire Farm Buildings

U.K.:	£25.00
U.S.:	$50.00
Can.:	$50.00

HOME FOR CHRISTMAS
(Sailor next to Route 66 signpost)

Model:	25621
Modeller:	Lowell Davis
Height:	5", 12.7 cm
Colour:	Navy blue, white, tan and black
Issued:	1993 - 1995
Series:	Route 66

U.K.:	£45.00
U.S.:	$90.00
Can.:	$90.00

HOME FROM MARKET
(Truck with various animals)

Model:	223-601
Modeller:	Lowell Davis
Height:	4 ½", 11.9 cm
Colour:	Black, brown, white, red, blue and grey
Issued:	1985 in a limited edition of 1,200
Series:	Farm Collection

U.K.:	£300.00
U.S.:	$600.00
Can.:	$600.00

HOME RUN

Model:	210-519
Modeller:	Boyd Perry
Height:	2 ¾", 7.0 cm
Colour:	Blue, black and brown
Issued:	c.1986 - Unknown
Series:	Little Heavyweights

U.K.:	£20.00
U.S.:	$40.00
Can.:	$40.00

HOME SQUEEZIN'S
(Two rats leaning on flagon of whisky)

Model:	225-504
Modeller:	Lowell Davis
Height:	3", 7.6 cm
Colour:	Blue, red, browns, grey and black
Issued:	1990 - 1993
Series:	The World of Little Critters

U.K.:	£30.00
U.S.:	$60.00
Can.:	$60.00

HONEYMOON'S OVER, THE

Model:	25370
Modeller:	Lowell Davis
Height:	4 ½", 11.9 cm
Colour:	Pink, white, light brown, black and green
Issued:	1992 in a limited edition of 1,950

U.K.:	£40.00
U.S.:	$80.00
Can.:	$80.00

HOOK, LINE AND SINKER
(Cat carrying fish in mouth)

Model:	25382
Modeller:	Lowell Davis
Height:	2 ¼", 5.7 cm
Colour:	Grey, white, orange, green and black
Issued:	1993 - Unknown
Series:	American Farm
U.K.:	£20.00
U.S.:	$40.00
Can.:	$40.00

HOPPER
(Frog)

Model:	210-560
Modeller:	Boyd Perry
Height:	2 ¾", 7.0 cm
Colour:	Terracotta, brown, yellow and green
Issued:	Unknown
Series:	Little Rascals
U.K.:	£20.00
U.S.:	$40.00
Can.:	$40.00

HOT DOG

Model:	210-512
Modeller:	Boyd Perry
Height:	2 ¾", 7.0 cm
Colour:	Greens, brown, red, white and silver
Issued:	c.1986 - Unknown
Series:	Little Heavyweights
U.K.:	£20.00
U.S.:	$40.00
Can.:	$40.00

HOT PURSUIT
(Warrior on Appaloosa horse)

Model:	Unknown
Modeller:	Don Polland
Height:	5 ½", 14.0 cm
Colour:	Brown, white, black, yellow, green, blue-grey and beige
Issued:	Unknown
Series:	Western Frontier Collection
U.K.:	£100.00
U.S.:	$200.00
Can.:	$200.00

HUH?
(Frog on lily pad, toad underneath)

Model:	225-242
Modeller:	Lowell Davis
Height:	1 ½", 3.8 cm
Colour:	Greens, white and blue-grey
Issued:	1984 - 1989
Series:	Farm Collection
U.K.:	£40.00
U.S.:	$80.00
Can.:	$80.00

HUMMINGBIRD
Style One

Model:	200-152
Modeller:	Frank Falco
Height:	7" 17.8 cm
Colour:	Yellow, green, grey, mauve, white and orange
Issued:	c.1986 in a limited edition of 950
Series:	Birds by Frank Falco
U.K.:	£175.00
U.S.:	$350.00
Can.:	$350.00

HUMMINGBIRD
Style Two

Model:	200-153
Modeller:	Frank Falco
Height:	6", 15.0 cm
Colour:	Red, reddish-brown, white, black and green
Issued:	c.1986 in a limited edition of 950
Series:	Birds by Frank Falco
U.K.:	£175.00
U.S.:	$350.00
Can.:	$350.00

Photograph not available at press time

HUNTER, THE

Model:	100-105
Modeller:	Don Polland
Height:	5", 12.7 cm
Colour:	Unknown
Issued:	1982 in a limited edition of 2,500 (UK)
Series:	Western Frontier Collection
U.K.:	£ 75.00
U.S.:	$150.00
Can.:	$150.00

IDLE HOURS
(Two lambs lying)
Model: 225-230 (094)
Modeller: Lowell Davis
Height: 2", 5.0 cm
Colour: 1. Black
2. White
3. White and black
Issued: 1981 - 1985 (USA)
07/82 - 12/82 (UK)
Series: American Farm

U.K.: £12.00
U.S.: $25.00
Can.: $25.00

IF YOU CAN'T BEAT 'EM, JOIN 'EM
(Hen with ducklings)
Model: 25279
Modeller: Lowell Davis
Height: 4 ¼", 10.8 cm
Colour: Yellow, black, tan and green
Issued: 1993 in a limited edition of 1,750
Series: American Farm

U.K.: £ 80.00
U.S.: $160.00
Can.: $160.00

IGNORANCE IS BLISS
(Cockerel on axe)
Model: 1. 225-031
2. 96843
Modeller: Lowell Davis
Height: 1. 6", 15.0 cm
2. 3 ¼", 8.3 cm
Colour: Red, green, and browns
Issued: 1. 1979 - 1983
2. 1993 - 1994
Series: 1. Farm Collection
2. 15th Anniv. of issue

	225-031	96843
U.K.:	£ 80.	£ 60.
U.S.:	$160.	$120.
Can.:	$160.	$120.

I'M THANKFUL FOR YOU
(Cat with turkey on plate)
Model: 27563
Modeller: Lowell Davis
Height: 2 ½", 6.4 cm
Colour: Grey, white, red and green
Issued: 1993 - 1995
Series: 1. Cats in Season
2. Farm Collection

U.K.: £20.00
U.S.: $40.00
Can.: $40.00

IN A PICKLE
(Cat with mouse)
Model: 225-284/LD33
Modeller: Lowell Davis
Height: 2 ¼", 5.7 cm
Colour: Grey, silver, black, white, green and brown
Issued: 1988 - 1991 (UK)
Series: Farm Collection

U.K.: £20.00
U.S.: $40.00
Can.: $40.00

INDIAN MAIDEN
Model: 100-111/AA0112
Modeller: Don Polland
Height: 7", 17.8 cm
Colour: Reddish-brown, green, black, light brown, yellow and white
Issued: 1984 in a limited edition of 2,500 (UK)
Series: The American West

U.K.: £200.00
U.S.: $400.00
Can.: $400.00

ITCHING POST
(Pig scratching on a post)
Model: 225-037
Modeller: Lowell Davis
Height: 3 ½", 8.9 cm
Colour: Black, white and tan
Issued: 1980 - 1988
Series: Farm Collection

U.K.: £30.00
U.S.: $60.00
Can.: $60.00

Photograph not
available
at press time

ITISKIT, ITASKIT
(Hen wearing bonnet, carrying basket)
Model: 225-511
Modeller: Lowell Davis
Height: 1 ½", 3.8 cm
Colour: Unknown
Issued: 1991 - 1993
Series: The World of Little Critters

U.K.: £25.00
U.S.: $50.00
Can.: $50.00

J.R.

Model: 210-511
Modeller: Boyd Perry
Height: 2 ¾", 7.0 cm
Colour: Light blue, brown, black and red
Issued: c.1986 - Unknown
Series: Little Heavyweights

U.K.: £20.00
U.S.: $40.00
Can.: $40.00

JOHNNY

Model: 210-510
Modeller: Boyd Perry
Height: 3", 7.6 cm
Colour: Black, white and red
Issued: c.1986 - Unknown
Series: Little Heavyweights

U.K.: £20.00
U.S.: $40.00
Can.: $40.00

JUST CHECK THE AIR *
(Old Phillips 66 Gas Station)

Model: 225-600
Modeller: Lowell Davis
Height: 3 ½", 8.9 cm
Colour: Browns, grey, yellow, black and blue
Issued: 1991 in a limited edition numbered 1 to 350
Series: Route 66

U.K.: £125.00
U.S.: $250.00
Can.: $250.00

Note: * Issued with a piece of Route 66 in a lucite block.

JUST CHECK THE AIR
(Old Phillips 66 gas station)

Model: 225-603
Modeller: Lowell Davis
Height: 3 ½", 8.9 cm
Colour: Browns, grey, yellow, black and blue
Issued: 1991 in a limited edition numbered 351 to 2,500
Series: Route 66

U.K.: £ 65.00
U.S.: $125.00
Can.: $125.00

KICKIN' HIMSELF
(Lowell's father walking to get gas)

Model: 25622
Modeller: Lowell Davis
Height: 4 ¾", 12.1 cm
Colour: Browns, blue, white, yellow, green and red
Issued: 1993 - 1995
Series: Route 66

U.K.: £40.00
U.S.: $80.00
Can.: $80.00

KING OF THE MOUNTAIN
(Goat and kid on wrecked car)

Model: 25380
Modeller: Lowell Davis
Height: 7", 17.8 cm
Colour: Green, browns, white, yellow and black
Issued: 1993 in a limited edition of 750
Series: American Farm

U.K.: £200.00
U.S.: $400.00
Can.: $400.00

KISSIN' COUSINS
(Two rabbits)

Model: 225-307/LD37
Modeller: Lowell Davis
Height: 2", 5.0 cm
Colour: Orange, white, browns and green
Issued: 1991 - 1993 (UK)
Series: Farm Collection

U.K.: £25.00
U.S.: $50.00
Can.: $50.00

LAST LAFF
(Lowell, tractor and horse)

Model: 23604
Modeller: Lowell Davis
Height: 6", 15.0 cm
Colour: Brown, cream, white, grey, blue, dark brown, green, beige and red
Issued: 1992 in a limited edition of 1,200
Series: American Farm

U.K.: £450.00
U.S.: $900.00
Can.: $900.00

LAST STRAW, THE
(Goat and scarecrow)
Model: 225-301/LD28
Modeller: Lowell Davis
Height: 6", 15.0 cm
Colour: White, yellow, black,
            pale blue and pale
            green
Issued: 1990 - 1993
Series: Farm Collection

U.K.:   £ 50.00
U.S.: $100.00
Can.: $100.00

LEAPIN' LIZARD, THE
(Lowell's van)
Model: Unknown
Modeller: Lowell Davis
Height: 2", 5.0 cm
Colour: Turquoise, grey, green,
            black, red and cream
Issued: 1993 - 1993
Series: Route 66

U.K.:   £35.00
U.S.: $70.00
Can.: $70.00

Note: Collector's Events only.

LEFTOVERS
(Cat on high chair)
Model: 225-290/LD25
Modeller: Lowell Davis
Height: 5 ¼", 13.3 cm
Colour: Black, white, tan
            and fawn
Issued: 1989 - 1995
Series: Farm Collection

U.K.:   £35.00
U.S.: $70.00
Can.: $70.00

LICKIN' GOOD
(Cat and milk churn)
Model: 225-234
Modeller: Lowell Davis
Height: 2 ¼", 5.7 cm
Colour: White, black and
            sivler
Issued: 1983 – 1985
Series: Farm Collection

U.K.:   £40.00
U.S.: $80.00
Can.: $80.00

LITTLE BIT OF SHADE
Model: 225-602
Modeller: Lowell Davis
Height: 5", 12.7 cm
Colour: Browns, white, black
            and green
Issued: 1991 - 1995
Series: Route 66

U.K.:   £10.00
U.S.: $20.00
Can.: $20.00

LONG DAYS, COLD NIGHTS
(Dog on kennel roof)
Model: 225-344
Modeller: Lowell Davis
Height: 5 ½", 14.0 cm
Colour: Black, brown, red,
            orange, green and
            beige
Issued: 1990 in a limited
            edition of 2,500
Series: Farm Collection

U.K.:   £45.00
U.S.: $90.00
Can.: $90.00

LONG HOT SUMMER
(Lowell in tub, cows and
windpump)
Model: 25343
Modeller: Lowell Davis
Height: 5 ½", 14.0 cm
Colour: Black, white, grey,
            tan, blue, green
            and browns
Issued: 1991 in a limited
            edition of 1,950

U.K.:   £ 65.00
U.S.: $125.00
Can.: $125.00

LOVE AT FIRST SIGHT
(Mouse looking into mirror)
Model: 225-267/LD24
Modeller: Lowell Davis
Height: 2", 5.0 cm
Colour: Browns, beige,
            blue-grey and red
Issued: 1985 - 1992
Series: Farm Collection

U.K.:   £35.00
U.S.: $70.00
Can.: $70.00

LUCKY SPOT
(Moose and person in boat)

Model: 210-416
Modeller: Boyd Perry
Height: 2", 5.0 cm
Colour: Blue-grey, brown,
            black, white, red
            and blue
Issued: c.1986 - Unknown
Series: Wind River Collection

U.K.:   £35.00
U.S.: $70.00
Can.: $70.00

MAD AS A WET HEN
(Goat standing on top of hen's house)

Model: 225-334
Modeller: Lowell Davis
Height: 6 ¾", 17.2 cm
Colour: Browns, grey, yellow
            and white
Issued: 1984 - 1986
Series: Farm Collection

U.K.:   £100.00
U.S.: $200.00
Can.: $200.00

MAIL ORDER BRIDE
(Hen in mail box with cockerel looking up)

Model: 225-263
Modeller: Lowell Davis
Height: 6 ¼", 15.9 cm
Colour: Black, yellow, red,
            grey and browns
Issued: 1987 - 1991
Series: Farm Collection

U.K.:   £35.00
U.S.: $70.00
Can.: $70.00

MAIN HOUSE

Model: 225-351
Modeller: Lowell Davis
Height: 3", 7.6 cm
Colour: Terracotta, grey, green
            and cream
Issued: 1985 - 1987
Series: FoxFire Farm Buildings

U.K.:   £45.00
U.S.: $90.00
Can.: $90.00

MAKIN' TRACKS
(Dog chased by turkey)

Model: 225-238
Modeller: Lowell Davis
Height: 2 ¾", 7.0 cm
Colour: Black, tan, white
            and red
Issued: 1983 - 1989
Series: Farm Collection

U.K.:   £30.00
U.S.: $60.00
Can.: $60.00

MAKING A BEE LINE
(Dog and bee hive)

Model: 225-274
Modeller: Lowell Davis
Height: 3", 7.6 cm
Colour: White, blue, reddish-
            brown, beige and green
Issued: 1988 - 1990
Series: Farm Collection

U.K.:   £35.00
U.S.: $70.00
Can.: $70.00

MAMA?
(Chicks and wellington boots)

Model: 225-277/LD1
Modeller: Lowell Davis
Height: 1 ¾", 4.4 cm
Colour: Black and yellow
Issued: 1986 - 1991
Series: Farm Collection

U.K.:   £15.00
U.S.: $30.00
Can.: $30.00

MAMA, CAN WILLIE STAY FOR SUPPER?
(Sow, piglets and chickens)

Model: Unknown
Modeller: Lowell Davis
Height: 2", 5.0 cm
Colour: Pink, black, white,
            orange, yellow, green
            and sandy brown
Issued: 1994 - 1995
Series: Farm Collection

U.K.:   £40.00
U.S.: $80.00
Can.: $80.00

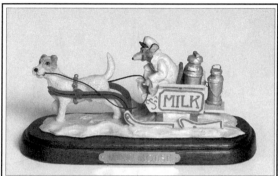

MAMA'S PRIZE LEGHORN
(Running fox with hen in mouth)

Model:	225-235
Modeller:	Lowell Davis
Height:	3", 7.6 cm
Colour:	Red-brown, yellow, red and white
Issued:	1983 - 1988
Series:	Farm Collection
U.K.:	£45.00
U.S.:	$90.00
Can.:	$90.00

MEETING OF SHELDON
(Calf and sparrow)

Model:	225-293/LD31
Modeller:	Lowell Davis
Height:	3 ½", 8.9 cm
Colour:	Dark cream, brown, green and black
Issued:	1989 - 1992
Series:	Farm Collection
U.K.:	£30.00
U.S.:	$60.00
Can.:	$60.00

MILK MOUSE
(Gus the dog pulling milk float driven by Mouse)

Model:	225-503
Modeller:	Lowell Davis
Height:	3 ¾", 9.5 cm
Colour:	White, red, silver-grey and brown
Issued:	1991 in a limited edition of 2,500
Series:	The World of Little Critters
U.K.:	£ 65.00
U.S.:	$125.00
Can.:	$125.00

MILKING TIME
(Cat on stool licking paw)

Model:	225-023
Modeller:	Lowell Davis
Height:	2 ¼", 5.7 cm
Colour:	Ginger tabby; white, brown and black
Issued:	1980 - 1985
Series:	Farm Collection
U.K.:	£25.00
U.S.:	$50.00
Can.:	$50.00

MISS PRIVATE TIME

Model:	225-517
Modeller:	Lowell Davis
Height:	2 ¾", 7.0 cm
Colour:	Brown, pink, white, green and blue
Issued:	1992 - 1993
Series:	The World of Little Critters
U.K.:	£25.00
U.S.:	$50.00
Can.:	$50.00

MISSOURI SPRING
(Suffolk Ewe and lambs)

Model:	225-278/LD30
Modeller:	Lowell Davis
Height:	3", 7.6 cm
Colour:	Black, white and browns
Issued:	1988 - 1992
Series:	Farm Collection
U.K.:	£40.00
U.S.:	$80.00
Can.:	$80.00

MOON RAIDERS
(Racoon and shed)

Model:	225-325
Modeller:	Lowell Davis
Height:	3 ¾", 9.5 cm
Colour:	Browns, black, white and red
Issued:	1982 in a limited edition of 900
Series:	Farm Collection
U.K.:	£ 65.00
U.S.:	$125.00
Can.:	$125.00

MOOSE

Model:	200-403
Modeller:	Daniel Parker
Height:	8", 20.3 cm
Colour:	Black, browns, grey and pink
Issued:	c.1986 in a limited edition of 1,450
Series:	North American Animals by Daniel Parker
U.K.:	£150.00
U.S.:	$300.00
Can.:	$300.00

MORNING CLOUD

Model:	210-525
Modeller:	Boyd Perry
Height:	2 ¾", 7.0 cm
Colour:	Sandy brown, black, white and red
Issued:	c.1986 - Unknown
Series:	Little Heavyweights
U.K.:	£20.00
U.S.:	$40.00
Can.:	$40.00

MOTHER HEN

Model:	225-292
Modeller:	Lowell Davis
Height:	2 ½", 6.4 cm
Colour:	Yellow, browns, red and green
Issued:	1989 - 1993
Series:	Farm Collection
U.K.:	£15.00
U.S.:	$30.00
Can.:	$30.00

MOTHER'S DAY
(Cat and kittens)

Model:	Unknown
Modeller:	Lowell Davis
Height:	1 ¾", 4.4 cm
Colour:	Black, white, orange, grey, green and beige
Issued:	1995 - 1995
Series:	1. Cats in Season
	2. Farm Collection
U.K.:	£20.00
U.S.:	$40.00
Can.:	$40.00

MOVING DAY
(Dog and cat)

Model:	225-225
Modeller:	Lowell Davis
Height:	2 ¾", 7.0 cm
Colour:	Black, white, browns and green
Issued:	1982 - 1984
Series:	Farm Collection
U.K.:	£40.00
U.S.:	$80.00
Can.:	$80.00

MY FAVOURITE CHORES

Model:	25362
Modeller:	Lowell Davis
Size:	5" x 13", 12.7 x 33.0 cm
Colour:	Dark brown, tan, white, black, blue, red and yellow
Issued:	1992 in a limited edition of 1,500
Series:	American Farm
U.K.:	£300.00
U.S.:	$600.00
Can.:	$600.00

NEL'S DINER*

Model:	225-601
Modeller:	Lowell Davis
Height:	3", 7.6 cm
Colour:	Red, blue, green, browns and black
Issued:	1991 in a limited edition numbered 1 to 350
Series:	Route 66
U.K.:	£100.00
U.S.:	$200.00
Can.:	$200.00

Note: * Issued with a piece of Route 66 in a lucite block.

NEL'S DINER

Model:	225-604
Modeller:	Lowell Davis
Height:	3", 7.6 cm
Colour:	Red, blue, green, browns and black
Issued:	1991 in a limited edition numbered 351 to 2500
Series:	Route 66
U.K.:	£ 80.00
U.S.:	$160.00
Can.:	$160.00

NEW FRIEND
(Puppy and hen)
Model: 225-288/LD12
Modeller: Lowell Davis
Height: 2 ½", 6.4 cm
Colour: Yellow, tan, white, black, green and red
Issued: 1989 - 1993
Series: Farm Collection

U.K.: £20.00
U.S.: $40.00
Can.: $40.00

NO HUNTING
(Bird of Prey on sign)
Model: 25375
Modeller: Lowell Davis
Height: 6 ½", 16.5 cm
Colour: Red-brown, black, white, green and browns
Issued: 1993 in a limited edition of 1,000
Series: American Farm

U.K.: £35.00
U.S.: $70.00
Can.: $70.00

NO HUNTING
(Fox and sign)
Model: 210-415
Modeller: Boyd Perry
Height: 4", 10.1 cm
Colour: Reddish-brown, black, white, grey, light brown and green
Issued: c.1986 - Unknown
Series: Wind River Collection

U.K.: £ 50.00
U.S.: $100.00
Can.: $100.00

NO PRIVATE TIME
Model: 225-316
Modeller: Lowell Davis
Height: 6", 15.0 cm
Colour: Red-brown, blue, black, white and red
Issued: 1988 in a limited edition of 1,250
Series: Farm Collection

U.K.: £45.00
U.S.: $90.00
Can.: $90.00

NOT A HAPPY CAMPER
(Racoon eating camper's lunch)
Model: Unknown
Modeller: Lowell Davis
Height: 2 ¾", 7.0 cm
Colour: Brown, black, navy blue, white, grey, beige and green
Issued: 1994 - 1995
Series: Farm Collection

U.K.: £30.00
U.S.: $60.00
Can.: $60.00

NOT A SHARIN' SOUL
(Pig in trough)
Model: 892-053/LD7
Modeller: Lowell Davis
Height: 1 ½", 3.84 cm
Colour: Pink pig with black spots; light brown trough
Issued: 1990 - 1991
Series: Lowell Davis Farm Club

U.K.: £25.00
U.S.: $50.00
Can.: $50.00

Note: Free to renewing members

OH MOTHER, WHAT IS IT?
(Cow, two calves, prairie dog)
Model: 96913
Modeller: Lowell Davis
Height: 3 ½", 8.9 cm
Colour: Black, white, red-brown and green
Issued: 1994 in a limited edition of 1,000
Series: Farm Collection

U.K.: £100.00
U.S.: $200.00
Can.: $200.00

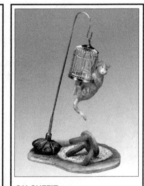

OH SHEEIT ...
(Cat climbing bird cage)
Model: 25363
Modeller: Lowell Davis
Height: 6", 15.0 cm
Colour: Orange, yellow, gold, browns, white and green
Issued: 1992 - 1995
Series: American Farm

U.K.: £40.00
U.S.: $80.00
Can.: $80.00

OH WHERE IS HE NOW?
(Bitch and pups)

Model: 95041
Modeller: Lowell Davis
Height: 3 ½", 8.9 cm
Colour: Black, grey, white,
            tan, red and green
Issued: 1993 in a limited
            edition of 1,250
Series: American Farm

U.K.:   £ 65.00
U.S.: $125.00
Can.: $125.00

OLD HOME PLACE, THE
(Three pigs and trough)

Model: 25802
Modeller: Lowell Davis
Height: 3 ½", 8.9 cm
Colour: Brown, pink, black,
            white and green
Issued: 1993 in a limited
            edition of 1,200
Series: American Farm

U.K.:   £ 65.00
U.S.: $125.00
Can.: $125.00

OLD HOME PLACE, THE
(Dated ornament, brown pig)

Model: 25806
Modeller: Lowell Davis
Height: 2 ¼", 5.7 cm
Colour: Brown and green
Issued: 1993 - 1993
Series: 1. American Farm
            2. Dated Ornament
            3. Miniature Figurine

U.K.:   £20.00
U.S.: $40.00
Can.: $40.00

ON THE MOVE
(Cat on steps)

Model: 225-206
Modeller: Lowell Davis
Height: 3", 7.6 cm
Colour: Browns, white, orange
            and red
Issued: 1982 in a limited
            edition of 4,000
Series: Farm Collection

U.K.:   £ 75.00
U.S.: $150.00
Can.: $150.00

ONE FOR THE ROAD
(Wren on cup)

Model: 225-241/LD20
Modeller: Lowell Davis
Height: 2 ½", 6.4 cm
Colour: Brown, white, fawn
            and pale green
Issued: 1984 - c.1995
Series: Farm Collection

U.K.:   £20.00
U.S.: $40.00
Can.: $40.00

OPEN THE LID
(Cat and goldfish bowl)

Model: 94106
Modeller: Lowell Davis
Height: 4 ¾", 12.1 cm
Colour: Grey, white, brown,
            orange, pink and blue
Issued: 1993 - 1993
Series: American Farm

U.K.:   £40.00
U.S.: $80.00
Can.: $80.00

ORPHANS, THE
(Two piglets)

Model: 1. 225-271
            2. LD17
Modeller: Lowell Davis
Height: 2 ¼", 5.7 cm
Colour: 1. Black and white
            2. Pink
Issued: 1. 1987 - 1992 (USA)
            2. 1987 - 1993 (UK)
Series: Farm Collection

U.K.:   £20.00
U.S.: $40.00
Can.: $40.00

OUT OF STEP
(Mother and six ducklings)

Model: 225-259/LD22
Modeller: Lowell Davis
Height: 2 ½", 6.4 cm
Colour: White, yellow, green
            and pink
Issued: 1985 - 1992
Series: Farm Collection

U.K.:   £25.00
U.S.: $50.00
Can.: $50.00

OUTING WITH GRANDPA
(Goats)

Model: 225-502
Modeller: Lowell Davis
Height: 6 ½", 16.5 cm
Colour: Red, browns, white, black and green
Issued: 1990 in a limited edition of 2,500
Series: The World of Little Critters

U.K.: £40.00
U.S.: $80.00
Can.: $80.00

OZARK BELLE
(Hound and teddy)

Model: 225-264/LD15
Modeller: Lowell Davis
Height: 2", 5.0 cm
Colour: Black, white, tan, yellow and beige
Issued: 1985 - 1990
Series: Farm Collection

U.K.: £20.00
U.S.: $40.00
Can.: $40.00

OZARK'S VITTLES
(Blue Jay on food bowl)

Model: 25818
Modeller: Lowell Davis
Height: 2 ½", 6.4 cm
Colour: Black, white, tan, blue and green
Issued: 1992 - 1993
Series: American Farm

U.K.: £20.00
U.S.: $40.00
Can.: $40.00

PASTURE PALS
(Cow, lying and rabbit)

Model: 225-245
Modeller: Lowell Davis
Height: 2 ¼", 5.7 cm
Colour: Black, white, green and brown
Issued: 1984 - 1990
Series: Farm Collection

U.K.: £30.00
U.S.: $60.00
Can.: $60.00

PEEP SHOW
(Chicks on basket)

Model: 25376
Modeller: Lowell Davis
Height: 2 ½", 6.4 cm
Colour: Yellow, browns and green
Issued: 1993 - 1993
Series: American Farm

U.K.: £30.00
U.S.: $60.00
Can.: $60.00

PEGGY

Model: 210-526
Modeller: Boyd Perry
Height: 1 ½", 3.8 cm
Colour: Blue, red, white black and silver
Issued: c.1986 - Unknown
Series: Little Heavyweights

U.K.: £20.00
U.S.: $40.00
Can.: $40.00

PERFECT TEN
(Cockerel and hen)

Model: 225-282
Modeller: Lowell Davis
Height: 3", 7.6 cm
Colour: Black, yellow, red, orange, light brown and green
Issued: 1988 - 1990
Series: Farm Collection

U.K.: £25.00
U.S.: $50.00
Can.: $50.00

PIGGIN' OUT
(Cow with piglets suckling)

Model: 225-345/LD35
Modeller: Lowell Davis
Height: 5 ½", 14.0 cm
Colour: Black, white, pink and green
Issued: 1990 in a limited edition of 1,250
Series: Farm Collection

U.K.: £ 75.00
U.S.: $150.00
Can.: $150.00

PIPELINE

Model:	210-527
Modeller:	Boyd Perry
Height:	3", 7.6 cm
Colour:	White, light blue, light sandy brown, red and yellow
Issued:	c.1986 - Unknown
Series:	Little Heavyweights
U.K.:	£20.00
U.S.:	$40.00
Can.:	$40.00

PIT STOP
(Birds on water pump with bucket)

Model:	20997
Modeller:	Lowell Davis
Height:	6 ½", 16.5 cm
Colour:	Browns, blue, grey, red, orange and green
Issued:	1990 – 1991
Series:	Lowell Davis Farm Club
U.K.:	£35.00
U.S.:	$70.00
Can.:	$70.00

Note: Available to club members only (5th Club Piece.)

PLAINS WARRIOR

Model:	100-114
Modeller:	Don Polland
Height:	10", 25.4 cm
Colour:	Dark reddish-black and white horse; Sandy yellow, red, blue and green
Issued:	1984 in a limited edition of 1,250 (UK)
Series:	The American West
U.K.:	£350.00
U.S.:	$700.00
Can.:	$700.00

PLUM TUCKERED OUT
(Dog and puppies)

Model:	225-201
Modeller:	Lowell Davis
Height:	4", 10.0 cm
Colour:	White, browns, black, tan and red
Issued:	1981 in a limited edition of 2,500
Series:	American Farm
U.K.:	£100.00
U.S.:	$200.00
Can.:	$200.00

POLLYWOGS
(Car, family in stream)

Model:	25617
Modeller:	Lowell Davis
Height:	4 ½", 11.9 cm
Colour:	Green, yellow, blue, browns and white
Issued:	1993 in a limited edition of 750
Series:	American Farm
U.K.:	£300.00
U.S.:	$600.00
Can.:	$600.00

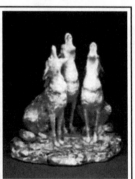

PRAIRIE CHORUS
(Three wild dogs)

Model:	225-333
Modeller:	Lowell Davis
Height:	4 ½", 11.9 cm
Colour:	Grey, white, brown and yellow
Issued:	1984 - 1986
Series:	Farm Collection
U.K.:	£100.00
U.S.:	$200.00
Can.:	$200.00

PRIVATE TIME
(Mouse reading, sitting on chamber pot)

Model:	225-506
Modeller:	Lowell Davis
Height:	1 ¾", 4.4 cm
Colour:	Brown, red, white and pink
Issued:	1990 - 1993
Series:	The World of Little Critters
U.K.:	£20.00
U.S.:	$40.00
Can.:	$40.00

PRIVY

Model:	225-348
Modeller:	Lowell Davis
Height:	1 ½", 3.8 cm
Colour:	Browns, green, yellow, black and blue
Issued:	1985 - 1987
Series:	FoxFire Farm Buildings
U.K.:	£15.00
U.S.:	$30.00
Can.:	$30.00

PUNKIN' PIG
(Ram pulling cart driven by pig)

Model:	225-505
Modeller:	Lowell Davis
Height:	5 ½", 14.0 cm
Colour:	White, green, orange, brown and pink
Issued:	1990 in a limited edition of 2,500
Series:	The World of Little Critters
U.K.:	£ 60.00
U.S.:	$120.00
Can.:	$120.00

PUNKIN' SEEDS
(Fish)

Model:	225-219
Modeller:	Lowell Davis
Height:	6 ½", 16.5 cm
Colour:	Yellow, black, red and light brown
Issued:	1981 in a limited edition of 750
Series:	Farm Collection
U.K.:	£125.00
U.S.:	$250.00
Can.:	$250.00

PUNKIN' WINE
(Two mice)

Model:	225-501
Modeller:	Lowell Davis
Height:	4", 10.1 cm
Colour:	Orange, white, brown, blue, black and green
Issued:	1990 - 1993
Series:	The World of Little Critters
U.K.:	£40.00
U.S.:	$80.00
Can.:	$80.00

QUACK
(Duckling)

Model:	210-553
Modeller:	Boyd Perry
Height:	1 ¾", 4.4 cm
Colour:	Reddish-brown, dark yellow, black and white
Issued:	Unknown
Series:	Little Rascals
U.K.:	£20.00
U.S.:	$40.00
Can.:	$40.00

QU'EST-CE QUE C'EST?
(Hen, chicks and turtle)

Model:	Unknown
Modeller:	Lowell Davis
Height:	3 ¼", 8.3 cm
Colour:	Orange-brown, brown, yellow, green and red
Issued:	1994 in a limited edition of 750
Series:	Farm Collection
U.K.:	£40.00
U.S.:	$80.00
Can.:	$80.00

QUIET DAY AT MAPLE GROVE
(Two dogs, cat at Coke machine)

Model:	225-618
Modeller:	Lowell Davis
Height:	Unknown
Colour:	Blue, brown, black, white and tan
Issued:	1992 - 1995
Series:	Route 66
U.K.:	£ 65.00
U.S.:	$125.00
Can.:	$125.00

RAIDERS
(Raccoons)

Model:	210-410
Modeller:	Boyd Perry
Height:	4", 10.1 cm
Colour:	Dark grey, black, white, sandy brown, reddish-brown, beige, yellow and green
Issued:	c.1986 - Unknown
Series:	Wind River Collection
U.K.:	£40.00
U.S.:	$80.00
Can.:	$80.00

RELIEF

Model:	225-605
Modeller:	Lowell Davis
Height:	2 ¼", 5.7 cm
Colour:	Black, tan, white and green
Issued:	1992 - 1995
Series:	Route 66
U.K.:	£15.00
U.S.:	$30.00
Can.:	$30.00

REMUS' CABIN

Model:	225-350
Modeller:	Lowell Davis
Height:	1 ¼", 3.1 cm
Colour:	Light brown, brown, blue-grey, green and white
Issued:	1985 - 1987
Series:	FoxFire Farm Buildings
U.K.:	£20.00
U.S.:	$40.00
Can.:	$40.00

RENOIR
(Cat on artist's palette)

Model:	225-261/LD19
Modeller:	Lowell Davis
Height:	3 ¼", 8.3 cm
Colour:	Black, grey, white, yellow and brown
Issued:	1985 - c.1995
Series:	Farm Collection
U.K.:	£25.00
U.S.:	$50.00
Can.:	$50.00

RFD BELL – BLOSSOM
(Cow)

Model:	225-040
Modeller:	Lowell Davis
Height:	4 ¾", 12.1 cm
Colour:	Browns, white, red and tan
Issued:	1980 - 1984
Series:	Farm Collection
U.K.:	£20.00
U.S.:	$40.00
Can.:	$40.00

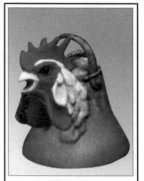

RFD BELL – CARUSO
(Cockeral)

Model:	225-043
Modeller:	Lowell Davis
Height:	3 ½", 8.9 cm
Colour:	White, red, yellow and browns
Issued:	1980 - 1984
Series:	Farm Collection
U.K.:	£20.00
U.S.:	$40.00
Can.:	$40.00

RFD BELL – KATE
(Mule)

Model:	225-041
Modeller:	Lowell Davis
Height:	4 ¼", 10.8 cm
Colour:	Browns, black and white
Issued:	1980 - 1984
Series:	Farm Collection
U.K.:	£20.00
U.S.:	$40.00
Can.:	$40.00

RFD BELL- OLD BLUE LEAD
(Two hounds)

Model:	225-045
Modeller:	Lowell Davis
Height:	3 ½", 8.9 cm
Colour:	White, black, tan, liver and brown
Issued:	1980 - 1984
Series:	Farm Collection
U.K.:	£20.00
U.S.:	$40.00
Can.:	$40.00

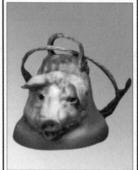

RFD BELL – WILBUR
(Pig)

Model:	225-044
Modeller:	Lowell Davis
Height:	4", 10.0 cm
Colour:	Pink, black and brown
Issued:	1980 - 1984
Series:	Farm Collection
U.K.:	£20.00
U.S.:	$40.00
Can.:	$40.00

RFD BELL - WILLY
(Goat)

Model:	225-042
Modeller:	Lowell Davis
Height:	3 ¾", 9.5 cm
Colour:	Tan, black, rust and brown
Issued:	1980 - 1984
Series:	Farm Collection
U.K.:	£20.00
U.S.:	$40.00
Can.:	$40.00

RIGHT CHURCH, WRONG PEW
(Hen looking at cats in hen
hut)

Model:	225-204
Modeller:	Lowell Davis
Height:	3", 7.6 cm
Colour:	Browns, white, red, black and orange
Issued:	1982 in a limited edition of 4,000
Series:	Farm Collection
U.K.:	£ 50.00
U.S.:	$100.00
Can.:	$100.00

ROOTED OUT
(Sow with piglets)

Model:	1. 225-217
	2. 091
Modeller:	Lowell Davis
Height:	1 ½", 3.8 cm
Colour:	1. Pink
	2. Pink with black spots
Issued:	1. 1981 - 1989 (USA)
	2. 07/82 - 12/82 (UK)
Series:	American Farm
U.K.:	£30.00
U.S.:	$60.00
Can.:	$60.00

RUFF (Puppy)

Model:	210-561
Modeller:	Boyd Perry
Height:	1 ¾", 4.4 cm
Colour:	Black, white, tan and red
Issued:	Unknown
Series:	Little Rascals
U.K.:	£20.00
U.S.:	$40.00
Can.:	$40.00

RUNNING WOLF, WAR CHIEF

Model:	100-111/AA0111
Modeller:	Don Polland
Height:	9", 22.9 cm
Colour:	Dark flesh tones; sandy-yellow, blue, black and white
Issued:	1984 in a limited edition of 2,500 (UK)
Series:	The American West
U.K.:	£250.00
U.S.:	$500.00
Can.:	$500.00

SAFE HAVEN
(Fox and trap)

Model:	25320
Modeller:	Lowell Davis
Height:	1 ¼", 3.1 cm
Colour:	Red-brown, green, black and browns
Issued:	1992 - 1995
Series:	American Farm
U.K.:	£40.00
U.S.:	$80.00
Can.:	$80.00

SAWIN' LOGS
(Dog on rocking chair)

Model:	225-260/LD26
Modeller:	Lowell Davis
Height:	3 ½", 8.9 cm
Colour:	Black, white, tan and pink
Issued:	1988 - 1992
Series:	Farm Collection
U.K.:	£25.00
U.S.:	$50.00
Can.:	$50.00

SCALLYWAGS
(Scarecrow with crows)

Model:	225-221
Modeller:	Lowell Davis
Height:	5 ¼", 13.3 cm
Colour:	Green, yellow, black, red and brown
Issued:	1981 - 1987
Series:	American Farm
U.K.:	£ 65.00
U.S.:	$125.00
Can.:	$125.00

SCHOOL BUS
(Possum and young)

Model:	210-401
Modeller:	Boyd Perry
Height:	2", 5.0 cm
Colour:	Grey, black, white, beige, pink and red
Issued:	c.1986 - Unknown
Series:	Wind River Collection
U.K.:	£35.00
U.S.:	$70.00
Can.:	$70.00

SCHOOL YARD DOGS

Model:	25369
Modeller:	Lowell Davis
Height:	8 ½", 21.6 cm
Colour:	Black, white, tan, red, blue and green
Issued:	1992 - 1995
Series:	Farm Collection
U.K.:	£ 50.00
U.S.:	$100.00
Can.:	$100.00

SCRAPPER (Raccoon)

Model:	210-557
Modeller:	Boyd Perry
Height:	1 ¾", 4.4 cm
Colour:	Dark grey, black, white, sandy brown and brown
Issued:	Unknown
Series:	Little Rascals
U.K.:	£20.00
U.S.:	$40.00
Can.:	$40.00

SCRATCH
(Kitten and teddy)

Moel:	210-559
Modeller:	Boyd Perry
Height:	1 ¾", 4.4 cm
Colour:	Brown, blue, white yellow and pink
Issued:	Unknown
Series:	Little Rascals
U.K.:	£20.00
U.S.:	$40.00
Can.:	$40.00

SECOND CHANCE
(North American Indian, pony and bison)

Model:	100-115
Modeller:	Don Polland
Height:	4 ½", 11.9 cm
Colour:	Black, white, blue, brown and yellow
Issued:	1984 in a limited edition of 2,000 (UK)
Series:	The American West
U.K.:	£150.00
U.S.:	$300.00
Can.:	$300.00

SEEIN' RED
(Puppy with red shoes)

Model:	225-296/LD6
Modeller:	Lowell Davis
Height:	1 ¾", 4.4 cm
Colour:	White, tan, red, green and black
Issued:	1990 - 1993
Series:	Farm Collection
U.K.:	£12.00
U.S.:	$25.00
Can.:	$25.00

SHE LAY LOW

Model:	25364
Modeller:	Lowell Davis
Height:	3 ¼", 8.3 cm
Colour:	Light brown, grey, yellow and green
Issued:	1992 - 1993
Series:	American Farm
U.K.:	£40.00
U.S.:	$80.00
CAn.:	$80.00

SHEEP SHEARIN' TIME
(Lowell, helper and sheep)

Model:	25388
Modeller:	Lowell Davis
Height:	4", 10.1 cm
Colour:	Blue, white, black, red and green
Issued:	1993 in a limited edition of 1,200
Series:	American Farm
U.K.:	£150.00
U.S.:	$300.00
Can.:	$300.00

SHOOTING THE RAPIDS /
RUNNING THE RAPIDS
(North American Indians in a canoe)

Model:	100-116/AA0101
Modeller:	Don Polland
Height:	5", 12.7 cm
Colour:	Browns, yellow, tan, white and blue
Issued:	1984 in a limited edition of 2,250 (UK)
Series:	The American West
U.K.:	£175.00
U.S.:	$350.00
Can.:	$350.00

SLEEPY (Owlet)
Model:	210-554
Modeller:	Boyd Perry
Height:	2 ¼", 5.7 cm
Colour:	Browns, orange, cream and white
Issued:	Unknown
Series:	Little Rascals
U.K.:	£20.00
U.S.:	$40.00
Can.:	$40.00

SLIM PICKIN'S
(Pig, trough and Cockerel)
Model:	1. 225-034
	2. 96846
Modeller:	Lowell Davis
Height:	1. 4", 10.0 cm
	2. 1 ¾", 4.4 cm
Colour:	Brown, white, and black
Issued:	1. 1979 - 1983
	2. 1994 - 1995
Series:	1. Farm Collection
	2. 15th Anniv. of issue

	225-034	96846
U.K.:	£ 75.	£40.
U.S.:	$150.	$80.
Can.:	$150.	$80.

SLY (Fox)
Model:	210-552
Modeller:	Boyd Perry
Height:	2 ¼", 5.7 cm
Colour:	Red-brown, black, white and tan
Issued:	Unknown
Series:	Little Rascals
U.K.:	£20.00
U.S.:	$40.00
Can.:	$40.00

SMOKE HOUSE
Model:	225-357
Modeller:	Lowell Davis
Height:	1 ½", 3.8 cm
Colour:	Terracotta, grey, green and turquoise
Issued:	1985 - 1987
Series:	FoxFire Farm Buildings
U.K.:	£20.00
U.S.:	$40.00
Can.:	$40.00

SMOKEY
Model:	210-501
Modeller:	Boyd Perry
Height:	2 ¾", 7.0 cm
Colour:	Orange-yellow, black, red and grey
Issued:	c.1986 - Unknown
Series:	Little Heavyweights
U.K.:	£20.00
U.S.:	$40.00
Can.:	$40.00

SMOKIN' JOE
Model:	210-507
Modeller:	Boyd Perry
Height:	2 ¼", 5.7 cm
Colour:	Black, light and dark blue, white and reddish-brown
Issued:	c.1986 - Unknown
Series:	Little Heavyweights
U.K.:	£20.00
U.S.:	$40.00
Can.:	$40.00

SNAKE DOCTOR
(Dragonfly on fishing line
bobber)
Model:	25365
Modeller:	Lowell Davis
Height:	2 ½", 6.4 cm
Colour:	Blue, brown, white and green
Issued:	1992 - 1995
Series:	American Farm
U.K.:	£25.00
U.S.:	$50.00
Can.:	$50.00

SNIP (Baby turtle)
Model:	210-558
Modeller:	Boyd Perry
Height:	1 ¼", 3.1 cm
Colour:	Reddish-brown, white and blue-grey
Issued:	Unknown
Series:	Little Rascals
U.K.:	£20.00
U.S.:	$40.00
Can.:	$40.00

"SPLIT DECISION"
(Cock and hens)

Model:	225-210/093
Modeller:	Lowell Davis
Height:	2", 5.0 cm
Colour:	Pink, red, black, white, green, yellow and blue-grey
Issued:	1981 - 1984 (USA) 07/82 - 12/82 (UK)
Series:	American Farm
U.K.:	£35.00
U.S.:	$70.00
Can.:	$70.00

STICKS AND STONES
(Cat, spade and bird)

Model:	Unknown
Modeller:	Lowell Davis
Height:	3 ¼", 8.3 cm
Colour:	Ginger tabby; orange and black bird; light brown and silver spade
Issued:	1995 - 1995
Series:	Farm Collection
U.K.:	£30.00
U.S.:	$60.00
Can.:	$60.00

STIRRING UP TROUBLE
(Two racoons on a rabbit's hutch)

Model:	225-331
Modeller:	Lowell Davis
Height:	5", 12.7 cm
Colour:	Browns, black, white and grey
Issued:	1983 in a limited edition of 2,500
Series:	Farm Collection
U.K.:	£ 65.00
U.S.:	$125.00
Can.:	$125.00

STRAWBERRY PATCH
(Tortoise and strawberries)

Model:	225-021
Modeller:	Lowell Davis
Height:	1", 2.5 cm
Colour:	Green, brown, red and beige
Issued:	1980 - 1989
Series:	Farm Collection
U.K.:	£20.00
U.S.:	$40.00
Can.:	$40.00

STRAY DOG
(Seated dog)

Model:	225-223
Modeller:	Lowell Davis
Height:	2", 5.0 cm
Colour:	Black, white and green
Issued:	1982 - 1988
Series:	Farm Collection
U.K.:	£25.00
U.S.:	$50.00
Can.:	$50.00

STRETCH

Model:	210-522
Modeller:	Boyd Perry
Height:	2 ¾", 7.0 cm
Colour:	Blue, white, brown and black
Issued:	c.1986 - Unknown
Series:	Little Heavyweights
U.K.:	£20.00
U.S.:	$40.00
Can.:	$40.00

STUDIO MOUSE

Model:	225-215
Modeller:	Lowell Davis
Height:	2 ½", 6.4 cm
Colour:	Browns, white, yellow and black
Issued:	1981 - 1984
Series:	Farm Collection
U.K.:	£30.00
U.S.:	$60.00
Can.:	$60.00

SUMMER DAYS
(Man selling tyres has cat in his lap)

Model:	Unknown
Modeller:	Lowell Davis
Height:	Unknown
Colour:	Blue, white, black, brown, ginger and tan
Issued:	1993 - 1993
Series:	Route 66
U.K.:	£ 50.00
U.S.:	$100.00
Can.:	$100.00

SUN WORSHIPPERS
(Cat lying next to potted plant)
Model: 223-621
Modeller: Lowell Davis
Height: 2 ¼", 5.7 cm
Colour: Black, white, red,
red-brown, green
and yellow
Issued: 1989 - Unknown
Series: 1. Dated Ornament
2. Friends of Mine
3. Miniature Figurines

U.K.: £15.00
U.S.: $30.00
Can.: $30.00

SUN WORSHIPPERS
(Three cats sitting on steps)
Model: 223-620
Modeller: Lowell Davis
Height: 3 ¼", 8.3 cm
Colour: Orange, black, white,
red, green and dark
terracotta
Issued: 1989 in a limited
edition of 5,000
Series: Friends of Mine

U.K.: £40.00
U.S.: $80.00
Can.: $80.00

SUNBURN
Model: 210-518
Modeller: Boyd Perry
Height: 1 ½", 3.8 cm
Colour: Red, green, black,
blue, yellow and whtie
Issued: c.1986 - Unknown
Series: Little Heavyweights

U.K.: £20.00
U.S.: $40.00
Can.: $40.00

SUNDAY AFTERNOON
**(Cat seated next to ice-cream
maker)**
Model: 225-024
Modeller: Lowell Davis
Height: 2", 5.0 cm
Colour: Black, white, tan
and grey
Issued: 1980 - 1985
Series: 1. Dated Ornament
2. Friends of Mine
3. Miniature Figurine

U.K.: £12.00
U.S.: $25.00
Can.: $25.00

SUNDAY AFTERNOON TREAT
**(Cat seated next to home made
ice-cream maker)**
Model: 223-625
Modeller: Lowell Davis
Height: 3", 7.6 cm
Colour: Ginger tabby; black,
brown, white, blue, red,
beige and green
Issued: 1990 in a limited
edition of 5,000
Series: Friends of Mine

U.K.: £35.00
U.S.: $70.00
Can.: $70.00

SUNDAY AFTERNOON TREAT
**(Cat sitting next to sack of
rock salt)**
Model: 223-626
Modeller: Lowell Davis
Height: 2 ¼", 5.7 cm
Colour: Ginger tabby; white,
beige, red and black
Issued: 1990 - Unknown
Series: 1. Dated Ornament
2. Friends of Mine
3. Miniature Figurine

U.K.: £15.00
U.S.: $30.00
Can.: $30.00

SURPRISE IN THE CELLAR
(Cat and kittens)
Model: 225-200
Modeller: Lowell Davis
Height: 3 ½", 8.9 cm
Colour: Orange, black, white,
blue and browns
Issued: 1981 in a limited
edition of 2,500
Series: 1. American Farm
2. Country Pride

U.K.: £ 80.00
U.S.: $160.00
Can.: $160.00

SWEET TOOTH
(Bear cub with Beehive)
Model: 25373
Modeller: Lowell Davis
Height: 2 ¾", 7.0 cm
Colour: Brown, white and
green
Issued: 1993 - 1995
Series: American Farm

U.K.: £25.00
U.S.: $50.00
Can.: $50.00

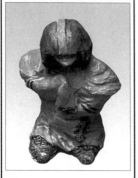

T.D.

Model:	210-505
Modeller:	Boyd Perry
Height:	2 ¾", 7.0 cm
Colour:	Red, blue and brown
Issued:	c.1986 - Unknown
Series:	Little Heavyweights
U.K.:	£20.00
U.S.:	$40.00
Can.:	$40.00

T.P.

Model:	210-513
Modeller:	Boyd Perry
Height:	2 ¾", 7.0 cm
Colour:	Red, green, white, browns, black and fleshtones
Issued:	c.1986 - Unknown
Series:	Little Heavyweights
U.K.:	£20.00
U.S.:	$40.00
Can.:	$40.00

TAX COLLECTOR
(Turkey on fence post)

Model:	210-407
Modeller:	Boyd Perry
Height:	4", 10.1 cm
Colour:	Dark grey, grey, light terracotta, blue, red and green
Issued:	c.1986 - Unknown
Series:	Wind River Collection
U.K.:	£35.00
U.S.:	$70.00
Can.:	$70.00

THINKING BIG
(Cockerel and chick)

Model:	225-231
Modeller:	Lowell Davis
Height:	2 ¾", 7.0 cm
Colour:	White, red, black, grey, yellow, blue and beige
Issued:	1982 - 1988
Series:	Farm Collection
U.K.:	£25.00
U.S.:	$50.00
Can.:	$50.00

THIRSTY
(Bird on flagon)

Model:	892-050
Modeller:	Lowell Davis
Height:	3", 7.6 cm
Colour:	Cream, black, yellow, brown and green
Issued:	1990 - Unknown
Series:	Lowell Davis Farm Club
U.K.:	£15.00
U.S.:	$30.00
Can.:	$30.00

Note: Free to members

TOAD STRANGLER
(Toad and umbrella)

Model:	225-509
Modeller:	Lowell Davis
Height:	2 ½", 6.4 cm
Colour:	Green, yellow-orange, purple and pink
Issued:	1991 - 1993
Series:	The World of Little Critters
U.K.:	£25.00
U.S.:	$50.00
Can.:	$50.00

TOO GOOD TO WASTE ON KIDS
(Cockerels eating water melon watched by chicks)

Model:	225-262
Modeller:	Lowell Davis
Height:	2 ½", 6.4 cm
Colour:	White, black, red, green and browns
Issued:	1985 - 1992
Series:	Farm Collection
U.K.:	£40.00
U.S.:	$80.00
Can.:	$80.00

TREED
(Cat and two dogs)

Model:	225-327
Modeller:	Lowell Davis
Height:	4 ½", 11.9 cm
Colour:	Black, white, red and orange
Issued:	1982 in a limited edition of 1,250
Series:	Farm Collection
U.K.:	£ 80.00
U.S.:	$160.00
Can.:	$160.00

TRIBUTE TO HOOKER
(Dog lying)

Model: 225-340
Modeller: Lowell Davis
Height: 2 ¾", 9.5 cm
Colour: Terracotta, brown,
            green, white and blue
Issued: 1989 in a limited
            edition of 2,500
Series: Farm Collection

U.K.:   £40.00
U.S.: $80.00
Can.: $80.00

TRICK OR TREAT?
(Cat and Jack O'lantern)

Model: 27565
Modeller: Lowell Davis
Height: 2 ¾", 7.0 cm
Colour: Black, orange and
            green
Issued: 1993 - 1995
Series: 1. Cats in Season
            2. Farm Collection

U.K.:   £20.00
U.S.: $40.00
Can.: $40.00

TRICKS OF THE TRADE
(Molly the mule with Lowell Davis)

Model: 225-346
Modeller: Lowell Davis
Height: 7 ½", 19.1 cm
Colour: Reddish-brown, grey,
            blue, green and black
Issued: 1990 in a limited
            edition of 1,250
Series: Farm Collection

U.K.:   £100.00
U.S.: $200.00
Can.: $200.00

TURKEY

Model: 200-150
Modeller: Frank Falco
Height: 7 ¼", 18.4 cm
Colour: Black, light and dark
            brown, white, red and
            beige
Issued: c.1986 in a limited
            edition of 950
Series: Birds by Frank Falco

U.K.:   £300.00
U.S.: $600.00
Can.: $600.00

TWO IN A BUSH
(Rabbits teasing dog)

Model: 225-337/LD33
Modeller: Lowell Davis
Height: 4 ½", 11.9 cm
Colour: Browns, grey, green,
            white and black
Issued: 1987 - 1988 (USA)
            1991 in a limited
            edition of 950 (UK)
Series: Farm Collection

U.K.:   £ 75.00
U.S.: $150.00
Can.: $150.00

TWO TIMER
(Three cats)

Model: 94119
Modeller: Lowell Davis
Height: 2 ½", 6.4 cm
Colour: Ginger, black, grey,
            white and green
Issued: 1994 - 1995
Series: Farm Collection

U.K.:   £30.00
U.S.: $60.00
Can.: $60.00

TWO'S COMPANY
(Two piglets and cockerel)

Model: 225-224
Modeller: Lowell Davis
Height: 2", 5.0 cm
Colour: Light brown, brown,
            white, red, green and
            grey
Issued: 1982 – 1986
Series: Farm Collection

U.K.:   £40.00
U.S.: $80.00
Can.: $80.00

UNDER THE WEATHER
(Piglet with apples)

Model: 225-212/LD8
Modeller: Lowell Davis
Height: 1 ¼", 3.1 cm
Colour: Pink, brown, green
            and grey
Issued: 1981 - 1991
Series: Farm Collection

U.K.:   £25.00
U.S.: $50.00
Can.: $50.00

UNINVITED CALLER
(Turtle and frog)

Model:	Unknown
Modeller:	Lowell Davis
Height:	2 ¾", 7.0 cm
Colour:	Browns, green, yellow, black, cream and light terracotta
Issued:	1995 - 1995
Series:	American Farm
U.K.:	£30.00
U.S.:	$60.00
Can.:	$60.00

UP TO NO GOOD
(Fox and hen house)

Model:	225-218
Modeller:	Lowell Davis
Height:	6 ¼", 15.9 cm
Colour:	Yellow, red-brown, black and white
Issued:	1981 - 1984
Series:	Farm Collection
U.K.:	£125.00
U.S.:	$250.00
Can.:	$250.00

WAITING FOR HIS MASTER
(Pup lying in front of a shed)

Model:	225-281
Modeller:	Lowell Davis
Height:	3 ¾", 9.5 cm
Colour:	Browns, black, white, red and green
Issued:	1982 – 1986
Series:	Farm Collection
U.K.:	£40.00
U.S.:	$80.00
Can.:	$80.00

Note: Version with unlocked door will command a premium of 30%.

WAR TROPHY

Model:	100-118
Modeller:	Don Polland
Height:	7 ½", 19.1 cm
Colour:	Grey, dark brown, orange, red, black, white, sandy yellow, blue and beige
Issued:	1984 in a limited edition of 2,250 (UK)
Series:	The American West
U.K.:	£350.00
U.S.:	$700.00
Can.:	$700.00

WARM MILK
(Cat standing next to bowl)

Model:	223-630
Modeller:	Lowell Davis
Height:	2 ¼", 5.7 cm
Colour:	Ginger tabby; white, red and sandy brown
Issued:	1991 - 1993
Series:	1. Dated Ornament
	2. Friends of Mine
	3. Miniature Figurine
U.K.:	£15.00
U.S.:	$30.00
Can.:	$30.00

WARM MILK
(Two cats)

Model:	223-629
Modeller:	Lowell Davis
Height:	4", 10.1 cm
Colour:	Ginger, browns, silver, white and red
Issued:	1991 in a limited edition of 5,000
Series:	Friends of Mine
U.K.:	£ 65.00
U.S.:	$125.00
Can.:	$125.00

WARMIN' THEIR BUNS
(Dog, cat, piglets in front of stove)

Model:	96911
Modeller:	Lowell Davis
Height:	5 ½", 14.0 cm
Colour:	Grey, black, white, pink, browns and orange
Issued:	1994 in a limited edition of 1,200
Series:	Farm Collection
U.K.:	£ 80.00
U.S.:	$160.00
Can.:	$160.00

WELCOME MAT
(Policeman hiding behind billboard)

Model:	225-606
Modeller:	Lowell Davis
Height:	5 ½", 14.0 cm
Colour:	Green, white, black and red
Issued:	1991 in a limited edition of 1,500
Series:	Route 66
U.K.:	£100.00
U.S.:	$200.00
Can.:	$200.00

333

WHAT ARE PALS FOR?
Model: 225-620
Modeller: Lowell Davis
Height: 2 ½", 6.4 cm
Colour: Blue, white, green, tan, red and black
Issued: 1992 - 1995
Series: Route 66

U.K.: £35.00
U.S.: $70.00
Can.: $70.00

WHAT RAT RACE?
(Horse drawn sleigh)
Model: 23603
Modeller: Lowell Davis
Height: 5 ½", 14.0 cm
Colour: Black, white, grey, green and red
Issued: 1991 in a limited edition of 1,200
Series: Farm Collection

U.K.: £425.00
U.S.: $850.00
Can.: $850.00

Photograph not available at press time

WHEN COFFEE NEVER TASTED SO GOOD
Model: 255-507
Modeller: Lowell Davis
Height: 6" x 10", 15.0 x 25.4 cm
Colour: Unknown
Issued: 1991 in a limited edition of 1,250
Series: The World of Little Critters

U.K.: £ 80.00
U.S.: $160.00
Can.: $160.00

WHEN MAMA GETS MAD
(Goat kid chewing hat)
Model: 225-228/096
Modeller: Lowell Davis
Height: 2 ¼", 5.7 cm
Colour: Reddish-brown, white, beige and green
Issued: 1981 - 1986 (USA) 07/82 - 12/82 (UK)
Series: American Farm

U.K.: £15.00
U.S.: $30.00
Can.: $30.00

WHEN THE CAT'S AWAY
Model: 225-276
Modeller: Lowell Davis
Height: 2 ½", 6.4 cm
Colour: Light and dark brown, red, white and green
Issued: 1987 - 1993
Series: Farm Collection

U.K.: £25.00
U.S.: $50.00
Can.: $50.00

WHEN THREE FOOT'S A MILE
(Geese and cockerel)
Model: 225-315
Modeller: Lowell Davis
Height: 4", 10.1 cm
Colour: White, brown, grey, black, red, orange and green
Issued: 1998 in a limited edition of 950
Series: Farm Collection

U.K.: £ 65.00
U.S.: $125.00
Can.: $125.00

WHITE-TAILED DEER
Model: 200-402
Modeller: Daniel Parker
Height: 8", 20.3 cm
Colour: Black, tan, grey and white
Issued: c.1986 in a limited edition of 1,450
Series: North American Animals by Daniel Parker

U.K.: £150.00
U.S.: $300.00
Can.: $300.00

WHITEY
Model: 210-520
Modeller: Boyd Perry
Height: 2 ¾", 7.0 cm
Colour: Light and dark blue and brown
Issued: c.1986 - Unknown
Series: Little Heavyweights

U.K.: £20.00
U.S.: $40.00
Can.: $40.00

WILBUR
(Pig and overturned bucket)

Model:	225-029
Modeller:	Lowell Davis
Height:	3 ¾", 9.5 cm
Colour:	Black, pink, orange and browns
Issued:	1980 - 1985
Series:	Farm Collection
U.K.:	£ 60.00
U.S.:	$120.00
Can.:	$120.00

WILL YOU RESPECT ME IN THE MORNING?
(Two cats)

Model:	225-265/LD34
Modeller:	Lowell Davis
Height:	3 ½", 8.9 cm
Colour:	White, black, orange, grey and green
Issued:	1985 - 01/91
Series:	Farm Collection
U.K.:	£20.00
U.S.:	$40.00
Can.:	$40.00

WINDMILL

Model:	225-349
Modeller:	Lowell Davis
Height:	4 ½", 11.9 cm
Colour:	Black, brown and red
Issued:	1985 - 1987
Series:	FoxFire Farm Buildings
U.K.:	£30.00
U.S.:	$60.00
Can.:	$60.00

WINTER LAMB
(Collie and lamb)

Model:	225-317
Modeller:	Lowell Davis
Height:	7", 17.8 cm
Colour:	Black, tan and white
Issued:	1991 in a limited edition of 1,750
Series:	Farm Collection
U.K.:	£125.00
U.S.:	$250.00
Can.:	$250.00

WISHFUL THINKING
(Cat seated on bird house)

Model:	225-285
Modeller:	Lowell Davis
Height:	4 ½", 11.9 cm
Colour:	Black and white cat; light brown bird house and tree trunk; green base
Issued:	1988 - 1992
Series:	Farm Collection
U.K.:	£20.00
U.S.:	$40.00
Can.:	$40.00

WOMAN'S WORK
(Chicken in barrel)

Model:	225-232/LD13
Modeller:	Lowell Davis
Height:	2 ½", 6.4 cm
Colour:	Brown, white, beige, grey, green and red
Issued:	1983 - 1988
Series:	Farm Collection
U.K.:	£25.00
U.S.:	$50.00
Can.:	$50.00

WOODSCOLT
(Mare and mule foal)

Model:	225-342
Modeller:	Lowell Davis
Height:	7 ½", 19.1 cm
Colour:	Dark brown, brown, black, cream and green
Issued:	1989 in a limited edition of 950
Series:	Farm Collection
U.K.:	£175.00
U.S.:	$350.00
Can.:	$350.00

ZSA ZSA

Model:	210-508
Modeller:	Boyd Perry
Height:	2 ¾", 7.0 cm
Colour:	Dark yellow, white and red
Issued:	c.1986 - Unknown
Series:	Little Heavyweights
U.K.:	£20.00
U.S.:	$40.00
Can.:	$40.00

CHAPTER THREE

STORYBOOK CHARACTERS

BEATRIX POTTER
Figurines

A LITTLE SHOE-HOUSE™

Model: 120010
Modeller: Richard Wawrzesta
Height: 4 ¾", 12.1 cm
Colour: Blue, brown, white, pink, blue, cream, brown, 22-carat gold
Issued: 1998 in a limited edition of 1,250

U.K.: £45.00
U.S.: $90.00
Can.: $90.00

A PARTING PRESENT FOR OLD BROWN™
(Old Mr. Brown and Squirrel Nutkin)

Model: 080105
Modeller: Richard Wawrzesta
Height: Unknown
Colour: Brown, cream, white, red-brown and green
Issued: Unknown in a limited edition of 250
Series: Tableau

U.K.: £115.00
U.S.: $230.00
Can.: $230.00

AMIABLE GUINEA PIG™

Model: BP12
Modeller: Richard Wawrzesta
Height: 3 ¾", 9.5 cm
Size: Large
Colour: White, yellow, mustard, blue, grey and brown
Issued: 01/87 - 12/89 (In Tins)

U.K.: £ 80.00
U.S.: $160.00
Can.: $160.00

APPLEY DAPPLY™
Style One

Model: A2352
Modeller: Richard Wawrzesta
Height: 2 ¼", 5.7 cm
Size: Miniature
Colour: Pink, white, blue and brown
Issued: 01/03 to the present

U.K.: £ 9.95
U.S.: $20.00
Can.: $20.00

APPLEY DAPPLY™
Style Two

Model: A8249
Modeller: Richard Wawrzesta
Height: 4 ½", 11.4 cm
Colour: Brown, white, pink, pale blue and red
Issued: 06/07 to the present

U.K.: £14.95
U.S.: $30.00
Can.: $30.00

AUNT PETTITOES AND PIGLETS™
Style One

Model: BP2
Modeller: Richard Wawrzesta
Height: 4 ¾", 12.1 cm
Size: Large
Colour: Pink, blue, white and grey
Issued: 01/87 - 12/93 (In Tins)

U.K.: £ 50.00
U.S.: $100.00
Can.: $100.00

AUNT PETTITOES AND PIGLETS™
Style Two

Model: BPM32, 271764
Modeller: Richard Wawrzesta
Height: 2 ½", 6.4 cm
Size: Miniature
Colour: Pink pigs; blue and white clothing
Issued: 01/94 - 12/01

Made in	U.K.	Abroad
U.K.:	£20.	£10.
U.S.:	$40.	$20.
Can.:	$40.	$20.

AUNT PETTITOES AND PIGLING BLAND™

Model: A3410
Modeller: Richard Wawrzesta
Height: 2 ½", 6.4 cm
Size: Miniature
Colour: Light blue, pink, cream, brown and green
Issued: 01/04 to the present

U.K.: £10.00
U.S.: $20.00
Can.: $20.00

BEATRIX POTTER MILLENNIUM TABLEAU™

Model:	669814
Modeller:	Richard Wawrzesta
Height:	6 ¼", 15.9 cm
Colour:	Rose-pink, blue, red, tan, yellowish-green and cream
Issued:	1999 in a limited edition of 2,000
Series:	Tableau

U.K.:	£ 65.00
U.S.:	$130.00
Can.:	$130.00

BENJAMIN BUNNY™
Style One

Model:	BP14
Modeller:	Richard Wawrzesta
Height:	4 ½", 11.9 cm
Size:	Large
Colour:	Brown and white rabbit; tan jacket; blue-green tam with a red pompon
Issued:	01/88 - 12/93 (In Tins)

U.K.:	£ 65.00
U.S.:	$130.00
Can.:	$130.00

BENJAMIN BUNNY™
Style Two

Model:	A1150
Modeller:	Richard Wawrzesta
Height:	3", 7.6 cm
Size:	Miniature
Colour:	Browns, blue and red
Issued:	06/01 to the present

U.K.:	£ 9.95
U.S.:	$20.00
Can.:	$20.00

BENJAMIN BUNNY™
Style Three

Model:	A2436
Modeller:	Richard Wawrzesta
Height:	4 ½", 11.9 cm
Colour:	Brown and beige rabbit; dark brown jacket; red blanket; green hat
Issued:	01/03 to the present
Medium:	Earthenware
Series:	Beatrix Potter Classics

U.K.:	£14.95
U.S.:	$30.00
Can.:	$30.00

BENJAMIN BUNNY™
Style Four

Model:	A2451/129754
Modeller:	Janet Miller
Height:	6 ½", 16.5 cm
Colour:	Browns, white, turquoise, red and black
Issued:	06/03 - 12/04
Medium:	Porcelain
Series:	Peter Rabbit and Friends Collection

U.K.:	£25.00
U.S.:	$50.00
Can.:	$50.00

BENJAMIN BUNNY™
Style Five

Model:	A4557
Modeller:	Richard Wawrzesta
Height:	11 ½", 29.2 cm
Size:	Large
Colour:	Browns, red and green
Issued:	06/04 - 12/05

U.K.:	£42.00
U.S.:	$85.00
Can.:	$85.00

BENJAMIN BUNNY EATING LETTUCE™

Model:	BP27
Modeller:	Richard Wawrzesta
Height:	4 ¾", 12.1 cm
Size:	Large
Colour:	Brown and white rabbit; brown jacket; green lettuce leaves
Issued:	01/94 - 12/95 (In Boxes)

U.K.:	£ 60.00
U.S.:	$120.00
Can.:	$120.00

BENJAMIN BUNNY SITTING WITH ONIONS™

Model:	A4075
Modeller:	Janet Miller
Height:	4 ½", 11.9 cm
Colour:	Browns, red, green and black
Issued:	01/04 - 12/04
Series:	Peter Rabbit and Friends Collection

U.K.:	£25.00
U.S.:	$50.00
Can.:	$50.00

CAT WITH WATERING CAN™

Model: BPM10
Modeller: Richard Wawrzesta
Height: 2 ½", 6.4 cm
Size: Miniature
Colour: White cat; green
watering can
Issued: 01/92 - 12/95

U.K.: £40.00
U.S.: $80.00
Can.: $80.00

CECILY PARSLEY™

Model: A0636
Modeller: Unknown
Height: 1 ¾", 4.5 cm
Size: Miniature
Colour: Pale blue, white, brown
and yellow
Issued: 01/01 - 12/06

U.K.: £10.00
U.S.: $20.00
Can.: $20.00

CECILY PARSLEY RAN AWAY™

Model: BP10
Modeller: Richard Wawrzesta
Height: 3 ½", 8.9 cm
Size: Large
Colour: Brown rabbit; blue
dress; white apron;
brown wheelbarrow
Issued: 01/87 - 12/89 (In Tins)

U.K.: £ 65.00
U.S.: $130.00
Can.: $130.00

CECILY PARSLEY WITH COWSLIPS™

Model: A7669
Modeller: Richard Wawrzesta
Height: 3", 7.6 cm
Size: Miniature
Colour: Light brown, white,
pale blue, yellow
and red
Issued: 01/07 to the present

U.K.: £ 9.95
U.S.: $20.00
Can.: $20.00

CHRISTMAS TREE DANCE MILLENNIUM TABLEAU™

Model: 120020
Modeller: Richard Wawrzesta
Height: 5 ½" x 7",
14.0 x 17.8 cm
Colour: Blue, brown, white,
rose-pink, green,
yellow tan, green,
white and gold
Issued: 2000 in a limited
edition of 500
Series: Tableau

U.K.: £125.00
U.S.: $250.00
Can.: $250.00

COTTON-TAIL AND PETER™

Model: A0754
Modeller: Unknown
Height: 2 ½", 6.4 cm
Size: Miniature
Colour: Light brown, red and
blue
Issued: 06/01 - 12/06

U.K.: £10.00
U.S.: $20.00
Can.: $20.00

COUSIN RIBBY™

Model: BP17
Modeller: Richard Wawrzesta
Height: 4 ¼", 10.8 cm
Size: Large
Colour: Ginger and brown
cat; pink dress;
green shawl, apron
and umbrella
Issued: 01/89 - 12/93 (In Tins)

U.K.: £ 65.00
U.S.: $130.00
Can.: $130.00

DUCHESS™

Model: A8414
Modeller: Richard Wawrzesta
Height: 3", 7.6 cm
Size: Miniature
Colour: Black, light brown,
multicoloured bouquet
Issued: 06/07 to the present

U.K.: £ 9.95
U.S.: $20.00
Can.: $20.00

FLOPSY BUNNIES, THE™
Style One

Model:	120015
Modeller:	Richard Wawrzesta
Height:	3 ¾", 9.5 cm
Colour:	Brown, white bunnies, green foliage
Issued:	1999 in a limited
edition	of 999

U.K.:	£ 50.00
U.S.:	$100.00
Can.:	$100.00

FLOPSY BUNNIES™, THE
Style Two

Model:	A3495
Modeller:	Unknown
Height:	2 ¼", 5.7 cm
Size:	Miniature
Colour:	Fawn, white green and red
Issued:	01/04 to the present

U.K.:	£ 9.95
U.S.:	$20.00
Can.:	$20.00

FLOPSY, MOPSY AND COTTON-TAIL™
Style One

Model:	CBP09
Modeller:	Richard Wawrzesta
Height:	3 ¾", 9.5 cm
Colour:	Brown rabbits; salmon cloaks
Issued:	01/93 - 12/93
Series:	100th Anniversary of Peter Rabbit (1893-1993)

U.K.:	£ 60.00
U.S.:	$120.00
Can.:	$120.00

FLOPSY, MOPSY AND COTTON-TAIL™
Style Two

Model:	A0623
Modeller:	Unknown
Height:	3 1/8", 8.0 cm
Colour:	Browns, red and green
Issued:	01/01 - 12/03 (In Tins)

U.K.:	£20.00
U.S.:	$40.00
Can.:	$40.00

FLOPSY, MOPSY AND COTTON-TAIL™
Style Three

Model:	A4074
Modeller:	Janet Miller
Height:	4 ½", 11.4 cm
Colour:	Light brown, white, pink, purple and green
Issued:	01/04 - 12/04
Series:	Peter Rabbit and Friends Collection

U.K.:	£30.00
U.S.:	$60.00
Can.:	$60.00

FLOPSY, MOPSY, COTTON-TAIL AND BOWL™

Model:	BPM12, 271845
Modeller:	Richard Wawrzesta
Height:	2", 5.0 cm
Series:	Miniature
Colour:	Brown rabbits; white bibs and bowl
Issued:	01/92 - 06/05

Made in	U.K.	Abroad
U.K.:	£20.	£10.
U.S.:	$40.	$20.
Can.:	$40.	$20.

FLOPSY, MOPSY AND COTTON-TAIL PICKING BLACKBERRIES™

Model:	BPM26, 271748
Modeller:	Richard Wawrzesta
Height:	2 ½", 6.4 cm
Size:	Miniature
Colour:	Brown rabbits; salmon pink cloaks
Issued:	01/94 to the present

Made in	U.K.	Abroad
U.K.:	£20.	£10.
U.S.:	$40.	$20.
Can.:	$40.	$20.

FOUR LITTLE RABBITS™
(Flopsy, Mopsy, Cotton-tail and Peter)

Model:	A2442
Modeller:	Richard Wawrzesta
Height:	4 ¾", 12.1 cm
Colour:	Brown, blue, pink, and green
Issued:	06/04 in a limited edition of 1,250
Series:	Beatrix Potter Classics

U.K.:	£ 50.00
U.S.:	$100.00
Can.:	$100.00

FOXY WHISKERED GENTLEMAN™
Style One

Model:	BP19
Modeller:	Richard Wawrzesta
Height:	5", 12.7 cm
Size:	Large
Colour:	Reddish-brown and white fox; green coat; red waistcoat; white trousers
Issued:	01/90 - 12/95 (In Tins)
U.K.:	£ 60.00
U.S.:	$120.00
Can.:	$120.00

FOXY WHISKERED GENTLEMAN™
Style Two

Model:	BPM3, 284149
Modeller:	Richard Wawrzesta
Height:	3", 7.6 cm
Size:	Miniature
Colour:	Reddish-brown fox; green coat; white paper
Issued:	01/92 - 12/01

Made in	U.K.	Abroad
U.K.:	£35.	£12.
U.S.:	$70.	$25.
Can.:	$70.	$25.

FOXY WHISKERED GENTLEMAN™
Style Three

Model:	A3947
Modeller:	Richard Wawrzesta
Height:	5 ¼", 13.3 cm
Colour:	Green, reddish-brown, white and red
Issued:	06/04 to the present
Series:	Beatrix Potter Classics
U.K.:	£14.95
U.S.:	$30.00
Can.:	$30.00

Earthenware

GENTLEMAN MOUSE™

Model:	A3105
Modeller:	Richard Wawrzesta
Height:	4 ¼", 10.8 cm
Colour:	Brown, white, blue, yellow and pink
Issued:	01/04 - 06/06
Series:	Beatrix Potter Classics
U.K.:	£15.00
U.S.:	$30.00
Can.:	$30.00

Earthenware

GENTLEMAN MOUSE BOWING™

Model:	BPM15
Modeller:	Richard Wawrzesta
Height:	2 ½", 6.4 cm
Size:	Miniature
Colour:	Brown mouse; violet coat; white frills
Issued:	01/92 - 12/96

Made in	U.K.	Abroad
U.K.:	£40.	£12.
U.S.:	$80.	$25.
Can.:	$80.	$25.

GINGER THE CAT™

Model:	BPM18
Modeller:	Richard Wawrzesta
Height:	2 ¾", 7.0 cm
Size:	Miniature
Colour:	Ginger tabby; olive green jacket; grey-blue parcel
Issued:	01/92 - 12/95
U.K.:	£35.00
U.S.:	$70.00
Can.:	$70.00

HENNY PENNY MEETS JEMIMA PUDDLE-DUCK™

Model:	BP18
Modeller:	Richard Wawrzesta
Height:	4", 10.1 cm
Size:	Large
Colour:	Yellow chicken and chicks; grey apron; white duck; blue bonnet; rose and blue shawl
Issued:	01/89 - 12/90 (In Tins)
U.K.:	£ 70.00
U.S.:	$140.00
Can.:	$140.00

HILL TOP COTTAGE™

Model:	CBP15
Modeller:	Richard Young
Height:	4", 10.1 cm
Colour:	Grey, brown and green
Issued:	01/93 in a limited edition of 1,993
Series:	100th Anniversary of Peter Rabbit (1893-1993)
U.K.:	£ 65.00
U.S.:	$130.00
Can.:	$130.00

HUNCA MUNCA AND BABIES™
Style One

Model:	BP5
Modeller:	Richard Wawrzesta
Height:	3", 7.6 cm
Size:	Large
Colour:	Brown mice; blue dress; white apron and nightdress; pink blanket
Issued:	01/87 - 12/95 (In Tins)
U.K.:	£ 50.00
U.S.:	$100.00
Can.:	$100.00

HUNCA MUNCA AND BABIES™
Style Two

Model:	BPM7, 271756
Modeller:	Richard Wawrzesta
Height:	2", 5.0 cm
Size:	Miniature
Colour:	Brown mice; blue dress with cream trim; pink blanket; brown cradle
Issued:	01/92 to the present

Made in	U.K.	Abroad
U.K.:	£20.	£10.
U.S.:	$40.	$20.
Can.:	$40.	$20.

HUNCA MUNCA AND BABY™
Style One

Model:	A2435
Modeller:	Richard Wawrzesta
Height:	3 ¾", 9.5 cm
Colour:	Brown, cream, pale blue and white
Issued:	01/03 to the present
Medium:	Earthenware
Series:	Beatrix Potter Classics
U.K.:	£14.95
U.S.:	$30.00
Can.:	$30.00

HUNCA MUNCA AND BABY™
Style Two

Model:	A4556
Modeller:	Unknown
Height:	11 ¼", 28.5 cm
Size:	Large
Colour:	Pale brown, white, turquoise and pink
Issued:	06/04 - 12/05
U.K.:	£40.00
U.S.:	$80.00
Can.:	$80.00

HUNCA MUNCA AND BABY™
Style Three

Model:	A3956
Modeller:	Richard Wawrzestra
Height:	2 ¾", 7.0cm
Size:	Miniature
Colour:	Lilac, white and brown
Issued:	01/05 to the present
U.K.:	£ 9.95
U.S.:	$20.00
Can.:	$20.00

HUNCA MUNCA SWEEPING™
Style One

Model:	BP20
Modeller:	Richard Wawrzesta
Height:	4 ½", 11.9 cm
Size:	Large
Colour:	Brown mouse; pink, white, green and cream clothing
Issued:	01/90 - 12/93 (In Tins)
U.K.:	£ 75.00
U.S.:	$150.00
Can.:	$150.00

HUNCA MUNCA SWEEPING™
Style Two

Model:	BPM8
Modeller:	Richard Wawrzesta
Height:	2 ¼", 5.7 cm
Size:	Miniature
Colour:	Brown mouse; lilac dress; white apron
Issued:	01/92 – 12/98

Made in	U.K.	Abroad
U.K.:	£20.	£10.
U.S.:	$40.	$20.
Can.:	$40.	$20.

HUNCA MUNCA SWEEPING™
Style Three

Model:	739510
Modeller:	Richard Wawrzesta
Height:	3 ¾", 9.5 cm
Size:	Medium
Colour:	Brown mouse; pink dress; white apron; brown broom and dustbin
Issued:	01/00 - 12/03 (In Tins)
U.K.:	£17.00
U.S.:	$35.00
Can.:	$35.00

HUNCA MUNCA WITH RICE JAR™

Model:	BPM22
Modeller:	Richard Wawrzesta
Height:	2 ½", 6.4 cm
Size:	Miniature
Colour:	Brown mouse; turquoise jar
Issued:	01/93 - 12/95

U.K.:	£ 50.00
U.S.:	$100.00
Can.:	$100.00

JANE AND CLOCK™

Model:	BPM6
Modeller:	Richard Wawrzesta
Height:	3", 7.6 cm
Size:	Miniature
Colour:	Pink dress; brown hair; tan clock
Issued:	01/92 - 12/93

U.K.:	£40.00
U.S.:	$80.00
Can.:	$80.00

JEMIMA PUDDLE-DUCK™
Style One

Model:	BPM2, 271799
Modeller:	Richard Wawrzesta
Height:	3", 7.6 cm
Size:	Miniature
Colour:	White duck; blue bonnet; rose and blue shawl
Issued:	01/92 to the present

Made in	U.K.	Abroad
U.K.:	£20.	£10.
U.S.:	$40.	$20.
Can.:	$40.	$20.

JEMIMA PUDDLE-DUCK™
Style Two

Model:	A2452/129756
Modeller:	Janet Miller
Height:	6", 15.0 cm
Colour:	White, rose-pink, blue and yellow
Issued:	06/03 - 12/04
Medium:	Porcelain
Series:	The Peter Rabbit and Friends Collection

U.K.:	£20.00
U.S.:	$40.00
Can.:	$40.00

JEMIMA PUDDLE-DUCK™
Style Three

Model:	A4555
Modeller:	Unknown
Height:	12 ¾", 32.4 cm
Size:	Large
Colour:	White, yellow, brown, deep pink, turquoise
Issued:	06/04 - 12/05

U.K.:	£40.00
U.S.:	$80.00
Can.:	$80.00

JEMIMA PUDDLE-DUCK AND DUCKLINGS™

Model:	739502
Modeller:	Richard Wawrzesta
Height:	3 ¾", 9.5 cm
Size:	Medium
Colour:	White, rose-pink, blue and green
Issued:	01/00 - 12/03 (In Tins)

U.K.:	£20.00
U.S.:	$40.00
Can.:	$40.00

JEMIMA PUDDLE-DUCK AND FOXGLOVES™

Model:	120005
Modeller:	Richard Wawrzesta
Height:	4 ½", 11.9 cm
Colour:	White, rose-pink, blue, pink, green, grey and gold
Issued:	1998 in a limited edition of 1,250

U.K.:	£35.00
U.S.:	$70.00
Can.:	$70.00

JEMIMA PUDDLE-DUCK AND FOXY-WHISKERED GENTLEMAN™

Model:	A0622
Modeller:	Unknown
Height:	3 ¾", 9.7 cm
Colour:	White, blue, red-brown, brown and yellow
Issued:	01/01 - 12/03 (In Tins)

U.K.:	£20.00
U.S.:	$40.00
Can.:	$40.00

JEMIMA PUDDLE-DUCK AND HER DUCKLINGS™

Model: A6610
Modeller: Richard Wawrzesta
Height: 4", 10.1 cm
Colour: White, pink, light blue, yellow and green
Issued: 01/06 - 12/06
Series: Friends of Peter Rabbit Member-only Figurine

U.K.: £20.00
U.S.: $40.00
Can.: $40.00

JEMIMA PUDDLE-DUCK SETS OFF™

Model: BP7
Modeller: Richard Wawrzesta
Height: 4", 10.1 cm
Size: Large
Colour: White, rose-pink, blue and green
Issued: 01/87 - 12/95 (In Tins)

U.K.: £ 60.00
U.S.: $120.00
Can.: $120.00

JEMIMA PUDDLE-DUCK WITH DUCKLINGS™

Model: A3955
Modeller: Richard Wawrzesta
Height: 3", 7.6 cm
Size: Miniature
Colour: White, pink, blue and yellow
Issued: 01/05 to the present

U.K.: £ 9.95
U.S.: $20.00
Can.: $20.00

JEMIMA PUDDLE-DUCK WITH HERBS™
Style One

Model: A2350
Modeller: Richard Wawrzesta
Height: 3 ¼", 8.3 cm
Size: Miniature
Colour: White, rose-pink, blue and green
Issued: 01/03 to the present

U.K.: £ 9.95
U.S.: $20.00
Can.: $20.00

JEMIMA PUDDLE-DUCK WITH HERBS™
Style Two

Model: A2432
Modeller: Richard Wawrzesta
Height: 4 ½", 11.9 cm
Colour: White, rose-pink, blue, green and yellow
Issued: 01/03 to the present
Medium: Earthenware
Series: Beatrix Potter Classics

U.K.: £14.95
U.S.: $30.00
Can.: $30.00

JEREMY FISHER PUNTING™

Model: BP9
Modeller: Richard Wawrzesta
Height: 2 ¾", 7.0 cm
Size: Large
Colour: Yellow frog; white jacket and shirt; pink waistcoat
Issued: 01/87 - 12/93 (In Tins)

U.K.: £ 60.00
U.S.: $120.00
Can.: $120.00

KEP THE COLLIE DOG™

Model: BPM1
Modeller: Richard Wawrzesta
Height: 2 ½", 6.4 cm
Size: Miniature
Colour: Brown, black and white dog; yellow ducklings
Issued: 01/92 - 12/93

U.K.: £40.00
U.S.: $80.00
Can.: $80.00

LADY MOUSE™
Style One

Model: BP24
Modeller: Richard Wawrzesta
Height: 3 ¼", 8.3 cm
Size: Large
Colour: Brown and white mouse; yellow, pink, blue and red clothing
Issued: 01/91 - 12/94 (In Boxes)

U.K.: £ 50.00
U.S.: $100.00
Can.: $100.00

LADY MOUSE™
Style Two

Model:	A3104
Modeller:	Richard Wawrzesta
Height:	4 ¼", 10.8 cm
Colour:	Brown, white, red and blue
Issued:	01/04 to the present
Medium:	Earthenware
Series:	Beatrix Potter Classics

U.K.:	£14.95
U.S.:	$30.00
Can.:	$30.00

LADY MOUSE™
Style Three

Model:	A3411
Modeller:	Richard Wawrzesta
Height:	2 ¼", 5.7 cm
Size:	Miniature
Colour:	White, lemon, pink, fawn and green
Issued:	01/04 - 12/06

U.K.:	£10.00
U.S.:	$20.00
Can.:	$20.00

LADY MOUSE CURTSEYING™

Model:	BPM14	
Modeller:	Richard Wawrzesta	
Height:	2 ¼", 5.7 cm	
Size:	Miniature	
Colour:	Brown mouse; cream and red dress; white apron and cap	
Issued:	01/92 - 12/98	

Made in	U.K.	Abroad
U.K.:	£30.	£12.
U.S.:	$60.	$25.
Can.:	$60.	$25.

LITTLE BLACK PIG (PIG-WIG)™

Model:	BP26
Modeller:	Richard Wawrzesta
Height:	5", 12.7 cm
Size:	Large
Colour:	Black and pink pig; blue dress
Issued:	01/94 - 12/95 (In Boxes)

U.K.:	£ 50.00
U.S.:	$100.00
Can.:	$100.00

LITTLE PIG ROBINSON™

Model:	A8044
Modeller:	Richard Wawrzesta
Height:	4 ¼", 10.8 cm
Colour:	Pink, blue, white, red and lemon
Issued:	01/07 to the present
Medium:	Earthenware
Series:	Beatrix Potter Classics

U.K.:	£14.95
U.S.:	$30.00
Can.:	$30.00

LUCINDA THE DOLL™

Model:	BPM5
Modeller:	Richard Wawrzesta
Height:	2 ¾", 7.0 cm
Size:	Miniature
Colour:	Blonde doll; blue and white dress
Issued:	01/92 - 12/93

U.K.:	£ 50.00
U.S.:	$100.00
Can.:	$100.00

MISS MOPPET AND THE MOUSE™

Model:	BP21
Modeller:	Richard Wawrzesta
Height:	4", 10.1 cm
Size:	Large
Colour:	Brown and white kitten; pink bow; lilac handkerchief; rose stool; brown mouse: light green jacket; pink bowtie
Issued:	01/90 - 12/93 (In Tins)

U.K.:	£ 55.00
U.S.:	$110.00
Can.:	$110.00

MITTENS™

Model:	A2494/129764
Modeller:	Janet Miller
Height:	5 ¼", 13.3 cm
Colour:	Light brown, mauve and white
Issued:	01/03 - 12/04
Medium:	Porcelain
Series:	The Peter Rabbit and Friends Collection

U.K.:	£20.00
U.S.:	$40.00
Can.:	$40.00

BFA CHARACTER - Cool Cats and Hot Dogs

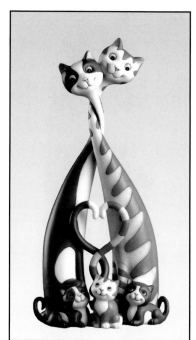

Our First Litter
[Wendy and Mortimer] (A5738)

The Love Knot
[Dido and Heneas] (A4432)

Big Hearted [Sophie] (A7591)

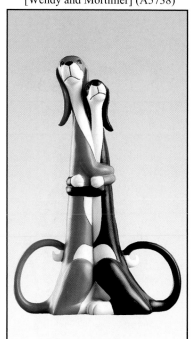

Huggy [Cuddles and Snuggles]
(A3403)

The Snuggle [Ella and Louis]
(A3693)

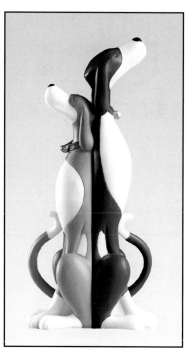

Their First Tiff
[Basie and Daisy] (A3285)

BFA STORYBOOK - Beatrix Potter

Amiable Guinea Pig (BP12)

Old Mr Benjamin Bunny,
Style One (BP28)

Tom Kitten with Butterfly,
Style One (BP23)

Benjamin Bunny, Style One (BP14)

Timmy Willie and the Strawberry,
Style One (BP4)

Cousin Ribby (BP17)

Jemima Puddle-Duck and
Foxgloves (120005)

Nutkin Tickling Old
Mr. Brown (BP15)

Foxy Whiskered Gentleman
Style One (BP19)

BFA STORYBOOK - Beatrix Potter

Mrs. Rabbit At Work (BP11)

A Little Shoe-House (120010)

Hunca Munca Sweeping, Style One (BP20)

Peter Squeezed Under Gate (BP29)

This One Is Moppet (BP8)

Cecily Parsley Ran Away (BP10)

BFA STORYBOOK - Thelwell

Danger Point (T49)

The Lone Stranger (T40)

Starting Point (T47)

Christmas Party (T50)

Four Hooves For Christmas (T25)

Penelope Carolling (T6)

Roomy Jodhpurs Are
Advisable (T21)

Smart Dude (T45)

Pony Not Yet Broken (T17)

Thelwell characters, names and images © Momentum Licensing

BFA CHARACTER - Merry Mice

Asparagus Pickers (A6241)

Currant Crop (A3262)

Lemon Chariot (A5020)

Mouse Band (A6244)

Not 'Mush-room' Under Here! (A1813)

Out of Reach (A3778)

Playing Gooseberry (A3784)

Puppet Show (A5897)

Tom Foolery (A6242)

BFA STORYBOOK - Winnie the Pooh

Pooh Sleeping (A0067)

Piglet With Balloon (A0060)

Eeyore Getting Dried (A0069)

Tigger and Bathtub (A0068)

Pooh With Umbrella
[Umbrella up]   (A0673)

Tiggers Don't Like Hunny (A0413)

Pooh Reading (A0065)

Eeyore Writing (A4169)

Piglet in Barrel of Apples (A6566)

BFA STORYBOOK - Winnie the Pooh

Piglet with Violets (A1342)

Birthday Party (A2391)

Eeyore and Snail (A6567)

Piglet and Eeyore (A2392)

Kanga and Roo (A1345)

Tigger Carrying Piglet in
Picnic Basket (A3939)

Pooh and Piglet Looking at Bee (A7883)

Tigger Jumping on Pooh's Bed (A1350)

Pooh Pushing Piglet in
Wheelbarrow (A1348)

BFA Character - Flower Fairies

Canterbury Bell Fairy (A0302)

Rose Fairy, Style Two (726966)

Primrose Fairy (A1908)

Columbine Fairy, Style Two (A1910)

MOPSY WITH BASKET OF BERRIES™

Model: A7155
Modeller: Richard Wawrzesta
Height: 4 ¾", 12.1 cm
Colour: Pale brown, white, red and green
Issued: 06/06 to the present
Series: Beatrix Potter Classics

U.K.: £14.95
U.S.: $30.00
Can.: $30.00

MR. JEREMY FISHER™
Style One

Model: A0621
Modeller: Unknown
Height: 4", 10.0 cm
Colour: Green, white and browns
Issued: 01/01 - 12/03 (In Tins)

U.K.: £20.00
U.S.: $40.00
Can.: $40.00

MR. JEREMY FISHER™
Style Two

Model: A1317
Modeller: Richard Wawrzesta
Height: 1 ¾", 4.5 cm
Size: Miniature
Colour: Light brown, pale blue, dark brown and green
Issued: 01/02 to the present

U.K.: £ 9.95
U.S.: $20.00
Can.: $20.00

MR. JEREMY FISHER™
Style Three

Model: A2434
Modeller: Richard Wawrzesta
Height: 3 ¾". 9.5 cm
Colour: Yellow-green frog; white, pink, yellow, red, green and pale blue
Issued: 01/03 to the present
Medium: Earthenware
Series: Beatrix Potter Classics

U.K.: £15.00
U.S.: $30.00
Can.: $30.00

MR. JEREMY FISHER™
Style Four

Model: A2454/129760
Modeller: Janet Miller
Height: 5 ½", 14.0 cm
Colour: Pale green, green, yellow, red, rust and brown
Issued: 06/03 - 12/04
Medium: Porcelain
Series: The Peter Rabbit and Friends Collection

U.K.: £20.00
U.S.: $40.00
Can.: $40.00

MR. JEREMY FISHER™
Style Five

Model: A4554
Modeller: Unknown
Height: 8 ½", 21.6 cm
Size: Large
Colour: Yellow, orange, green, white and brown
Issued: 06/04 - 12/05

U.K.: £40.00
U.S.: $80.00
Can.: $80.00

MR. JEREMY FISHER™
Style Six

Model: B1007
Modeller: Richard Wawrzesta
Height: 2 ¼", 5.7 cm
Colour: Light golden, brown and green
Issued: 01/06 - 12/06
Series: Membership: Friends of Peter Rabbit Club

U.K.: £10.00
U.S.: $20.00
Can.: $20.00

MR. JEREMY FISHER ON A BISCUIT TIN™

Model: BPM17, 271772
Modeller: Richard Wawrzesta
Height: 2 ½", 6.4 cm
Size: Miniature
Colour: Green frog; rose-pink jacket; brown biscuit tin
Issued: 01/92 - 12/03

Made in	U.K.	Abroad
U.K.:	£20.	£10.
U.S.:	$40.	$20.
Can.:	$40.	$20.

MR. TOD™

Model: A8248
Modeller: Richard Wawrzesta
Height: 5 ¼", 13.3 cm
Colour: Brown, red, yellow,
          grey and white
Issued: 06/07 to the present

U.K.:   £14.95
U.S.: $30.00
Can.: $30.00

MRS. RABBIT™
Style One

Model: BPM11, 284076
Modeller: Richard Wawrzesta
Height: 2 ½", 6.4 cm
Size: Miniature
Colour: Brown rabbit; orange-
          brown dress; blue
          overdress; red and
          white shawl
Issued: 01/92 - 06/04

Made in	U.K.	Abroad
U.K.:	£20.	£10.
U.S.:	$40.	$20.
Can.:	$40.	$20.

MRS. RABBIT™
Style Two

Model: A2431
Modeller: Richard Wawrzesta
Height: 4 ¼", 10.8 cm
Colour: Brown, cream, red,
          white and green
Issued: 01/03 to the present
Medium: Earthenware
Series: Beatrix Potter Classics

U.K.:   £14.95
U.S.: $30.00
Can.: $30.00

MRS. RABBIT AND BABIES™

Model: A7657
Modeller: Richard Wawrzesta
Height: 5 ¼", 13.3 cm
Colour: Pale brown, white,
          pale pink and blue
Issued: 01/07 to the present
Medium: Earthenware
Series: Beatrix Potter Classics

U.K.:   £14.95
U.S.: $30.00
Can.: $30.00

MRS. RABBIT AND FLOPSY
BUNNY™

Model: A1313
Modeller: Richard Wawrzesta
Height: 3", 7.5 cm
Size: Miniature
Colour: Brown, white, blue
          and red
Issued: 01/02 to the present

U.K.:   £ 9.95
U.S.: $20.00
Can.: $20.00

MRS. RABBIT AND HER
CHILDREN™

Model: BPLE01
Modeller: Richard Wawrzesta
Height: 4 ¾", 12.1 cm
Colour: Brown rabbits; blue,
          white and red clothing
Issued: 07/95 in a limited
          edition of 2,500

U.K.:   £ 75.00
U.S.: $150.00
Can.: $150.00

MRS. RABBIT AND PETER™
Style One, First Variation

Model: CBP11
Modeller: Richard Wawrzesta
Height: 3 ¼", 8.3 cm
Colour: Brown rabbits; blue
          and white clothing
Issued: 01/93 – 12/93
Series: 100th Anniversary of
          Peter Rabbit
          (1893-1993)

U.K.:   £ 50.00
U.S.: $100.00
Can.: $100.00

MRS. RABBIT AND PETER™
Style one, Second Variation

Model: BPM28, 271780
Modeller: Richard Wawrzesta
Height: 2 ¾", 7.0 cm
Size: Miniature
Colour: Brown rabbits; blue
          and white clothing
Issued: 01/94 to the present

Made in	U.K.	Abroad
U.K.:	£40.	£10.
U.S.:	$80.	$20.
Can.:	$80.	$20.

MRS. RABBIT AND PETER™
Style Two

Model:	A8413
Modeller:	Richard Wawrzesta
Height:	2 ½", 6.4 cm
Size:	Miniature
Colour:	Blue, white, green pink and brown
Issued:	06/07 to the present

U.K.:	£ 9.95
U.S.:	$20.00
Can.:	$20.00

MRS. RABBIT AT WORK™

Model:	BP11
Modeller:	Richard Wawrzesta
Height:	4", 10.1 cm
Series:	Large
Colour:	Blue dress; white and pink shawl; brown rabbits and table
Issued:	01/87 - 12/93 (In Tins)

U.K.:	£ 70.00
U.S.:	$140.00
Can.:	$140.00

MRS. RABBIT COOKING™

Model:	A2353
Modeller:	Richard Wawrzesta
Height:	3", 7.6 cm
Size:	Miniature
Colour:	Turquoise, white, brown and green
Issued:	01/03 - 12/06

U.K.:	£10.00
U.S.:	$20.00
Can.:	$20.00

MRS. RABBIT IN ROCKING CHAIR™

Model:	739537
Modeller:	Richard Wawrzesta
Height:	3 ½", 8.9 cm
Size:	Medium
Colour:	Brown and white rabbits; blue dress; white apron; green lettuce in grey bowl
Issued:	01/00 - 06/03 (In Tins)

U.K.:	£20.00
U.S.:	$40.00
Can.:	$40.00

MRS. TIGGY-WINKLE™
Style One

Model:	BPM20
Modeller:	Richard Wawrzesta
Height:	2 ½", 6.4 cm
Size:	Miniature
Colour:	Brown hedgehog; pink and white clothing; brown sack
Issued:	01/92 - 12/95

U.K.:	£25.00
U.S.:	$50.00
Can.:	$50.00

MRS. TIGGY-WINKLE™
Style Two

Model:	739529
Modeller:	Richard Wawrzesta
Height:	2 ¾", 7.0 cm
Size:	Medium
Colour:	Brown hedgehog; white cap; rose-pink, yellow and blue clothing; white cloth with blue trim
Issued:	01/00 - 12/03 (In Tins)

U.K.:	£20.00
U.S.:	$40.00
Can.:	$40.00

MRS. TIGGY-WINKLE™
Style Three

Model:	A1149
Modeller:	Richard Wawrzesta
Height:	2 ½", 6.4 cm
Size:	Miniature
Colour:	White, pink, yellow and brown
Issued:	06/01 - 06/04

U.K.:	£10.00
U.S.:	$20.00
Can.:	$20.00

MRS. TIGGY-WINKLE™
Style Four

Model:	A4553
Modeller:	Unknown
Height:	11 ½", 29.2 cm
Size:	Large
Colour:	Brown, white, pink, lemon and pale blue
Issued:	06/04 - 12/05

U.K.:	£40.00
U.S.:	$80.00
Can.:	$80.00

MRS. TIGGY-WINKLE™
Style Five

Model: A5086
Modeller: Unknown
Height: 2 ½", 6.4 cm
Colour: White, pink, green, yellow and gold
Issued: 01/05 - 12/05
Series: Friends of Peter Rabbit: Symbol of Membership 2005

U.K.: £10.00
U.S.: $20.00
Can.: $20.00

MRS. TIGGY-WINKLE™
Style Six

Model: A6276
Modeller: Richard Wawrzesta
Height: 4", 10.1 cm
Colour: White, pink, grey and brown
Issued: 01/06 to the present
Series: Beatrix Potter Classics

U.K.: £14.95
U.S.: $30.00
Can.: $30.00

MRS. TIGGY-WINKLE
DRINKING TEA™

Model: A1316
Modeller: Richard Wawrzesta
Height: 2 ½", 6.4 cm
Size: Miniature
Colour: Brown, pink, white and cream
Issued: 01/02 to the present

U.K.: £ 9.95
U.S.: $20.00
Can.: $20.00

MRS. TIGGY-WINKLE POURING
TEA™

Model: A2351
Modeller: Richard Wawrzesta
Height: 2 ¼", 5.7 cm
Size: Miniature
Colour: Pink, white, blue and brown
Issued: 01/03 to the present

U.K.: £ 9.95
U.S.: $20.00
Can.: $20.00

MRS. TIGGY-WINKLE, THE
WASHERWOMAN™

Model: BP6
Modeller: Richard Wawrzesta
Height: 4", 10.1 cm
Size: Large
Colour: Brown hedgehog; tan dresser and basket; white cap; pink, white, yellow and blue clothing; white apron
Issued: 01/87 - 12/90 (In Tins)

U.K.: £ 70.00
U.S.: $140.00
Can.: $140.00

MRS. TIGGY-WINKLE WITH
BASKET™

Model: A2433
Modeller: Richard Wawrzesta
Height: 4 ½", 11.9 cm
Colour: White, pink, yellow, blue and brown
Issued: 01/03 - 06/05
Medium: Earthenware
Series: Beatrix Potter Classics

U.K.: £12.00
U.S.: $25.00
Can.: $25.00

MRS. TITTLEMOUSE™

Model: A2453/129758
Modeller: Janet Miller
Height: 5", 12.7 cm
Colour: Light brown, pink, blue and beige
Issued: 06/03 - 12/04
Medium: Porcelain
Series: The Peter Rabbit and Friends Collection

U.K.: £20.00
U.S.: $40.00
Can.: $40.00

NUTKIN TICKLING OLD MR.
BROWN™

Model: BP15
Modeller: Richard Wawrzesta
Height: 3 ½", 8.9 cm
Size: Large
Colour: Brown and cream owl; reddish-brown squirrel
Issued: 01/88 - 12/90 (In Tins)

U.K.: £ 80.00
U.S.: $160.00
Can.: $160.00

OLD MR. BENJAMIN BUNNY™
Style One

Model: BP28
Modeller: Richard Wawrzesta
Height: 5 ¼", 13.3 cm
Size: Large
Colour: Brown rabbit; violet
jacket; cream and
brown waistcoat;
red handkerchief
Issued: 01/94 - 12/95
(In Boxes)

U.K.: £ 55.00
U.S.: $110.00
Can.: $110.00

OLD MR. BENJAMIN BUNNY™
Style Two

Model: A1314
Modeller: Richard Wawrzesta
Height: 2 ½", 6.4 cm
Size: Miniature
Colour: Beige, purple, cream
and green
Issued: 01/02 - 12/06
(In Tins)

U.K.: £10.00
U.S.: $20.00
Can.: $20.00

OLD MR. BENJAMIN BUNNY™
Style Three

Model: A3103
Modeller: Richard Wawrzesta
Height: 5", 12.7 cm
Colour: Brown, cream, purple,
pink and green
Issued: 06/03 - 06/07
Medium: Earthenware
Series: Beatrix Potter Classics

U.K.: £15.00
U.S.: $30.00
Can.: $30.00

OLD WOMAN WHO LIVED IN A
SHOE™
Style One, First Version

Model: BP13
Modeller: Richard Wawrzesta
Height: 4 ¾", 12.1 cm
Size: Large
Colour: Blue shoe; brown mice;
cream bonnet with
pink bow
Issued: 01/88 - 12/95 (In Tins)

U.K.: £45.00
U.S.: $90.00
Can.: $90.00

OLD WOMAN WHO LIVED IN A
SHOE™
Style One, Second Version

Model: 643904
Modeller: Richard Wawrzesta
Height: 2 ¾", 7.0 cm
Size: Miniatures
Colour: Blue shoe; brown mice;
cream bonnet with
pink bow
Issued: 06/99 - 12/03

U.K.: £10.00
U.S.: $20.00
Can.: $20.00

OLD WOMAN WHO LIVED IN A
SHOE™
Style Two

Model: A2440
Modeller: Richard Wawrzesta
Height: 3 ¼", 8.3 cm
Colour: Turquoise shoe; brown
bunnies; and white
Issued: 01/03 to the present
Medium: Earthenware
Series: Beatrix Potter Classics

U.K.: £14.95
U.S.: $30.00
Can.: $30.00

ONE SPOONFUL TO BE TAKEN
AT BEDTIME™

Model: 091011
Modeller: Richard Wawrzesta
Height: 7", 17.8 cm
Colour: Light brown, green,
dark blue-green, light
blue, white and beige
Issued: 2002 Ltd. Ed. of 250
Series: Tableau

U.K.: £125.00
U.S.: $250.00
Can.: $250.00

PETER AND WHEELBARROW™

Model: BP33
Modeller: Richard Wawrzesta
Height: 5 ¾", 14.6 cm
Colour: Brown and white
rabbit; brown wheelbarrow;
green leaves
Issued: 01/95 in a limited
edition of 9,500

U.K.: £40.00
U.S.: $80.00
Can.: $80.00

PETER POSTING LETTER™
Model: A7154
Modeller: Richard Wawrzesta
Height: 5 ¼", 13.3 cm
Colour: Pale brown, turquoise, white, red and green
Issued: 06/06 to the present
Series: Beatrix Potter Classics

U.K.: £14.95
U.S.: $30.00
Can.: $30.00

PETER RABBIT ATE SOME RADISHES™
Model: A2430
Modeller: Richard Wawrzesta
Height: 5", 12.7 cm
Colour: Beige, white, blue, green and red
Issued: 01/03 to the present
Medium: Earthenware
Series: Beatrix Potter Classics

U.K.: £45.00
U.S.: $90.00
Can.: $90.00

Note: Models produced in 2004 carry the "100 Years" blue button on base.

PETER RABBIT CARRYING ONIONS™
Model: A2349
Modeller: Richard Wawrzesta
Height: 3 ¼", 8.3 cm
Size: Miniatures
Colour: Brown, blue, white and red
Issued: 01/03 - 06/07

U.K.: £10.00
U.S.: $20.00
Can.: $20.00

PETER RABBIT EATING A RADISH™
Style One, First Version
Model: BP16
Modeller: Richard Wawrzesta
Height: 5", 12.7 cm
Size: Large
Colour: Brown and white rabbit; blue jacket; red and brown robin on cream spade
Issued: 01/89 – 12/95 (In Tins)

U.K.: £ 50.00
U.S.: $100.00
Can.: $100.00

PETER RABBIT EATING A RADISH™
Style One, Second Version
Model: CBP01
Modeller: Richard Wawrzesta
Height: 7 ½", 19.1 cm
Colour: Brown, white, blue red, brown and cream
Issued: 01/93 in a limited edition of 1,993
Series: 100th Anniversary of Peter Rabbit (1893-1993)

U.K.: £ 60.00
U.S.: $120.00
Can.: $120.00

PETER RABBIT™ (EATING A RADISH)
Style Two, First Version
Model: BPM9, 284238
Modeller: Richard Wawrzesta
Height: 3 ¼", 8.3 cm
Size: Miniature
Colour: Brown, white, blue, red brown and cream
Issued: 01/92 - 12/03

Made in	U.K.	Abroad
U.K.:	£20.	£10.
U.S.:	$40.	$20.
Can.:	$40.	$20.

PETER RABBIT EATING A RADISH™
Style Two, Second Version
Model: CBP10
Modeller: Richard Wawrzesta
Height: 3 ¾", 9.5 cm
Colour: Brown, white, blue red, brown and cream
Issued: 01/93 - 12/93
Series: 100th Anniversary of Peter Rabbit (1893-1993)

U.K.: £45.00
U.S.: $90.00
Can.: $90.00

PETER RABBIT EATING LETTUCE™
First Variation
Model: CBP12
Modeller: Richard Wawrzesta
Height: 3 ¼", 8.3 cm
Colour: Brown rabbit; blue jacket; green lettuce leaves
Issued: 01/93 - 12/93
Series: 100th Anniversary of Peter Rabbit (1893-1993)

U.K.: £ 50.00
U.S.: $100.00
Can.: $100.00

PETER RABBIT EATING LETTUCE™
Second Variation

Model:	BPM27, 284157	
Modeller:	Richard Wawrzesta	
Height:	3 ¼", 8.3 cm	
Size:	Miniature	
Colour:	Brown rabbit; blue jacket; green lettuce leaves	
Issued:	01/94 - 12/99	

Made in	U.K.	Abroad
U.K.:	£40.	£12.
U.S.:	$80.	$25.
Can.:	$80.	$25.

PETER RABBIT IN MR. MCGREGOR'S GARDEN™

Model:	BP25
Modeller:	Richard Wawrzesta
Height:	5 ¾", 14.6 cm
Colour:	Brown rabbit; blue jacket; red radishes; tan spade; brown and red robin
Issued:	01/96 in a limited edition of 9,500

U.K.:	£45.00
U.S.:	$90.00
Can.:	$90.00

PETER RABBIT IN THE GARDEN™
Style One

Model:	BP1
Modeller:	Richard Wawrzesta
Height:	4 ½", 11.9 cm
Size:	Large
Colour:	Brown and white rabbit; blue jacket; red handkerchief
Issued:	01/87 - 12/95 (In Tins)

U.K.:	£ 55.00
U.S.:	$110.00
Can.:	$110.00

PETER RABBIT IN THE GARDEN™
Style Two

Model:	739499
Modeller:	Richard Wawrzesta
Height:	3 ¾", 9.5 cm
Size:	Medium
Colour:	Brown and white rabbit; blue jacket; red flowers; green leaves; brown and red bird; terracotta planters
Issued:	01/00 - 12/03 (In Tins)

U.K.:	£20.00
U.S.:	$40.00
Can.:	$40.00

PETER RABBIT IN WATERING CAN™
Style One, First Version

Model:	CBP07
Modeller:	Richard Wawrzesta
Height:	3 ½", 8.9 cm
Colour:	Brown rabbit; green watering can; brown pots
Issued:	01/93 - 12/93
Series:	100th Anniversary of Peter Rabbit (1893-1993)

U.K.:	£ 50.00
U.S.:	$100.00
Can.:	$100.00

PETER RABBIT IN WATERING CAN™
Style one, Second Version

Model:	BPM24, 271837	
Modeller:	Richard Wawrzesta	
Height:	2 ¾", 7.0 cm	
Size:	Miniature	
Colour:	Brown rabbit and pots; green watering can	
Issued:	01/94 to the present	
Varieties:	Also called Peter's Hiding Place	

Made in	U.K.	Abroad
U.K.:	£ 50.	£10.
U.S.:	$100.	$20.
Can.:	$100.	$20.

PETER RABBIT IN WATERING CAN™
Style Two

Model:	A6275
Modeller:	Richard Wawrzesta
Height:	4 ½", 10.8 cm
Colour:	Green, brown and white
Issued:	01/06 to the present
Series:	Beatrix Potter Classics

U.K.:	£14.95
U.S.:	$30.00
Can.:	$30.00

PETER RABBIT IN WHEELBARROW™
First Version

Model:	CBP08
Modeller:	Richard Wawrzesta
Height:	3 ½", 8.9 cm
Colour:	Brown rabbit and wheelbarrow; green leaves; white cloth
Issued:	01/93 - 12/93
Series:	100th Anniversary of Peter Rabbit (1893-1993)

U.K.:	£ 50.00
U.S.:	$100.00
Can.:	$100.00

PETER RABBIT IN WHEELBARROW™
Second Version

Model:	BPM25, 271810	
Modeller:	Richard Wawrzesta	
Height:	2 ¾", 7.0 cm	
Size:	Miniature	
Colour:	Brown rabbit; green leaves	
Issued:	01/94 to the present	

Made in	U.K.	Abroad
U.K.:	£35.	£10.
U.S.:	$70.	$20.
Can.:	$70.	$20.

PETER RABBIT LOVES RADISHES™

Model:	A2654/129766
Modeller:	Janet Miller
Height:	6 ¼", 15.9 cm
Colour:	Brown and white rabbit; blue coat, red radish; green leaves
Issued:	06/03 - 12/04
Medium:	Porcelain
Series:	The Peter Rabbit and Friends Collection

U.K.:	£25.00
U.S.:	$50.00
Can.:	$50.00

PETER RABBIT POSTING A LETTER™

Model:	A3486
Modeller:	Richard Wawrzesta
Height:	3", 7.6 cm
Size:	Miniature
Colour:	Fawn, white, turquoise, red and brown
Issued:	01/04 to the present

U.K.:	£10.00
U.S.:	$20.00
Can.:	$20.00

PETER RABBIT RUNNING™
Style One, First Version

Model:	CBP13
Modeller:	Richard Wawrzesta
Height:	3 ½", 8.9 cm
Colour:	Brown rabbit; blue jacket and slippers
Issued:	01/93 - 12/93
Series:	100th Anniversary of Peter Rabbit (1893-1993)

U.K.:	£ 50.00
U.S.:	$100.00
Can.:	$100.00

PETER RABBIT RUNNING™
Style One, Second Version

Model:	BPM29, 284246	
Modeller:	Richard Wawrzesta	
Height:	3", 7.6 cm	
Size:	Miniature	
Colour:	Brown rabbit; blue jacket and slippers	
Issued:	01/94 - 12/99	

Made in	U.K.	Abroad
U.K.:	£25.	£10.
U.S.:	$50.	$20.
Can.:	$50.	$20.

PETER RABBIT RUNNING™
Style Two

Model:	A3093
Modeller:	Richard Wawrzesta
Height:	1 ½", 3.84 cm
Size:	Miniature
Colour:	Light blue, white, brown, green and gold (metal)
Issued:	01/03 - 12/03
Series:	Charter Club Symbol Membership Figurine

U.K.:	£10.00
U.S.:	$20.00
Can.:	$20.00

PETER RABBIT STANDING™
First Variation

Model:	CBP14
Modeller:	Richard Wawrzesta
Height:	3 ¾", 9.5 cm
Colour:	Brown rabbit; blue jacket and slippers
Issued:	01/93 - 12/93
Series:	100th Anniversary of Peter Rabbit (1893-1993)

U.K.:	£ 50.00
U.S.:	$100.00
Can.:	$100.00

PETER RABBIT STANDING™
Second Variation

Model:	BPM30	
Modeller:	Richard Wawrzesta	
Height:	3", 7.6 cm	
Size:	Miniature	
Colour:	Brown rabbit; blue jacket	
Issued:	01/94 - 12/98	

Made in	U.K.	Abroad
U.K.:	£25.	£10.
U.S.:	$50.	$20.
Can.:	$50.	$20.

PETER RABBIT WITH CHRISTMAS STOCKING™

Model:	A3369/129768
Modeller:	Janet Miller
Height:	6 ¾", 17.2 cm
Colour:	Light brown, white, blue, red and green
Issued:	06/03 - 12/04
Medium:	Porcelain
Series:	The Peter Rabbit and Friends Collection
U.K.:	£25.00
U.S.:	$50.00
Can.:	$50.00

PETER RABBIT WITH DAFFOLDILS™

Model:	A7798
Modeller:	Richard Wawrzesta
Height:	3", 7.6 cm
Size:	Miniature
Colour:	Light brown, white, turquoise, yellow and green
Issued:	01/07 to the present
U.K.:	£ 9.95
U.S.:	$20.00
Can.:	$20.00

PETER RABBIT WITH FAMILY™

Model:	Unknown
Modeller:	Richard Wawrzesta
Height:	4", 10.1 cm
Colour:	Brown rabbits; blue dress and jacket; white apron and bottle
Issued:	1991 in a limited edition of 1,200
U.K.:	£ 80.00
U.S.:	$160.00
Can.:	$160.00

PETER RABBIT WITH ONIONS™
Style One

Model:	BPM31, 284165
Modeller:	Richard Wawrzesta
Height:	3", 7.6 cm
Size:	Miniature
Colour:	Brown rabbit; blue jacket; red handkerchief
Issued:	01/94 - 06/04

Made in	U.K.	Abroad
U.K.:	£25.	£10.
U.S.:	$50.	$20.
Can.:	$50.	$20.

PETER RABBIT WITH ONIONS™
Style Two

Model:	A5686
Modeller:	Richard Wawrzesta
Height:	4 ¼", 10.8 cm
Colour:	Blue, white, brown, red and green
Issued:	01/05 - 12/05
Series:	Peter Rabbit and Friends Member-only Figurine 2005
U.K.:	£20.00
U.S.:	$40.00
Can.:	$40.00

PETER RABBIT WITH ONIONS™
Style Three

Model:	A6189
Modeller:	Unknown
Height:	4 ¾", 12.1 cm
Colour:	Brown, blue and red
Issued:	06/05 to the present
Series:	Beatrix Potter Classics
U.K.:	£14.95
U.S.:	$30.00
Can.:	$30.00

PETER RABBIT WITH PLANT POT™

Model:	A1312
Modeller:	Richard Wawrzesta
Height:	3", 7.6 cm
Size:	Miniature
Colour:	Brown, white, blue, terracotta, red and green
Issued:	01/02 to the present
U.K.:	£ 9.95
U.S.:	$20.00
Can.:	$20.00

PETER RABBIT WITH RADISHES™

Model:	A4552
Modeller:	Unknown
Height:	11 ½", 29.2 cm
Size:	Large
Colour:	Pale brown, turquoise, white, green, orange
Issued:	06/04 - 12/05
U.K.:	£40.00
U.S.:	$80.00
Can.:	$80.00

PETER RABBIT™ WITH ROBIN
Model: A2450/129752
Modeller: Janet Miller
Height: 2 ¾", 7.0 cm
Colour: Brown, light blue, red
             and green
Issued: 06/03 - 12/04
Medium: Porcelain
Series: The Peter Rabbit and
             Friends Collection

U.K.:   £25.00
U.S.: $50.00
Can.: $50.00

PETER RABBIT™ WITH SPADE
Style One
Model: A0620
Modeller: Unknown
Height: 4 ¼", 10.8 cm
Colour: Blue, white, browns
             and yellow
Issued: 01/01 - 12/03 (In Tins)

U.K.:   £20.00
U.S.: $40.00
Can.: $40.00

PETER RABBIT™ WITH SPADE
Style Two
Model: A6615
Modeller: Richard Wawrzesta
Height: 3 ¼", 8.3 cm
Size: Miniature
Colour: Light brown, turquoise,
             green and grey
Issued: 01/06 to the present

U.K.:   £ 9.95
U.S.: $20.00
Can.: $20.00

PETER SQUEEZED UNDER GATE™
Model: BP29
Modeller: Richard Wawrzesta
Height: 5", 12.7 cm
Colour: Brown rabbit; blue
             jacket; yellowish-brown
             gate; green foliage
Issued: 01/95 in a limited
             edition of 9,500

U.K.:   £ 60.00
U.S.: $120.00
Can.: $120.00

PETER'S HIDING PLACE™
Model: BP32
Modeller: Richard Wawrzesta
Height: 5", 12.7 cm
Colour: Brown rabbit; grey-
             green watering can;
             brown flower pots
Issued: 01/95 in a limited
             edition of 9,500
Varieties: Also called Peter
             Rabbit in Watering Can

U.K.:   £ 50.00
U.S.: $100.00
Can.: $100.00

PICKLES THE DOG™
Model: BPM23
Modeller: Richard Wawrzesta
Height: 3", 7.6 cm
Size: Miniature
Colour: Brown and white dog;
             tan coat; white apron
Issued: 01/93 - 12/95

U.K.:   £ 80.00
U.S.: $160.00
Can.: $160.00

PIGLING BLAND™
Style One
Model: BPM33
Modeller: Richard Wawrzesta
Height: 3", 7.6 cm
Size: Miniature
Colour: Pink pig; blue and
             white waistcoat;
             umber jacket
Issued: 01/94 - 12/98

Made in	U.K.	Abroad
U.K.:	£35.	£12.
U.S.:	$70.	$25.
Can.:	$70.	$25.

PIGLING BLAND™
Style Two
Model: A4696
Modeller: Richard Wawrzesta
Height: 4 ¾", 12.1 cm
Colour: Red, yellow, blue
             and white
Issued: 01/05 to the present
Series: Beatrix Potter Classics

U.K.:   £14.95
U.S.: $30.00
Can.: $30.00

PIG-WIG DANCING™
Model: BPM34
Modeller: Richard Wawrzesta
Height: 3", 7.6 cm
Size: Miniature
Colour: Black and pink pig; blue and white dress
Issued: 01/94 - 12/96

Made in	U.K.	Abroad
U.K.:	£35.	£12.
U.S.:	$70.	$25.
Can.:	$70.	$25.

RABBIT SHOVELLING SNOW™
Model: A7668
Modeller: Richard Wawrzesta
Height: 3", 7.6 cm
Size: Miniature
Colour: Light brown, white, grey and red
Issued: 01/07 to the present

U.K.: £ 9.95
U.S.: $20.00
Can.: $20.00

RABBIT WITH BASKET OF GIFTS™
Model: A3487
Modeller: Unknown
Height: 3 ¼", 8.3 cm
Size: Miniature
Colour: Fawn, brown, white, green, red and blue
Issued: 01/04 to the present

U.K.: £ 9.95
U.S.: $20.00
Can.: $20.00

REBECCA AND DUCKLINGS™
Model: BPM21
Modeller: Richard Wawrzesta
Height: 2 ¾", 7.0 cm
Size: Miniature
Colour: White duck; yellow ducklings
Issued: 01/93 - 12/95

U.K.: £ 70.00
U.S.: $140.00
Can.: $140.00

RUNNING PETER RABBIT™
Model: A3946
Modeller: Unknown
Height: 4 ¾", 12.1 cm
Colour: Pale brown, turquoise, white, green, red
Issued: 01/04 to the present
Series: Beatrix Potter Classics

U.K.: £14.95
U.S.: $30.00
Can.: $30.00

SAILING HOME™
(Squirrel Nutkin and Friends)
Model: A2443
Modeller: Richard Wawrzesta
Height: 8", 20.3 cm
Colour: Red-brown, cream, brown, green, white and blue-grey
Issued: 01/03 in a limited edition of 1,250
Series: Beatrix Potter Classics

U.K.: £ 60.00
U.S.: $120.00
Can.: $120.00

SALLY HENNY PENNY™
Model: BPM19
Modeller: Richard Wawrzesta
Height: 3", 7.6 cm
Size: Miniature
Colour: Yellow hen; black apron; yellow chicks
Issued: 01/92 - 12/95

U.K.: £25.00
U.S.: $50.00
Can.: $50.00

SAMUEL WHISKERS™
Model: A6279
Modeller: Richard Wawrzesta
Height: 2 ¼", 5.7 cm
Size: Miniature
Colour: Light brown, yellow and green
Issued: 01/06 to the present

U.K.: £ 9.95
U.S.: $20.00
Can.: $20.00

SIMPKIN HOLDING A CUP™

Model: BPM16
Modeller: Richard Wawrzesta
Height: 2 ½", 6.4 cm
Size: Miniature
Colour: Tabby cat; white and pink cup
Issued: 01/92 - 12/95

U.K.:	£ 60.00
U.S.:	$120.00
Can.:	$120.00

SQUIRREL NUTKIN™

Model: A2437
Modeller: Richard Wawrzesta
Height: 4 ½", 11.9 cm
Colour: Red-brown, white and green
Issued: 01/03 to the present
Medium: Earthenware
Series: Beatrix Potter Classics

U.K.:	£14.95
U.S.:	$30.00
Can.:	$30.00

Note: Models produced in 2004 carry the "100 Years" blue button on base.

TABITHA TWITCHIT™

Model: A4697
Modeller: Richard Wawrzesta
Height: 5 ¼", 13.3 cm
Colour: Lilac, white and cream
Issued: 01/05 to the present
Medium: Earthenware
Series: Beatrix Potter Classics

U.K.:	£14.95
U.S.:	$30.00
Can.:	$30.00

TABITHA TWITCHIT AND KITTENS™

Model: A0625
Modeller: Unknown
Height: 3 ½", 8.9 cm
Colour: Lilac, white, browns and grey
Issued: 01/01 - 12/03 (In Tins)

U.K.:	£40.00
U.S.:	$80.00
Can.:	$80.00

TAILOR OF GLOUCESTER™
Style One

Model: BP3
Modeller: Richard Wawrzesta
Height: 4 ½", 11.9 cm
Size: Large
Colour: Brown mouse; tan spool of fuchsia thread; grey thimble
Issued: 01/87 - 12/95 (In Tins)

U.K.:	£ 55.00
U.S.:	$110.00
Can.:	$110.00

TAILOR OF GLOUCESTER™
Style Two

Model: BPM13, 271829
Modeller: Richard Wawrzesta
Height: 3", 7.6 cm
Size: Miniature
Colour: Brown mouse; tan spool of fuchsia thread
Issued: 01/92 to the present

Made in	U.K.	Abroad
U.K.:	£20.	£10.
U.S.:	$40.	$20.
Can.:	$40.	$20.

TAILOR OF GLOUCESTER™
Style Three

Model: A0624
Modeller: Unknown
Height: 3 ½", 8.9 cm
Colour: Browns, white and grey
Issued: 01/02 - 12/03 (In Tins)

U.K.:	£20.00
U.S.:	$40.00
Can.:	$40.00

TAILOR OF GLOUCESTER™
Style Four

Model: A2222
Modeller: Richard Wawrzesta
Height: 3 ¾", 9.5 cm
Colour: Brown, white, fuchsia, turquoise, pink, yellow and gold
Issued: 01/03 - 12/03
Series: Beatrix Potter Classic Centenary Collection

U.K.:	£20.00
U.S.:	$40.00
Can.:	$40.00

TAILOR OF GLOUCESTER™
Style Five

Model: A2439
Modeller: Richard Wawrzesta
Height: 4 ½", 11.9 cm
Colour: Brown, cream, white, rose-pink and grey
Issued: 01/03 to the present
Medium: Earthenware
Series: Beatrix Potter Classics

U.K.: £14.95
U.S.: $30.00
Can.: $30.00

Note: Models produced in 2004 carry the "100 Years" blue button on base.

TAILOR OF GLOUCESTER™
Style Six

Model: A3101
Modeller: Richard Wawrzesta
Height: 5 ¼", 13.3 cm
Colour: Brown, white, pink, yellow and blue
Issued: 06/03 in a limited edition of 1,250
Series: Beatrix Potter Classics

U.K.: £ 50.00
U.S.: $100.00
Can.: $100.00

THE TALE OF A FIERCE BAD RABBIT™

Model: 545945
Modeller: Richard Wawrzesta
Height: 3 ½", 8.9 cm
Colour: Brown rabbit; blue-grey bench
Issued: 01/99 - 12/02
Series: Storybook

U.K.: £15.00
U.S.: $30.00
Can.: $30.00

THE TALE OF BENJAMIN BUNNY™
Style One

Model: BPM53, 199540
Modeller: Richard Wawrzesta
Height: 3 ½", 8.9 cm
Colour: Brown rabbit and jacket; black tam with red pompon
Issued: 01/95 - 12/02
Series: Storybook

Made in	U.K.	Abroad
U.K.:	£40.	£12.
U.S.:	$80.	$25.
Can.:	$80.	$25.

THE TALE OF BENJAMIN BUNNY™
Style Two

Model: A3287
Modeller: Richard Wawrzesta
Height: 3 ½", 8.9 cm
Colour: Browns, green, cream, orange and red
Issued: 01/04-12/04
Series: 2004 Centenary Figurines

U.K.: £20.00
U.S.: $40.00
Can.: $40.00

THE TALE OF BENJAMIN BUNNY™
Style Three

Model: A3945
Modeller: Richard Wawrzesta
Height: 6 ¾", 17.2 cm
Colour: Browns, grey, blue, red and green
Issued: 01/05 in a limited edition of 1,250
Series: Beatrix Potter Classics

U.K.: £ 55.00
U.S.: $110.00
Can.: $110.00

THE TALE OF GINGER AND PICKLES™
(Storybook)

Model: 545929
Modeller: Richard Wawrzesta
Height: 2 ¾", 7.0 cm
Colour: Brown rabbit; blue coat; tan basket; green window frame; red brick
Issued: 01/99 - 12/02
Series: Storybook

U.K.: £12.00
U.S.: $25.00
Can.: $25.00

THE TALE OF GINGER AND PICKLES™
(Tableau)

Model: A0460
Modeller: Richard Wawrzesta
Height: 7", 17.8 cm
Colour: Green, yellow, brown, blue, pink and white
Issued: 01/02 in a limited edition of 2,000
Series: Tableau

U.K.: £ 60.00
U.S.: $120.00
Can.: $120.00

THE TALE OF JEMIMA PUDDLE-DUCK™

Model:	BPM58, 268674
Modeller:	Richard Wawrzesta
Height:	3 ½", 8.9 cm
Colour:	White duck; blue bonnet; pink and blue shawl
Issued:	01/96 - 12/02
Series:	Storybook

Made in	U.K.	Abroad
U.K.:	£25.	£12.
U.S.:	$50.	$25.
Can.:	$50.	$25.

THE TALE OF JOHNNY TOWN-MOUSE™

Model:	467553
Modeller:	Richard Wawrzesta
Height:	3", 7.6 cm
Colour:	Brown mouse, coat and hat; yellow waistcoat; tan briefcase
Issued:	01/98 - 12/02
Series:	Storybook

U.K.:	£12.00
U.S.:	$25.00
Can.:	$25.00

THE TALE OF LITTLE PIG ROBINSON™

Model:	545937
Modeller:	Richard Wawrzesta
Height:	3", 7.6 cm
Colour:	Pink pig; blue and white striped outfit; rose-pink chair; tan telescope
Issued:	01/99 - 12/02
Series:	Storybook

U.K.:	£12.00
U.S.:	$25.00
Can.:	$25.00

THE TALE OF MR. JEREMY FISHER™
Style One

Model:	BPM56, 199486
Modeller:	Richard Wawrzesta
Height:	2 ¾", 7.0 cm
Colour:	Greenish-yellow frog; white coat; brown pack; blue books
Issued:	01/96 - 12/02
Series:	Storybook

Made in	U.K.	Abroad
U.K.:	£25.	£12.
U.S.:	$50.	$25.
Can.:	$50.	$25.

THE TALE OF MR. JEREMY FISHER™
Style Two

Model:	A6224
Modeller:	Richard Wawrzesta
Height:	4 ¼", 10.8 cm
Colour:	Light golden brown, green, red, yellow and white
Issued:	01/06 - 12/06
Series:	2006 Centenary Figurines

U.K.:	£20.00
U.S.:	$40.00
Can.:	$40.00

THE TALE OF MR. TOD™

Model:	467561
Modeller:	Richard Wawrzesta
Height:	3 ½", 8.9 cm
Colour:	Reddish-brown fox; brown coat, trousers and fencing; red waistcoat
Issued:	01/98 - 12/02
Series:	Storybook

U.K.:	£12.00
U.S.:	$25.00
Can.:	$25.00

THE TALE OF MRS. TIGGY-WINKLE™
Style One

Model:	BPM55, 199559
Modeller:	Richard Wawrzesta
Height:	3", 7.6 cm
Colour:	Browns, white, pink, yellow and blue
Issued:	01/95 - 12/02
Series:	Storybook

Made in	U.K.	Abroad
U.K.:	£25.	£12.
U.S.:	$50.	$25.
Can.:	$50.	$25.

THE TALE OF MRS. TIGGY-WINKLE™
Style Two

Model:	A3953
Modeller:	Richard Wawrzesta
Height:	5 ¼", 13.3 cm
Colour:	White, brown, blue and green
Issued:	06/05 in a limited edition of 1,250
Series:	Beatrix Potter Classics

U.K.:	£40.00
U.S.:	$80.00
Can.:	$80.00

THE TALE OF MRS. TIGGY-WINKLE™
Style Three

Model:	A5087
Modeller:	Unknown
Height:	3 ¾, 9.5 cm
Colour:	Pink, white, brown, and blue
Issued:	01/05 - 12/05
Series:	2005 Centenary Figurines
U.K.:	£20.00
U.S.:	$40.00
Can.:	$40.00

THE TALE OF MRS. TITTLEMOUSE™

Model:	BPM60, 268682	
Modeller:	Richard Wawrzesta	
Height:	3", 7. 6 cm	
Colour:	Brown mouse; white, pale blue and red clothing	
Issued:	01/96 - 12/98	
Series:	Storybook	
Made in	**U.K.**	**Abroad**
U.K.:	£25.	£12.
U.S.:	$50.	$25.
Can.:	$50.	$25.

THE TALE OF PETER RABBIT™
Style One (Storybook)

Model:	BPM50, 199443	
Modeller:	Richard Wawrzesta	
Height:	3 ½", 8.9 cm	
Colour:	Brown rabbit; blue jacket	
Issued:	01/95 - 12/02	
Series:	Storybook	
Made in	**U.K.**	**Abroad**
U.K.:	£25.	£12.
U.S.:	$50.	$25.
Can.:	$50.	$25.

THE TALE OF PETER RABBIT™
Style Two (To celebrate the film "Miss Potter")

Model:	A7799
Modeller:	Richard Wawrzesta
Height:	4", 10.1 cm
Colour:	Light brown, turquoise, green and orange
Issued:	01/07-12/07
U.K.:	£25.00
U.S.:	$50.00
Can.:	$50.00

THE TALE OF PETER RABBIT™
TABLEAU

Model:	A1306
Modeller:	Richard Wawrzesta
Height:	5 ¼", 13.3 cm
Colour:	Browns, green, blues and red
Issued:	01/02 in a limited edition of 2,002
Series:	Peter Rabbit Centenary Collection Tableau
U.K.:	£ 65.00
U.S.:	$130.00
Can.:	$130.00

THE TALE OF PIGLING BLAND™

Model:	467545
Modeller:	Richard Wawrzesta
Height:	3 ½", 8.9 cm
Colour:	Pink pig; lilac coat; blue and white striped waistcoat; red handkerchief; tan stick
Issued:	01/98 - 12/02
Series:	Storybook
U.K.:	£12.00
U.S.:	$25.00
Can.:	$25.00

THE TALE OF SAMUEL WHISKERS™

Model:	467537
Modeller:	Richard Wawrzesta
Height:	2 ½", 6.4 cm
Colour:	Brown mouse; green coat; yellow waistcoat; brown pantaloons
Issued:	01/98 - 12/02
Series:	Storybook
U.K.:	£12.00
U.S.:	$25.00
Can.:	$25.00

THE TALE OF SQUIRREL NUTKIN™
Style One (Storybook)

Model:	BPM51, 199494	
Modeller:	Richard Wawrzesta	
Height:	3 ½", 8.9 cm	
Colour:	Reddish-brown and white squirrel	
Issued:	01/95 - 12/98	
Series:	Storybook	
Made in	**U.K.**	**Abroad**
U.K.:	£25.	£12.
U.S.:	$50.	$25.
Can.:	$50.	$25.

THE TALE OF SQUIRREL NUTKIN™

Style Two (Centenary Figure)

Model:	A2221
Modeller:	Richard Wawrzesta
Height:	3 ¾", 9.5 cm
Colour:	Red-brown and white squirrel; brown, green, pink and blue-grey
Issued:	01/03 limited to the year of manufacture 2003
Series:	Beatrix Potter Classic Centenary Figures

U.K.:	£20.00
U.S.:	$40.00
Can.:	$40.00

THE TALE OF THE FLOPSY BUNNIES™

Model:	BPM59, 268704
Modeller:	Richard Wawrzesta
Height:	3 ¼", 8.3 cm
Colour:	Brown rabbits; salmon jacket; blue frock
Issued:	01/96 - 12/02
Series:	Storybook

Made in	U.K.	Abroad
U.K.:	£30.	£15.
U.S.:	$60.	$30.
Can.:	$60.	$30.

THE TALE OF THE PIE AND THE PATTY PAN™

Style One (Duchess)

Model:	545910
Modeller:	Richard Wawrzesta
Height:	3 ¼", 8.3 cm
Colour:	Black dog; red, blue, yellow and green bouquet
Issued:	01/99 - 12/02
Series:	Storybook

U.K.:	£12.00
U.S.:	$25.00
Can.:	$25.00

THE TALE OF THE PIE AND THE PATTY PAN™

Style Two (Miss Moppet)

Model:	A5088
Modeller:	Richard Wawrzesta
Height:	4", 10.1 cm
Colour:	Blue, white, pink , red, green, blue and yellow
Issued:	01/05 - 12/05
Series:	2005 Centenary Figurines

U.K.:	£20.00
U.S.:	$40.00
Can.:	$40.00

THE TALE OF THE TAILOR OF GLOUCESTER™

Model:	BPM52, 199532
Modeller:	Richard Wawrzesta
Height:	3 ½", 8.9 cm
Colour:	Brown mouse; tan spool of fuchsia thread
Issued:	01/95 - 12/02
Series:	Storybook

Made in	U.K.	Abroad
U.K.:	£25.	£12.
U.S.:	$50.	$25.
Can.:	$50.	$25.

THE TALE OF TIMMY TIPTOES™

Model:	BPM61, 268690
Modeller:	Richard Wawrzesta
Height:	3 ¼", 8.3 cm
Colour:	Brown, white and pink squirrel; salmon jacket
Issued:	01/96 - 12/98
Series:	Storybook

Made in	U.K.	Abroad
U.K.:	£25.	£12.
U.S.:	$50.	$25.
Can.:	$50.	$25.

THE TALE OF TOM KITTEN™

Style One

Model:	BPM57, 199478
Modeller:	Richard Wawrzesta
Height:	3 ¼", 8.3 cm
Colour:	Ginger tabby cat; blue suit
Issued:	01/96 - 12/02
Series:	Storybook

Made in	U.K.	Abroad
U.K.:	£25.	£12.
U.S.:	$50.	$25.
Can.:	$50.	$25.

THE TALE OF TOM KITTEN™

Style Two

Model:	A7667
Modeller:	Richard Wawrzesta
Height:	3 ¼", 8.3 cm
Colour:	Light brown, turquoise, green, red and blue
Issued:	01/07 - 12/07
Series:	2007 Centenary Figurine

U.K.:	£22.00
U.S.:	$45.00
Can.:	$45.00

THE TALE OF TWO BAD MICE™
Style One

Model:	BPM54, 199516
Modeller:	Richard Wawrzesta
Height:	3", 7.6 cm
Colour:	Brown mouse; lilac and white clothing
Issued:	01/95 - 12/02
Varieties:	1. Base: "Hunca Munca" 2. Base: "The Tale of Two Bad Mice"
Series:	Storybook

Made in	U.K.	Abroad
U.K.:	£25.	£12.
U.S.:	$50.	$25.
Can.:	$50.	$25.

THE TALE OF TWO BAD MICE™
(Hunca Munca and Babies)
Style Two

Model:	A3288
Modeller:	Unknown
Height:	3 ½", 8.9 cm
Colour:	Brown, cream, blue, green, cream pink and white
Issued:	01/04 - 12/04
Series:	2004 Centenary Figurines

U.K.:	£20.00
U.S.:	$40.00
Can.:	$40.00

THE TALE OF TWO BAD MICE™
Style Three

Model:	A3948
Modeller:	Unknown
Height:	5 ¾", 14.6 cm
Colour:	Pink, brown, pale blue, lilac, white and lemon
Issued:	06/04 in a limited edition of 1,250
Medium:	Earthenware
Series:	Beatrix Potter Classics

U.K.:	£ 60.00
U.S.:	$120.00
Can.:	$120.00

THIS ONE IS MOPPET™

Model:	BP8
Modeller:	Richard Wawrzesta
Height:	3 ¾", 9.5 cm
Size:	Large
Colour:	Tabby and ginger cats; purple dress; white apron and bowl; brown dresser
Issued:	01/87 - 12/93 (In Tins)

U.K.:	£ 80.00
U.S.:	$160.00
Can.:	$160.00

TIMMY WILLIE™

Model:	739545
Modeller:	Richard Wawrzesta
Height:	3 ¼", 8.3 cm
Size:	Medium
Colour:	Brown mouse; yellowish-green leaf; pink and white flowers
Issued:	01/00 - 06/03 (In Tins)

U.K.:	£20.00
U.S.:	$40.00
Can.:	$40.00

TIMMY WILLIE AND THE STRAWBERRY™
Style One

Model:	BP4
Modeller:	Richard Wawrzesta
Height:	3 ½", 8.9 cm
Size:	Large
Colour:	Brown and white mouse; red strawberry; green leaves
Issued:	01/87 - 12/95 (In Tins)

U.K.:	£ 55.00
U.S.:	$110.00
Can.:	$110.00

TIMMIE WILLIE AND THE STRAWBERRY™
Style Two

Model:	A3102
Modeller:	Richard Wawrzesta
Height:	4 ¾", 12.1 cm
Colour:	Red-brown, white, green and dark pink
Issued:	06/03 to the present
Medium:	Earthenware
Series:	Beatrix Potter Classics

U.K.:	£14.95
U.S.:	$30.00
Can.:	$30.00

TIMMY WILLIE SLEEPING IN A PEA POD™
First Version

Model:	BP22
Modeller:	Richard Wawrzesta
Height:	2", 5.0 cm
Size:	Large
Colour:	Brown mouse; green pea pod
Issued:	01/91 - 12/95 (In Tins)

U.K.:	£ 55.00
U.S.:	$110.00
Can.:	$110.00

TIMMY WILLIE SLEEPING IN A PEA POD™
Second Version

Model: 643920
Modeller: Richard Wawrzesta
Height: 1 ½", 3.9 cm
Size: Miniature
Colour: Brown and white mouse; green pea pod
Issued: 06/99 to the present

U.K.: £ 9.95
U.S.: $20.00
Can.: $20.00

TIMMIE WILLIE SLEEPING IN A PEA POD™
Third Version

Model: A1084
Modeller: Unknown
Height: 1 ¾", 4.4 cm
Colour: Brown, white, green, yellow and lilac
Issued: 01/02 - 12/03 (In Tins)

U.K.: £20.00
U.S.: $40.00
Can.: $40.00

TIMMIE WILLIE SLEEPING IN A PEA POD™
Fourth Version

Model: A2441
Modeller: Richard Wawrzesta
Length: 4 ¾", 12.1 cm
Colour: Beige, cream and green
Issued: 01/03 to the present
Medium: Earthenware
Series: Beatrix Potter Classics

U.K.: £14.95
U.S.: $30.00
Can.: $30.00

TIMMIE WILLIE UNDER LEAF™

Model: A2354
Modeller: Richard Wawrzesta
Height: 2 ½", 6.4 cm
Size: Miniature
Colour: Beige, white and green
Issued: 01/03 to the present

U.K.: £ 9.95
U.S.: $20.00
Can.: $20.00

TOM KITTEN™

Model: A2493/129762
Modeller: Janet Miller
Height: 5 ½", 14.0 cm
Colour: Brown, blue and white
Issued: 06/03 - 12/04
Medium: Porcelain
Series: The Peter Rabbit and Friends Collection

U.K.: £24.99
U.S.: $50.00
Can.: $50.00

TOM KITTEN WITH BUTTERFLY™
Style One

Model: BP23
Modeller: Richard Wawrzesta
Height: 4 ½", 11.9 cm
Size: Large
Colour: Brown kitten; blue suit; white collar; straw hat
Issued: 01/91 - 12/94 (In Boxes)

U.K.: £ 55.00
U.S.: $110.00
Can.: $110.00

TOM KITTEN WITH BUTTERFLY™
Style Two

Model: A1315
Modeller: Richard Wawrzesta
Height: 2 ½", 6.4 cm
Size: Miniature
Colour: Brown, white, blue, orange and black
Issued: 01/02 to the present

U.K.: £ 9.95
U.S.: $20.00
Can.: $20.00

TOM KITTEN WITH BUTTERFLY™
Style Three

Model: A2438
Modeller: Richard Wawrzesta
Height: 4 ½", 11.9 cm
Colour: Brown, blue, white, red and black
Issued: 01/03 to the present
Medium: Earthenware
Series: Beatrix Potter Classics

U.K.: £14.95
U.S.: $30.00
Can.: $30.00

TOM THUMB AND TONGS™

Model:	BPM4
Modeller:	Richard Wawrzesta
Height:	3", 7.6 cm
Size:	Miniature
Colour:	Brown and white mouse; gold tongs
Issued:	01/92 - 12/95

U.K.:	£30.00
U.S.:	$60.00
Can.:	$60.00

WE WISHED THEM GOODBYE IN THE YARD™

Model:	120025
Modeller:	Richard Wawrzesta
Height:	6 ½", 16.5 cm
Colour:	Green, black, white, pale blue, lilac, rust, dark green and yellow
Issued:	01/01 in a limited edition of 500
Series:	Tableau

U.K.:	£150.00
U.S.:	$300.00
Can.:	$300.00

YOCK-YOCK IN CLOTHES BASKET™

Model:	BPM35
Modeller:	Richard Wawrzesta
Height:	1 ¾", 4.4 cm
Size:	Miniature
Colour:	Pink pig; white towel; brown basket
Issued:	01/94 – 12/96

Made in	UK	Abroad
U.K.:	£ 75.	£20.
U.S.:	$150.	$40.
Can.:	$150.	$40.

Archways

AUNT PETTITOES™

Model: 739553
Modeller: Richard Wawrzesta
Height: 3 ½", 8.9 cm
Colour: Pink pig; blue and white striped dress; white apron; green archway with blue flowers
Issued: 01/00 - 12/01

U.K.: £15.00
U.S.: $30.00
Can.: $30.00

JEMIMA PUDDLE-DUCK™

Model: 512044
Modeller: Richard Wawrzesta
Height: 4", 10.1 cm
Colour: White duck; blue bonnet; rose and blue shawl; rose-pink, green and brown archway
Issued: 01/99 - 12/02

U.K.: £15.00
U.S.: $30.00
Can.: $30.00

MR. JEREMY FISHER™

Model: 511897
Modeller: Richard Wawrzesta
Height: 3 ½", 8.9 cm
Colour: Yellow frog; rose-pink jacket; white paper; yellow, green, and brown archway
Issued: 01/99 - 12/01

U.K.: £15.00
U.S.: $30.00
Can.: $30.00

MRS. TIGGY-WINKLE™

Model: 512656
Modeller: Richard Wawrzesta
Height: 3 ½", 8.9 cm
Colour: White cap; pink, white, yellow and blue outfit; lilac, blue and green archway
Issued: 01/99 - 12/02

U.K.: £15.00
U.S.: $30.00
Can.: $30.00

PETER RABBIT™

Model: 511900
Modeller: Richard Wawrzesta
Height: 3 ½", 8.9 cm
Colour: Brown rabbit; blue coat; rose-pink kerchief; green and rose-pink archway
Issued: 01/99 - 12/02

U.K.: £15.00
U.S.: $30.00
Can.: $30.00

PETER RABBIT WITH RADISH™

Model: 739596
Modeller: Richard Wawrzesta
Height: 3 ¾", 9.5 cm
Colour: Brown rabbit; blue jacket; red radishes; orange and brown bird; green leaves
Issued: 01/00 - 12/02

U.K.: £15.00
U.S.: $30.00
Can.: $30.00

TAILOR OF GLOUCESTER, THE™

Model: 739561
Modeller: Richard Wawrzesta
Height: 3 ½", 8.9 cm
Colour: Brown mouse; white paper; tan spool of fuchsia thread; brown window frame with blue curtains
Issued: 01/00 - 12/02

U.K.: £15.00
U.S.: $30.00
Can.: $30.00

TIMMY WILLIE™

Model: 739588
Modeller: Richard Wawrzesta
Height: 3 ¼", 8.3 cm
Colour: Brown mouse; red strawberries; green leaves with white flowers
Issued: 01/00 - 12/02

U.K.: £15.00
U.S.: $30.00
Can.: $30.00

Growing Up

NEW BABY (HUNCA MUNCA)™

Model:	269425
Modeller:	Richard Wawrzesta
Height:	2 ¾", 7.0 cm
Colour:	Mother: brown; blue dress; white apron and trim
	Baby: brown; white nightgown
Issued:	06/97 - 12/00
Series:	Nursery Collection
U.K.:	£30.00
U.S.:	$60.00
Can.:	$60.00

AGE 1 (CURIOUS RABBIT)™

Model:	269433
Modeller:	Richard Wawrzesta
Height:	3 ¼", 8.3 cm
Colour:	Brown rabbit; blue coat; red handkerchief
Issued:	06/97 - 12/00
Series:	Nursery Collection
U.K.:	£30.00
U.S.:	$60.00
Can.:	$60.00

AGE 2 (BAD MICE)™

Model:	269441
Modeller:	Richard Wawrzesta
Height:	3 ½", 8.9 cm
Colour:	Brown mouse; tan plate; grey fish; brown chair
Issued:	06/97 - 12/99
U.K.:	£30.00
U.S.:	$60.00
Can.:	$60.00

AGE 3 (PLAYFUL KITTEN)™

Model:	269468
Modeller:	Richard Wawrzesta
Height:	2 ¾", 7.0 cm
Colour:	Brown kitten; blue suit; white collar; yellow straw hat
Issued:	06/97 - 12/99
U.K.:	£30.00
U.S.:	$60.00
Can.:	$60.00

AGE 4 (LITTLE RABBITS)™

Model:	269476
Modeller:	Richard Wawrzesta
Height:	3", 7.6 cm
Colour:	Brown rabbits; blue jacket; red handkerchief
Issued:	06/97 - 12/99
U.K.:	£30.00
U.S.:	$60.00
Can.:	$60.00

AGE 5 (MENDING MICE)™

Model:	269484
Modeller:	Richard Wawrzesta
Height:	2 ½", 6.4 cm
Colour:	Brown mouse; white cloth with blue and red designs; white candle; gold candleholder
Issued:	06/97 - 12/99
U.K.:	£30.00
U.S.:	$60.00
Can.:	$60.00

AGE 6 (SLEEPING BUNNIES)™

Model:	269492
Modeller:	Richard Wawrzesta
Height:	2 ½", 6.4 cm
Colour:	Brown bunny; green foliage
Issued:	06/97 - 12/99
U.K.:	£30.00
U.S.:	$60.00
Can.:	$60.00

BRAMBLY HEDGE
Figurines

AUTUMN TABLEAU™

Model:	B0631
Designer:	Jill Barklem
Modeller:	Richard Wawrzesta
Size:	6 ¼" x 8", 15.9 x 20.3 cm
Colour:	Brown, yellow, white, tan, rust, burnt orange,
Issued:	11/00 in a limited edition of 999
Series:	Four Seasons Tableau Collection

U.K.:	£100.00
U.S.:	$200.00
Can.:	$200.00

BABIES IN THE BATH™

Model:	BH73
Designer:	Jill Barklem
Modeller:	Richard Wawrzesta
Height:	2 ¼", 5.7 cm
Colour:	Brown, white and pink mice in blue tub; yellow sponge
Issued:	01/96 - 12/97 (In Box)
Series:	Poppy's Babies Collection

U.K.:	£ 50.00
U.S.:	$100.00
Can.:	$100.00

BASIL RECLINING™

Model:	BH38
Designer:	Jill Barklem
Modeller:	Richard Wawrzesta
Height:	2 ¼", 5.7 cm
Colour:	Brown, white and pink mouse; red waistcoat; white and blue trousers; brown jacket
Issued:	07/91 - 12/95 (In Tin)
Series:	Midwinter Collection

U.K.:	£ 80.00
U.S.:	$160.00
Can.:	$160.00

BASIL WITH BASKET™

Model:	BH64
Designer:	Jill Barklem
Modeller:	Richard Wawrzesta
Height:	2 ½", 6.4 cm
Colour:	Green jacket; red waistcoat; blue and white striped trousers; brown baskets
Issued:	01/93 - 12/95 (In Tin)
Series:	Picnic Collection

U.K.:	£40.00
U.S.:	$80.00
Can.:	$80.00

BASIL WITH BOTTLES™

Model:	BH26
Designer:	Jill Barklem
Modeller:	Richard Wawrzesta
Height:	2 ½", 6.4 cm
Colour:	Brown, white, pink, red and blue
Issued:	01/91 - 12/96 (In Tin or Box)
Series:	Store Stump Kitchen Collection

U.K.:	£35.00
U.S.:	$70.00
Can.:	$70.00

BEST MAN - CONKER™

Model	BH15
Designer:	Jill Barklem
Modeller:	Richard Wawrzesta
Height:	2 ½", 6.4 cm
Colour:	Green waistcoat; green and white striped trousers; blue and pink present
Issued:	01/90 - 12/96 (In Tin or Box)
Series:	Wedding Collection

U.K.:	£30.00
U.S.:	$60.00
Can.:	$60.00

BRIDE - POPPY EYEBRIGHT™

Model:	BH9
Designer:	Jill Barklem
Modeller:	Richard Wawrzesta
Height:	2 ½", 6.4 cm
Colour:	Pink and white striped dress; white and blue apron
Issued:	01/89 - 12/96 (In Tin or Box)
Series:	Wedding Collection

U.K.:	£25.00
U.S.:	$50.00
Can.:	$50.00

BRIDE AND GROOM - POPPY AND DUSTY™

Model:	BH11
Designer:	Jill Barklem
Modeller:	Richard Wawrzesta
Height:	2 ½", 6.4 cm
Colour:	Pink, white, blue, violet and rose
Issued:	01/90 -12/95 (In Tin or Box)
Series:	Wedding Collection

U.K.:	£40.00
U.S.:	$80.00
Can.:	$80.00

BRIDESMAID - PRIMROSE™

Model: BH14
Designer: Jill Barklem
Modeller: Richard Wawrzesta
Height: 2 ¼", 5.7 cm
Colour: Pink dress; white apron; multicoloured flowers
Issued: 01/90 - 12/96 (In Tin or Box)
Series: Wedding Collection

U.K.: £30.00
U.S.: $60.00
Can.: $60.00

BUNK BEDS, THE™

Model: BH35
Designer: Jill Barklem
Modeller: Richard Wawrzesta
Height: 4 ¼", 10.8 cm
Colour: Brown frame; pink and white and blue and white bedclothes
Issued: 01/91 - 12/95 (In Box)
Series: Nursery Collection

U.K.: £100.00
U.S.: $200.00
Can.: $200.00

CANOPY BED, THE™

Model: BH34
Designer: Jill Barklem
Modeller: Richard Wawrzesta
Height: 6", 15.0 cm
Colour: Multicoloured
Issued: 01/91 - 12/95 (In Box)
Series: Nursery Collection

U.K.: £125.00
U.S.: $250.00
Can.: $250.00

CLOVER AND CATKIN™

Model: BH32
Designer: Jill Barklem
Modeller: Richard Wawrzesta
Height: 2 ½", 6.4 cm
Colour: Brown mice in white and pink bedclothes
Issued: 01/91 - 12/95 (In Tin)
Series: Nursery Collection

U.K.: £40.00
U.S.: $80.00
Can.: $80.00

DRESSER, THE™

Model: BH6
Designer: Jill Barklem
Modeller: Richard Wawrzesta
Height: 5", 12.7 cm
Colour: Cream dresser with multicoloured contents
Issued: 01/88 - 12/95 (In Box)
Series: Store Stump Kitchen Collection

U.K.: £100.00
U.S.: $200.00
Can.: $200.00

DRESSING TABLE, THE™

Model: BH33
Designer: Jill Barklem
Modeller: Richard Wawrzesta
Height: 2 ¾", 7.0 cm
Colour: Brown table; multicoloured accessories
Issued: 01/91 - 12/95 (In Box)
Series: Nursery Collection

U.K.: £ 80.00
U.S.: $160.00
Can.: $160.00

DUSTY PUSHING PRAM™

Model: BH75
Designer: Jill Barklem
Modeller: Richard Wawrzesta
Height: 3", 7.6 cm
Colour: Brown and white mouse; grey, blue and white clothing; brown pram; pink and white blanket
Issued: 01/96 - 12/97 (In Box)
Series: Poppy's Babies Collection

U.K.: £ 50.00
U.S.: $100.00
Can.: $100.00

FIREPLACE, THE™

Model: BH8
Designer: Jill Barklem
Modeller: Richard Wawrzesta
Height: 5", 12.7 cm
Colour: Cream hearth with multicoloured contents
Issued: 01/88 - 12/95 (In Box)
Series: Store Stump Kitchen Collection

U.K.: £ 80.00
U.S.: $160.00
Can.: $160.00

FLORAL ARCH™

Model: BH16
Designer: Jill Barklem
Modeller: Richard Wawrzesta
Height: 5 ½", 14.0 cm
Colour: Green, pink, yellow and blue
Issued: 01/90 - 12/95 (In Box)
Series: Wedding Collection

U.K.: £ 60.00
U.S.: $120.00
Can.: $120.00

GROOM - DUSTY DOGWOOD™

Model: BH10
Designer: Jill Barklem
Modeller: Richard Wawrzesta
Height: 2 ½", 6.4 cm
Colour: Blue suit; rose waistcoat; white shirt
Issued: 01/89 - 12/96 (In Tin or Box)
Series: Wedding Collection

U.K.: £25.00
U.S.: $50.00
Can.: $50.00

HAPPY BIRTHDAY WILFRED™

Model: Unknown
Designer: Jill Barklem
Modeller: Richard Wawrzesta
Height: Unknown
Colour: Light brown, dark blue, red, green, light blue and yellow
Issued: 2001 in a limited edition of 500

U.K.: £20.00
U.S.: $40.00
Can.: $40.00

LADY WOODMOUSE™

Model: BH2
Designer: Jill Barklem
Modeller: Richard Wawrzesta
Height: 2 ½", 6.4 cm
Colour: Pink dress; white apron; straw hat and basket
Issued: 01/88 - 12/96 (In Tin or Box)
Series: Store Stump Kitchen Collection

U.K.: £25.00
U.S.: $50.00
Can.: $50.00

LADY WOODMOUSE AND PRIMROSE™

Model: BH29
Designer: Jill Barklem
Modeller: Richard Wawrzesta
Height: 2 ¾", 7.0 cm
Colour: Lady Woodmouse: pink, white and blue Primrose: yellow and white
Issued: 01/91 - 12/94 (In Tin)
Series: Nursery Collection

U.K.: £ 80.00
U.S.: $160.00
Can.: $160.00

LADY WOODMOUSE EATING CAKE™

Model: BH28
Designer: Jill Barklem
Modeller: Richard Wawrzesta
Height: 2 ¾", 7.0 cm
Colour: Tan bonnet; blue frock; white apron
Issued: 01/91 - 12/96 (In Tin or Box)
Series: Wedding Collection

U.K.: £25.00
U.S.: $50.00
Can.: $50.00

LADY WOODMOUSE IN A CHAIR™

Model: BH21
Designer: Jill Barklem
Modeller: Richard Wawrzesta
Height: 3", 7.6 cm
Colour: Brown, white and pink mouse; buff clothing
Issued: 07/90 - 12/93 (In Tin)
Series: Midwinter Collection

U.K.: £125.00
U.S.: $250.00
Can.: $250.00

LADY WOODMOUSE LOOKING IN THE CRADLE™

Model: BH71
Designer: Jill Barklem
Modeller: Richard Wawrzesta
Height: 3", 7.6 cm
Colour: White, red, blue and yellow clothing; brown cradle; multicoloured blanket
Issued: 01/96 - 12/97 (In Box)
Series: Poppy's Babies Collection

U.K.: £ 50.00
U.S.: $100.00
Can.: $100.00

LORD AND LADY WOODMOUSE RESTING™

Model: BH67
Designer: Jill Barklem
Modeller: Richard Wawrzesta
Height: 2 ¼", 5.7 cm
Colour: Pink and white striped dress; white apron;
blue trousers; red waistcoat
Issued: 01/93 - 12/95 (In Tin)
Series: Picnic Collection

U.K.: £ 80.00
U.S.: $160.00
Can.: $160.00

LORD WOODMOUSE IN A CHAIR™

Model: BH22
Designer: Jill Barklem
Modeller: Richard Wawrzesta
Height: 3", 7.6 cm
Colour: Brown, white and pink mouse; orange, blue and yellow clothing
Issued: 07/90 - 12/93 (In Tin)
Series: Midwinter Collection

U.K.: £125.00
U.S.: $250.00
Can.: $250.00

MERRY WINTER TABLEAU™

Model: Unknown
Designer: Jill Barklem
Modeller: Unknown
Height: 6 ½", 16.5 cm
Colour: Beige, brown, red, white, green, yellow and blue
Issued: 2001 in a limited edition of 500
Series: Tableau Collection

U.K.: £100.00
U.S.: $200.00
Can.: $200.00

MIDWINTER FIREPLACE™

Model: BH24
Designer: Jill Barklem
Modeller: Richard Wawrzesta
Height: 4 ¾", 12.1 cm
Colour: Yellow and brown with multicoloured ornaments
Issued: 07/90 - 12/93 (In Box)
Series: Midwinter Collection

U.K.: £100.00
U.S.: $200.00
Can.: $200.00

MIDWINTER TREE™

Model: BH23
Designer: Jill Barklem
Modeller: Richard Wawrzesta
Height: 5 ½", 14.0 cm
Colour: Green tree; yellow, orange and pink decorations
Issued: 07/90 - 12/93 (In Box)
Series: Midwinter Collection

U.K.: £100.00
U.S.: $200.00
Can.: $200.00

MILLENNIUM SNOW BALL TABLEAU™

Model: B0555
Designer: Jill Barklem
Modeller: Richard Wawrzesta
Size: 6 ½" x 9", 16.5 cm x 22.9 cm
Colour: Brown, green, red, blue, yellow, cream and green
Issued: 01/99 in a limited edition of 999
Series: Tableau Collection

U.K.: £100.00
U.S.: $200.00
Can.: $200.00

MINISTER - OLD VOLE™

Model: BH12
Modeller: Richard Wawrzesta
Height: 2 ¼", 5.7 cm
Colour: Brown; green jacket and waistcoat; blue trousers
Issued: 01/90 - 12/96 (In Tin or Box)
Series: Wedding Collection

U.K.: £40.00
U.S.: $80.00
Can.: $80.00

MR. APPLE IN ROCKING CHAIR™

Model: BH5
Designer: Jill Barklem
Modeller: Richard Wawrzesta
Height: 3 ¼", 8.3 cm
Colour: Blue trousers and waistcoat; pale blue shirt; white tablecloth; red checkered cloth
Issued: 01/88 - 12/95 (In Tin)
Series: Store Stump Kitchen Collection

U.K.: £ 50.00
U.S.: $100.00
Can.: $100.00

MR. APPLE PROPOSING A TOAST™

Model: BH27
Designer: Jill Barklem
Modeller: Richard Wawrzesta
Height: 2 ¾", 7.0 cm
Colour: Blue jacket and trousers; white shirt; red bowtie
Issued: 01/91 - 12/96 (In Tin or Box)
Series: Wedding Collection

U.K.: £25.00
U.S.: $50.00
Can.: $50.00

MR. TOADFLAX™

Model: BH61
Designer: Jill Barklem
Modeller: Richard Wawrzesta
Height: 2 ¾", 7.0 cm
Colour: Blue waistcoat; pink and white striped shirt; brown basket
Issued: 01/93 - 12/95 (In Tin)
Series: Picnic Collection

U.K.: £ 50.00
U.S.: $100.00
Can.: $100.00

MRS. APPLE™

Model: BH1
Designer: Jill Barklem
Modeller: Richard Wawrzesta
Height: 2 ½", 6.4 cm
Colour: Blue striped dress; white apron; green tea service
Issued: 01/88 - 12/96 (In Tin or Box)
Series: Store Stump Kitchen Collection

U.K.: £25.00
U.S.: $50.00
Can.: $50.00

MRS. APPLE AND THE CHILDREN™

Model: BH37
Designer: Jill Barklem
Modeller: Richard Wawrzesta
Height: 2 ½", 6.4 cm
Colour: Brown, white and pink mice; blue and white, red and white and yellow and white clothing
Issued: 07/91 - 12/95 (In Tin)
Series: Midwinter Collection

U.K.: £100.00
U.S.: $200.00
Can.: $200.00

MRS. APPLE AND WILFRED™

Model: BH65
Designer: Jill Barklem
Modeller: Richard Wawrzesta
Height: 2 ¾", 7.0 cm
Colour: Blue and white striped dress; white apron; red and white striped shirt; blue trousers; brown wheelbarrow
Issued: 01/93 - 12/95 (In Tin)
Series: Picnic Collection

U.K.: £100.00
U.S.: $200.00
Can.: $200.00

MRS. CRUSTY BREAD WITH MIXING BOWL™

Model: BH25
Designer: Jill Barklem
Modeller: Richard Wawrzesta
Height: 2 ½", 6.4 cm
Colour: Brown and white mouse; white apron; yellow dress; white bowl
Issued: 01/91 - 12/96 (In Tin or Box)
Series: Store Stump Kitchen Collection

U.K.: £25.00
U.S.: $50.00
Can.: $50.00

MRS. TOADFLAX WITH HAMPER™

Model: BH62
Designer: Jill Barklem
Modeller: Richard Wawrzesta
Height: 2 ½", 6.4 cm
Colour: White dress with yellow flowers; white apron; brown picnic hamper
Issued: 01/93 - 12/95 (In Tin)
Series: Picnic Collection

U.K.: £ 80.00
U.S.: $160.00
Can.: $160.00

PAGEBOY - WILFRED™

Model: BH13
Designer: Jill Barklem
Modeller: Richard Wawrzesta
Height: 2 ¼", 5.7 cm
Colour: Brown and white mouse; blue clothing
Issued: 01/90 - 12/96 (In Tin or Box)
Series: Wedding Collection

U.K.: £ 50.00
U.S.: $100.00
Can.: $100.00

PICNIC BLANKET™

Model:	BH60
Designer:	Jill Barklem
Modeller:	Richard Wawrzesta
Height:	1 ½", 3.8 cm
Colour:	Multicoloured food on white blanket; green grass
Issued:	01/93 - 12/95 (In Box)
Series:	Picnic Collection

U.K.:	£30.00
U.S.:	$60.00
Can.:	$60.00

POPPY AND BABIES™

Model:	BH70
Designer:	Jill Barklem
Modeller:	Richard Wawrzesta
Height:	3", 7.6 cm
Colour:	Brown, white and pink mice; blue, white and red clothing
Issued:	01/96 - 12/97 (In Box)
Series:	Poppy's Babies Collection

U.K.;	£ 50.00
U.S.:	$100.00
Can.:	$100.00

POPPY ASLEEP IN CHAIR™

Model:	BH72
Designer:	Jill Barklem
Modeller:	Richard Wawrzesta
Height:	2 ¼", 5.7 cm
Colour:	Brown and white mouse; blue and white clothing; green chair; brown cushion
Issued:	01/96 - 12/97 (In Box)
Series:	Poppy's Babies Collection

U.K.:	£ 50.00
U.S.:	$100.00
Can.:	$100.00

POPPY PACKING NIGHT CLOTHES™

Model:	BH74
Designer:	Jill Barklem
Modeller:	Richard Wawrzesta
Height:	2 ½", 6.4 cm
Colour:	Brown and white mouse; blue, white and red clothing; brown trunk
Issued:	01/96 - 12/97 (In Box)
Series:	Poppy's Babies Collection

U.K.:	£ 50.00
U.S.:	$100.00
Can.:	$100.00

PRETENDERS TO THE THRONE TABLEAU™

Model:	Unknown
Designer:	Jill Barklem
Modeller:	Unknown
Height:	Unknown
Colour:	Tan, brown, pink, rose-pink, grey, white, cream and yellow
Issued:	2001 in a limited edition of 250

U.K.:	£100.00
U.S.:	$200.00
Can.:	$200.00

PRIMROSE™

Model:	BH3
Designer:	Jill Barklem
Modeller:	Richard Wawrzesta
Height:	2 ¼", 5.7 cm
Colour:	Yellow dress; white apron and cloth
Issued:	01/88 - 12/96 (In Tin or Box)
Series:	Store Stump Kitchen Collection

U.K.:	£25.00
U.S.:	$50.00
Can.:	$50.00

PRIMROSE RECITING™

Model:	BH20
Designer:	Jill Barklem
Modeller:	Richard Wawrzesta
Height:	2 ½", 6.4 cm
Colour:	Brown, white and pink mouse; cream, blue and yellow hat
Issued:	07/90 - 12/93 (In Tin)
Series:	Midwinter Collection

U.K.:	£100.00
U.S.:	$200.00
Can.:	$200.00

PRIMROSE - TEDDY MOUSE™

Model:	BH40
Designer:	Jill Barklem
Modeller:	Richard Wawrzesta
Height:	2 ¼", 5.7 cm
Colour:	Brown mouse in white and blue pyjamas
Issued:	01/92 - 12/96 (In Tin or Box)
Series:	Nursery Collection

U.K.:	£ 50.00
U.S.:	$100.00
Can.:	$100.00

SEA STORY TABLEAU™

Model:	Unknown
Designer:	Jill Berklem
Modeller:	Unknown
Height:	6 ½", 16.5 cm
Colour:	Light brown, green, blue-white, blue, yellow, cream and red
Issued:	2001 in a limited edition of 500
Series:	Tableau Collection
U.K.:	£100.00
U.S.:	$200.00
Can.:	$200.00

SNOWMOUSE™

Model:	BH18
Designer:	Jill Barklem
Modeller:	Richard Wawrzesta
Height:	2 ½", 6.4 cm
Colour:	White mouse; orange and white scarf; brown pipe
Issued:	07/90 - 12/93 (In Tin)
Series:	Midwinter Collection
U.K.:	£40.00
U.S.:	$80.00
Can.:	$80.00

SPRING TABLEAU™

Model:	B0630
Designer:	Jill Barklem
Modeller:	Richard Wawrzesta
Size:	6 ½" x 7 ¾", 16.5 cm x 19.7 cm
Colour:	Brown, blue, white, green, red, yellow and pink
Issued:	04/00 in a limited edition of 999
Series:	Four Seasons Tableau Collection
U.K.:	£100.00
U.S.:	$200.00
Can.:	$200.00

SUMMER TABLEAU™

Model:	B0514
Designer:	Jill Barklem
Modeller:	Richard Wawrzesta
Size:	6 ½" x 7 ¼", 16.5 cm x 18.4 cm
Colour:	Brown, green, red, yellow, pink, blue, yellow, white and green
Issued:	1999 in a limited edition of 999
Series:	Four Seasons Tableau Collection
U.K.:	£100.00
U.S.:	$200.00
Can.:	$200.00

TABLE, THE™

Model:	BH7
Designer:	Jill Barklem
Modeller:	Richard Wawrzesta
Height:	3", 7.6 cm
Colour:	Cream table with multicoloured contents
Issued:	01/88 - 12/95 (In Box)
Series:	Store Stump Kitchen Collection
U.K.:	£ 60.00
U.S.:	$120.00
Can.:	$120.00

TEASEL™

Model:	BH30
Designer:	Jill Barklem
Modeller:	Richard Wawrzesta
Height:	2 ½", 6.4 cm
Colour:	Pink and white pyjamas; baby in blue
Issued:	01/91 - 12/96 (In Tin or Box)
Series:	Nursery Collection
U.K.:	£25.00
U.S.:	$50.00
Can.:	$50.00

TEASEL AND CLOVER™

Model:	BH66
Designer:	Jill Barklem
Modeller:	Richard Wawrzesta
Height:	2 ½", 6.4 cm
Colour:	Rose-pink dress; white apron; blue dungarees; white and blue striped shirt
Issued:	01/93 - 12/95 (In Tin)
Series:	Picnic Collection
U.K.:	£ 80.00
U.S.:	$160.00
Can.:	$160.00

Note: A few figurines exist with Teasel wearing a red striped shirt – very rare.

TOY CHEST, THE™
Model: BH36
Designer: Jill Barklem
Modeller: Richard Wawrzesta
Height: 2 ½", 6.4 cm
Colour: Green chest with tan trim; multicoloured contents
Issued: 01/91 - 12/95 (In Tin)
Series: Nursery Collection

U.K.: £ 50.00
U.S.: $100.00
Can.: $100.00

WEDDING TABLE AND CANOPY™
Model: BH17
Designer: Jill Barklem
Modeller: Richard Wawrzesta
Height: 5 ¼", 13.3 cm
Colour: Pink and white awning; blue background; multicoloured food
Issued: 01/90 - 12/95 (In Box)
Series: Wedding Collection

U.K.: £100.00
U.S.: $200.00
Can.: $200.00

WILFRED™
Model: BH4
Designer: Jill Barklem
Modeller: Richard Wawrzesta
Height: 2 ¼", 5.7 cm
Colour: Blue dungarees; red and white striped shirt
Issued: 01/88 - 12/96 (In Tin or Box)
Series: Store Stump Kitchen Collection

U.K.: £25.00
U.S.: $50.00
Can.: $50.00

WILFRED JIGGING™
Model: BH31
Designer: Jill Barklem
Modeller: Richard Wawrzesta
Height: 2 ½", 6.4 cm
Colour: Brown mouse; red and white striped shirt
Issued: 01/91 - 12/96 (In Tin or Box)
Series: Nursery Collection

U.K.: £30.00
U.S.: $60.00
Can.: $60.00

WILFRED RECITING™
Model: BH19
Designer: Jill Barklem
Modeller: Richard Wawrzesta
Height: 2 ½", 6.4 cm
Colour: Brown and pink mouse; blue and yellow hat; red clothing
Issued: 07/90 - 12/93 (In Tin)
Series: Midwinter Collection

U.K.: £100.00
U.S.: $200.00
Can.: $200.00

WILFRED - TEDDY MOUSE™
Model: BH39
Designer: Jill Barklem
Modeller: Richard Wawrzesta
Height: 2 ½", 6.4 cm
Colour: Red and white striped pyjamas; baby in blue
Issued: 01/92 - 12/96 (In Tin or Box)
Series: Nursery Collection

U.K.: £ 50.00
U.S.: $100.00
Can.: $100.00

WILFRED WITH TOYS™
Model: BH63
Designer: Jill Barklem
Modeller: Richard Wawrzesta
Height: 2", 5.0 cm
Colour: Blue dungarees; white and red striped shirt; multicoloured toys
Issued: 01/93 - 12/95 (In Tin)
Series: Picnic Collection

U.K.: £100.00
U.S.: $200.00
Can.: $200.00

WINTER TABLEAU™
Model: B0554
Designer: Jill Barklem
Modeller: Richard Wawrzesta
Size: 6 ½" x 7 ¼", 16.5 cm x 18.4 cm
Colour: Blue, white, red, orange-yellow, brown
Issued: 10/99 in a limited edition of 999
Series: Four Seasons Tableau Collection

U.K.: £125.00
U.S.: $250.00
Can.: $250.00

COMIC AND CURIOUS CATS

A BIRD IN THE HAND

Model: A2185
Designer: Linda Jane Smith
Modeller: Janet Miller
Height: 5 ¼", 13.3 cm
Colour: Reddish-brown, black, white, pale green and green
Issued: 01/03 - 06/05

U.K.:   £20.00
U.S.: $40.00
Can.: $40.00

A FINE ROMANCE

Model: A0911
Designer: Linda Jane Smith
Modeller: Janet Miller
Height: 4 ¾", 12.1 cm
Colour: Yellowy-orange, white, black and blue
Issued: 06/01 - 12/03

U.K.:   £20.00
U.S.: $40.00
Can.: $40.00

A PIECE OF CAKE

Model: A6866
Designer: Linda Jane Smith
Modeller: Janet Miller
Height: 4", 10.1 cm
Colour: Grey, white, lemon, brown, violet, orange and green
Issued: 06/06 to the present

U.K.:   £20.00
U.S.: $40.00
Can.: $40.00

A TIGHT SQUEEZE

Model: A7378
Designer: Linda Jane Smith
Modeller: Unknown
Height: 3 ¾", 9.5 cm
Colour: Brown and white
Issued: 01/07 to the present

U.K.:   £16.00
U.S.: $32.00
Can.: $32.00

ALL TIED UP
(Cat on Toilet)

Model: A0483
Designer: Linda Jane Smith
Modeller: Raewyn Greggain
Height: 6", 15.0 cm
Colour: Orange, white and brown
Issued: 01/01 to the present

U.K.:   £24.00
U.S.: $50.00
Can.: $50.00

ALL WASHED UP

Model: A5963
Designer: Linda Jane Smith
Modeller: Janet Miller
Height: 7 ½", 19.1 cm
Colour: Grey, brown, blue, green and white
Issued: 06/05 - 12/06

U.K.:   £30.00
U.S.: $60.00
Can.: $60.00

ALLEY CAT
(Cat in Garbage)

Model: A0482
Designer: Linda Jane Smith
Modeller: Raewyn Greggain
Height: 4", 10.1 cm
Colour: Grey, white and brown
Issued: 01/01 - 12/03

U.K.:   £20.00
U.S.: $40.00
Can.: $40.00

ANGEL FACE

Model: A6039
Designer: Linda Jane Smith
Modeller: Janet Miller
Height: 4 ¼", 10.8 cm
Colour: Light brown, white and multicoloured
Issued: 06/05 - 12/06
Series: Christmas Figurines

U.K.:   £15.00
U.S.: $30.00
Can.: $30.00

ANY UMBRELLAS?
Model: A3086
Designer: Linda Jane Smith
Modeller: Janet Miller
Height: 5 ½", 14.0 cm
Colour: Fawn, white, grey and black
Issued: 01/04 - 12/04
Series: Annual Figurine 2004

U.K.: £45.00
U.S.: $90.00
Can.: $90.00

BAD HAIR DAY
Model: A4956
Designer: Linda Jane Smith
Modeller: Janet Miller
Height: 4", 10.1 cm
Colour: Grey, turquoise, white and cream
Issued: 01/05 to the present

U.K.: £20.00
U.S.: $40.00
Can.: $40.00

BALANCING ACT
Model: A1292
Designer: Linda Jane Smith
Modeller: Janet Miller
Height: 8", 20.3 cm
Colour: Brown, white, orange, yellow, grey, blue, black and pink
Issued: 01/03 - 12/05

U.K.: £25.00
U.S.: $50.00
Can.: $50.00

BATHING BEAUTY
Model: A3090
Designer: Linda Jane Smith
Modeller: Janet Miller
Height: 5 ½", 14.0 cm
Colour: Tan, white, green and grey
Issued: 01/04 - 12/06

U.K.: £25.00
U.S.: $50.00
Can.: $50.00

BED HEAD
Model: A7690
Designer: Linda Jane Smith
Modeller: Unknown
Height: 3 ¾", 9.5 cm
Colour: White, blue and brown
Issued: 01/07 to the present

U.K.: £16.00
U.S.: $32.00
Can.: $32.00

BEDTIME STORIES
Model: A4955
Designer: Linda Jane Smith
Modeller: Janet Miller
Height: 7 ¾", 19.7cm
Colour: Multicoloured
Issued: 01/05 - 12/05
Series: Annual Figurine 2005

U.K.: £ 50.00
U.S.: $100.00
Can.: $100.00

BEES AND ROSES
Model: A4958
Designer: Linda Jane Smith
Modeller: Janet Miller
Height: 5 ¼", 13.3 cm
Colour: Black, white, green and yellow
Issued: 01/05 - 12/06

U.K.: £30.00
U.S.: $60.00
Can.: $60.00

BIG SPENDER (Money Bank)
Model: A6253
Designer: Linda Jane Smith
Modeller: Janet Miller
Height: 6", 15.2 cm
Colour: Grey, white, gold green, blue and pink
Issued: 01/06 - 06/07

U.K.: £25.00
U.S.: $50.00
Can.: $50.00

BIRD'S EYE VIEW

Model:	A0913, 1770
Designer:	Linda Jane Smith
Modeller:	Janet Miller
Height:	12 ¾", 32.4 cm
Colour:	Black, white, ginger, grey, browns, yellow and green
Issued:	A0913 01/02 in a ltd. ed. of 1,500 (UK) A1770 01/02 in a ltd. ed. of 850 (Int'l.)
U.K.:	£125.00
U.S.:	$250.00
Can.:	$250.00

BOOKKEEPER (The) (Bookstop)

Model:	A1890
Designer:	Linda Jane Smith
Modeller:	Janet Miller
Height:	6", 15.2 cm
Colour:	Grey, white, black and multicoloured
Issued:	01/05 - 12/05
U.K.:	£25.00
U.S.:	$50.00
Can.:	$50.00

CAT CALLS

Model:	A6042 (Uk Ed.) A6043 (Int'l Ed.)
Designer:	Linda Jane Smith
Modeller:	Janet Miller
Height:	9 ¼", 23.5 cm
Colour:	Red, black, white, browns, grey, green
Issued:	A6042 01/06 Ltd ed 1,500 A6043 01/06 Ltd ed 1,100
U.K.:	£ 90.00
U.S.:	$175.00
Can.:	$175.00

CAT'S CRADLE

Model:	A7379
Designer:	Linda Jane Smith
Modeller:	Unknown
Height:	5 ¾", 14.6 cm
Colour:	White, lemon, pink and blue
Issued:	01/07 to the present
U.K.:	£24.00
U.S.:	$50.00
Can.:	$50.00

CAT'S WHISKERS, THE

Model:	A1896
Designer:	Linda Jane Smith
Modeller:	Janet Miller
Height:	4", 10.1 cm
Colour:	Grey, white and brown
Issued:	01/04 - 06/06
U.K.:	£20.00
U.S.:	$40.00
Can.:	$40.00

CHIP BUTTY

Model:	A5316
Designer:	Linda Jane Smith
Modeller:	Janet Miller
Height:	3 ½", 8.9 cm
Colour:	Grey, cream, yellow, brown and red
Issued:	01/05 to the present
U.K.:	£17.50
U.S.:	$35.00
Can.:	$35.00

CHOCOHOLIC

Model:	A3089
Designer:	Linda Jane Smith
Modeller:	Janet Miller
Height:	4", 10.1 cm
Colour:	White, pink and black
Issued:	01/04 to the present
U.K.:	£23.00
U.S.:	$45.00
Can.:	$45.00

CHRISTMAS FEAST

Model:	A7175
Designer:	Linda Jane Smith
Modeller:	Janet Miller
Height:	4", 10.1 cm
Colour:	White, brown, green, red, grey and silver
Issued:	06/06 to the present
Series:	Christmas Figurine 2006
U.K.:	£17.50
U.S.:	$35.00
Can.:	$35.00

COLLECTOR, THE
Model: A3562
Designer: Linda Jane Smith
Modeller: Janet Miller
Height: 5 ½", 13.3 cm
Colour: Ginger, white and grey
Issued: 01/04 to the present

U.K.: £28.00
U.S.: $55.00
Can.: $55.00

CONTENTMENT
Model: A1895
Designer: Linda Jane Smith
Modeller: Janet Miller
Height: 5 ¼". 13.3 cm
Colour: Rusty-brown, white, terracotta, blue, green and yellow
Issued: 01/03 to the present

U.K.: £30.00
U.S.: $60.00
Can.: $60.00

DINNER IS SERVED
Model: A3088
Designer: Linda Jane Smith
Modeller: Janet Miller
Height: 3 ¼", 8.3 cm
Colour: Grey, white, black, green and orange
Issued: 01/04 - 06/06

U.K.: £20.00
U.S.: $40.00
Can.: $40.00

DIRECT HIT
Model: A6045
Designer: Linda Jane Smith
Modeller: Janet Miller
Height: 4", 10.1 cm
Colour: Grey, white, green, blue, yellow, maroon and pink
Issued: 01/06 to the present

U.K.: £20.00
U.S.: $40.00
Can.: $40.00

DOWN THE PAN
Model: A1297
Designer: Linda Jane Smith
Modeller: Janet Miller
Height: 4 ¾", 12.1 cm
Colour: Black, white, yellow and green
Issued: 01/02 to the present

U.K.: £24.00
U.S.: $50.00
Can.: $50.00

FAT CAT
(Cat seated on cushion)
Model: A0480
Designer: Linda Jane Smith
Modeller: Raewyn Greggain
Height: 3 ½", 8.9 cm
Colour: Grey, white, red and yellow
Issued: 01/01 - 12/04

U.K.: £20.00
U.S.: $40.00
Can.: $40.00

FIRST CLASS CATS
Model: A1894, 2601
Designer: Linda Jane Smith
Modeller: Janet Miller
Height: 10", 25.4 cm
Colour: Red, brown striped, grey striped, black and white
Issued: A1894 01/03 in a Ltd ed. of 1,500 (UK)
A2601 01/03 in a Ltd. ed. of 1,000 (Int'l)

U.K.: £ 60.00
U.S.: $120.00
Can.: $120.00

FISH AND CHIPS
Model: A7377
Designer: Linda Jane Smith
Modeller: Unknown
Height: 3 ½", 8.9 cm
Colour: Black, white and brown
Issued: 01/07 to the present

U.K.: £16.00
U.S.: $32.00
Can.: $32.00

GIFT WRAPPED (Money box)

Model: A7688
Designer: Linda Jane Smith
Modeller: Unknown
Height: 6 ¼", 15.9 cm
Colour: Grey, white and brown
Issued: 01/07 to the present

U.K.:   £25.00
U.S.: $50.00
Can.: $50.00

GOING CUCKOO

Model: A4959
Designer: Linda Jane Smith
Modeller: Janet Miller
Height: 5 ¼", 13.3 cm
Colour: Ginger, turquoise,
           brown, yellow, white
Issued: 01/05 to the present

U.K.:   £28.00
U.S.: $55.00
Can.: $55.00

GOING FOR A SONG (Musical)

Model: A7382
Designer: Linda Jane Smith
Modeller: Unknown
Height: 5 ½", 14.0 cm
Colour: Grey, brown, black
           and white
Issued: 01/07 to the present

U.K.:   £ 49.00
U.S.: $100.00
Can.: $100.00

GOLD TOP

Model: A7174
Designer: Linda Jane Smith
Modeller: Unknown
Height: 4 ¼", 10.8 cm
Colour: Ginger, white, grey,
           yellow and blue
Issued: 06/06 to the present

U.K.:   £24.00
U.S.: $50.00
Can.: $50.00

GONE FISHING

Model: A7383 (UK Ed.)
           A8306 (Int'l Ed.)
Designer: Linda Jane Smith
Modeller: Janet Miller
Height: 5 ½", 14.0 cm
Colour: Grey, brown, black,
           white and blue
Issued: A7383
           01/07 Ltd ed 1,500
           A8306
           01/07 Ltd ed 900

U.K.:   £ 70.00
U.S.: $140.00
Can.: $140.00

HAPPY BIRTHDAY

Model: A2715
Designer: Linda Jane Smith
Modeller: Janet Miller
Height: 6", 15.2 cm
Colour: Fawn, brown and red
Issued: 01/05 - 12/06

U.K.:   £20.00
U.S.: $40.00
Can.: $40.00

HIDE AND SEEK

Model: A4957
Designer: Linda Jane Smith
Modeller: Janet Miller
Height: 4 ½", 11.4 cm
Colour: Brown, green, yellow
           and white
Issued: 01/05 to the present

U.K.:   £35.00
U.S.: $70.00
Can.: $70.00

HOUSE OF CARDS

Model: A6049
Designer: Linda Jane Smith
Modeller: Janet Miller
Height: 4 ½", 11.4 cm
Colour: Browns, white, red
           and green
Issued: 01/06 to the present

U.K.:   £20.00
U.S.: $40.00
Can.: $40.00

HUNG OUT TO DRY

Model: A6125
Designer: Linda Jane Smith
Modeller: Janet Miller
Height: 7 ¼", 18.4 cm
Colour: Multicoloured
Issued: 06/05 to the present

U.K.: £ 65.00
U.S.: $130.00
Can.: $130.00

IN THE BAG

Model: A2184
Designer: Linda Jane Smith
Modeller: Janet Miller
Height: 3 ¾", 9.5 cm
Colour: Brown, black, yellow, reddish-brown, white and green
Issued: 01/03 - 12/06

U.K.: £15.00
U.S.: $30.00
Can.: $30.00

IN THE SINK

Model: A1294
Designer: Linda Jane Smith
Modeller: Janet Miller
Height: 6", 15.0 cm
Colour: Black, white, blue, green and yellow
Issued: 01/02 to the present

U.K.: £30.00
U.S.: $60.00
Can.: $60.00

IN THE TUB

Model: A3884 (UK ed.)
A3927 (Int'l ed.)
Designer: Linda Jane Smith
Modeller: Janet Miller
Height: 10", 25.4 cm
Colour: Multicoloured
Issued: A3884
01/04 Ltd ed 1,500
A3927
01/04 Ltd ed 1,500

U.K.: £ 70.00
U.S.: $140.00
Can.: $140.00

IT'S FOR YOU

Model: A1897
Designer: Linda Jane Smith
Modeller: Janet Miller
Height: 4", 10.1 cm
Colour: Grey, white, black, yellow and pink
Issued: 01/03 - 12/05

U.K.: £15.00
U.S.: $30.00
Can.: $30.00

JUST A MINUTE
(Perpetual Calendar)

Model: A1892
Designer: Linda Jane Smith
Modeller: Janet Miller
Height: 4", 10.1 cm
Colour: Black, white, multicoloured
Issued: 01/05 - 12/05

U.K.: £30.00
U.S.: $60.00
Can.: $60.00

LAUNDRY DAY

Model: A7173
Designer: Linda Jane Smith
Modeller: Janet Miller
Height: 7", 17.8 cm
Colour: Ginger, white, green, grey, black and silver
Issued: 06/06 to the present

U.K.: £ 49.00
U.S.: $100.00
Can.: $100.00

LUCKY CAT
(Cat Under Table)

Model: A0484
Designer: Linda Jane Smith
Modeller: Raewyn Greggain
Height: 4", 10.1 cm
Colour: Grey, brown, blue and white
Issued: 01/01 - 12/03

U.K. £20.00
U.S. $40.00
Can. $40.00

MODEL, THE
(Cat on Chair)
Model: A0485
Designer: Linda Jane Smith
Modeller: Raewyn Greggain
Height: 5 ¾", 14.6 cm
Colour: Tan, brown, purple
            and red
Issued: 01/01 – 06/03

U.K.:   £15.00
U.S.: $30.00
Can.: $30.00

OUTSIDE PRIVY
Model: A4961 (UK ed.)
            A4962 (Int'l ed.)
Designer: Linda Jane Smith
Modeller: Janet Miller
Height: 9", 22.9 cm
Colour: Browns, grey, black,
            white and green
Issued: A4961
                01/05 Ltd ed 1,500
            A4962
                01/05 Ltd ed 2,000

U.K.:   £ 75.00
U.S.: $150.00
Can.: $150.00

PERFECT PESTS
Model: A4500
Designer: Linda Jane Smith
Modeller: Janet Miller
Height: 4 ¾", 12.1 cm
Colour: Grey, white, tan, pink,
            green and black
Issued: 06/04 - 06/06

U.K.:   £30.00
U.S.: $60.00
Can.: $60.00

PERFUME BOTTLE
Model: A1898
Designer: Linda Jane Smith
Modeller: Janet Miller
Height: 3 ½", 8.9 cm
Colour: Ginger, white, green
            and grey
Issued: 01/03 - 12/05

U.K.:   £20.00
U.S.: $40.00
Can.: $40.00

RUNAWAY ROMANCE
Model: A3085
Designer: Linda Jane Smith
Modeller: Janet Miller
Height: 4 ½", 11.9 cm
Colour: Grey, white, black, tan,
            red, green and lilac
Issued: 06/03 - 12/05

U.K.:   £25.00
U.S.: $50.00
Can.: $50.00

SANTA CLAWS
Model: A6038
Designer: Linda Jane Smith
Modeller: Janet Miller
Height: 4 ½", 8.9 cm
Colour: Browns, red, white,
            grey and yellow
Issued: 06/05 - 12/06
Series: Christmas Figurine
            2005

U.K.:   £15.00
U.S.: $30.00
Can.: $30.00

SCROUNGER, THE
(Money Bank)
Model: A7689
Designer: Linda Jane Smith
Modeller: Unknown
Height: 6 ¼", 15.9 cm
Colour: Grey, white and brown
Issued: 01/07 to the present

U.K.:   £25.00
U.S.: $50.00
Can.: $50.00

SECOND HAND ROSE
Model: A1900
Designer: Linda Jane Smith
Modeller: Janet Miller
Height: 3 ¾", 9.5 cm
Colour: Grey, white, yellow,
            blue, pink and mauve
Issued: 01/03 to the present

U.K.:   £17.50
U.S.: $35.00
Can.: $35.00

SECOND POST
Model: A8377
Designer: Linda Jane Smith
Modeller: Unknown
Height: 9", 22.8 cm
Colour: Black, white, red and green
Issued: 06/07 to the present

U.K.: £26.00
U.S.: $50.00
Can.: $50.00

SHALL WE DANCE?
(Ginger)
Model: A1296
Designer: Linda Jane Smith
Modeller: Janet Miller
Height: 3 ¼", 8.3 cm
Colour: Ginger, black, white, blue and pink
Issued: 01/02 - 12/03

U.K.: £15.00
U.S.: $30.00
Can.: $30.00

SPEAK YOUR WEIGHT
Model: A3561
Designer: Linda Jane Smith
Modeller: Janet Miller
Height: 7 ¼", 18.4 cm
Colour: Ginger, white and pale blue
Issued: 01/04 - 06/06

U.K.: £20.00
U.S.: $40.00
Can.: $40.00

SPIKE
Model: A6046
Designer: Linda Jane Smith
Modeller: Janet Miller
Height: 3 ¾", 9.5 cm
Colour: Black, green, browns, grey and white
Issued: 01/06 to the present

U.K.: £17.50
U.S.: $35.00
Can.: $35.00

SPOILED FOR CHOICE
Model: A1295
Designer: Linda Jane Grey
Modeller: Janet Miller
Height: 4", 10.1 cm
Colour: Black, brown, white, orange and blue
Issued: 01/02 to the present

U.K.: £24.00
U.S.: $50.00
Can.: $50.00

TEE'D OFF
Model: A7380
Designer: Linda Jane Smith
Modeller: Unknown
Height: 7 ¼", 18.4 cm
Colour: Brown, grey and white
Issued: 01/07 to the present

U.K.: £26.00
U.S.: $50.00
Can.: $50.00

THREE'S A CROWD
Model: A1709
Designer: Linda Jane Smith
Modeller: Janet Miller
Height: 5 ¼", 13.3 cm
Colour: Orange, white, Beige, brown, blue-grey and green
Issued: 01/03 - 12/06

U.K.: £25.00
U.S.: $50.00
Can.: $50.00

THROUGH THE LOOKING GLASS
Model: A4960
Designer: Linda Jane Smith
Modeller: Janet Miller
Height: 5 ¾", 14.6 cm
Colour: Cream, purple, black and green
Issued: 01/05 to the present

U.K.: £38.00
U.S.: $75.00
Can.: $75.00

TOP HAT AND TAILS (Fred)

Model: A1293
Designer: Linda Jane Smith
Modeller: Janet Miller
Height: 5 ¼", 13.3 cm
Colour: Black, white, blue-grey and dark blue
Issued: 01/02 - 12/03

U.K.: £15.00
U.S.: $30.00
Can.: $30.00

TRULY TROPICAL

Model: A6044
Designer: Linda Jane Smith
Modeller: Janet Miller
Height: 7 ¼", 18.4 cm
Colour: Multicoloured
Issued: 01/06 - 12/06
Series: Annual Figurine 2006

U.K.: £ 60.00
U.S.: $120.00
Can.: $120.00

(Batteries required)

TWO TERRORS

Model: A7376
Designer: Linda Jane Smith
Modeller: Unknown
Height: 6", 15.2 cm
Colour: Black, white, brown and cream
Issued: 01/07 to the present

U.K.: £26.00
U.S.: $50.00
Can.: $50.00

WAITING FOR SANTA

Model: A7387
Designer: Linda Jane Smith
Modeller: Unknown
Height: 3 ¼", 7.9 cm
Colour: Black, white, maroon pink and purple
Issued: 06/07 to the present

U.K.: £20.00
U.S.: $40.00
Can.: $40.00

WASH DAY BLUES

Model: A6719
Designer: Linda Jane Smith
Modeller: Janet Miller
Height: 3 ½", 8.9 cm
Colour: Black, white, yellow, and silver
Issued: 01/06 to the present

U.K.: £24.00
U.S.: $50.00
Can.: $50.00

**WATCHING YOU, WATCHING ME!
(Cat and Mouse)**

Model: A0481
Designer: Linda Jane Smith
Modeller: Raewyn Greggain
Height: 5", 12.7 cm
Colour: Black, white, grey, brown and yellow
Issued: 01/01 - 12/03

U.K.: £20.00
U.S.: $40.00
Can.: $40.00

**WHODUNNIT?
(Cat on Book Pile)**

Model: A0486
Designer: Linda Jane Smith
Modeller: Raewyn Greggain
Height: 15", 38.1 cm
Colour: Black, white, blue, gold, green, red and tan
Issued: 01/01 in a limited edition of 1,250

U.K.: £ 50.00
U.S.: $100.00
Can.: $100.00

WITH LOVE

Model: A6041
Designer: Linda Jane Smith
Modeller: Janet Miller
Height: 6", 15.2 cm
Colour: Black, white, green and pink
Issued: 01/06 to the present

U.K.: £22.00
U.S.: $45.00
Can.: $45.00

COOL CATS, HOT DOGS AND PORKIE PIES

A BUNCH OF LOVE
(Rosie)
Model: A5741
Designer: Toni Goffe
Modeller: Janet Miller
Height: 7", 17.8 cm
Colour: Pink, red and green
Issued: 01/05 - 12/06
Series: Porkie Pies

U.K.: £10.00
U.S.: $20.00
Can.: $20.00

BIG HEARTED
(Sophie)
Model: A7951
Designer: Toni Goffe
Modeller: Janet Miller
Height: 7 ¾", 19.7 cm
Colour: White, black, pink
and red
Issued: 01/07 to the present
Series: Cool Cats

U.K.: £20.00
U.S.: $40.00
Can.: $40.00

BONDING
(Kirk and Michael)
Model: A7375
Designer: Toni Goffe
Modeller: Janet Miller
Height: 7 ¾", 19.7 cm
Colour: Brown, cream,
black and white
Issued: 01/06 to the present
Series: Cool Cats

U.K.: £17.00
U.S.: $35.00
Can.: $35.00

CHEERS
(Kenneth)
Model: A7374
Designer: Toni Goffe
Modeller: Janet Miller
Height: 8", 20.3 cm
Colour: Cream and black
Issued: 06/06 to the present
Series: Cool Cats

U.K.: £17.00
U.S.: $35.00
Can.: $35.00

COMFORT
(Charles and Camilla)
Model: A3405
Designer: Toni Goffe
Height: 7 ¾", 19.7 cm
Colour: Brown, beige, blue,
yellow and white
Issued: 06/03 to the present
Series: Cool Cats

U.K.: £19.00
U.S.: $40.00
Can.: $40.00

CONGRATULATIONS
(Adam and Eve)
Model: A5639
Designer: Toni Goffe
Modeller: Unknown
Height: 8", 20.3 cm
Colour: Orange, lilac, white
and light blue
Issued: 01/05 to the present
Series: Cool Cats

U.K.: £22.00
U.S.: $45.00
Can.: $45.00

FISH I'D PREFER
(Finkle and Winkle)
Model: A3409
Designer: Toni Goffe
Height: 8 ¼", 21.0 cm
Colour: Brown, beige, slate
blue, white, red and
orange
Issued: 06/03 to the present
Series: Cool Cats

U.K.: £22.00
U.S.: $45.00
Can.: $45.00

FORGIVE ME
(Dizzy and Jackson)
Model: A3402
Modeller: Toni Goffe
Height: 8 ½", 21.6 cm
Colour: Brown, white, red
and dusty rose
Issued: 06/03 - 12/06
Series: Hot Dogs

U.K.: £18.00
U.S.: $35.00
Can.: $35.00

FUR WRAP, THE
(Phil and Liza)

Model:	A4433
Designer:	Toni Goffe
Modeller:	Unknown
Height:	7 ¼", 18.4 cm
Colour:	Orange, white and black
Issued:	01/04 to the present
Series:	Cool Cats
U.K.:	£22.00
U.S.:	$45.00
Can.:	$45.00

GIVE US A HUG
(Rosemary and Thyme)

Model:	A5648
Designer:	Toni Goffe
Modeller:	Janet Miller
Height:	7 ¼", 18.4 cm
Colour:	Pink
Issued:	01/05 - 12/06
Series:	Porkie Pies
U.K.:	£12.00
U.S.:	$25.00
Can.:	$25.00

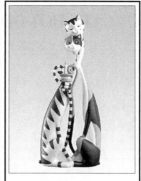

HAPPY BIRTHDAY
(Buzz and Mrs. Nesbit)

Model:	A4434
Designer:	Toni Goffe
Modeller:	Unknown
Height:	11 ¼", 28.5 cm
Colour:	Orange, black and white
Issued:	01/04 to the present
Series:	Cool Cats
U.K.:	£34.00
U.S.:	$65.00
Can.:	$65.00

HAPPY BIRTHDAY
(Jodie)

Model:	A6365
Designer:	Toni Goffe
Modeller:	Janet Miller
Height:	8", 20.3 cm
Colour:	Cream, dark brown, pink, yellow and blue
Issued:	01/06 to the present
Series:	Cool Cats
U.K.:	£19.00
U.S.:	$40.00
Can.:	$40.00

HAPPY BIRTHDAY
(Swine and Spritza)

Model:	A5402
Designer:	Toni Goffe
Modeller:	Janet Miller
Height:	6 ¾", 17.2 cm
Colour:	Pink, green and orange
Issued:	01/05 - 06/06
Series:	Porkie Pies
U.K.:	£15.00
U.S.:	$30.00
Can.:	$30.00

HE LOVES ME

Model:	A5740
Designer:	Toni Goffe
Modeller:	Janet Miller
Height:	6 ¾", 17.2 cm
Colour:	Pink, green, brown and yellow
Issued:	01/05 - 06/06
Series:	Porkie Pies
U.K.:	£10.00
U.S.:	$20.00
Can.:	$20.00

HOWLING AT THE MOON
(Bunny and Hutch)

Model:	A3401
Designer:	Toni Goffe
Height:	8 ¼", 21.0 cm
Colour:	Browns, blue, red and white
Issued:	06/03 - 12/04
Series:	Hot Dogs
U.K.:	£15.00
U.S.:	$30.00
Can.:	$30.00

HUGGING
(Richard and Judy)

Model:	A3286
Designer:	Toni Goffe
Height:	8", 20.3 cm
Colour:	Orange, pale yellow, white and black
Issued:	06/03 to the present
Series:	Cool Cats
U.K.:	£19.00
U.S.:	$40.00
Can.:	$40.00

HUGGY
(Cuddles and Snuggles)

Model: A3403
Designer: Toni Goffe
Modeller: Unknown
Height: 8 ¾", 22.2 cm
Colour: Red, brown, black
            and white
Issued: 06/04 - 12/06
Series: Hot Dogs

U.K.:   £20.00
U.S.: $40.00
Can.: $40.00

I HEARD IT ON THE
GRAPEVINE
(Sam amd Kookie)

Model: A4430
Designer: Toni Goffe
Modeller: Unknown
Height: 8 ¼", 21.0 cm
Colour: Tan, brown, black,
            white and red
Issued: 01/04 - 12/06
Series: Hot Dogs

U.K.:   £20.00
U.S.: $40.00
Can.: $40.00

I LOVE YOU
(Charlotte and Lancelot)

Model: A5404
Designer: Toni Goffe
Modeller: Unknown
Height: 7 ¼", 18.4 cm
Colour: Pink
Issued: 01/05 - 12/06
Series: Porkie Pies

U.K.:   £12.00
U.S.: $25.00
Can.: $25.00

I LOVE YOU
(David and Victoria)

Model: A3408
Designer: Toni Goffe
Height: 7 ¾", 19.7 cm
Colour: Red, burnt orange,
            tan, white and blue
Issued: 06/03 to the present
Series: Cool Cats

U.K.:   £22.00
U.S.: $45.00
Can.: $45.00

KISS, THE
(Ginger and Spice)

Model: A3694
Designer: Toni Goffe
Modeller: Unknown
Height: 11 ¾", 29.2 cm
Colour: Dark orange, pale
            yellow, black and white
Issued: 01/04 to the present
Series: Cool Cats

U.K.:   £29.00
U.S.: $60.00
Can.: $60.00

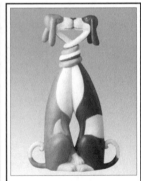

KISS AND MAKE UP
(Homer and Marge)

Model: A3404
Designer: Toni Goffe
Height: 8", 20.3 cm
Colour: Dark and light brown
            and white
Issued: 06/03 - 12/06
Series: Hot Dogs

U.K.:   £15.00
U.S.: $30.00
Can.: $30.00

LOVE AT FIRST SIGHT
(Woofer and Tweeter)

Model: A4989
Designer: Toni Goffe
Modeller: Unknown
Height: 8", 20.3 cm
Colour: Tan, fawn, dark brown,
            white, red and gold
Issued: 01/05 - 12/06
Series: Hot Dogs

U.K.:   £23.00
U.S.: $45.00
Can.: $45.00

LOVE KNOT, THE
(Dido and Aeneas)

Model: A4432
Designer: Toni Goffe
Modeller: Janet Miller
Height: 7 ¼", 18.4 cm
Colour: Pale brown, red-brown,
            black and white
Issued: 06/04 to the present
Series: Cool Cats

U.K.:   £22.00
U.S.: $45.00
Can.: $45.00

MADONNA AND CHILD
(Madonna and Pavlova)

Model:	A5737
Designer:	Toni Goffe
Modeller:	Unknown
Height:	8", 20.3 cm
Colour:	Tan, white, black and grey
Issued:	01/05 to the present
Series:	Cool Cats
U.K.:	£18.00
U.S.:	$35.00
Can.:	$35.00

MISSING YOU MADLY
(Jo Jo)

Model:	A6235
Designer:	Toni Goffe
Modeller:	Unknown
Height:	4 ¼", 10.8 cm
Colour:	Black, white, brown, blue and gold
Issued:	06/05 to the present
Series:	Cool Cats
U.K.:	£16.00
U.S.:	$35.00
Can.:	$35.00

MISSING YOU TRULY
(Kylie)

Model:	A8051
Designer:	Toni Goffe
Modeller:	Unknown
Height:	7 ¼", 18.4 cm
Colour:	Brown, white and black
Issued:	01/07 to the present
Series:	Cool Cats
U.K.:	£18.00
U.S.:	$35.00
Can.:	$35.00

MY HEART IS YOURS
(Fluffy)

Model:	A5638
Designer:	Toni Goffe
Modeller:	Janet Miller
Height:	8", 20.3 cm
Colour:	Dark grey, purple, white and red
Issued:	01/05 to the present
Series:	Cool Cats
U.K.:	£16.00
U.S.:	$35.00
Can.:	$35.00

MY HERO
(Daddy and Paddy)

Model:	A5640
Designer:	Toni Goffe
Modeller:	Unknown
Height:	8", 20.3 cm
Colour:	Tan, white, black and grey
Issued:	06/05 to the present
Series:	Cool Cats
U.K.:	£18.00
U.S.:	$35.00
Can.:	$35.00

NURTURE
(Morag)

Model:	A7373
Designer:	Toni Goffe
Modeller:	Unknown
Height:	7 ¾", 19.7 cm
Colour:	Dark cream, black and white
Issued:	06/06 to the present
Series:	Cool Cats
U.K.:	£17.00
U.S.:	$35.00
Can.:	$35.00

ONLY FOR YOU
(Roxanne)

Model:	A5637
Designer:	Toni Goffe
Modeller:	Janet Miller
Height:	8", 20.3 cm
Colour:	Black, white, red and green
Issued:	01/05 to the present
Series:	Cool Cats
U.K.:	£16.00
U.S.:	$35.00
Can.:	$35.00

OUR FIRST LITTER
(Wendy and Mortimer)

Model:	A5738
Designer:	Toni Goffe
Modeller:	Unknown
Height:	8", 20.3 cm
Colour:	Orange, cream, dark grey, brown and white
Issued:	01/05 to the present
Series:	Cool Cats
U.K.:	£26.00
U.S.:	$50.00
Can.:	$50.00

PEEK-A-BOO
(Tiddles and Widdles)
Model: A3407
Designer: Toni Goffe
Height: 5 ½", 14.0 cm
Colour: Brown, white, pink
            and blue
Issued: 06/03 to the present
Series: Cool Cats

U.K.:   £22.00
U.S.: $45.00
Can.: $45.00

PIGGY BACK RIDER
(Grumble and Grunt)
Model: A5650
Designer: Toni Goffe
Modeller: Unknown
Height: 9", 22.9 cm
Colour: Pink
Issued: 01/05 - 12/06
Series: Porkie Pies

U.K.:   £15.00
U.S.: $30.00
Can.: $30.00

PLAYTIME
(Peaches and Apple)
Model: A7950
Designer: Toni Goffe
Modeller: Unknown
Height: 7 ¾", 19.7 cm
Colour: Blue, white and ginger
Issued: 01/07 to the present
Series: Cool Cats

U.K.:   £18.00
U.S.: $35.00
Can.: $35.00

PORKY POLKA, THE
Model: A5649
Designer: Toni Goffe
Modeller: Unknown
Height: 7 ¾", 19.7 cm
Colour: Pink and green
Issued: 01/05 - 12/06
Series: Porkie Pies

U.K.:   £15.00
U.S.: $30.00
Can.: $30.00

PROUD FATHER
(Harvey, Wally and the Little
Bangers)
Model: A5739
Designer: Toni Goffe
Modeller: Unknown
Height: 8", 20.3 cm
Colour: Grey, tan, white,
            red and gold
Issued: 01/05 - 12/06
Series: Hot Dogs

U.K.:   £20.00
U.S.: $40.00
Can.: $40.00

SEALED WITH A KISS
(Romeo and Juliet)
Model: A3406
Designer: Toni Goffe
Modeller: Unknown
Height: 7 ¼", 18.4 cm
Colour: Orange, white
            and black
Issued: 06/04 to the present
Series: Cool Cats

U.K.:   £22.00
U.S.: $45.00
Can.: $45.00

SHUT YOUR EYES AND OPEN
YOUR MOUTH
Model: A5647
Designer: Toni Goffe
Modeller: Janet Miller
Height: 7 ¼", 18.4 cm
Colour: Pink, red and green
Issued: 01/05 - 06/06
Series: Porkie Pies

U.K.:   £15.00
U.S.: $30.00
Can.: $30.00

SNUGGLE, THE
(Ella and Louis)
Model: A3693
Designer: Toni Goffe
Height: 12", 30.5 cm
Colour: Browns, white and red
Issued: 06/03 - 12/06
Series: Hot Dogs

U.K.:   £25.00
U.S.: $50.00
Can.: $50.00

**TENDER LOVING CARE
(Gin and Tonic)**

Model: A5641
Designer: Toni Goffe
Modeller: Unknown
Height: 5 ¼", 13.3 cm
Colour: Brown, orange, white,
           red and gold
Issued: 01/05 - 12/06
Series: Hot Dogs

U.K.:   £20.00
U.S.: $40.00
Can.: $40.00

**THANK YOU SO MUCH
(Maximillian)**

Model: A6366
Designer: Toni Goffe
Modeller: Unknown
Height: 8", 20.3 cm
Colour: Grey, white, pink
           and green
Issued: 01/06 to the present
Series: Cool Cats

U.K.:   £16.00
U.S.: $32.00
Can.: $32.00

**THEIR FIRST TIFF
(Basie and Daisy)**

Model: A3285
Designer: Toni Goffe
Height: 8 ¼, 21.0 cm
Colour: Beige, white and blue
Issued: 06/03 - 12/04
Series: Hot Dogs

U.K.:   £15.00
U.S.: $30.00
Can.: $30.00

**THINKING OF YOU
(Old Blue Eyes)**

Model: A5642
Designer: Toni Goffe
Modeller: Unknown
Height: 8 ¼", 21.0 cm
Colour: Light and dark brown,
           white, red and gold
Issued: 01/05 - 12/06
Series: Hot Dogs

U.K.:   £15.00
U.S.: $30.00
Can.: $30.00

**WANT TO PLAY?
(Hydie and Zeeky)**

Model: A3937
Designer: Toni Goffe
Modeller: Unknown
Height: 4", 10.1 cm
Colour: Dark blue-grey, red,
           brown and white
Issued: 01/04 - 12/06
Series: Hot Dogs

U.K.:   £20.00
U.S.: $40.00
Can.: $40.00

**WHAT?
(Rhett and Scarlett)**

Model: A4429
Designer: Toni Goffe
Modeller: Unknown
Height: 8", 20.3 cm
Colour: Reddish brown,
           black and white
Issued: 06/04 - 12/06
Series: Hot Dogs

U.K.:   £20.00
U.S.: $40.00
Can.: $40.00

**WRONG AGAIN
(Bart and Lisa)**

Model: A3400
Designer: Toni Goffe
Height: 6 ¼", 15.9 cm
Colour: Brown, white, blue
           and tan
Issued: 06/03 - 12/06
Series: Hot Dogs

U.K.:   £20.00
U.S.: $40.00
Can.: $40.00

**YOU, I ADORE
(Eleanor and Theodore)**

Model: A4992
Designer: Toni Goffe
Modeller: Unknown
Height: 13 ¼", 33.6 cm
Colour: Orange, cream,
           dark gey and white
Issued: 01/05 - 06/07
Series: Cool Cats

U.K.:   £40.00
U.S.: $80.00
Can.: $80.00

DAPPER DOGS

ANNABEL

Model: A6834
Designer: Toni Goffe
Modeller: Unknown
Height: 6 ½", 16.5 cm
Colour: Light brown, cream
            and pink
Issued: 06/06 to the present

U.K.:   £12.00
U.S.: $25.00
Can.: $25.00

BILLY

Model: A6835
Designer: Toni Goffe
Modeller: Unknown
Height: 5 ¼", 13.3 cm
Colour: Brown, blue, white
            and black
Issued: 06/06 to the present

U.K.:   £12.00
U.S.: $25.00
Can.: $25.00

BOB

Model: A7317
Designer: Toni Goffe
Modeller: Unknown
Height: 4", 10.1 cm
Colour: Brown, red, black,
            white and gold
Issued: 06/06 to the present

U.K.:   £ 7.95
U.S.: $15.00
Can.: $15.00

CLYDE

Model: A6842
Designer: Toni Goffe
Modeller: Unknown
Height: 5 ½", 14.0 cm
Colour: Black, white, dark
            blue and brown
Issued: 06/06 to the present

U.K.:   £12.00
U.S.: $25.00
Can.: $25.00

DUNCAN

Model: A6836
Designer: Toni Goffe
Modeller: Unknown
Height: 4", 10.1 cm
Colour: White, black, red
            and blue
Issued: 06/06 to the present

U.K.:   £ 7.95
U.S.: $15.00
Can.: $15.00

REX

Model: A7318
Designer: Toni Goffe
Modeller: Unknown
Height: 7", 17.8 cm
Colour: Brown, black
            and white
Issued: 06/06 to the present

U.K.:   £12.00
U.S.: $25.00
Can.: $25.00

RORY

Model: A6837
Designer: Toni Goffe
Modeller: Unknown
Height: 8", 20.3 cm
Colour: Cream, green,
            brown and black
Issued: 06/06 to the present

U.K.:   £14.00
U.S.: $28.00
Can.: $28.00

SHERLOCK

Model: A6838
Designer: Toni Goffe
Modeller: Unknown
Height: 5 ¼", 13.3 cm
Colour: Tan, brown, grey
            and black
Issued: 06/06 to the present

U.K.:   £14.00
U.S.: $28.00
Can.: $28.00

FAIRIES

ALMOND BLOSSOM FAIRY™

Model: A1902
Designer: Cicely Mary Barker
Modeller: Unknown
Height: 5 ¼", 13.3 cm
Colour: Pink, red and green
Issued: 2003 - 12/04
Series: Flower Fairies

U.K.:   £15.00
U.S.: $30.00
Can.: $30.00

APPLE BLOSSOM FAIRIES™
Style One

Model: CF6
Designer: Cicely Mary Barker
Modeller: David Geenty
Height: 6 ¾", 17.2 cm
Colour: Green and pink
             clothing; pink flowers
Issued: 01/86 - 12/87
Series: Flower Fairies

U.K.:   £125.00
U.S.: $250.00
Can.: $250.00

APPLE BLOSSOM FAIRIES™
Style Two

Model: 726958
Designer: Cicely Mary Barker
Modeller: Unknown
Height: 4 ½", 11.9 cm
Colour: Green and pink
             clothing; pink flowers
Issued: 01/00 - 12/02
Series: Miniature Fairies

U.K.:   £25.00
U.S.: $50.00
Can.: $50.00

BLACKBERRY FAIRY™
Style One

Model: CF23
Designer: Cicely Mary Barker
Modeller: Glenis Devereux
Height: 5 ¾", 14.6 cm
Colour: Blackberry dress; lilac
             wings; orange-brown
             leaves; purple berries
Issued: 01/93 in a limited
             edition of 1,950
Series: Flower Fairies

U.K.:   £175.00
U.S.: $350.00
Can.: $350.00

BLACKBERRY FAIRY™
Style Two

Model: A1912
Designer: Cicely Mary Barker
Modeller: Unknown
Height: 2 ¾", 7.0 cm
Colour: Black, pink, rusty-
             brown and purple
Issued: 01/03 - 12/04
Series: Miniature Fairies

U.K.:   £12.00
U.S.: $25.00
Can.: $25.00

BLACKTHORN FAIRY™

Model: CF5
Designer: Cicely Mary Barker
Modeller: David Geenty
Height: 9", 22.9 cm
Colour: Dark blue shirt; white
             skirt with red dots; pink
             blossoms; brown stem
             and thorns
Issued: 01/86 - 12/87
Series: Flower Fairies

U.K.:   £125.00
U.S.: $250.00
Can.: $250.00

BOX TREE FAIRY™

Model: A0745
Designer: Cicely Mary Barker
Modeller: Unknown
Height: 5", 12.7 cm
Colour: Green, blue and yellow
Issued: 01/02 - 12/04
Series: Flower Fairies

U.K.:   £15.00
U.S.: $20.00
Can.: $20.00

BUGLE FAIRY™
Style One

Model: CF10
Designer: Cicely Mary Barker
Modeller: David Geenty
Height: 7 ½", 19.1 cm
Colour: Blue and lilac clothing;
             blue flowers; green
             stem and leaves
Issued: 01/88 - 12/89
Series: Flower Fairies

U.K.:   £100.00
U.S.: $200.00
Can.: $200.00

BUGLE FAIRY™
Style Two
Model: A0303
Designer: Cicely Mary Barker
Modeller: Unknown
Height: 5 ¾", 14.6 cm
Colour: Purple, lilac, pink and green
Issued: 01/01 - 12/02
Series: Flower Fairies

U.K.: £20.00
U.S.: $40.00
Can.: $40.00

BUTTERCUP FAIRY™
Model: B0114
Designer: Cicely Mary Barker
Modeller: Glenis Devereux
Height: 7 ½", 19.1 cm
Colour: Yellow dress and buttercups; green wings, stem and leaves
Issued: 01/97 in a limited edition of 1,950
Series: Flower Fairies

U.K.: £100.00
U.S.: $200.00
Can.: $200.00

CANDYTUFT FAIRY™
Style One
Model: CF2
Designer: Cicely Mary Barker
Modeller: David Geenty
Height: 5", 12.7 cm
Colour: Pink clothing and wings
Issued: 01/86 - 12/87
Series: Flower Fairies

U.K.: £100.00
U.S.: $200.00
Can.: $200.00

CANDYTUFT FAIRY™
Style Two
Model: 726974
Designer: Cicely Mary Barker
Modeller: Unknown
Height: 4", 10.1 cm
Colour: Pink clothing and wings
Issued: 01/00 - 12/02
Series: Miniature Fairies

U.K.: £20.00
U.S.: $40.00
Can.: $40.00

CANTERBURY BELL FAIRY™
Model: A0302
Designer: Cicely Mary Barker
Modeller: Unknown
Height: 5", 12.7 cm
Colour: Lilac, pink and green
Issued: 01/01 - 12/05
Series: Flower Fairies

U.K.: £20.00
U.S.: $40.00
Can.: $40.00

CHICORY FAIRY™
Style One
Model: CF22
Designer: Cicely Mary Barker
Modeller: Glenis Devereux
Height: 6 ¼", 15.9 cm
Colour: Lilac dress, cap and flowers; cream and lilac wings; green leaves
Issued: 01/93 in a limited edition of 1,950
Series: Flower Fairies

U.K.: £125.00
U.S.: $250.00
Can.: $250.00

CHICORY FAIRY™
Style Two
Model: A1911
Designer: Cicely Mary Barker
Modeller: Unknown
Height: 5", 12.7 cm
Colour: Pastel blue, yellow, white and green
Issued: 01/03 - 12/05
Series: Miniatures Fairies

U.K.: £15.00
U.S.: $30.00
Can.: $30.00

CHRISTMAS TREE FAIRY™
Model: A1101
Designer: Cicely Mary Barker
Modeller: Unknown
Height: 4 ½", 11.9 cm
Colour: White, green, red, blue and pale pink
Issued: 06/01 - 12/02
Series: Flower Fairies

U.K.: £20.00
U.S.: $40.00
Can.: $40.00

COLUMBINE FAIRY™
Style One

Model:	CF11
Designer:	Cicely Mary Barker
Modeller:	David Geenty
Height:	6 ¾", 17.2 cm
Colour:	Orange, rose-pink and green clothing; rose-pink flowers
Issued:	01/88 - 12/89
Series:	Flower Fairies

U.K.:	£100.00
U.S.:	$200.00
Can.:	$200.00

COLUMBINE FAIRY™
Style Two

Model:	A1910
Designer:	Cicely Mary Barker
Modeller:	Unknown
Height:	6", 15.2 cm
Colour:	Pink, lilac, lemon and green
Issued:	01/04 - 12/05

U.K.:	£25.00
U.S.:	$50.00
Can.:	$50.00

CROCUS FAIRIES™

Model:	A0300
Designer:	Cicely Mary Barker
Modeller:	Unknown
Height:	4 ½", 11.9 cm
Colour:	Yellow, purple, pale yellow and white
Issued:	01/01 - 12/02
Series:	Flower Fairies

U.K.:	£25.00
U.S.:	$50.00
Can.:	$50.00

DAISY FAIRY™

Model:	A0747
Designer:	Cicely Mary Barker
Modeller:	Unknown
Height:	4 ¼", 10.8 cm
Colour:	Pink, white, green and yellow
Issued:	01/02 - 12/03
Series:	Miniature Fairies

U.K.:	£15.00
U.S.:	$30.00
Can.:	$30.00

FORGET-ME-NOT FAIRY™

Model:	A1904
Designer:	Cicely Mary Barker
Modeller:	Unknown
Height:	3", 7.6 cm
Colour:	Purple, blue, pink, green and beige
Issued:	06/02 - 12/04
Series:	Miniature Fairies

U.K.:	£15.00
U.S.:	$30.00
Can.:	$30.00

FUCHSIA FAIRY™

Model:	CF12
Designer:	Cicely Mary Barker
Modeller:	David Geenty
Height:	6 ¾", 17.2 cm
Colour:	Rose-pink and purple clothing; lilac wings; rose-pink and purple flower
Issued:	01/88 - 12/89
Series:	Flower Fairies

U.K.:	£100.00
U.S.:	$200.00
Can.:	$200.00

GERANIUM FAIRY™

Model:	726923
Designer:	Cicely Mary Barker
Modeller:	Unknown
Height:	4 ½", 11.9 cm
Colour:	Green and peach dress, flowers and leaves
Issued:	01/00 - 12/04
Series:	Flower Fairies

U.K.:	£20.00
U.S.:	$40.00
Can.:	$40.00

GORSE FAIRIES™
Style One

Model:	CF21
Designer:	Cicely Mary Barker
Modeller:	Glenis Devereux
Height:	8", 20.3 cm
Colour:	Yellow, brown and green clothing; green-brown wings; yellow gorse
Issued:	01/93 in a limited edition of 1,950
Series:	Flower Fairies

U.K.:	£175.00
U.S.:	$350.00
Can.:	$350.00

GORSE FAIRIES™
Style Two

Model: A1909
Designer: Cicely Mary Barker
Modeller: Unknown
Height: 4 ¾", 12.1 cm
Colour: Yellow, pink, green
           and white
Issued: 01/03 - 12/05
Series: Flower Fairies

U.K.:   £25.00
U.S.: $50.00
Can.: $50.00

HELIOTROPE FAIRY™

Model: CF4
Designer: Cicely Mary Barker
Modeller: David Geenty
Height: 6 ¾", 17.2 cm
Colour: Pink dress; lilac flowers
Issued: 01/86 - 12/87
Series: Flower Fairies

U.K.:   £125.00
U.S.: $250.00
Can.: $250.00

HOLLY FAIRY™
(WINTER)

Model: B0417
Designer: Cicely Mary Barker
Modeller: Glenis Devereux
Height: 8 ¼", 21.0 cm
Colour: Green, red and orange
           clothing
Issued: 01/99 in a limited
           edition of 1,950
Series: Flower Fairies of
           the Seasons

U.K.:   £175.00
U.S.: $350.00
Can.: $350.00

IRIS FAIRY™

Model: CF9
Designer: Cicely Mary Barker
Modeller: David Geenty
Height: 7 ½", 19.1 cm
Colour: Yellow dress and
           flowers
Issued: 01/88 - 12/89
Series: Flower Fairies

U.K.:   £100.00
U.S.: $200.00
Can.: $200.00

JASMINE FAIRY™
(SUMMER)

Model: B0415
Designer: Cicely Mary Barker
Modeller: Glenis Devereux
Height: 6 ½", 16.5 cm
Colour: Peach clothing;
           green leaves; white
           flowers with pink
Issued: 01/99 in a limited
           edition of 1,950
Series: Flower Fairies of
           the Seasons

U.K.:   £125.00
U.S.: $250.00
Can.: $250.00

LAVENDER FAIRY™
Style One

Model: CF1
Designer: Cicely Mary Barker
Modeller: David Geenty
Height: 8 ¾", 22.2 cm
Colour: Lilac and green dress;
           lilac wings
Issued: 01/86 - 12/87
Series: Flower Fairies

U.K.:   £125.00
U.S.: $250.00
Can.: $250.00

LAVENDER FAIRY™
Style Two

Model: 726915
Designer: Cicely Mary Barker
Modeller: Unknown
Height: 6", 15.0 cm
Colour: Lilac and green dress;
           cream and lilac wings;
           lilac flowers
Issued: 01/00 - 12/04
Series: Flower Fairies

U.K.:   £20.00
U.S.: $40.00
Can.: $40.00

MALLOW FAIRY™
Style One

Model: CF8
Designer: Cicely Mary Barker
Modeller: David Geenty
Height: 7", 17.8 cm
Colour: Green and lilac
           clothing; lilac flowers;
           green leaves
Issued: 01/88 - 12/89
Series: Flower Fairies

U.K.:   £100.00
U.S.: $200.00
Can.: $200.00

MALLOW FAIRY™
Style Two

Model: A0301
Designer: Cicely Mary Barker
Modeller: Unknown
Height: 5 ¼", 13.3. cm
Colour: Green, pink and yellow
Issued: 01/01 - 12/02
Series: Flower Fairies

U.K.: £40.00
U.S.: $80.00
Can.: $80.00

MARIGOLD FAIRY™
Style One

Model: CF28
Designer: Cicely Mary Barker
Modeller: Glenis Devereux
Height: 6", 15.0 cm
Colour: Green dress, wings and leaves
Issued: 01/96 in a limited edition of 1,950
Series: Flower Fairies

U.K.: £175.00
U.S.: $350.00
Can.: $350.00

MARIGOLD FAIRY™
Style Two

Model: A0305
Designer: Cicely Mary Barker
Modeller: Unknown
Height: 5 ¾", 14.5 cm
Colour: Orange, yellow, pink and green
Issued: 01/01 - 12/04
Series: Flower Fairies

U.K.: £20.00
U.S.: $40.00
Can.: $40.00

MILLENNIUM CHRISTMAS FAIRY™

Model: B0536
Designer: Cicely Mary Barker
Modeller: Glenis Devereux
Height: 7 ½", 19.1 cm
Colour: White dress; peach wings
Issued: 01/00 in a limited edition of 500
Series: Flower Fairies

U.K.: £150.00
U.S.: $300.00
Can.: $300.00

MOUNTAIN ASH FAIRY™

Model: B0925
Modeller: Sue Norton
Height: 8" x 5 ½"
20.3 x 16.0 cm
Colour: Orange, peach, green and red
Issued: 01/05 in a limited edition of 500

U.K.: £125.00
U.S.: $250.00
Can.: $250.00

NARCISSUS FAIRY™
Style One

Model: CF24
Designer: Cicely Mary Barker
Modeller: Glenis Devereux
Height: 8 ¼", 21.0 cm
Colour: White, yellow and red dress
Issued: 01/94 in a limited edition of 950
Series: Flower Fairies

U.K.: £175.00
U.S.: $350.00
Can.: $350.00

NARCISSUS FAIRY™
Style two

Model: A1905
Designer: Cicely Mary Barker
Modeller: Unknown
Height: 6 ¼", 15.9 cm
Colour: White, yellow, red and green
Issued: 01/03 - 12/05
Series: Flower Fairies

U.K.: £20.00
U.S.: $40.00
Can.: $40.00

NASTURTIUM FAIRY™
Style One

Model: CF7
Designer: Cicely Mary Barker
Modeller: David Geenty
Height: 6", 15.0 cm
Colour: Orange, yellow and green clothing
Issued: 01/88 - 12/89
Series: Flower Fairies

U.K.: £100.00
U.S.: $200.00
Can.: $200.00

NASTURTIUM FAIRY™
Style Two

Model:	A0744
Designer:	Cicely Mary Barker
Modeller:	Unknown
Height:	4 ¾", 12.1 cm
Colour:	Orange-red, yellow, green and orange-yellow
Issued:	01/02 - 12/04
Series:	Flower Fairies
U.K.:	£15.00
U.S.:	$30.00
Can.:	$30.00

PANSY FAIRY™

Model:	CF29
Designer:	Cicely Mary Barker
Modeller:	Glenis Devereux
Height:	7 ¼", 18.4 cm
Colour:	Lilac and yellow dress; violet wings
Issued:	Jan. 1996 in a limited edition of 1,950
Series:	Flower Fairies
U.K.:	£175.00
U.S.:	$350.00
Can.:	$350.00

POPPY FAIRY™

Model:	B0790
Designer:	Cicely Mary Barker
Modeller:	Unknown
Height:	8", 20.3 cm
Colour:	Red, black, green and beige
Issued:	01/03 in a limited edition of 500
Series:	Flower Fairies
U.K.:	£125.00
U.S.:	$250.00
Can.:	$250.00

PRIMROSE FAIRY™

Model:	A1908
Modeller:	Unknown
Height:	6", 15.2 cm
Colour:	Lemon, yellow and green
Issued:	01/04 - 12/05
Series:	Flower Fairies
U.K.:	£20.00
U.S.:	$40.00
Can.:	$40.00

PRIMROSE FAIRY (SPRING)™

Model:	B0416
Designer:	Cicely Mary Barker
Modeller:	Glenis Devereux
Height:	7 ½", 19.1 cm
Colour:	Yellow and green clothing and flowers
Issued:	01/99 in a limited edition of 1,950
Series:	Flower Fairies of the Seasons
U.K.:	£150.00
U.S.:	$300.00
Can.:	$300.00

ROSE FAIRY™
Style One

Model:	CF20
Designer:	Cicely Mary Barker
Modeller:	Glenis Devereux
Height:	7 ½", 19.1 cm
Colour:	Pink and cream dress and flowers
Issued:	01/93 in a limited edition of 1,950
Series:	Flower Fairies
U.K.:	£150.00
U.S.:	$300.00
Can.:	$300.00

ROSE FAIRY™
Style Two

Model:	726966
Designer:	Cicely Mary Barker
Modeller:	Unknown
Height:	4 ¾", 12.1 cm
Colour:	Pink dress, rose and wings
Issued:	01/00 - 12/05
Series:	Miniature Fairies
U.K.:	£15.00
U.S.:	$30.00
Can.:	$30.00

SCILLA FAIRY™

Model:	A1097
Designer:	Cicely Mary Barker
Modeller:	Unknown
Height:	3 ¾", 9.5 cm
Colour:	Deep violet, light brown, black, green and yellow
Issued:	01/02 - 12/04
Series:	Miniature Fairies
U.K.:	£15.00
U.S.:	$30.00
Can.:	$30.00

SLOE FAIRY™ (AUTUMN)
Style One

Model: B0418
Designer: Cicely Mary Barker
Modeller: Glenis Devereux
Height: 7 ¾", 19.7 cm
Colour: Lilac, beige and purple
                clothing
Issued: 01/99 in a limited
                edition of 1,950
Series: Flower Fairies of
                the Seasons

U.K.:   £125.00
U.S.: $250.00
Can.: $250.00

SLOE FAIRY™
Style Two

Model: A1901
Designer: Cicely Mary Barker
Modeller: Unknown
Height: 6 ¼", 15.9 cm
Colour: Purple, green and lilac
Issued: 2003 - 12/04
Series: Flower Fairies

U.K.:   £20.00
U.S.: $40.00
Can.: $40.00

SNAPDRAGON FAIRY™

Model: A0743
Designer: Cicely Mary Barker
Modeller: Unknown
Height: 5", 12.7 cm
Colour: Yellow, pink and green
Issued: 01/02 - 12/04
Series: Flower Fairies

U.K.:   £20.00
U.S.: $40.00
Can.: $40.00

STRAWBERRY FAIRY™
Style One

Model: B0115
Designer: Cicely Mary Barker
Modeller: Glenis Devereux
Height: 7 ¼", 18.4 cm
Colour: Red strawberries and
                dress; white sleeves
and   wings; green leaves
Issued: 01/97 in a limited
                edition of 1,950
Series: Flower Fairies

U.K.:   £125.00
U.S.: $250.00
Can.: $250.00

STRAWBERRY FAIRY™
Style Two

Model: A0748
Designer: Cicely Mary Barker
Modeller: Unknown
Height: 3 ¾", 9.5 cm
Colour: Red, green and white
Issued: 01/02 - 12/03
Series: Miniature Fairies

U.K.:   £15.00
U.S.: $30.00
Can.: $30.00

SWEET PEA FAIRIES™
Style One

Model: CF3
Designer: Cicely Mary Barker
Modeller: David Geenty
Height: 7 ¼", 18.4 cm
Colour: Green, rose-pink
                and lilac clothing
Issued: 01/86 - 12/87
Series: Flower Fairies

U.K.:   £100.00
U.S.: $200.00
Can.: $200.00

SWEET PEA FAIRIES™
Style Two

Model: 726931
Designer: Cicely Mary Barker
Modeller: Unknown
Height: 5", 12.7 cm
Colour: Lilac, pink and green
Issued: 01/00 - 12/03
Series: Flower Fairies

U.K.:   £25.00
U.S.: $50.00
Can.: $50.00

WALLFLOWER FAIRY™
Style One

Model: CF27
Designer: Cicely Mary Barker
Modeller: Glenis Devereux
Height: 7 ½", 19.1 cm
Colour: Rust and yellow
                clothing
Issued: 01/95 in a limited
                edition of 1,950
Series: Flower Fairies

U.K.:   £150.00
U.S.: $300.00
Can.: $300.00

WALLFLOWER FAIRY™
Style Two

Model:	A0304
Designer:	Cicely Mary Barker
Modeller:	Unknown
Height:	4 ¾", 12.1 cm
Colour:	Red, greens, yellow and brown
Issued:	01/01 - 12/02
Series:	Miniature Fairies

U.K.:	£15.00
U.S.:	$30.00
Can.:	$30.00

WHITE BINDWEED FAIRY™
Style One

Model:	CF26
Designer:	Cicely Mary Barker
Modeller:	Glenis Devereux
Height:	5 ½", 14.0 cm
Colour:	Pink dress and wings; white flowers
Issued:	01/95 in a limited edition of 1,950
Series:	Flower Fairies

U.K.:	£150.00
U.S.:	$300.00
Can.:	$300.00

WHITE BINDWEED FAIRY™
Style Two

Model:	A1906
Designer:	Cicely Mary Barker
Modeller:	Unknown
Height:	3 ¾", 9.5 cm
Colour:	White, pink and green
Issued:	01/03 - 12/05
Series:	Flower Fairies

U.K.:	£15.00
U.S.:	$30.00
Can.:	$30.00

WILD CHERRY FAIRY™

Model:	CF25
Designer:	Cicely Mary Barker
Modeller:	Glenis Devereux
Height:	8", 20.3 cm
Colour:	White and red dress; white flowers
Issued:	01/94 in a limited edition of 1,950
Series:	Flower Fairies

U.K.:	£175.00
U.S.:	$350.00
Can.:	$350.00

WINDFLOWER FAIRY™

Model:	B0847
Modeller:	Sue Norton
Height:	8 ½", 21.6 cm
Colour:	Pink, green, orange, beige, green and white
Issued:	01/04 in a limited edition of 500
Series:	Flower Fairies

U.K.:	£125.00
U.S.:	$250.00
Can.:	$250.00

WINTER ACONITE FAIRY™

Model:	A1903
Designer:	Cicely Mary Barker
Modeller:	Unknown
Height:	3 ¾", 9.5 cm
Colour:	Green, yellow, white and beige
Issued:	06/02 - 12/03
Series:	Miniature Fairies

U.K.:	£12.00
U.S.:	$25.00
Can.:	$25.00

WOOD SORREL FAIRY™

Model:	A1096
Designer:	Cicely Mary Barker
Modeller:	Unknown
Height:	2 ½", 6.4 cm
Colour:	Pink, green and yellow
Issued:	01/02 - 12/04
Series:	Miniature Fairies

U.K.:	£12.00
U.S.:	$25.00
Can.:	$25.00

ZINNIA FAIRY™

Model:	A0746
Designer:	Cicely Mary Barker
Modeller:	Unknown
Height:	5 ¼", 13.3 cm
Colour:	Green, pink, black, orange, and light brown,
Issued:	01/02 - 12/04
Series:	Flower Fairies

U.K.:	£20.00
U.S.:	$40.00
Can.:	$40.00

Fairies By Linda Pagett

FAIRY AND FROG™

Model:	UK# F2
	USA# 225-301
Designer:	Linda Pagett
Modeller:	David Geenty
Height:	6", 15.0 cm
Colour:	Pink dress and cap; yellow-brown frog; green lilypad
Issued:	01/81 - 12/82

U.K.:	£ 75.00
U.S.:	$150.00
Can.:	$150.00

FAIRY AND MUSHROOM™

Model:	UK# F3
	USA# 225-304
Designer:	Linda Pagett
Modeller:	David Geenty
Height:	5", 12.7 cm
Colour:	Yellow dress; beige mushroom with brown cap
Issued:	01/81 - 12/82

U.K.:	£ 75.00
U.S.:	$150.00
Can.:	$150.00

FAIRY AND PIPE™

Model:	UK# F4
	USA# 225-303
Designer:	Linda Pagett
Modeller:	David Geenty
Height:	4", 10.1 cm
Colour:	Lilac outfit and cap; cream wings
Issued:	01/81 - 12/82

U.K.:	£ 75.00
U.S.:	$150.00
Can.:	$150.00

FAIRY AND POPPY™

Model:	UK# F1
	USA# 225-300
Designer:	Linda Pagett
Modeller:	David Geenty
Height:	4 ½", 11.9 cm
Colour:	Yellow outfit and flower; cream wings; green leaves
Issued:	01/81 - 12/82

U.K.:	£ 75.00
U.S.:	$150.00
Can.:	$150.00

LEGEND OF KING ARTHUR

GUINEVERE™
Model: KA02
Modeller: Mark Newman
Height: 9", 22.9 cm
Colour: Lilac dress; yellow
          cloak; brown hair;
          gold crown
Issued: 01/91 - 12/93

U.K.:   £ 75.00
U.S.: $150.00
Can.: $150.00

KING ARTHUR™
Model: KA01
Modeller: Mark Newman
Height: 9 ½", 24.0 cm
Colour: Grey armour; purple
          cloak; silver sword;
          gold crown; blonde
          hair
Issued: 01/91 - 12/93

U.K.:   £ 75.00
U.S.: $150.00
Can.: $150.00

MERLIN™
Model: KA03
Modeller: Mark Newman
Height: 9", 22.9 cm
Colour: Dark green robe;
          orange, tan and
          brown cloak; grey
          beard; brown and
          white owl
Issued: 01/91 - 12/93

U.K.:   £ 75.00
U.S.: $150.00
Can.: $150.00

MORDRED™
Model: KA07
Modeller: Mark Newman
Height: 7 ½", 19.1 cm
Colour: Grey armour; orange
          shirt; tan cloak;
          brown hair and beard
Issued: 01/91 - 12/93

U.K.:   £ 75.00
U.S.: $150.00
Can.: $150.00

MORGAN LE FAY™
Model: KA08
Modeller: Mark Newman
Height: 9", 22.9 cm
Colour: Yellow skirt; pale
          blue shirt; green
          cloak; pink headdress;
          strawberry blonde hair
Issued: 01/91 - 12/93

U.K.:   £ 75.00
U.S.: $150.00
Can.: $150.00

SIR GALAHAD™
Model: KA05
Modeller: Mark Newman
Height: 8 ½", 21.6 cm
Colour: Grey armour; pale
          green cloak
Issued: 01/91 - 12/93

U.K.:   £ 75.00
U.S.: $150.00
Can.: $150.00

SIR GAWAINE™
Model: KA06
Modeller: Mark Newman
Height: 9", 22.9 cm
Colour: Grey armour; light
          brown cloak; grey
          moustache
Issued: 01/91 - 12/93

U.K.:   £ 75.00
U.S.: $150.00
Can.: $150.00

SIR LANCELOT™
Model: KA04
Modeller: Mark Newman
Height: 9 ½", 24.0 cm
Colour: Golden armour;
          grey cloak; silver
          sword and shield
Issued: 01/91 - 12/93

U.K.:   £ 75.00
U.S.: $150.00
Can.: $150.00

400

LOCAL HEROES

BIG RESPECT FOR MR. TIBBS™
Model: A8158
Designer: Philip Stuttard
Modeller: Unknown
Height: 8 ½", 21.6 cm
Colour: Black white and tan
Issued: 01/07 the present

U.K.: £25.00
U.S.: $50.00
Can.: $55.00

CITY SLICKER™
Model: A8093
Designer: Philip Stuttar
Modeller: Unknown
Height: 9 ¼", 23.5 cm
Colour: Mottled black, white and red
Issued: 01/07 the present

U.K.: £25.00
U.S.: $50.00
Can.: $55.00

DINNER FOR TWO™
Model: A8250
Designer: Philip Stuttar
Modeller: Unknown
Height: 5 ½", 13.7 cm
Colour: Mottled black and white
Issued: 01/07 the present

U.K.: £30.00
U.S.: $60.00
Can.: $65.00

HOME JAMES™
Model: A8163
Designer: Philip Stuttar
Modeller: Unknown
Height: 7 ¼", 18.4 cm
Colour: Black, white and silver
Issued: 01/07 the present

U.K.: £30.00
U.S.: $60.00
Can.: $65.00

MAN AND MACHINE™
Model: A8160
Designer: Philip Stuttar
Modeller: Unknown
Height: 8 ¾", 22.2 cm
Colour: Mottled black and white
Issued: 01/07 the present

U.K.: £30.00
U.S.: $60.00
Can.: $65.00

NIGHT WATCH, THE™
Model: A8164
Designer: Philip Stuttar
Modeller: Unknown
Height: 4 ¾", 12.1 cm
Colour: Mottled black and yellowish-white, yellow, red and brown
Issued: 01/07 the present

U.K.: £30.00
U.S.: $60.00
Can.: $65.00

MERRIE MICE

A "GNAWING HABIT"

Model: A1814
Modeller: Janet Miller
Height: 4", 10.1 cm
Colour: Beige, white, brown and green
Issued: 06/02 - 12/03
Series: Funguys

U.K.: £12.00
U.S.: $25.00
Can.: $25.00

ASPARAGUS PICKERS

Model: A6241
Modeller: Janet Miller
Height: 3 ¾", 9.5 cm
Colour: Brown, white, green, pink and red
Issued: 01/06 - 06/07
Series: Vegging Out

U.K.: £22.00
U.S.: $45.00
Can.: $45.00

BABY ROSE HIP

Model: A3773
Modeller: Janet Miller
Height: 3", 7.6 cm
Colour: Light brown, white, green, yellow, red and pale blue
Issued: 01/04 - 06/06
Series: Happy Families

U.K.: £15.00
U.S.: $30.00
Can.: $30.00

BALANCING ACT

Model: A1815
Modeller: Janet Miller
Height: 3 ¼", 8.3 cm
Colour: Orange-brown, white, dark brown, grey, green and yellow
Issued: 01/03 - 12/06
Series: Funguys

U.K.: £15.00
U.S.: $30.00
Can.: $30.00

BE BERRY CAREFUL!

Model: A0605
Modeller: Raewyn Greggain
Height: 4 ¼", 10.8 cm
Colour: Brown, white, dark purple and green
Issued: 01/01 - 12/06
Series: Fruit Fun

U.K.: £15.00
U.S.: $30.00
Can.: $30.00

BLACKCURRENT JUICE

Model: A3785
Modeller: Janet Miller
Height: 3 ½", 8.9 cm
Colour: Light brown, white, pink, black and green
Issued: 06/04 - 06/06
Series: Fruit Fun

U.K.: £15.00
U.S.: $30.00
Can.: $30.00

BOBBING APPLES

Model: A3776
Modeller: Janet Miller
Height: 3", 7.6 cm
Colour: Light brown, white, green, brown and turquoise
Issued: 01/04 - 06/06
Series: Happy Families

U.K.: £18.00
U.S.: $35.00
Can.: $35.00

COCKTAIL PARTY

Model: A0603
Modeller: Raewyn Greggain
Height: 4 ½", 11.9 cm
Colour: Brown, white, orange, and yellow
Issued: 01/01 - 12/04
Series: Fruit Fun

U.K.: £15.00
U.S.: $30.00
Can.: $30.00

CONKER CRADLE

Model: A3775
Modeller: Janet Miller
Height: 3 ½", 8.9 cm
Colour: Light brown, green,
            white and yellow
Issued: 01/04 - 06/06
Series: Happy Families

U.K.:   £15.00
U.S.: $30.00
Can.: $30.00

CORE BLIMEY

Model: A0604
Modeller: Raewyn Greggain
Height: 3", 7.6 cm
Colour: Brown, white, red and
            green
Issued: 01/01 - 06/05
Series: Fruit Fun

U.K.:   £15.00
U.S.: $30.00
Can.: $30.00

CURRANT CROP

Model: A3262
Modeller: Janet Miller
Height: 3 ¼", 8.3 cm
Colour: Brown, white, red and
            green
Issued: 06/03 - 12/05
Series: Fruit Fun

U.K.:   £12.00
U.S.: $25.00
Can.: $25.00

FEEDING TIME

Model: A5024
Modeller: Janet Miller
Height: 3", 7.6 cm
Colour: Brown, white, pink,
            green yellow and red
Issued: 01/05 - 06/07
Series: Happy Families

U.K.:   £20.00
U.S.: $40.00
Can.: $40.00

FUNGISLIDE

Model: A1816
Modeller: Janet Miller
Height: 4 ¼", 10.8 cm
Colour: Rusty-brown, white,
            grey, yellow and green
Issued: 01/03 - 12/05
Series: Funguys

U.K.:   £12.00
U.S.: $25.00
Can.: $25.00

GRAPE ESCAPE, THE

Model: A1631
Modeller: Janet Miller
Height: 2 ½", 6.4 cm
Colour: Purple grapes; brown,
            white and cream mice;
            white and yellow
            flowers and green grass
Issued: 01/02 - 06/06
Series: Fruit Fun

U.K.:   £15.00
U.S.: $30.00
Can.: $30.00

HITCHIN' A RIDE

Model: A0440
Modeller: Raewyn Greggain
Height: 3 ¼", 8.3 cm
Colour: Brown, white, red and
            green
Issued: 01/01 - 12/05
Series: Fruit Fun

U.K.:   £12.00
U.S.: $25.00
Can.: $25.00

HOBBY HORSE RACES

Model: A5025
Modeller: Janet Miller
Height: 3 ¼", 8.3 cm
Colour: Brown, white, green,
            yellow and red
Issued: 01/05 - 06/07
Series: Happy Families

U.K.:   £20.00
U.S.: $40.00
Can.: $40.00

KIWI QUIVER

Model: A5021
Modeller: Janet Miller
Height: 3 ¼", 8.3 cm
Colour: Brown, white, green, pink and red
Issued: 01/05 - 06/06
Series: Fruit Farm

U.K.: £15.00
U.S.: $30.00
Can.: $30.00

LAND AHOY!

Model: A0606
Modeller: Raewyn Greggain
Height: 3 ¼", 8.3 cm
Colour: Brown, white, yellow and green
Issued: 01/01 - 06/07
Series: Fruit Fun

U.K.: £25.00
U.S.: $50.00
Can.: $50.00

LAZY DAYS

Model: A1811
Modeller: Janet Miller
Height: 3 ¼", 8.3 cm
Colour: Light brown, white, yellow, red and green
Issued: 06/02 - 12/06
Series: Funguys

U.K.: £15.00
U.S.: $30.00
Can.: $30.00

LEMON CHARIOT

Model: A5020
Modeller: Janet Miller
Height: 3 ½", 8.9 cm
Colour: Brown, white, yellow and green
Issued: 01/05 - 12/06
Series: Fruit Farm

U.K.: £15.00
U.S.: $30.00
Can.: $30.00

MARCHING ORDERS

Model: A3260
Modeller: Janet Miller
Height: 3 ¼", 8.3 cm
Colour: Brown, white, grey, golden yellow and green
Issued: 06/03 - 06/05
Series: Funguys

U.K.: £15.00
U.S.: $30.00
Can.: $30.00

MELON ROCK'N'ROLL

Model: A0441
Modeller: Raewyn Greggain
Height: 5 ½", 14.0 cm
Colour: Brown, white, red and green
Issued: 01/01 - 12/04
Series: Fruit Fun

U.K.: £20.00
U.S.: $40.00
Can.: $40.00

MOUSE BAND

Model: A6244
Modeller: Janet Miller
Height: 3", 7.6 cm
Colour: Brown, white, green and pink
Issued: 01/06 - 06/07
Series: Happy Families

U.K.: £20.00
U.S.: $40.00
Can.: $40.00

NOT 'MUSH-ROOM' UNDER HERE!

Model: A1813
Modeller: Janet Miller
Height: 3 ½", 8.9 cm
Colour: Brown, white, grey, yellow and green
Issued: 06/02 - 12/04
Series: Funguys

U.K.: £15.00
U.S.: $30.00
Can.: $30.00

ONION DIGGERS

Model: A5896
Modeller: Janet Miller
Height: 3 ¼", 8.3 cm
Colour: Browns, white and green
Issued: 06/05 - 06/07
Series: Vegging Out

U.K.: £18.00
U.S.: $35.00
Can.: $35.00

OUT OF REACH

Model: A3778
Modeller: Janet Miller
Height: 4 ¼", 10.8 cm
Colour: Light brown, white, yellow, green and blue
Issued: 06/04 - 06/06
Series: Funguys

U.K.: £15.00
U.S.: $30.00
Can.: $30.00

PEAR DROP

Model: A1630
Modeller: Janet Miller
Height: 4 ¼", 10.8 cm
Colour: Yellow, browns, white, green and pink
Issued: 01/02 - 12/04
Series: Fruit Fun

U.K.: £15.00
U.S.: $30.00
Can.: $30.00

PIGGY BACK

Model: A5898
Modeller: Janet Miller
Height: 3", 7.6 cm
Colour: Brown, white, red and pale blue
Issued: 06/05 - 06/07
Series: Happy Families

U.K.: £10.00
U.S.: $20.00
Can.: $20.00

PLAYING GOOSEBERRY

Model: A3784
Modeller: Janet Miller
Height: 4 ¼", 10.8 cm
Colour: Light brown, white and green
Issued: 06/04 - 06/06
Series: Fruit Fun

U.K.: £17.00
U.S.: $35.00
Can.: $35.00

PLUM PUDDINGS

Model: A1810
Modeller: Janet Miller
Height: 2 ¼", 5.7 cm
Colour: Black, purple, brown, white and green
Issued: 01/03 - 12/05
Series: Fruit Fun

U.K.: £12.00
U.S.: $25.00
Can.: $25.00

PUPPET SHOW

Model: A5897
Modeller: Janet Miller
Height: 3", 7.6 cm
Colour: Brown, white, green, blue, red and yellow
Issued: 06/05 - 06/07
Series: Happy Families

U.K.: £20.00
U.S.: $40.00
Can.: $40.00

RASPBERRY FOOL

Model: A3261
Modeller: Janet Miller
Height: 6 ½", 16.5 cm
Colour: Brown, white, pink, green and red
Issued: 06/03 - 06/07
Series: Fruit Fun

U.K.: £20.00
U.S.: $40.00
Can.: $40.00

SEE-SAW
Model: A6243
Modeller: Janet Miller
Height: 2 ¾", 7.0 cm
Colour: Browns, green, pink and white
Issued: 01/06 - 06/07
Series: Happy Families

U.K.: £20.00
U.S.: $40.00
Can.: $40.00

SOAP STAR
Model: A1812
Modeller: Janet Miller
Height: 4 ½", 11.9 cm
Colour: Yellow, white, brown and green
Issued: 06/02 - 12/04
Series: Funguys

U.K.: £15.00
U.S.: $30.00
Can.: $30.00

STORING CARROTS
Model: A5895
Modeller: Janet Miller
Height: 4 ¼", 10.8 cm
Colour: Brown, orange and green
Issued: 06/05 - 06/07
Series: Vegging Out

U.K.: £20.00
U.S.: $40.00
Can.: $40.00

STRAWBERRY BED
Model: A1809
Modeller: Janet Miller
Height: 2 ½", 6.4 cm
Colour: Brown, white, red and green
Issued: 01/03 - 06/06
Series: Fruit Fun

U.K.: £15.00
U.S.: $30.00
Can.: $30.00

TEA FOR TWO
Model: A3259
Modeller: Janet Miller
Height: 4 ¼", 10.8 cm
Colour: Brown, white, pink, red, blue, green and yellow
Issued: 06/03 - 12/05
Series: Funguys

U.K.: £15.00
U.S.: $30.00
Can.: $30.00

TICKLED PINK
Model: A3777
Modeller: Janet Miller
Height: 4 ¼", 10.8 cm
Colour: Light brown, white, green and red
Issued: 06/04 - 06/06
Series: Funguys

U.K.: £15.00
U.S.: $30.00
Can.: $30.00

TOM FOOLERY
Model: A6242
Modeller: Janet Miller
Height: 3 ½", 8.9 cm
Colour: Brown, pink, green and red
Issued: 01/06 - 06/07
Series: Fruit Farm

U.K.: £22.00
U.S.: $45.00
Can.: $45.00

WALNUT WASH
Model: A3774
Modeller: Janet Miller
Height: 2 ¾", 7.0 cm
Colour: Light brown, white, green, red, yellow and pale blue
Issued: 01/04 - 06/06
Series: Happy Families

U.K.: £15.00
U.S.: $30.00
Can.: $30.00

OLIVER OTTER AND FRIENDS

DIGSBY THE MOLE™
Model: 330825
Designer: Kate Veale
Modeller: Richard Wawrzesta
Height: 3 ½", 8.9 cm
Colour: Brown mole; red vest and strawberries; blue and white bowl
Issued: 06/97 - 12/98

U.K.: £15.00
U.S.: $30.00
Can.: $30.00

DREW THE SHREW™
Model: 330787
Designer: Kate Veale
Modeller: Richard Wawrzesta
Height: 2 ¾", 7.0 cm
Colour: Brown shrew; white shirt with red ladybugs; blue sneakers; blue and white bowl
Issued: 06/97 - 12/98

U.K.: £15.00
U.S.: $30.00
Can.: $30.00

OLIVER OTTER™
Model: 330809
Designer: Kate Veale
Modeller: Richard Wawrzesta
Height: 4 ½", 11.9 cm
Colour: Brown and white otter; white shirt with heart and fish; blue sandals; orange bottles
Issued: 06/97 - 12/98

U.K.: £15.00
U.S.: $30.00
Can.: $30.00

WILL SQUIRREL™
Model: 330817
Designer: Kate Veale
Modeller: Richard Wawrzesta
Height: 4 ¼", 10.8 cm
Colour: Brown and white squirrel; blue shirt; white and blue lunchbox
Issued: 06/97 - 12/98

U.K.: £15.00
U.S.: $30.00
Can.: $30.00

OLIVER OTTER™ BOOKENDS
Model: 330833
Designer: Kate Veale
Modeller: Richard Wawrzesta
Height: 5", 12.7 cm
Colour: Brown, red, white, blue and green
Issued: 06/97 - 12/98
Series: Bookends

U.K.: £ 50.00
U.S.: $100.00
Can.: $100.00

OLIVER OTTER™ SUNFLOWER CLOCK
Model: 330795
Designer: Kate Veale
Modeller: Richard Wawrzesta
Height: 7 ¾", 19.7 cm
Colour: Brown, blue, white, green and yellow
Issued: 06/97 - 12/98
Series: Clocks

U.K.: £40.00
U.S.: $80.00
Can.: $80.00

PETER PAN

CROCODILE™

Model:	PP06
Modeller:	Glenis Devereux
Height:	1 ½", 3.8 cm
Colour:	Green body; pink tongue
Issued:	07/94 - 12/95
U.K.:	£ 50.00
U.S.:	$100.00
Can.:	$100.00

HOOK™

Model:	PP04
Modeller:	Glenis Devereux
Height:	6 ½", 16.5 cm
Colour:	Cream shirt; red vest and belt; grey pantaloons and sword; black hat with white plume
Issued:	07/94 - 12/95
U.K.:	£30.00
U.S.:	$60.00
Can.:	$60.00

PETER PAN™

Model:	PP01
Modeller:	Glenis Devereux
Height:	5", 12.7 cm
Colour:	Green clothing and shoes; black hat with red band
Issued:	07/94 - 12/95
U.K.:	£40.00
U.S.:	$80.00
Can.:	$80.00

SMEE™

Model:	PP05
Modeller:	Glenis Devereux
Height:	3", 7.6 cm
Colour:	Blue and white striped clothing; red neckerchief; black shoes with gold buckles
Issued:	07/94 - 12/95
U.K.:	£25.00
U.S.:	$50.00
Can.:	$50.00

TINKER BELL™

Model:	PP03
Modeller:	Glenis Devereux
Height:	4 ¾", 12.1 cm
Colour:	Lilac frock with gold bells; brown and beige mushroom
Issued:	07/94 - 12/95
U.K.:	£40.00
U.S.:	$80.00
Can.:	$80.00

WENDY™

Model:	PP02
Modeller:	Glenis Devereux
Height:	5 ¾", 14.6 cm
Colour:	Pink frock; blue kite; tan rope with pink bows
Issued:	07/94 - 12/95
U.K.:	£40.00
U.S.:	$80.00
Can.:	$80.00

RATS THE WAY WE DO IT!

FAT RAT

Model:	A7910
Modeller:	Unknown
Height:	4", 10.1 cm
Colour:	Light brown, green and burgundy
Issued:	01/07 to the present
U.K.:	£20.00
U.S.:	$40.00
Can.:	$40.00

KING RAT

Model:	A7905
Modeller:	Unknown
Height:	5 ¼", 13.3 cm
Colour:	White, blue, black and green
Issued:	01/07 to the present
U.K.:	£20.00
U.S.:	$40.00
Can.:	$40.00

LOVE RAT

Model:	A7911
Modeller:	Unknown
Height:	4 ¼", 10.8 cm
Colour:	Light brown, green, pink and black
Issued:	01/07 to the present
U.K.:	£22.00
U.S.:	$45.00
Can.:	$45.00

NORA RATTY

Model:	A7912
Modeller:	Unknown
Height:	4 ¾", 12.1 cm
Colour:	Grey, pink, black and white
Issued:	01/07 to the present
U.K.:	£20.00
U.S.:	$40.00
Can.:	$40.00

RAT PACK

Model:	A7907
Modeller:	Unknown
Height:	4 ¼", 10.8 cm
Colour:	Grey, brown, green and black
Issued:	01/07 to the present
U.K.:	£45.00
U.S.:	$90.00
Can.:	$90.00

RAT RACE

Model:	A7908
Modeller:	Unknown
Height:	4 ½", 11.4 cm
Colour:	Light brown, black and pink
Issued:	01/07 to the present
U.K.:	£18.00
U.S.:	$35.00
Can.:	$35.00

RAT-AT-TWEE

Model:	A7909
Modeller:	Unknown
Height:	5 ¼", 13.3 cm
Colour:	White, grey, brown and blue
Issued:	01/07 to the present
U.K.:	£20.00
U.S.:	$40.00
Can.:	$40.00

SEWER RAT

Model:	A8303
Modeller:	Unknown
Height:	5 ¼", 13.3 cm
Colour:	Grey, yellow and green
Issued:	01/07 to the present
U.K.:	£18.00
U.S.:	$35.00
Can.:	$35.00

THE REYNARD ESTATE

DUKE OF REYNARD, THE

Model: A8388
Modeller: Unknown
Height: 6", 15.2 cm
Colour: Red, white, black
            and brown
Issued: 01/07 to the present

U.K.:   £20.00
U.S.: $40.00
Can.: $40.00

LADY REYNARD

Model: A7654
Modeller: Unknown
Height: 7 ¼", 18.4 cm
Colour: Black, brown and white
Issued: 01/07 to the present

U.K.:   £20.00
U.S.: $40.00
Can.: $40.00

LORD REYNARD

Model: A7653
Modeller: Unknown
Height: 7 ¾", 19.7 cm
Colour: Red, white, black
            and brown
Issued: 01/07 to the present

U.K.:   £20.00
U.S.: $40.00
Can.: $40.00

MASTER REYNARD

Model: A7655
Modeller: Unknown
Height: 6 ¼", 15.9 cm
Colour: Red, white, black
            and brown
Issued: 01/07 to the present

U.K.:   £18.00
U.S.: $35.00
Can.: $35.00

MISS REYNARD

Model: A7656
Modeller: Unknown
Height: 6 ¼", 15.9 cm
Colour: Black, white and
            brown
Issued: 01/07 to the present

U.K.:   £18.00
U.S.: $35.00
Can.: $35.00

DUCHESS OF REYNARD, THE

Model: A8387
Modeller: Unknown
Height: 6 ¾, 17.2 cm
Colour: Black, white, brown
            and red
Issued: 01/07 to the present

U.K.:   £25.00
U.S.: $50.00
Can.: $50.00

RUFF and REDDY

HELPING HANDS

Model: RR05
Modeller: Anne Wall
Height: 4", 10.1 cm
Colour: Black and white collie; ginger cat; grey tool box
Issued: 01/95 - 12/99

U.K.: £30.00
U.S.: $60.00
Can.: $60.00

HEN PECKED

Model: RR06
Modeller: Anne Wall
Height: 3 ½", 8.9 cm
Colour: Black and white collie; ginger cat; white and black hen; white feed bowl
Issued: 01/95 - 12/00

U.K.: £30.00
U.S.: $60.00
Can.: $60.00

HIDE AND SEEK

Model: RR08
Modeller: Anne Wall
Height: 3 ¼", 8.3 cm
Colour: Black and white collie; ginger cat in grey pail
Issued: 01/96 - 12/99

U.K.: £25.00
U.S.: $50.00
Can.: $50.00

HIGH JINKS

Model: RR03
Modeller: Anne Wall
Height: 5 ½", 14.0 cm
Colour: Black and white collie; ginger cat; brown tree stump
Issued: 01/95 - 12/00

U.K.: £30.00
U.S.: $60.00
Can.: $60.00

IF THE CAP FITS

Model: RR07
Modeller: Anne Wall
Height: 3 ¾", 9.5 cm
Colour: Black and white collie wearing cloth cap; ginger cat
Issued: 01/96 - 12/97

U.K.: £25.00
U.S.: $50.00
Can.: $50.00

NOT MY SIZE

Model: RR02
Modeller: Anne Wall
Height: 3 ¾", 9.5 cm
Colour: Black and white collie; ginger cat with dark grey wellingtons
Issued: 01/95 - 12/00

U.K.: £30.00
U.S.: $60.00
Can.: $60.00

SCARECROW SCALLYWAGS

Model: B0085
Modeller: Anne Wall
Height: 6 ¾", 17.2 cm
Colour: Black and white collie; ginger cat; scarecrow wears brown and blue clothing
Issued: 01/97 - 06/99

U.K.: £35.00
U.S.: $70.00
Can.: $70.00

TAKING THE BISCUIT

Model: B0295
Modeller: Anne Wall
Height: 5 ½", 14.0 cm
Colour: Black and white collie; ginger cat; beige sacks
Issued: 06/98 - 12/00

U.K.: £35.00
U.S.: $70.00
Can.: $70.00

TYRED OUT

Model:	RR01
Modeller:	Anne Wall
Height:	2 ¾", 7.0 cm
Colour:	Black and white collie; ginger cat in a black tyre
Issued:	01/95 - 12/97

U.K.:	£30.00
U.S.:	$60.00
Can.:	$60.00

WASHDAY BLUES

Model:	RR04
Modeller:	Anne Wall
Height:	3", 7.6 cm
Colour:	Black and white collie; ginger cat; blue dungarees
Issued:	01/95 - 06/99

U.K.:	£30.00
U.S.:	$60.00
Can.:	$60.00

THELWELL

A WELL HANDLED PONY™

Model: T15
Modeller: Fred Moore
Height: 3", 7.6 cm
Colour: 1. Bay; red, green, blue and tan clothing
2. Grey; red, green, blue and tan clothing
Issued: 1987 - 12/89
Series: Thelwell's Riding Academy

U.K.: £45.00
U.S.: $90.00
Can.: $90.00

AMONG THE PRIZES™

Model: T35
Modeller: Richard Wawrzesta
Height: 3", 7.6 cm
Colour: 1. Bay; maroon and cream clothing
2. Grey; maroon and cream clothing
Issued: 06/91 - 12/93
Series: Thelwell's Riding Academy

U.K.: £35.00
U.S.: $70.00
Can.: $70.00

BOILING POINT™

Model: T48
Modeller: Richard Wawrzesta
Height: 2 ¼", 5.7 cm
Colour: 1. Bay; blue and cream clothing
2. Grey; blue and cream clothing
Issued: 07/92 - 12/93
Series: Thelwell's Riding Academy

U.K.: £40.00
U.S.: $80.00
Can.: $80.00

BRONCO BUSTER™

Model: T43
Modeller: Richard Wawrzesta
Height: 3", 7.6 cm
Colour: 1. Bay; brown, blue and tan clothing
2. Grey; brown, blue and tan clothing
Issued: 06/91 - 12/93
Series: Thelwell Goes West

U.K.: £40.00
U.S.: $80.00
Can.: $80.00

BRUSH VIGOROUSLY - HE'LL ENJOY IT™

Model: T10/140-709
Modeller: Fred Moore
Height: 2 ½", 6.4 cm
Colour: 1. Bay; green jacket; brown brush
2. Grey; green jacket; brown brush
Issued: 1985-Dec. 1993
Series: Thelwell's Riding Academy

U.K.: £20.00
U.S.: $40.00
Can.: $40.00

CHRISTMAS DELIVERY™
Style One

Model: T22
Modeller: Fred Moore
Height: 3", 7.6 cm
Colour: 1. Bay; red clothing; multi. packages
2. Grey; red clothing; multi. packages
Issued: 12/88 - 12/89
Series: Thelwell's Riding Academy

U.K.: £45.00
U.S.: $90.00
Can.: $90.00

CHRISTMAS DELIVERY™
Style Two

Model: T53
Modeller: Richard Wawrzesta
Height: 3 ¼", 8.3 cm
Colour: 1. Bay; red clothing; multi. packages
2. Grey; red clothing; multi. packages
Issued: 01/94 - 12/94
Series: Thelwell's Riding Academy

U.K.: £45.00
U.S.: $90.00
Can.: $90.00

CHRISTMAS FAIRY™

Model: T46
Modeller: Richard Wawrzesta
Height: 2 ½", 6.4 cm
Colour: 1. Bay; red and green clothing
2. Grey; red and green clothing
Issued: 07/92 - 12/93
Series: Thelwell's Riding Academy

U.K.: £45.00
U.S.: $90.00
Can.: $90.00

CHRISTMAS PARTY™
Model: T50
Modeller: Richard Wawrzesta
Height: 2 ½", 6.4 cm
Colour: 1. Bay; blue and cream clothing; orange carrot
2. Grey; blue and cream clothing; orange carrot
Issued: 07/93 - 12/93
Series: Thelwell's Riding Academy

U.K.: £ 60.00
U.S.: $120.00
Can.: $120.00

CHRISTMAS TREAT™
Model: T11
Modeller: Fred Moore
Height: 3", 7.6 cm
Colour: 1. Bay; blue, rose and cream clothing
2. Grey; blue, rose and cream clothing
Issued: 12/85 - 12/86
Series: Thelwell's Riding Academy

U.K.: £45.00
U.S.: $90.00
Can.: $90.00

DANGER POINT™
Model: T49
Modeller: Richard Wawrzesta
Height: 2 ¾", 7.0 cm
Colour: 1. Bay; red and cream clothing
2. Grey; red and cream clothing
Issued: 07/92 - 12/93
Series: Thelwell's Riding Academy

U.K.: £45.00
U.S.: $90.00
Can.: $90.00

DON'T EXPECT HIM TO READ YOUR MIND™
Model: T55
Modeller: Richard Wawrzesta
Height: 2 ½", 6.4 cm
Colour: 1. Bay; red and cream clothing
2. Grey; red and cream clothing
Issued: 01/95 - 12/95
Series: Thelwell's Riding Academy

U.K.: £ 60.00
U.S.: $120.00
Can.: $120.00

DON'T PANIC OVER HIS SIMPLE AILMENTS™
Model: T9/140-708
Modeller: Fred Moore
Height: 3", 7.6 cm
Colour: 1. Bay; white coat; brown stethoscope
2. Grey; white coat; brown stethoscope
Issued: 1985 - 12/89
Series: Thelwell's Riding Academy

U.K.: £45.00
U.S.: $90.00
Can.: $90.00

DON'T PLAY WITH YOUR PONY IN THE GARDEN™
Model: T24
Modeller: Richard Wawrzesta
Height: 3", 7.6 cm
Colour: 1. Bay; red jacket; yellow, red and blue flowers
2. Grey; red jacket; yellow, red and blue flowers
Issued: 12/89 - 12/93
Series: Thelwell's Riding Academy

U.K.: £35.00
U.S.: $70.00
Can.: $70.00

DON'T TIRE YOUR PONY™
Model: T1/140-706
Modeller: Fred Moore
Height: 2", 5.0 cm
Colour: 1. Bay; tan and cream clothing
2. Grey; tan and cream clothing
Issued: 1984 - 12/89
Series: Thelwell's Riding Academy

U.K.: £35.00
U.S.: $70.00
Can.: $70.00

EASY JUMPS FIRST™
Model: T13
Modeller: Fred Moore
Height: 3", 7.6 cm
Colour: 1. Bay; tan, blue and cream clothing
2. Grey; tan, blue and cream clothing
Issued: 1986 - 12/93
Series: Thelwell's Riding Academy

U.K.: £35.00
U.S.: $70.00
Can.: $70.00

FAT PONIES ARE HARD ON THE LEGS™

Model: T52
Modeller: Richard Wawrzesta
Height: 2 ½", 6.4 cm
Colour: 1. Bay; red and cream
clothing
2. Grey; red and cream
clothing
Issued: 07/93 - 12/93
Series: Thelwell's Riding
Academy

U.K.: £ 60.00
U.S.: $120.00
Can.: $120.00

FOUR FAULTS™

Model: T8/140-707
Modeller: Fred Moore
Height: 3", 7.6 cm
Colour: 1. Bay; blue and cream
clothing; red, blue
and yellow flowers
2.Grey; blue and
cream clothing; red,
blue and yellow
flowers
Issued: 1985 - 12/93
Series: Thelwell's Riding
Academy

U.K.: £25.00
U.S.: $50.00
Can.: $50.00

FOUR HOOVES FOR CHRISTMAS™

Model: T25
Modeller: Richard Wawrzesta
Height: 3", 7.6 cm
Colour: 1. Bay; maroon and
cream clothing
2. Grey; maroon and
cream clothing
Issued: 12/89 - 12/91
Series: Thelwell's Riding
Academy

U.K.: £30.00
U.S.: $60.00
Can.: $60.00

GARDENERS, THE™

Model: T36
Modeller: Richard Wawrzesta
Height: 2 ½", 6.4 cm
Colour: 1. Bay; red, tan and
cream clothing
2. Grey; red, tan and
cream clothing
Issued: 06/91 - 12/93
Series: Thelwell's Riding
Academy

U.K.: £35.00
U.S.: $70.00
Can.: $70.00

GOOD MANNERS ARE ESSENTIAL IN A PONY™

Model: T18
Modeller: Fred Moore
Height: 2", 5.0 cm
Colour: 1. Bay; blue and cream
clothing; grey fence
2. Grey; blue and
cream clothing; grey fence
Issued: 1987 - 12/93
Series: Thelwell's Riding
Academy

U.K.: £25.00
U.S.: $50.00
Can.: $50.00

GREATEST, THE™

Model: T5/140-702
Modeller: Fred Moore
Height: 3", 7.6 cm
Colour: 1. Bay; burgundy and
cream clothing
2. Grey; burgundy and
cream clothing
Issued: 1984 - 12/93
Series: Thelwell's Riding
Academy

U.K.: £25.00
U.S.: $50.00
Can.: $50.00

GROOM DAILY™

Model: T12
Modeller: Fred Moore
Height: 3", 7.6 cm
Colour: 1. Bay; tan and cream
clothing; grey pail
2. Grey; tan and cream
clothing; grey pail
Issued: 1986 - 12/93
Series: Thelwell's Riding
Academy

U.K.: £25.00
U.S.: $50.00
Can.: $50.00

HALLOA AWAY™

Model: T7/140-701
Modeller: Fred Moore
Height: 3", 7.6 cm
Colour: 1. Bay; red and cream
clothing; brown fox
2. Grey; red and cream
clothing; brown fox
Issued: 1985 - 12/93
Series: Thelwell's Riding
Academy

U.K.: £25.00
U.S.: $50.00
Can.: $50.00

HE'LL FIND YOU™

Model:	T3/140-704
Modeller:	Fred Moore
Height:	3", 7.6 cm
Colour:	1. Bay; green and cream clothing
	2. Grey; green and cream clothing
Issued:	1984 - 12/93
Series:	Thelwell's Riding Academy
U.K.:	£30.00
U.S.:	$60.00
Can.:	$60.00

IN A DEEP DRIFT™

Model:	T19
Modeller:	Fred Moore
Height:	3", 7.6 cm
Colour:	1. Bay; green and cream clothing; brown log
	2. Grey; green and cream clothing; brown log
Issued:	1987 - 12/89
Series:	Thelwell's Riding Academy
U.K.:	£40.00
U.S.:	$80.00
Can.:	$80.00

IT SHOULD BE CLEARLY UNDERSTOOD WHO'S BOSS™

Model:	T23
Modeller:	Richard Wawrzesta
Height:	3", 7.6 cm
Colour:	1. Bay; green and cream clothing
	2. Grey; green and cream clothing
Issued:	12/89 - 12/93
Series:	Thelwell's Riding Academy
U.K.:	£30.00
U.S.:	$60.00
Can.:	$60.00

LEARN WHAT HE'S SAYING™

Model:	T41
Modeller:	Richard Wawrzesta
Height:	2 ½", 6.4 cm
Colour:	1. Bay; tan and blue clothing
	2. Grey; tan and blue clothing
Issued:	06/91 - 12/93
Series:	Thelwell Goes West
U.K.:	£40.00
U.S.:	$80.00
Can.:	$80.00

LONE STRANGER, THE™

Model:	T40
Modeller:	Richard Wawrzesta
Height:	3", 7.6 cm
Colour:	1. Bay; red and blue clothing; black and white skunk
	2. Grey; red and blue clothing; black and white skunk
Issued:	06/91 - 12/93
Series:	Thelwell Goes West
U.K.:	£40.00
U.S.:	$80.00
Can.:	$80.00

NEVER USE SPURS™

Model:	T51
Modeller:	Richard Wawrzesta
Height:	2 ¼", 7.0 cm
Colour:	1. Bay; red and cream clothing
	2. Grey; red and cream clothing
Issued:	07/93 - 12/93
Series:	Thelwell's Riding Academy
U.K.:	£ 60.00
U.S.:	$120.00
Can.:	$120.00

NIGHT BEFORE CHRISTMAS™

Model:	T26
Modeller:	Richard Wawrzesta
Height:	1 ½", 3.8 cm
Colour:	1. Bay; red and cream clothing
	2. Grey; red and cream clothing
Issued:	07/90 - 12/91
Series:	Thelwell's Riding Academy
U.K.:	£45.00
U.S.:	$90.00
Can.:	$90.00

NO MORE THAN THREE REFUSALS ARE PERMITTED™

Model:	T28
Modeller:	Richard Wawrzesta
Height:	2 ¾", 7.0 cm
Colour:	1. Bay; blue and cream clothing
cream	2. Grey; blue and clothing
Issued:	07/90 - 12/93
Series:	Thelwell's Riding Academy
U.K.:	£45.00
U.S.:	$90.00
Can.:	$90.00

PARTY TIME (Christmas)™
Model: T14
Modeller: Fred Moore
Height: 3", 7.6 cm
Colour: 1. Bay; red and cream
            clothing; yellow and
            orange party hats
            2. Grey; red and cream
            clothing; yellow and
            orange party hats
Issued: 12/86 - 12/89
Series: Thelwell's Riding
            Academy

U.K.:   £30.00
U.S.: $60.00
Can.: $60.00

PENELOPE CAROLLING™
Model: T6
Modeller: Fred Moore
Height: 2 ¾", 7.0 cm
Colour: 1. Bay; orange, red and
            cream clothing
            2. Grey; orange, red
            and cream clothing
Issued: 12/84 - 12/85
Series: Thelwell's Riding
            Academy

U.K.:   £ 75.00
U.S.: $150.00
Can.: $150.00

PICNIC, THE™
Model: T27
Modeller: Richard Wawrzesta
Height: 2 ¼", 5.7 cm
Colour: 1. Bay; green and
            cream clothing
            2. Grey; green and
            cream clothing
Issued: 07/90 - 12/93
Series: Thelwell's Riding
            Academy

U.K.:   £40.00
U.S.: $80.00
Can.: $80.00

POINT OF DEPARTURE™
Model: T4/140-703
Modeller: Fred Moore
Height: 3", 7.6 cm
Colour: 1. Bay; red and cream
            clothing
            2. Grey; red and cream
            clothing
Issued: 1984 - 12/93
Series: Thelwell's Riding
            Academy

U.K.:   £40.00
U.S.: $80.00
Can.: $80.00

**PONIES ARE INCREDIBLY
SENSITIVE™**
Model: T29
Modeller: Richard Wawrzesta
Height: 2 ½", 6.4 cm
Colour: 1. Bay; blue and cream
            clothing
            2. Grey; blue and
            cream clothing
Issued: 06/91 - 12/93
Series: Thelwell's Riding
            Academy

U.K.:   £30.00
U.S.: $60.00
Can.: $60.00

PONY NOT YET BROKEN™
Model: T17
Modeller: Fred Moore
Height: 3", 7.6 cm
Colour: 1. Bay; green, blue and
            red clothing
            2. Grey; green, blue
            and red clothing
Issued: 1987 - 12/93
Series: Thelwell's Riding
            Academy

U.K.:   £ 50.00
U.S.: $100.00
Can.: $100.00

REMEMBER TO PRAISE HIM™
Model: T20
Modeller: Fred Moore
Height: 3", 7.6 cm
Colour: 1. Bay; red jacket; blue
            and red ribbons;
            silver cup
            2. Grey; red jacket;
            blue and red
            ribbons; silver cup
Issued: 12/88 - 12/93
Series: Thelwell's Riding
            Academy

U.K.:   £25.00
U.S.: $50.00
Can.: $50.00

**ROOMY JODHPURS ARE
ADVISABLE™**
Model: T21
Modeller: Fred Moore
Height: 3", 7.6 cm
Colour: 1. Bay; maroon and
            cream clothing
            2. Grey; maroon and
            cream clothing
Issued: 12/88 - 12/93
Series: Thelwell's Riding
            Academy

U.K.:   £ 50.00
U.S.: $100.00
Can.: $100.00

SMART DUDE™
Model: T45
Modeller: Richard Wawrzesta
Height: 3 ½", 8.9 cm
Colour: 1. Bay; red, blue and tan clothing
2. Grey; red. blue and tan clothing
Issued: 06/91 - 12/93
Series: Thelwell Goes West

U.K.: £40.00
U.S.: $80.00
Can.: $80.00

STARTING POINT™
Model: T47
Modeller: Richard Wawrzesta
Height: 3", 7.6 cm
Colour: 1. Bay; maroon and cream clothing
2. Grey; maroon and cream clothing
Issued: 07/92 - 12/93
Series: Thelwell's Riding Academy

U.K.: £40.00
U.S.: $80.00
Can.: $80.00

TALK TO YOUR PONY™
Model: T2/140-705
Modeller: Fred Moore
Height: 2 ½", 6.4 cm
Colour: 1. Bay; blue and cream clothing
2. Grey; blue and cream clothing
Issued: 1984 - 12/93
Series: Thelwell's Riding Academy

U.K.: £20.00
U.S.: $40.00
Can.: $40.00

TREAT HIM LIKE A PAL™
Model: T44
Modeller: Richard Wawrzesta
Height: 3", 7.6 cm
Colour: 1. Bay; black clothing
2. Grey; black clothing
Issued: 06/91 - 12/93
Series: Thelwell Goes West

U.K.: £40.00
U.S.: $80.00
Can.: $80.00

TREAT YOUR PONY AS YOU LIKE TO BE TREATED YOURSELF™
Model: T16
Modeller: Fred Moore
Height: 2 ½", 6.4 cm
Colour: 1. Bay; blue and cream clothing; red scarf
2. Grey; blue and cream clothing; red scarf
Issued: 1987 - 12/93
Series: Thelwell's Riding Academy

U.K.: £25.00
U.S.: $50.00
Can.: $50.00

TUMBLEWEED™
Model: T42
Modeller: Richard Wawrzesta
Height: 3", 7.6 cm
Colour: 1. Bay; blue, brown and red clothing
2. Bay; blue, brown and red clothing
Issued: 06/91 - 12/93
Series: Thelwell Goes West

U.K.: £40.00
U.S.: $80.00
Can.: $80.00

WINTER SPORTS™
Model: T37
Modeller: Richard Wawrzesta
Height: 3", 7.6 cm
Colour: 1. Bay; red, blue, green and cream clothing
2. Grey; red, blue, green and cream clothing
Issued: 06/91 - 12/93
Series: Thelwell's Riding Academy

U.K.: £ 60.00
U.S.: $120.00
Can.: $120.00

YOU'LL HAVE TO WAIT FOR CHRISTMAS™
Model: T54
Modeller: Richard Wawrzesta
Height: 2 ½", 6.4 cm
Colour: 1. Bay; green tree; blue jacket
2. Grey; green tree; blue jacket
Issued: 01/95 - 12/95
Series: Thelwell's Riding Academy

U.K.: £45.00
U.S.: $90.00
Can.: $90.00

WIND IN THE WILLOWS

BADGER™

Model:	M33
Modeller:	David Fryer
Height:	Unknown
Colour:	Black and white; green jacket; tan trousers; brown accordion
Issued:	06/83 - 12/83
Series:	Miniatures on Bronze
U.K.:	£40.00
U.S.:	$80.00
Can.:	$80.00

MOLE™

Model:	M31
Modeller:	David Fryer
Height:	Unknown
Colour:	Brown; yellow jacket and waistcoat; lilac trousers; red cap
Issued:	07/83 - 12/83
Series:	Miniatures on Bronze
U.K.:	£40.00
U.S.:	$80.00
Can.:	$80.00

RATTY™

Model:	M30
Modeller:	David Fryer
Height:	Unknown
Colour:	Brown; blue jacket; green trousers
Issued:	07/83 - 12/83
Series:	Miniatures on Bronze
U.K.:	£40.00
U.S.:	$80.00
Can.:	$80.00

RIVERBANK PICNIC, THE™

Model:	Unknown
Modeller:	Richard Wawrzesta
Size:	8" x 5", 20.3 x 12.7 cm
Colour:	Mr. Toad: Green frog; yellow and brown suit, red waistcoat; Mole: Blue suit, black shoes, white shirt; Ratty: White shirt and trousers, red belt; Mr. Badger: Yellow and brown jacket; red waistcoat and green neckerchief; Base: Green, brown, grey, yellow and white
Issued:	2002 in a limited edition of 500
Series:	Tableau
U.K.:	£ 50.00
U.S.:	$100.00
Can.:	$100.00

TOAD™

Model:	M32
Modeller:	David Fryer
Height:	Unknown
Colour:	Green; yellow jacket; blue waistcoat; lilac trousers
Issued:	07/83 - 12/83
Series:	Miniatures on Bronze
U.K.:	£40.00
U.S.:	$80.00
Can.:	$80.00

WINNIE THE POOH

A HOME FOR EEYORE™ (Pooh and Piglet)

Model: A0939
Modeller: Richard Wawrzesta
Height: 4", 10.1 cm
Colour: Honey-brown, red, pink, green, brown and cream
Issued: 06/01 - 12/02
Series: Winter Collection

U.K.: £12.00
U.S.: $25.00
Can.: $25.00

AFTER THE PICNIC™

Model: A1711
Modeller: Richard Wawrzesta
Height: 2 ¾", 7.0 cm
Colour: Honey-brown, brown, green, yellow and rusty-brown
Issued: 06/03 - 12/06
Series: Classic Pooh

U.K.: £12.00
U.S.: $25.00
Can.: $25.00

BIRTHDAY PARTY™

Model: A2391
Modeller: Richard Wawrzesta
Height: 2 ½", 6.4 cm
Colour: Honey-brown, orange, black, pink, green, grey, blue, red and yellow
Issued: 01/03 - 12/06
Series: Classic Pooh

U.K.: £25.00
U.S.: $50.00
Can.: $50.00

BLOWING DANDELIONS™

Model: A0676
Modeller: Richard Wawrzesta
Height: 3", 7.6 cm
Colour: Honey-brown, pink, green, yellow and white
Issued: 01/01 - 12/03
Series: Best Friends Pooh and Piglet Collection

U.K.: £12.00
U.S.: $25.00
Can.: $25.00

DO YOU THINK IT'S A-A- A WOOZLE?™

Model: A0936
Modeller: Richard Wawrzesta
Height: 3 ¾", 9.5 cm
Size: Miniature
Colour: Golden-brown, red, pink and green
Issued: 06/01 - 12/02
Series: Winter Collection

U.K.: £12.00
U.S.: $25.00
Can.: $25.00

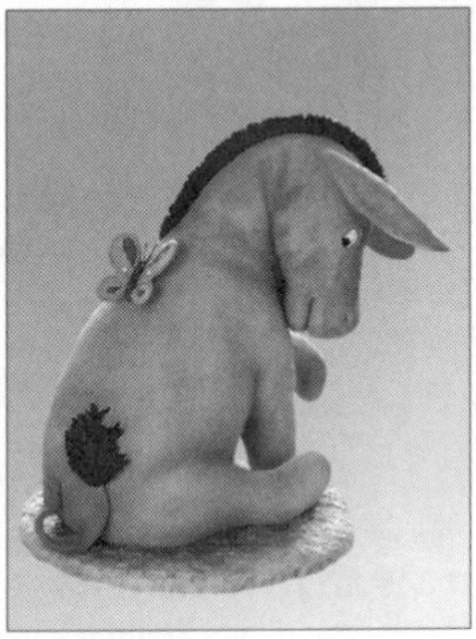

EEYORE™

Model: A2387
Modeller: Richard Wawrzesta
Height: 11 ½", 29.2 cm
Size: Large
Colour: Grey, black and yellow
Issued: 01/03 - 06/06
Series: Classic Pooh

U.K.: £ 60.00
U.S.: $120.00
Can.: $120.00

EEYORE™ AND SNAIL

Model: A6567
Modeller: Richard Wawrzesta
Height: 2 ½", 6.4 cm
Colour: Grey, black, white and red
Issued: 01/06 to the present

U.K.: £ 9.95
U.S.: $20.00
Can.: $20.00

EEYORE™ GETTING DRIED

Model: A0069
Modeller: Richard Wawrzesta
Height: 4", 10.8 cm
Colour: Eeyore: grey and black; Pooh: golden brown; Piglet: pink with green clothing; red, blue and white towels; green grass
Issued: 01/00 - 12/05

U.K.: £15.00
U.S.: $30.00
Can.: $30.00

EEYORE™ HAPPY BIRTHDAY

Model: A6398
Modeller: Richard Wawrzesta
Height: 2 ½", 6.4 cm
Colour: Grey, cream, red and blue
Issued: 01/06 to the present
Series: Classic Pooh It's a Gift

U.K.: £ 7.50
U.S.: $15.00
Can.: $15.00

EEYORE™ WITH BUTTERFLY

Model: A2389
Modeller: Richard Wawrzesta
Height: 3 ¼", 8.3 cm
Size: Small
Colour: Grey, black and yellow
Issued: 01/03 to the present
Series: Classic Pooh

U.K.: £ 9.95
U.S.: $20.00
Can.: $20.00

EEYORE™ WRITING

Model: A4169
Modeller: Richard Wawrzesta
Height: 2 ¾", 7.0 cm
Colour: Grey, black, red, pale blue and white
Issued: 01/05 -06/07
Series: Classic Pooh

U.K.: £10.00
U.S.: $20.00
Can.: $20.00

EEYORE'S™ TAIL

Model: A2717
Modeller: Richard Wawrzesta
Height: 3 ¾", 9.5 cm
Colour: White, grey, green, blue and red
Issued: 01/05 to the present
Series: Classic Pooh

U.K.: £15.00
U.S.: $30.00
Can.: $30.00

HAVING A REST
(Pooh™ and Piglet™ sitting back to back)

Model: A0677
Modeller: Richard Wawrzesta
Height: 2 ¾", 7.0 cm
Colour: Golden-brown, pink and green
Issued: 01/01 - 12/02
Series: Best Friends, Pooh and Piglet Collection

U.K.: £12.00
U.S.: $25.00
Can.: $25.00

IT'S HARD TO BE BRAVE
(Pooh™ and Piglet™ with bucket and stick)
First Version - Small

Model: A0675
Modeller: Richard Wawrzesta
Height: 3 ¾", 9.5 cm
Size: Small
Colour: Golden-yellow, pink, green and grey
Issued: 01/01 - 12/03
Series: Best Friends, Pooh and Piglet Collection

U.K.: £12.00
U.S.: $25.00
Can.: $25.00

IT'S HARD TO BE BRAVE
(Pooh™ and Piglet™ with bucket and stick)
Second Version - Large

Model: A2384
Modeller: Richard Wawrzesta
Height: 16 ½", 41.9 cm
Size: Large
Colour: Golden-brown, pink, green and silver-grey
Issued: 01/03 - 12/05
Series: Classic Pooh

U.K.: £ 60.00
U.S.: $120.00
Can.: $120.00

KANGA™ AND ROO™

Model: A1345
Modeller: Richard Wawrzesta
Height: 2 ¾", 7.0 cm
Colour: Brown, white, green, red, blue and yellow
Issued: 01/02 - 12/04
Series: Classic Pooh

U.K.: £10.00
U.S.: $20.00
Can.: $20.00

LET'S GO WOOZLE HUNTING
(Pooh™ and Piglet™)

Model:	A0937
Modeller:	Richard Wawrzesta
Height:	3", 7.6 cm
Size:	Miniature
Colour:	Golden-brown, red, pink, green, brown and cream
Issued:	06/01 - 12/02
Series:	Winter Collection
U.K.:	£12.00
U.S.:	$25.00
Can.:	$25.00

LOOK AT THE TRACKS
(Pooh™ and Piglet™)

Model:	A0938
Modeller:	Richard Wawrzesta
Height:	4 ¼", 10.8 cm
Size:	Miniature
Colour:	Golden-brown, red, pink, green and cream
Issued:	06/01 - 12/02
Series:	Winter Collection
U.K.:	£12.00
U.S.:	$25.00
Can.:	$25.00

PICKING FLOWERS
(Pooh™ and Piglet™ looking at flowers)

Model:	A0678
Modeller:	Richard Wawrzesta
Height:	3", 7.6 cm
Colour:	Honey-brown, pink, green and red
Issued:	01/01 - 12/03
Series:	Best Friends Pooh and Piglet Collection
U.K.:	£12.00
U.S.:	$25.00
Can.:	$25.00

PIGLET™ AND EEYORE™

Model:	A2392
Modeller:	Richard Wawrzesta
Height:	3 ¼", 8.3 cm
Colour:	Grey, pink, green, brown and red
Issued:	01/03 - 12/05
Series:	Classic Pooh
U.K.:	£12.00
U.S.:	$25.00
Can.:	$25.00

PIGLET™ AND TIGGER™ CATCHING BUTTERFLIES

Model:	A2718
Modeller:	Richard Wawrzesta
Height:	4", 10.1 cm
Colour:	Orange, pink, green, blue, red, yellow, grey
Issued:	01/05 to the present
Series:	Classic Pooh
U.K.:	£15.00
U.S.:	$30.00
Can.:	$30.00

PIGLET™ CARRYING BALLOON

Model:	A0411
Modeller:	Richard Wawrzesta
Height:	3", 7.6 cm
Colour:	Piglet: pink with green clothing; blue balloon
Issued:	06/00 - 12/04
U.K.:	£10.00
U.S.:	$20.00
Can.:	$20.00

PIGLET™ CARRYING A WATERING CAN

Model:	A2388
Modeller:	Richard Wawrzesta
Height:	2 ½", 6.4 cm
Colour:	Pink, green and silver-grey
Issued:	01/03 - 12/05
Series:	Classic Pooh
U.K.:	£10.00
U.S.:	$20.00
Can.:	$20.00

PIGLET™ IN BARREL OF APPLES

Model:	A6566
Modeller:	Richard Wawrzesta
Height:	3", 7.6 cm
Colour:	Brown, green, red, pink and turquoise
Issued:	01/06 to the present
Series:	Classic Pooh
U.K.:	£ 9.95
U.S.:	$20.00
Can.:	$20.00

PIGLET™ SITTING ON EEYORE™

Model: A7882
Modeller: Richard Wawrzesta
Height: 3 ½", 8.9 cm
Colour: Grey, black, pink and green
Issued: 01/07 to the present

U.K.: £ 9.95
U.S.: $20.00
Can.: $20.00

PIGLET™ THANK YOU

Model: A6526
Modeller: Richard Wawrzesta
Height: 2 ½", 6.4 cm
Colour: Pink, white and green
Issued: 01/06 to the present
Series: It's A Gift

U.K.: £ 6.50
U.S.: $12.00
Can.: $12.00

PIGLET™ WITH BALLOON

Model: A0060
Modeller: Richard Wawrzesta
Height: 4", 10.8 cm
Colour: Piglet: pink with green clothing; Pooh: golden brown; Tigger: orange with black stripes; red balloon
Issued: 01/00 - 12/05

U.K.: £15.00
U.S.: $30.00
Can.: $30.00

PIGLET™ WITH TROWEL

Model: A3942
Modeller: Richard Wawrzesta
Height: 3 ¼", 8.3 cm
Colour: Pink, green and brown
Issued: 01/04 - 12/06

U.K.: £10.00
U.S.: $20.00
Can.: $20.00

PIGLET™ WITH VIOLETS

Model: A1342
Modeller: Richard Wawrzesta
Height: 2 ½", 6.4 cm
Colour: Pink, green, violet and brown
Issued: 01/02 - 06/06
Series: Classic Pooh

U.K.: £10.00
U.S.: $20.00
Can.: $20.00

POOH™ AND BUTTERFLY

Model: A6568
Modeller: Richard Wawrzesta
Height: 2 ¾", 7.0 cm
Colour: Yellow, red, blue and green
Issued: 01/06 to the present
Series: Classic Pooh

U.K.: £ 9.95
U.S.: $20.00
Can.: $20.00

POOH™ AND MIRROR

Model: A0070
Modeller: Richard Wawrzesta
Height: 4", 10.8 cm
Colour: Pooh: golden brown; Piglet: pink with green clothing; silver mirror; white and red mat; brown base
Issued: 01/00 - 12/04

U.K.: £12.00
U.S.: $25.00
Can.: $25.00

POOH™ AND PIGLET™ LEANING OVER FENCE

Model: A3941
Modeller: Richard Wawrzesta
Height: 4 ¼", 10.8 cm
Colour: Yellow, pink, green and light brown
Issued: 01/04 - 12/06

U.K.: £15.00
U.S.: $30.00
Can.: $30.00

POOH™ AND PIGLET™ LOOKING AT BEE

Model: A7883
Modeller: Unknown
Height: 3", 7.6 cm
Colour: Yellow, pink, green and brown
Issued: 01/07 to the present

U.K.: £ 9.95
U.S.: $20.00
Can.: $20.00

POOH™ AND PIGLET™ SITTING IN A CHAIR

Model: A2719
Modeller: Richard Wawrzesta
Height: 4 ¼", 10.8 cm
Colour: Yellow, brown, green, pink, orange and grey
Issued: 01/05 to the present
Series: Classic Pooh

U.K.: £18.00
U.S.: $35.00
Can.: $35.00

POOH™ AND PIGLET™ SITTING IN UMBRELLA

Model: A3943
Modeller: Richard Wawrzesta
Height: 3 ¾", 9.5 cm
Colour: Yellow, pink, green, blue, white and red
Issued: 06/04 - 12/06
Series: Classic Pooh

U.K.: £12.00
U.S.: $25.00
Can.: $25.00

POOH™ AND PIGLET™ SITTING ON A BENCH

Model: A2393
Modeller: Richard Wawrzesta
Height: 4 ¼", 10.8 cm
Colour: Honey-brown, pink, green, blue and yellow
Issued: 01/03 - 12/05
Series: Classic Pooh

U.K.: £12.00
U.S.: $25.00
Can.: $25.00

POOH™ AND PIGLET™ SITTING ON LOG

MODEL: A0674
Modeller: Richard Waawrzesta
Height: 4", 10.1 cm
Colour: Golden-brown, brown, pink, green, red and yellow
Issued: 01/01 - 12/04
Series: Classic Pooh

U.K.: £15.00
U.S.: $30.00
Can.: $30.00

POOH™ BALANCING HUNNY POTS

Model: A7881
Modeller: Unknown
Height: 5", 12.7 cm
Colour: Yellow, red, white and green
Issued: 01/07 to the present

U.K.: £ 9.95
U.S.: $20.00
Can.: $20.00

POOH™ DRINKING TEA

Model: A7880
Modeller: Unknown
Height: 3", 7.6 cm
Colour: Yellow, red, white, blue and green
Issued: 01/07 to the present

U.K.: £ 9.95
U.S.: $20.00
Can.: $20.00

POOH™ EATING HUNNY

Model: A1339
Modeller: Richard Wawrzesta
Height: 3 ½", 8.9 cm
Colour: Honey brown, brown and green
Issued: 01/02 - 06/06
Series: Classic Pooh

U.K.: £12.00
U.S.: $25.00
Can.: $25.00

POOH™, EEYORE™ AND HUNNY

Model: A0063
Modeller: Richard Wawrzesta
Size: 4" x 3", 10.0 x 7.6 cm
Colour: Pooh: golden brown; Eeyore: grey and black; red and brown "hunny" jars; brown base
Issued: 01/00 - 12/05

U.K.: £15.00
U.S.: $30.00
Can.: $30.00

POOH™ HOLDING BALLOON

Model: A1665
Modeller: Richard Wawrzesta
Height: 6 ¼", 15.9 cm
Colour: Honey-brown, red, blue, yellow and green
Issued: 06/02 - 06/06
Series: Classic Pooh

U.K.: £12.00
U.S.: $25.00
Can.: $25.00

POOH™ HOLDING PIGLET™

Model: A1346
Modeller: Richard Wawrzesta
Height: 3 ¾", 9.5 cm
Colour: Honey-brown, pink, green, blue and yellow
Issued: 06/02 - 12/05
Series: Best Friends, Pooh and Piglet Collection

U.K.: £12.00
U.S.: $25.00
Can.: $25.00

POOH™, HUNNY AND FOXGLOVES

Model: A0062
Modeller: Richard Wawrzesta
Height: 3 ¼", 8.3 cm
Colour: Pooh: golden brown; yellow, brown, and tan jars of "hunny"; green grass with multicoloured flowers and pink foxgloves
Issued: 01/00 - 12/03

U.K.: £15.00
U.S.: $30.00
Can.: $30.00

POOH™ LYING DOWN WITH HUNNY JAR

Model: A0102
Modeller: Richard Wawrzesta
Height: 2 ¼", 7.0 cm
Colour: Pooh: golden brown; brown and yellow jars of "hunny"; green grass
Issued: 01/00 - 12/06

U.K.: £10.00
U.S.: $20.00
Can.: $20.00

POOH™, PIGLET™ AND FLOWERS

Model: A0066
Modeller: Richard Wawrzesta
Height: 4", 10.1 cm
Colour: Pooh: golden brown; Piglet: pink with green clothing; red, blue and yellow flowers; brown log; green grass
Issued: 01/00 - 12/02

U.K.: £15.00
U.S.: $30.00
Can.: $30.00

POOH™, PIGLET™ AND TIGGER™ TABLEAU

Model: A0410
Modeller: Richard Wawrzesta
Height: 5 ½", 14.0 cm
Colour: Pooh: golden brown; Piglet: pink and green Tigger: orange, black, blue, pink, brown, green and yellow
Issued: 06/00 - 12/02

U.K.: £30.00
U.S.: $60.00
Can.: $60.00

POOH™ PUSHING PIGLET™ IN WHEELBARROW

Model: A1348
Modeller: Richard Wawrzesta
Height: 3 ¼", 8.3 cm
Colour: Honey-brown, brown, pink, green and violet
Issued: 01/02 - 06/06
Series: Classic Pooh

U.K.: £15.00
U.S.: $30.00
Can.: $30.00

POOH™ READING

Model:	A0065
Modeller:	Richard Wawrzesta
Height:	4 ¼", 10.8 cm
Colour:	Pooh: golden brown; Piglet: pink with green clothing; Tigger: orange with black stripes; red, green and blue books
Issued:	01/00 - 12/06
U.K.:	£18.00
U.S.:	$35.00
Can.:	$35.00

POOH™ SITTING ON LOG

Model:	A6569
Modeller:	Richard Wawrzesta
Height:	3 ¾", 9.5 cm
Colour:	Yellow, red, brown and green
Issued:	01/06 - 12/06
Series:	Classic Pooh
U.K.:	£10.00
U.S.:	$20.00
Can.:	$20.00

Note: Issued to celebrate 80 years of Classic Pooh Adventures.

POOH™ SLEEPING

Model:	A0067
Modeller:	Richard Wawrzesta
Height:	2 ¾", 7.0 cm
Colour:	Pooh: golden brown; Piglet: pink with green clothing; red armchair; white pillow; red and blue books
Issued:	01/00 - 12/05
U.K.:	£12.00
U.S.:	$25.00
Can.:	$25.00

POOH™ STANDING ON CHAIR

Model:	A1338
Modeller:	Richard Wawrzesta
Height:	4 ¼", 10.8 cm
Colour:	Honey-brown, brown, red, green and white
Issued:	01/02 - 12/05
Series:	Classic Pooh
U.K.:	£12.00
U.S.:	$25.00
Can.:	$25.00

POOH™ WITH BEES

Model:	A3940
Modeller:	Richard Wawrzesta
Height:	4", 10.0 cm
Colour:	Yellow, brown, green and ginger
Issued:	01/04 - 12/06
Series:	Classic Pooh
U.K.:	£12.00
U.S.:	$25.00
Can.:	$25.00

POOH™ WITH HUNNY JAR ON FOOT

Model:	A3938
Modeller:	Richard Wawrzesta
Height:	3 ½", 8.9 cm
Colour:	Yellow, black, green and red
Issued:	06/04 - 06/06
Series:	Classic Pooh
U.K.:	£12.00
U.S.:	$25.00
Can.:	$25.00

POOH™ WITH HUNNY POTS

Model:	A2385
Modeller:	Richard Wawrzesta
Height:	15 ¾", 40.0 cm
Size:	Large
Colour:	Honey-brown, reddish-brown, brown, yellow and green
Issued:	01/03 - 06/06
Series:	Classic Pooh
U.K.:	£ 50.00
U.S.:	$100.00
Can.:	$100.00

POOH™ WITH LOVE

Model:	A6397
Modeller:	Richard Wawrzesta
Height:	3 ¼", 8.3 cm
Colour:	Lemon and red
Issued:	01/06 to the present
Series:	It's a Gift
U.K.:	£ 7.50
U.S.:	$15.00
Can.:	$15.00

POOH™ WITH UMBRELLA
(Umbrella Down)

Model: A2390
Modeller: Richard Wawrzesta
Height: 3 ¾", 9.5 cm
Colour: Yellow, blue, black,
            pink, yellow and green
Issued: 01/03 - 12/04
Series: Classic Pooh

U.K.:   £12.00
U.S.: $25.00
Can.: $25.00

POOH™ WITH UMBRELLA
(Umbrella Up)

Model: A0673
Modeller: Richard Wawrzesta
Height: 4 ¼", 10.8 cm
Colour: Honey-brown, dark
            blue, grey, blue, red
            and yellow
Issued: 01/01 - 06/06
Series"   Classic Pooh

U.K.:   £15.00
U.S.: $30.00
Can.: $30.00

POOH™ WRITING

Model: A0064
Modeller: Richard Wawrzesta
Height: 2 ½", 6.4 cm
Colour: Pooh: golden brown;
            white paper with black
            ink; grey quill; blue pot
            of ink
Issued: 01/00 - 12/04

U.K.:   £12.00
U.S.: $25.00
Can.: $25.00

POOH'S™ PICNIC

Model: A0061
Modeller: Richard Wawrzesta
Height: 3 ¼", 8.3 cm
Colour: Pooh: golden brown;
            Piglet: pink with green
            clothing; yellow and
            red jars of "hunny";
            pink blanket; brown
            picnic basket
Issued: 01/00 - 12/03

U.K.:   £15.00
U.S.: $30.00
Can.: $30.00

POOH'S™ WISHING WELL

Model: A0103
Modeller: Richard Wawrzesta
Height: 7 ½", 19.1 cm
Colour: Pooh: golden brown;
            Piglet: pink and green
            Tigger: orange, black
            Eeyore: grey and black;
            grey well, brown roof
Issued: 01/00 - 12/01

U.K.:   £ 60.00
U.S.: $120.00
Can.: $120.00

THAT'S THE WAY TO BUILD A
HOUSE™

Model: A0940
Modeller: Richard Wawrzesta
Height: 4", 10.1 cm
Size: Miniature
Colour: Golden-brown, pink,
            green, brown and red
Issued: 06/01 - 12/02
Series: Winter Collection

U.K.:   £20.00
U.S.: $40.00
Can.: $40.00

TIGGER™ AND BATHTUB

Model: A0068
Modeller: Richard Wawrzesta
Height: 3 ½", 8.9 cm
Colour: Tigger: orange with
            black stripes;
            Pooh: golden brown;
            Piglet: pink with green
            clothing; grey bathtub;
            white mat with red trim
Issued: 01/00 - 06/04

U.K.:   £15.00
U.S.: $30.00
Can.: $30.00

TIGGER™ CARRYING PIGLET™
IN A PICNIC BASKET

Model: A3939
Modeller: Richard Wawrzesta
Height: 4", 10.0 cm
Colour: Orange, black, pink,
            green and fawn
Issued: 06/04 - 06/06
Series: Classic Pooh

U.K.:   £15.00
U.S.: $30.00
Can.: $30.00

TIGGER™ JUMPING ON POOH'S™ BED

Model: A1350
Modeller: Richard Wawrzesta
Height: 4", 10.0 cm
Colour: Orange, black, honey-brown, brown, blue and white
Issued: 01/02 to the present
Series: Classic Pooh

U.K.: £24.00
U.S.: $50.00
Can.: $50.00

TIGGER™ JUST FOR YOU

Model: A6527
Modeller: Richard Wawrzesta
Height: 2 ¾", 7.0 cm
Colour: Orange and black
Issued: 01/06 to the present
Series: It's a Gift

U.K.: £ 7.50
U.S.: $15.00
Can.: $15.00

TIGGER™, POOH™ AND PIGLET™

Model: A0059
Modeller: Richard Wawrzesta
Height: 3", 7.6 cm
Colour: Tigger: orange with black stripes; Pooh: golden brown; Piglet: pink with green clothing; green grass with blue, yellow and red flowers
Issued: 01/00 - 12/02

U.K.: £20.00
U.S.: $40.00
Can.: $40.00

TIGGER™ WITH FLOWERS

Model: A2386
Modeller: Richard Wawrzesta
Height: 14 ½", 36.8 cm
Size: Large
Colour: Orange, black, white and green
Issued: 01/03 - 12/04
Series: Classic Pooh

U.K.: £ 50.00
U.S.: $100.00
Can.: $100.00

TIGGERS™ DON'T LIKE HUNNY

Model: A0413
Modeller: Richard Wawrzesta
Height: 2 ¼", 5.7 cm
Colour: Tigger: orange with black stripes; brown and yellow pot; green grass with multicoloured flowers
Issued: 06/00 - 06/04

U.K.: £12.00
U.S.: $25.00
Can.: $25.00

WINNIE THE POOH™ WITH HUNNY POT

Model: A0412
Modeller: Richard Wawrzesta
Height: 3 ½", 8.9 cm
Colour: Pooh: golden brown; brown and cream and red pots; green grass with multicoloured flowers
Issued: 06/00 - 06/06

U.K.: £12.00
U.S.: $25.00
Can.: $25.00

WINTER SLEIGH RIDE (Pooh™ and Piglet™)

Model: A0941
Modeller: Richard Wawrzesta
Height: 4 ¼", 10.8 cm
Size: Miniature
Colour: Honey-brown, red, pink, green, black and cream
Issued: 06/01 - 12/02
Series: Winter Collection

U.K.: £20.00
U.S.: $40.00
Can.: $40.00

WINTER TABLEAU™

Model: A0931
Modeller: Richard Wawrzesta
Height: 6 ¼", 15.9 cm
Colour: Honey-brown, red, pink, green, gold, orange and black
Issued: 06/01 - 12/02
Series: 1. Tableau
2. Winter Collection

U.K.: £30.00
U.S.: $60.00
Can.: $60.00

BROWN SITE DEVELOPMENT
(JCB Mark I Major Loader)
(B1003)

INDEX

A

H

452

P

Symbol of Loyalty
by Ray Ayres

Border
F I N E 🖐 A R T S
Society™

What is the Border Fine Arts Society?

Jenny Wren
Membership Figure 2007/2008

The Border Fine Arts Society was established in 1989. By joining the Border Fine Arts Society you will be joining a worldwide 'family' of like-minded enthusiasts who share a common interest: the beauty and detail of our art. Our full-colour Society magazine, *The Borderer,* includes fascinating in-depth feature articles and it keeps you up to date with the latest news from Border Fine Arts. You can also buy exlusive figurines that are only available to, and which are designed specially for, Society members by Master Sculptor, Ray Ayres.

To join the Society, or to find out more about what it can offer you, contact the Society office at the address below. Don't forget, too, that your membership includes our delightful Symbol of Membership figurine.

Benefits

As a member of the Border Fine Arts Society you will receive

- Subscription to the Society's exclusive magazine The Borderer
- The opportunity, but no obligation, to purchase the exclusive Society Member-only figurines details of which will be sent to you with a reservation card
- Full Membership kit including a membership card and a copy of Welcome to Border Fine Arts, an exclusive magazine explaining the history of the company.
- Personal invitations to Special Events in you area held throughout the year.
- The complete Border Fine Arts catalogues and price lists as they are published.
- A Society 'hotline' for any queries you may have.
- The chance to participate in the 'Seek 'n' Sell' Collectors' Exchange.

And not forgetting

The Society Symbol of Membership figure for 2007/2008 is *Jenny Wren*. The Nineteenth Annual Classic Society Member-only Figurine for 2007/2008 is *September Fruits*. The fifteenth year of continuous membership 'thank-you' gift is *Symbol of Loyalty*.

Plus lots more

For further information on how to join this exclusive Society please contact:

The Border Fine Arts Society
Brunhill Road, Kingstown, Carlisle, Cumbria, England CA3 0EN
Telephone 01228 404370
Website: www.borderfinearts.com